W9-DFD-433

Freshman Mathematics for University Students

Freshman Mathematics for University Students

Frederick M. Lister
Associate Professor of Mathematics, Western Washington State College.

Sheldon T. Rio
Professor of Mathematics, and Chairman of the Department, Southern Oregon College.

Walter J. Sanders
Assistant Professor of Mathematics, University of Illinois.

PRENTICE-HALL, INC., *Englewood Cliffs, N. J.*

Current printing (last digit):
10 9 8 7 6 5 4 3 2 1

Library of Congress Catalog Card 66-13533
Printed in the United States of America
C—33130

To our gal, Val

Preface

With the advent of calculus courses which stress concepts and proof to a greater extent than ever before, it has become evident that the regular preparatory calculus course no longer fulfills the needs of the student. This text is written for the express purpose of preparing students so that they will be able to read and understand such a course in calculus.

In a calculus preparatory course, it is presumed that the student is familiar with high school algebra and geometry. [Because of the distinctive nature of the material presented in this text, students who have completed a course in college algebra and trigonometry frequently benefit from a study of this material.] The text does not contain a review as such of algebra and geometry. Such a review may be conducted as the exercises of the first three chapters are worked, depending on the needs of a particular class.

The method of presentation of materials is informal. There is a great reliance on intuition and imagination for working the exercises. To do a set of exercises on mathematical sentences, for example, the gamut of concepts of the real, rational, and whole numbers is run. The examples for logic and for sets are nearly all chosen to be within the context of the mathematics with which the student is familiar. These examples should reinforce the student's knowledge of those topics as well as indicate any need of review.

Nearly all of the material in this edition has been classroom tested by various instructors for a variety of needs. For a two-quarter precalculus course, chapters 1 through 7, with chapter 9 have been used. In other cases, where the students have had an adequate background in trigonometry, chapter 6 has been omitted in favor of parts of Chapter 8. For a one-quarter course, Chapters 1–4 have been reviewed, with a concentration of Chapters 5 and 7.

At the secondary level, the text has been used for senior students who have had from three to four years of high school mathematics including two years of algebra.

The instructor will find that there is considerable freedom in the ordering of chapters even though an effort has been made to relate them. Chapter 9, as a case in point, is often taught immediately after chapter 4.

There has been an effort, and a purposeful one, not to cover too many topics in this text. This was not designed to be an "all things for all people" type of text. Rather, it was designed especially to prepare students for calculus. Linear algebra [including matrices] has been omitted in the belief that this topic best fits in the calculus sequence just prior to the study of the calculus of several variables where, indeed, it appears in many calculus texts.

The text fulfills several other needs also. It is being used in part to prepare students for business courses. It has been used for non-mathematics majors as an introduction to mathematics, and, with surprising success, has been used with practicing teachers of junior and senior high schools as an introduction to modern mathematics.

The authors are indebted to the many persons who made helpful suggestions and who used the materials in their classrooms.

F. M. Lister
S. T. Rio
W. J. Sanders

Contents

0 Basic Concepts **2**

1 Logic **4**

1.1 Constants, variables, 5
1.2 Quantifiers, 6
1.3 Symbols for quantifiers, 8
1.4 Open sentences; instance of proof; counterexample, 11
1.5 Conjunctions, 16
1.6 Disjunctions and denials, 17
1.7 Conditionals, 20
1.8 Truth of conjunctions and disjunctions, 22
1.9 Truth of conditionals, 25
1.10 Converse, contrapositive, and biconditionals, 31
1.11 Synonyms, 33
1.12 Denials of generalizations, 36
1.13 Denials of conditionals; denials of biconditionals, 41

2 Sets 46

2.1 Introduction, 47
2.2 Notation, 47
2.3 The roster notation, 50
2.4 Intervals, half lines, rays, 51
2.5 Graphs of sets of real numbers, 53
2.6 Subsets, 55
2.7 Set intersection, 59
2.8 Set union, 61
2.9 The universal set, complement of sets, 63

3 Algebraic Properties of the Real Numbers 68

3.1 Introduction, 69
3.2 Real numbers that are not fractions, 71
3.3 Representation of real numbers by infinite decimals, 74
3.4 Operations, 78
3.5 Closure, 79
3.6 The associative and commutative principals, 83
3.7 Identities, 87
3.8 Inverse elements, 88
3.9 Distributive principle, 92

4 Order Properties of the Real Numbers 94

4.1 Introduction, 95
4.2 Solution sets, 95
4.3 Properties of order, 99
4.4 Solution of polynomial inequalities, 102
4.5 The multiplication transformation principle, 106
4.6 Absolute value, 110
4.7 Inequalities involving absolute value, 111

5 Subsets of the Plane; an Introduction to Analytic Geometry 116

5.1 Introduction, 117
5.2 Rectangular coordinates, 117
5.3 Graphing solution sets, 119
5.4 Symmetry, 125

5.5 Distance, 131
5.6 Using distance to obtain analytic descriptions of points, 133
5.7 Slope and intercepts, 139
5.8 Writing linear equations, 145
5.9 Circles, 148
5.10 The ellipse, 153
5.11 Hyperbolas, 157
5.12 Parabolas, 160
5.13 Conics, 162

6 Trigonometry **164**

6.1 Introduction, 165
6.2 Polar coordinates, 165
6.3 Degrees, radians, revolutions, 168
6.4 Sine and cosine, 174
6.5 Tables of values for sine and cosine, 179
6.6 Interpolation, 182
6.7 Reduction identities, 184
6.8 General coordinate relations, 191
6.9 Solution of right triangles, 193
6.10 The tangent function, 195
6.11 Reciprocal functions, 196
6.12 Graphs of trigonometric functions, 198
6.13 Pythagorean identities, 203
6.14 Addition identities, 209
6.15 Half-angle identities, 213
6.16 Law of sines and law of cosines, 219

7 Functions **224**

7.1 Introduction, 225
7.2 Graphs of functions, 227
7.3 $f(x)$ notation, 231
7.4 The trigonometric functions, 233
7.5 Restrictions on the domain and range of a function, 237
7.6 Mapping notation for functions, 242
7.7 Composition of functions, 248
7.8 Writing a function as a composition, 256
7.9 The identity function, 261
7.10 Inverse functions; restricted identity, 261

7.11 Properties of composition, 273
7.12 Inverse of a composition, 274
7.13 Restricting domains to obtain inverses, 278
7.14 Inverse trigonometric functions, 279
7.15 Exponential functions, 285
7.16 Logarithmic functions, 289
7.17 Algebra of functions, 298
7.18 Expressing relationships with functions, 303

8 Rules of Inference **310**

8.1 Introduction, 311
8.2 Sentential variables and tautologies, 311
8.3 Inference patterns, validity, 316
8.4 Patterns of inference involving disjunction and conditionals, 322
8.5 Proof, 326
8.6 Proof of conditionals, 330
8.7 The paragraph proof, 334
8.8 Indirect proof, 337
8.9 Order properties of the real numbers, 340
8.10 More order theorems, 344

9 Mathematical Induction and the Binomial Theorem **348**

9.1 Introduction, 349
9.2 Sigma notation, 349
9.3 The $P(n)$ notation, 355
9.4 The axiom of mathematical induction, 357
9.5 The binomial theorem, 366

Appendix **371**

Index **443**

Freshman Mathematics for University Students

Basic Concepts

CHAPTER ZERO

Throughout the text, references will be made to various sets and systems of numbers. These numbers will be studied in detail in later chapters, and, until then, the student will have to rely on his previous knowledge of numbers from the study of arithmetic, algebra, and geometry.

The numbers referred to include:

The counting numbers: $1, 2, 3, \ldots$

The natural numbers: $0, 1, 2, \ldots$

The integers: The positive integers,
$1, 2, 3, \ldots$
the negative integers,
$-1, -2, -3, \ldots$
and 0.

The rational numbers: All numbers which can be expressed as a fraction of integers (where the denominator is not zero).

The real numbers: All numbers with a decimal representation.

The real numbers can be represented by the *real number line*. This line may be pictured as follows:

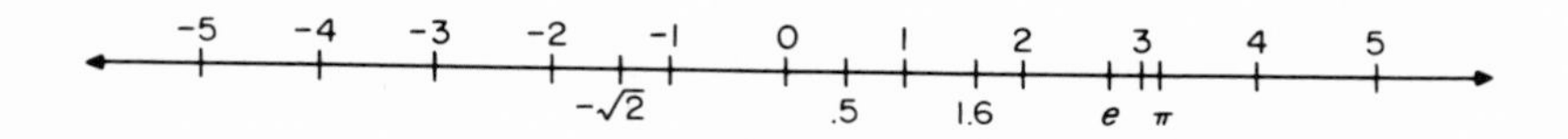

Each point on this line represents a real number (in appropriate order), and each real number represents a point on this line.

Whenever a sentence which refers to *numbers* is given, it is to be assumed that the sentence is concerned with the *real numbers* unless it is stated otherwise. In the examples and problems involving geometry, it is assumed that the discussion is of the ordinary (Euclidean) geometry of the plane. Some examples and exercises involving trigonometry precede the trigonometry chapter (Chapter Six). If the reader is not acquainted with the basic trigonometric functions, he will be able to proceed without difficulty by omitting the material involving trigonometry from the first five chapters.

Logic

CHAPTER ONE

1.1 Constants, Variables

In mathematical writings, specific numbers, lines, angles, and so forth are referred to as *constants*. Often symbols such as letters of the alphabet are also used; these do not refer to specific objects and are generally called *variables*. In the sentence

$$3 + 2x = 7,$$

3, 2, and 7 are constants while x is a variable.

The variable x in the sentence

$$2 + x = 7$$

is a "place holder" for a number, so that the equation is a "form" for equations such as

$$2 + 4 = 7,$$

$$2 + 5 = 7,$$

$$2 + 6 = 7,$$

$$2 + (-\tfrac{3}{2}) = 7,$$

$$2 + (5\pi) = 7,$$

and so forth, each of which arises by substituting a specific number (constant) for the variable.

The sentence

$$x > 3 \quad \text{and} \quad x < 4$$

has the variable x and constants 3 and 4, while

$$5x + 4 = y$$

has variables x, y and constants 5 and 4.

The variables in

Point P is on line L

are P and L; there are no constants.

The use of the terms "variable" and "constant" is not always as clear as the above examples may suggest. The sentence

$$5x + b = 0$$

has variables x and b and constants 0 and 5. Nevertheless, many times b is referred to as an "arbitrary constant" while x is called the "variable." This distinction simply tells the reader which variable to "solve" for. It does not mean that b is a constant. The solution

$$\frac{-b}{5}$$

is not a specific number at all since b is not a specific number. Only when b is replaced by a number will $-b/5$ be a number. b is a variable in the original problem and remains a variable in the solution.

1.2 Quantifiers

Statements about objects such as numbers, lines, points, and so forth often specify whether the sentence is concerned with all such objects or with at least one such object. Phrases which relate to all objects of a specific kind, such as "for each point," "for all numbers," "every line," and "all integers," are called *universal quantifiers*. The sentence

For each number x, $1 + x^2$ is positive

contains the universal quantifier "for each number x." The sentence asserts that one more than the square of a number will be positive regardless of the number chosen. Other sentences having a universal quantifier are:

Each number x is even or odd

and

$$(x - 2)(x - 3) = x^2 - 5x + 6, \text{ for each } x.$$

Phrases which relate to at least one of a number of objects, such as "for some angle," "there is a number," "there exists a line," and so on, are called *existential quantifiers*. The sentence

There is a number x such that $2x = x$

has the existential quantifier "there is a number x." The sentence asserts that there is at least one number that is equal to twice itself. Other sentences having existential quantifiers are:

Some point p is on the line L

and

At least one positive number is even.

A sentence may contain more than one quantifier. The sentence

For some x, and for some y, $x - y = 0$

contains two quantifiers: "for some x" and "for some y," both of which are existential, while

There is a number x such that for each number y, $x + y = y$

contains both the existential quantifier "there is a number x" and the universal quantifier "for each number y."

Those sentences in which the first quantifier is an existential quantifier are called *existential generalizations*; those in which the first quantifier is a universal quantifier are called *universal generalizations*. The sentence

For each number x and for some number y, x is greater than y

is a universal generalization since the first quantifier, "for each number x," is universal. The first (and only) quantifier in

For some number x, $x^2 = 2$

is existential; therefore the sentence is an existential generalization.

EXERCISE SET 1.1

In Exercises 1–12, list each variable and tell whether it is universally quantified, existentially quantified, or unquantified.

1. $x - 3 = 7$.
2. Each x is less than 3.
3. There is a number x which is less than 3.

4. Two is less than 3.
5. There is a number x such that x is less than 3.
6. x is less than y.
7. There is an x which is less than b.
8. For each x, for some y, x is less than y.
9. There is an x and there is a y such that x is less than y.
10. For some x, for each y, x is less than $y + a$.
11. For every x, for each y, x is less than $y + a$.
12. There is an x such that for each y, $x + y = y$.

Classify each sentence in Exercises 13–20 as a universal generalization, an existential generalization, or an unquantified sentence.

13. Some x is less than 4.
14. At least one number y is greater than 0 and less than 1.
15. Each number is less than 3.
16. Some numbers are perfect squares.
17. Some number is less than 3.
18. At least one number is less than 3.
19. For some x, for each y, x is less than y.
20. For each x, for some y, x is less than y.
21. Is the variable x in the sentence, "No number x is both positive and negative," quantified universally, existentially, or neither? Explain.
22. Discuss the quantification of the variable y in the sentence, "Not all numbers y are rational."

1.3 Symbols for Quantifiers

Sentences in mathematics are often abbreviated by the use of symbols. Since each of the phrases "for all," "for each," "all numbers," and so forth refer to the same idea—namely, the universal generalization—mathematicians use the special symbol

(read "for each") in place of each of these phrases. To specify the objects referred to by the quantifier, it is convenient to use a variable along with it. Using the variable x, the complete quantifying phrase would be symbolized as

$$\forall x.$$

Employing this symbolism,

Every number has a nonnegative square

can be written as

$\forall x$, x has a nonnegative square.

The sentence

For each x and for each y, $x + y = y + x$

would appear as

$\forall x \, \forall y, \, x + y = y + x.$

Similarly, each existential quantifier is represented by the symbol

$\exists$

or, employing the variable x, by

$\exists x$

(read "there is an x such that" or "for some x"). The sentence

There is a number larger than 2

can be written as

$\exists z$, z is larger than 2.

EXAMPLE 1.1 Rewrite each sentence using symbols for the quantifiers.

(a) All numbers are positive or negative.
$\forall x$, x is positive or negative.

(b) For each number x there is a number y such that $x + y = 0$ and $x - y > 0$.
$\forall x \, \exists y$, $x + y = 0$ and $x - y > 0$.

Notice that the meaning of a sentence containing one quantified variable is unchanged when different variables are employed. Thus,

$$\forall x,\ x > 3,$$

$$\forall y,\ y > 3,$$

and

$$\forall a,\ a > 3$$

say the same thing: namely, that each number is greater than 3.

In all the above examples, it is understood that $\forall x$ means "for each number x" since all the sentences were about numbers. Symbolizing the quantifier of

Each triangle has 3 vertices

gives

$\forall t$, t has 3 vertices.

However, this form does not make plain what t refers to—triangles, rectangles, or whatever. For clarity, one writes

$\forall t$ (t is a triangle), t has 3 vertices.

EXAMPLE 1.2 Write the sentence

Some integers are even

using symbols for the quantifiers.

$\exists x$ (x is an integer), x is even.

EXERCISE SET 1.2

Write each sentence using symbols for the quantifiers. Introduce variables as needed.

1. Each number is less than 3.
2. Each number is larger than its square.
3. Some numbers are perfect squares.
4. All numbers are perfect squares.
5. There is a number x such that $x^2 = 2$.
6. For each number x, there is a number larger than x.

7. At least one number is larger than its square.
8. There is a number x which is larger than y.
9. For some number x, there is a number y so that xy is 0, but y is not 0.
10. There is a number x such that for each number y, xy is 0, but y is not 0.
11. Any number is either positive or negative.
12. Some number is positive and also negative.
13. Some number is positive and some number is negative.
14. At least one number is larger than any given number.
15. The square of each number is positive.
16. Some integer is not 0 and is not positive.
17. All natural numbers are 0 or positive.
18. All triangles have three interior angles.
19. For each angle A, A is acute or obtuse.
20. Some rectangles are squares, and all squares are rectangles.
21. Each line L is parallel to L_1 or it is not parallel to L_1.
22. No triangles have four sides.
23. Not all rectangles are squares.

1.4 Open Sentences; Instance of Proof; Counterexample

A sentence which contains an unquantified variable is called an *open sentence*. The sentence

$$x + 2 < 5$$

is open (or open in x) since the variable x is not quantified. Open sentences do not have truth values. To change an open sentence into a sentence with a truth value, either constants are substituted for the variables or else the variables are quantified.

Substituting constants for the variables produces an instance of the open sentence. Instances of

$$x + 2 < 5$$

include

$$1 + 2 < 5,$$

$$2 + 2 < 5,$$

$$3 + 2 < 5,$$

and

$$\pi + 2 < 5.$$

Notice in this case that some instances are true and some are false.

The instances of a quantified sentence such as

$$\forall y, y > 3 \quad \text{and} \quad y < 5$$

are the instances of its open sentence

$$y > 3 \quad \text{and} \quad y < 5.$$

The instance obtained by letting $y = 2$ is

$$2 > 3 \quad \text{and} \quad 2 < 5,$$

and the instance for $y = \pi$ is

$$\pi > 3 \quad \text{and} \quad \pi < 5.$$

Instances of the sentence

Some numbers are greater than 5

are found by first rewriting the sentence with a variable as

$\exists x$, x is greater than 5.

Some instances are

3 is greater than 5,

7 is greater than 5,

and

8 is greater than 5.

Using one's previous knowledge of particular numbers and operations on them, it is possible to prove many existential generalizations. All that is needed is a single true instance.

The existential statement

For some x, $x^2 < 28$

is true since the number 4, among others, provides a true instance,

$$4^2 < 28.$$

A true instance of an existential generalization is called an *instance of proof*.

It is not possible in general to prove universal generalizations by instances, since in this case every possible instance (and usually these are infinite in number) would have to be checked.

The universal statement

For each x, $x(x + 3) = x^2 + 3x$

is *not* proven to be true by the instances

$$2(2 + 3) = 2^2 + (3)(2),$$

$$-3(-3 + 3) = (-3)^2 + (3)(-3),$$

and

$$5(5 + 3) = 5^2 + (3)(5),$$

nor by any finite number of instances even though they are all true. A proof of the statement must be based on some general assumptions about the collection of all numbers. The question of formal proof based on explicitly stated assumptions (axioms) is considered in Chapter 8.

Informal proofs of universal statements frequently appear in mathematical writing. The above statement can be proved informally by using familiar rules of algebra—in particular, the distributive law and the commutative law.

Proof:
For each number x,

$$x(x + 3) = (x)(x) + (x)(3) = x^2 + 3x.$$

It is possible to disprove universal statements (which are false) in a manner similar to that used in proving true existential statements. One false instance of a universal generalization disproves it.

The sentence

For each number x, $x^2 > 0$

is not true since $0^2 > 0$ is a *false* instance. The number 0 here is called a *counterexample*.

As with proofs of true universal generalizations, formal disproofs of false existential generalizations require some general assumptions, but again informal disproofs of such statements are frequently given.

The sentence

For some x, $x + 1 = x$

is false, for if it were true, elementary algebraic manipulation would yield $1 = 0$.

EXAMPLE 1.3 Label each sentence *true*, *false*, or *open sentence* appropriately. Give a counterexample for each false generalization having only universal quantifiers. Give an instance of proof for each true generalization having only existential quantifiers.

(a) For each x, for each y, $x < y$.
False. Counterexample: $x = 2$, $y = 2$.

(b) For each x, for each y, $x + y = y + x$.
True.

(c) $\exists x \exists y$, $x + y < 0$.
True. Instance of proof: $-2 + (-3) < 0$.

(d) For each x, there is a y such that

$$x = \frac{1}{y}$$

False. Let $x = 0$; then no number y will provide a true instance.

(e) $x + 3 > 7$.
Open sentence. x is not quantified.

EXERCISE SET 1.3

In Exercises 1–38, label each sentence *true*, *false*, or *open sentence*. Give a counterexample for each false generalization having only universal quantifiers. Give an instance of proof for each true generalization having only existential quantifiers.

1. Each number is less than 3.
2. Some numbers are perfect squares.

3. There is a number x such that $x^2 = 2$.
4. For each number x, there is a number larger than x.
5. For each x, $x + y > y$.
6. At least one number is larger than its square.
7. For each x, $x + x = 2x$.
8. All numbers are either even or odd.
9. Any number that has a square root is positive.
10. All even numbers are larger than x.
11. For each number x, if x is greater than 3, then x is greater than 2.
12. $3x - 2 = 10$.
13. $\exists x,\ 3x - 2 = 10$.
14. $\exists x$ (x is a counting number), $3x - 2 = 10$.
15. $\exists y,\ y = y + 1$.
16. $\exists x,\ 3 + x = x + 3$.
17. $\exists x,\ 2x - 5 = 0$ and $5x - 2 = 0$.
18. $\exists x,\ 2x - 3 = y$.
19. $\forall x,\ x + 0 = 0$.
20. $\exists x,\ x + 0 = 0$.
21. $x \cdot 0 = 0$.
22. $\forall x,\ x \cdot 0 = 0$.
23. $x \cdot 0 = x$.
24. $\exists x,\ x \cdot 0 = x$.
25. $\forall x\ \forall y,\ x + y = y + x$.
26. $\forall x\ \exists y,\ x + y = 3$.
27. $\exists x\ \forall y,\ x + y = 3$.
28. $\forall x\ \exists y,\ x \cdot y = 0$.
29. $\exists y\ \forall x,\ x \cdot y = 0$.
30. $\exists x\ \forall y,\ x - y = y - x$.
31. $\forall x\ \exists y,\ x - y = y - x$.
32. $\exists z,\ z^2 = z$ and $z \neq 0$.
33. $\forall x,\ 2 = 3$.
34. $\exists y,\ 4 - 3 = 1$.
35. $\forall x\ \forall y\ \forall z,\ x + y = z$.
36. $\forall x\ \forall y\ \exists z,\ x + y = z$.
37. $\exists x\ \exists y\ \exists z,\ x + y = z$.
38. $\forall x\ \exists y$ (y is an integer), $y > x$.

In Exercises 39–48 determine whether each sentence is true or false. Using your knowledge of real numbers and algebra, justify your answer.

39. $\forall x\ \exists y,\ x - y = 0$.
40. $\forall x,\ (x^2 - 1)(x + 1) = (x + 1)^2(x - 1)$.

41. $\exists x, x(x + 1) = x^2$.
42. $\exists x$ (x is an integer), $x + 3 = 3x - 2$.
43. $\forall x\ \exists y, x \cdot y = 1$.
44. $\exists x\ \forall y, x \cdot y = 0$.
45. $\forall t, t^2 > 0$.
46. $\forall x\ \exists y, x < y$ and $y < x + 1$.
47. $\forall x$ (x is a natural number), $2x$ is even.
48. $\forall x\ \forall y\ \exists z, x = y + z$.
49. Find an open sentence with one variable which is true whether quantified universally or existentially.
50. Find an open sentence with one variable which is true when quantified existentially, but false when quantified universally.
51. An algebra student is likely to say that $x + x = 2x$ is a true statement. Is he correct?

1.5 Conjunctions

Many of the mathematical statements used previously in the text have been simple sentences. To express ideas more clearly, it is often appropriate to use compound sentences—that is, sentences composed of several simple sentences together with suitable connecting words. Complete statements (independent clauses) which have no connective words such as "not," "and," "or," "but," and "if . . . then" are called *components* of the compound sentence. The connecting words are referred to as *connectives*.

The compound sentence

x is greater than 5 and x is less than 6

consists of two complete sentences (components),

x is greater than 5

and

x is less than 6,

joined by the connective "and." The sentence is called the *conjunction* of the two components.

In order to understand a mathematical statement, it is often helpful to identify the components and the connectives and to find their position in the sentence. Writing the above sentence as

(x is greater than 5) and (x is less than 6)

shows that it is a conjunction of two components. Further abbreviation is possible by symbolizing the connective "and" as "&," obtaining

(x is greater than 5) & (x is less than 6).

The sentence

Some numbers are even and positive

can be rewritten with a variable as

$\exists x$, x is even and positive.

The components of the conjunction are the open sentences

x is even

and

x is positive.

(Notice that the latter component is not explicitly stated in the original sentence.) The sentence written symbolically, i.e., with the components isolated and the connective symbolized, is

$\exists x$, (x is even) & (x is positive).

1.6 Disjunctions and Denials

A disjunction is a compound sentence in which the two components (or subordinate clauses) are joined by the connective "or." The sentence

x is even or x is odd and positive

has the connective "or" between the two clauses (not necessarily component sentences)

x is even

and

x is odd and positive.

Separating the sentence into components, it appears as

(x is even) or [(x is odd) & (x is positive)]

(Notice that this sentence is a disjunction of a single component and a conjunction.)

The connective "or" is written symbolically as "$\vee$." Its use is illustrated in the following example.

EXAMPLE 1.4 Write each sentence symbolizing the connectives and quantifiers and setting off the completed components with parentheses.

(a) Each number is even or is odd.
$\forall x$, [(x is even) $\vee$ (x is odd)].

(b) Each number is positive or is negative, or else it is zero.
$\forall x$, [(x is positive) $\vee$ (x is negative)] $\vee$ (x is zero).

(c) Some angle A is a right angle, or it is obtuse or acute.
$\exists A$ (A is an angle), (A is a right angle) $\vee$ [(A is obtuse) $\vee$ (A is acute)].

Notice how the parentheses correspond to the punctuation of the original sentence in the last two sentences.

The denial of the sentence

x is even

is the sentence

x is not even.

Symbolizing "not" as "$\sim$," the sentence "x is not even" becomes

$\sim$ (x is even).

This reads, "It is not the case that x is even." The sentence

For some x, it is false that x is greater than 2 and less than 3 can be written

$$\text{E}x, \sim [(x > 2) \ \& \ (x < 3)].$$

Notice that the denial applies to the whole conjunction, as indicated by the use of brackets.

EXAMPLE 1.5 Write the sentence symbolically.

For some integer x, x is not even and not odd.

$\exists x$ (x is an integer), $\sim$ (x is even) & $\sim$ (x is odd).

EXERCISE SET 1.4

Write the following sentences (Excercises 1–22) symbolizing the connective and the quantifiers and setting off the completed components with parentheses.

1. Some number is rational and is a perfect square.
2. For every number x, x is less than 3 or x is even.
3. $2 < 3$ and $3 < 4$.
4. The square of x is positive or 0.
5. For each counting number x, $x^2 > 0$ and $-x^2 < 0$.
6. For some number A, A^2 is not greater than 0 or $-A^2$ is not less than 0.
7. $\exists x$, $x > 3$ or $x = 3$, and $x < 5$.
8. Line L_1 is parallel to line L_2 and does not intersect L_2.
9. The absolute value of each number is positive or zero, and is not negative.
10. For each x and for each y, $x < y$ or $y < x$.
11. For some x and some y, x is not less than y and y is not less than x.
12. For each whole number n, there is a whole number m so that $n + m = 1$.
13. For some number a, each number b is larger than a or is not positive.
14. $x < y$ or $y < x$ or $x = y$.
15. $2 < 3$ or $2 = 3$.
16. $2 \leq 3$.
17. $2 \nless 3$.
18. Every integer has a square root.
19. Some integers do not have a square root.
20. Sometimes the square root of a number is not positive.

21. Some number is not negative and is not positive.
22. For each number x, $0 < x$ and $x < x^2$, or $x \nless 0$ and $x \nless x^2$.
23. The open sentence

    x is positive and negative or even

    can be interpreted as a conjunction or as a disjunction. Does the sentence have the same meaning in either case? Explain.
24. Which pairs of sentences have the same meaning?

    (a) $x < 0$. (e) $x \geq 0$.

    (b) $x > 0$. (f) $x \leq 0$.

    (c) $\sim (x < 0)$. (g) $\sim (x \leq 0)$.

    (d) $\sim (x > 0)$. (h) $\sim (x \geq 0)$.
25. Determine whether each sentence of Exercises 1–15 is true, false, or an open sentence.

1.7 Conditionals

Compound sentences in which the connective is "if . . . then" are called *conditional sentences*, or simply *conditionals*. The symbol for the connective "if . . . then" is "$\rightarrow$," which can be read "arrow" or "if . . . then." The sentence

If x is rational, then x is not irrational

has the two components "x is rational" and "x is irrational" together with the connective "if . . . then" and the connective "not." It can be rewritten in symbolic form as

$$(x \text{ is rational}) \rightarrow [\sim (x \text{ is irrational})].$$

The sentence preceding the arrow, "x is rational," is called the *antecedent* of the conditional, while the sentence after the arrow, "x is not irrational," is called the *consequent*.

The conditional

If x is positive, then x^2 is positive and $-x$ is negative

symbolizes as

$$(x \text{ is positive}) \rightarrow [(x^2 \text{ is positive}) \ \& \ (-x \text{ is negative})].$$

The parentheses and brackets are used to clarify the intent of the original sentence. The antecedent of the conditional is "x is positive," while the consequent is "(x^2 is positive) & ($-x$ is negative)." The connective "if . . . then" does not occur as part of the antecedent or consequent.

$$x^2 > 3 \text{ if } x > 2 \text{ or } x < -2$$

has as an antecedent,

$$x > 2 \quad \text{or} \quad x < -2$$

and as a consequent,

$$x^2 > 3.$$

Symbolically, the sentence is written

$$[(x > 2) \lor (x < -2)] \rightarrow x^2 > 3.$$

In this example, the antecedent of the conditional appears last in the word order of the sentence. Word order should not be used to determine the order of the conditional. The word "if" determines which part of the sentence is the antecedent and which is the consequent. The sentence means the same as

$$\text{If } x > 2 \text{ or } x < -2, \text{ then } x^2 > 3.$$

The use of connectives in mathematical writing is usually restricted to the four connectives already mentioned, "and," "or," "not," "if . . . then," together with a fifth, "if and only if." This last connective will be considered in a later section.

EXERCISE SET 1.5

Rewrite the following sentences symbolizing the quantifiers and connectives and setting off the completed components with parentheses.

1. For each x, if $x > 3$, then $x > 2$.
2. If x is positive, then x^3 is positive.
3. A number is negative if it is less than 0.
4. For each x, if x is even or x is odd, then $x + x$ is even.

5. If $x > 2$ and x is even, then $x > 3$.
6. If $x > 2$, then x is even and $x > 3$.
7. If x is even and $x > 3$, then $x > 2$.
8. If $x > 2$, then $x^2 > 4$, and if $x < 2$, $x^2 < 4$.
9. If $x > 0$, then $-x < 0$, and if $x < 0$, then $-x > 0$.
10. If $x > 0$, then $x + 1 > 0$, and if $x < 0$ then $x - 1 < 0$.
11. A number is a perfect square if it is an integer and has an integral (whole number) square root.
12. Some number is larger than π, and if it is an even integer, it is divisible by 4.
13. An angle A is a straight angle if it is the sum of two right angles.
14. If $A > 0$ and $A < \pi/2$, then $\sin A > 0$ and $\cos A > 0$.
15. Sin $A = \cos A$ if $A = \pi/4$ or $A = 5\pi/4$.

1.8 Truth of Conjunctions and Disjunctions

To determine whether the sentence

Each number is less than 5 or greater than 3

is true or not, consider the two components

$$x < 5.$$

and

$$x > 3$$

Surely, neither is universally true, for many numbers are not less than 5 and many are not greater than 3. The generalization does not assert that each number is less than 5, however; and it does not assert that each number is greater than 3. It merely insists that each number must be greater than 3 *or* it must be less than 5. No matter which number one chooses, it is not possible that both components would be false. The statement, then, is universally true.

As a universally true statement, each instance is true. In the instance

$$4 < 5 \quad \text{or} \quad 4 > 3.$$

both components are true. In some writings this use of the word "or" is not acceptable in that "or" is taken to mean "one or the other but not both." In this text, as in most mathematical writing, "or" will mean "one or the other or both," as described in the example.

The sentence

$\forall x$, x is negative or x has a square root

is a true statement since each number is either negative or nonnegative, and each nonnegative number has a square root. Are there instances of this generalization where both components are true?

The existential statement

$$\exists x, x^2 < 0 \quad \text{or} \quad x + 1 = x$$

can be proved to be true by finding just one instance where one of the components is true. Unfortunately, neither of the components,

$$x^2 < 0$$

nor

$$x + 1 = x$$

has true instances, i.e., each is universally false. The original sentence is therefore false.

The sentence

$\exists x$, $x > 0$ and x is even

asserts that *both* components, $x > 0$, x is even, are true for some x. Such a number x is easy to find—2, 4, 6, 8, 10, and so on, for example. Each of these produces a true instance of $x > 0$ and of x is even.

The sentence

$$\forall x, x^2 > 0 \quad \text{and} \quad x + 1 > x$$

asserts that each number has two properties: it has a positive square *and* one added to it yields a number larger than the original. The number 0 is a counter-example since the instance

$$0^2 > 0 \quad \text{and} \quad 0 + 1 > 0$$

is not true. That is, it is not so that both components are true.

The existential generalization

$$\exists x, x < 0 \quad \text{and} \quad x > 0$$

is false since no one number x exists which is *both* less than 0 and greater than 0.

EXERCISE SET 1.6

Classify each sentence (Excercises 1–16) as true or false. Give a counterexample for each false generalization having only universal quantifiers. Give an instance of proof for each true generalization having only existential quantifiers.

1. $\forall x, x \neq 0$ or $x^2 > 0$.
2. $\exists x, x < 0$ or $\sqrt{x^2} = x$.
3. $\exists x, x \not> 0$ or $x = 0$ or $x > 0$.
4. $\forall x, x < 0$ or $x = 0$ or $x > 0$.
5. $\forall x$, x is not even or $2x$ is even.
6. $\exists x$, x is even and $2x$ is even.
7. Some number is an even integer and is less than 0.
8. Each number is positive or is negative.
9. $\forall x\, \exists y, x < y$ and $y < x + 1$.
10. $\exists x\, \forall y, x < y$ and $y < x + 1$.
11. $\forall x\, \exists y$, x is nonpositive or $0 < y < x$.
12. $\exists x, x + 2 = 5$ and $x - 1 = 7$.
13. $\exists x, x^2 + 3x + 2 = 0$ and $x^2 - 4x - 5 = 0$.
14. $\forall x, \sqrt{x^2} = x$ or $x < 0$.
15. $\exists A$, $\sin A = \cos A$ and $\tan A = 1$.
16. $\exists A$, $\sin A = \cos A$ and $\tan A = -1$.

Write each sentence (Excercises 17–22) symbolically and determine whether it is true or false. Justify your answer.

17. There is a number which is positive, or else it is negative and has a positive square.
18. Each number is positive, or else it is negative and has a positive square.
19. Each number has a square root or is negative.
20. Each triangle is isosceles or has three angles, no two of which are equal.
21. At least one triangle is an isosceles, an equilateral, and a right triangle.
22. Each triangle is isosceles or else it is not equilateral.
23. $\exists x, x < 3$ and x is even.
    (a) Is this sentence true?
    (b) Does the number 4 give an instance of proof that this sentence is true?
    (c) Is 4 a counterexample?
    (d) Is 1 a counterexample?
    (e) Why doesn't 6 give an instance that proves the sentence?
    (f) Why doesn't 1 give an instance that proves the sentence?

(g) Does the sentence assert that some number is less than 3?
(h) Describe all the numbers which prove the sentence to be true.

24. $\exists x$, $x < 3$ or x is even.
(a) Is the sentence true?
(b) Does 4 give an instance of proof? Does 2? Does 1?
(c) Does 5 give an instance of proof?
(d) Is 5 a counterexample to the sentence?
(e) Does the sentence assert that there is a number less than 3?
(f) Describe the numbers which give instances of proof.

25. For each x, x is less than 3 and x is even.
(a) Write the sentence symbolically.
(b) Does the sentence assert that each number is less than 3?
(c) Is each number less than 3?
(d) Is the sentence true?
(e) Is 2 a counterexample?
(f) Does 2 give an instance of proof of the generalization?

26. Each number has a square greater than zero or is such that twice itself equals itself.
(a) Write the sentence symbolically.
(b) Does the sentence assert that each number has a square greater than zero?
(c) Does the sentence assert that some number has a square greater than zero?
(d) Is there a number whose square is not greater than zero? If there is one, is it a counterexample to the generalization?
(e) Does the sentence assert that twice a number equals the number for each number?
(f) Is the sentence true?

1.9 Truth of Conditionals

Conditional sentences were introduced in section 1.7. It is most essential to gain an understanding of what the mathematician means by the use of the conditional.

Is the sentence

For each x, if x is greater than 4, then x is greater than 3

true or not? The average person would accept this sentence as one that is true, for certainly any number that is greater than 4 must be greater than 3. Mathematicians (presumably they are not average persons) also accept this statement as true.

This sentence, being a true universal generalization, must be true for each of its instances. That is, whenever a number is substituted for x, a true statement is obtained. Both

If 8 is greater than 4, then 8 is greater than 3

and

If 29 is greater than 4, then 29 is greater than 3

must be true sentences since they are instances of this true universal generalization. In the first case, it is observed that "8 is greater than 4" and "8 is greater than 3." That is, both components are true statements. To disprove the common misconception that both components must be true for the conditional to be true, one need only observe other instances of the above generalization, such as

If -2 is greater than 4, then -2 is greater than 3

and

If 0 is greater than 4, then 0 is greater than 3.

These sentences, since they are instances of a *true* universal generalization, must be true. But in both cases, neither of the components is true. Each component, "-2 is greater than 4," "-2 is greater than 3," "0 is greater than 4," and "0 is greater than 3," is false. The conditional sentence, of course, did *not* assert that any of these *components* were true.

It is a common temptation to call such instances false. If any instance were accepted as false, then it would of course be a counterexample to the universal generalization

$\forall x$, if $x > 4$, then $x > 3$;

that is, it would prove this generalization to be false. To avoid this predicament, *all* the instances are accepted as true.

Finally, the instances

If 4 is greater than 4, then 4 is greater than 3

and

If π is greater than 4, then π is greater than 3

illustrate cases in which the antecedent is false, but the consequent is true. These, too, as instances of a true universal generalization, are true.

The universal generalization

For each x, if x is greater than 3, then x is greater than 7

is not a true sentence. (Do you agree?) It is false because there are numbers greater than 3 which are *not* greater than 7; 5 is such a number. The instance generated by 5,

If $5 > 3$, then $5 > 7$,

is a false sentence.

Some other counterexamples to the generalization are the numbers 4, $4\frac{1}{2}$, 6, $6\frac{1}{2}$, and π. (Note that numbers such as 0, 1, 2, 9, 11, 72, and 100 are not counterexamples.) The only instances of this generalization which are false are those in which the antecedent is true and the consequent is false. It is consistent to accept all other instances as true.

[NOTE: In writing generalizations whose instances are conditionals, the universal quantifiers are generally omitted. In the text to follow, all conditionals will be assumed to be universally quantified if quantifiers do not appear. The order of the quantifiers follows the order of occurrence of the variables.]

EXERCISE SET 1.7

In Exercises 1–20, tell whether the sentence is true or false. Justify your answer. Each variable is assumed to be universally quantified if not explicitly quantified.

1. There is an x such that if x is less than 5, then x is negative.
2. If line L_1 is not line L_2, then L_1 is parallel to L_2, or else the lines intersect at one point.
3. If a number is divisible by 2, then it is divisible by 6.
4. If a number is divisible by 6, then it is divisible by 2.
5. If $x = 0$, then $(x - 2)x = 0$.
6. If $x(x - 2) = 0$, then $x = 0$.
7. If $x \neq 0$, then $(x - 2)x \neq 0$.
8. $\exists x$, if $x > 2$, then $(x - 2)x \neq 0$.
9. If $x = 0$, then $xy = 0$.
10. If $xy = 0$, then $x = 0$.
11. If $x \neq 0$, then $xy \neq 0$.

12. If $xy \neq 0$, then $x \neq 0$.
13. $\exists y$, if $xy = 0$, $x = 0$.
14. If $xy = 0$, then $x = 0$ and $y = 0$.
15. If $x = 2$, then $x^2 = 4$.
16. If $x^2 = 4$, then $x = 2$.
17. If $a < 0$, then $1/a < 0$.
18. If $A = 30°$, then $\sin A = \frac{1}{2}$.
19. If A is a multiple of π, then $\sin A = 0$.
20. If $\sin A = 0$, then A is a multiple of π.
21. $\forall x$, if x is even, then $2x$ is even.
    (a) Write the sentence symbolically.
    (b) Is the sentence true?
    (c) Does the sentence assert that the double of each even number is even?
    (d) Does the sentence assert that $2x$ is even for each x?
    (e) Is $2x$ even for each x?
    (f) Does the sentence assert that x is even for each x?
    (g) Is x even for each x?
    (h) Considering the fact that 2 is an even number, does the sentence assert that $2 \cdot 2$ is an even number?
    (i) Considering the fact that 3 is not an even number, does the sentence assert that $2 \cdot 3$ is an even number?
    (j) Since $2 \cdot 3$ is an even number, is the sentence wrong in that it does not assert that $2 \cdot 3$ is an even number?
    (k) Is the instance, "if 3 is even, then $2 \cdot 3$ is even," a true instance?
    (l) Find a false instance of the generalization.
22. For each x, if x is an integer, then x is positive.
    (a) Write the sentence symbolically.
    (b) Is the sentence true?
    (c) Does the sentence assert that each integer is positive? Is each integer positive?
    (d) Does the sentence assert that each positive number is an integer?
    (e) Since 5 is an integer, does the sentence assert that 5 is positive?
    (f) Since -6 is an integer, does the sentence assert that -6 is positive?
    (g) Find a false instance of the generalization.
    (h) Would the number 18 provide a counterexample for the sentence? Would -18 provide a counterexample?
23. For each x, if $x^2 > 0$, then $x > 0$.
    (a) Write the sentence symbolically.
    (b) Does the sentence say that each number is greater than 0?
    (c) Since 4 is greater than 0, and $4 = 2^2$, does the sentence assert that 2 is greater than 0?

(d) Does the sentence assert that $0 > 0$? Explain.
(e) For the sentence to be true, must -2 be greater than 0?
(f) Is the sentence true? Justify your answer.

24. For each triangle T, if T is congruent to an equilateral triangle with sides of length 2, then T is similar to that triangle.
(a) Write the sentence symbolically.
(b) Does the sentence assert that each triangle T is similar to the equilateral triangle with side length 2?
(c) Does the sentence say that each triangle T is congruent to the equilateral triangle with side length 2?
(d) Can you find a triangle which is congruent to an equilateral triangle with side length 2 and is not similar to that triangle? Would such a triangle give a counterexample to the sentence?
(e) Is the sentence true or false?
(f) Can you find a triangle which is similar to an equilateral triangle with side length 2, but is not congruent to it? Would such a triangle give a counterexample to the sentence?
(g) Would the sentence be true if the words "for each" were changed to "for some"?

1.10 Converse, Contrapositive, and Biconditionals

The *converse* of a conditional is the conditional obtained by interchanging the antecedent and the consequent of the original conditional. (Only conditionals have converses—conjunctions, disjunctions, and so forth do not.)

The converse of

$$\forall x, (x \leq 2) \rightarrow (x \leq 3)$$

is

$$\forall x, (x \leq 3) \rightarrow (x \leq 2).$$

The converse of

For each integer x, if x is even, then $2x$ is even

is the conditional

For each integer x, if $2x$ is even, then x is even.

Upon consideration of several conditionals together with their converses, one should note that the original sentence may be true while its converse is false, or vice versa. On the other hand, the original sentence and its converse may both be true or both be false. Although both the above conditionals were true, neither of the converses were. Both the conditional

If $x \neq 0$, $x^2 \neq 0$

and its converse

If $x^2 \neq 0$, then $x \neq 0$

are true.

Sentences in which the principal connective is "if and only if" are called *biconditional* sentences or *statements of equivalence*. Each biconditional can be considered as the conjunction of a conditional together with its converse as illustrated herewith. The biconditional

$x < y$ if and only if $x + a < y + a$

means the same as

If $x < y$, then $x + a < y + a$, and if $x + a < y + a$, then $x < y$.

For a biconditional to be true, the two components (or clauses) must have identical truth values for each instance. If for some instance the truth values were different (that is, one true and the other false), one conditional would have a true antecedent and a false consequent, making it false. If both components are true, or both false, however, then both conditionals of these components are true. Since the two sentences of a true biconditional have the same truth values in each instance, they are said to be *equivalent* or *logically equivalent sentences*.

The sentence

$\forall x, x < 3 \rightarrow x < 4$

is a generalization sentence (it is a universal generalization), but each of its instances is a conditional. For this reason we will also refer to the generalization sentence as a "conditional." Similarly, generalization sentences each of whose instances is a biconditional will be referred to as "biconditionals." Furthermore, universal quantifiers are assumed for all unquantified variables in biconditional sentences just as in the case of conditionals.

The biconditional

$$\forall x,\ x < 3 \leftrightarrow x < 4$$

is false since the conditional

$$\forall x,\ x < 4 \rightarrow x < 3$$

is false. A counterexample for this conditional, such as the number 3, will be a counterexample for the biconditional. Notice that one component of the biconditional is false and the other is true when $x = 3$.

The biconditional

$$x^2 > 0 \leftrightarrow x \neq 0$$

is true. (Why?) The two sentences, $x^2 > 0$, $x \neq 0$, are equivalent sentences.

The *contrapositive* of a conditional sentence is the conditional obtained by replacing the antecedent by the denial of the consequent, and replacing the consequent by the denial of the antecedent. The contrapositive of

$$\forall x,\ (x < 2) \rightarrow (x < 3)$$

is the conditional

$$\forall x,\ \sim (x < 3) \rightarrow \sim (x < 2),$$

or, written in the usual way,

$$\forall x,\ (x \nless 3) \rightarrow (x \nless 2).$$

The contrapositive of

If x is even, then $2x$ is even

is the conditional

If $2x$ is not even, then x is not even.

The relation of the truth value of a conditional to that of its contrapositive is developed in the exercises to follow.

EXERCISE SET 1.8

Write the converse of each conditional and compare the truth value of the original conditional to that of the converse.

1. If $x < 3$, then $x + 2 < 5$.
2. If $x < 3$, then $x < 5$.
3. If $x < 2$, then $x^2 < 4$.
4. If there is a number less than 7, then there is a number less than 5.
5. If $x < 3$ or $x = 3$, then $-x > 3$.
6. If an integer is a multiple of 3, then it is a multiple of 6.
7. $\forall x$, if $x > 2$, then $(x - 2)x \neq 0$.
8. $xy = 0$ if $x = 0$.
9. If line L is parallel to M, and M is parallel to N, then L is parallel to N.
10. If line L is perpendicular to line M, and M is perpendicular to N, then M is perpendicular to N.
11. If $x = y$, then $xz = yz$.
12. If x is an integer, then $2x$ is an integer.
13. If x is not an integer, then nx is an integer for some integer n.
14. If n is a natural number, n is an integer or n is zero.

Write each biconditional symbolically, including explicit or understood quantifiers. Determine the truth value of each sentence; justify your answer.

15. For each x, $x < 0$ if and only if $-x > 0$.
16. $x < y$ if and only if $x < 0$ and $y > 0$.
17. $2x$ is even if and only if x is even.
18. $2x$ is even if and only if x is an integer.
19. $x > 0$ if and only if $x^2 > 0$.
20. $x = y$ if and only if $y^2 = x^2$.
21. A triangle is equilateral if and only if it is equiangular.
22. A natural number x is odd if and only if $x = 2n + 1$ for some natural number n.
23. $2x = 5$ is equivalent to $x = \frac{5}{2}$.
24. Each integer m is a prime number and is even if and only if $m + m = m^2$.
25. A conditional is true if and only if its consequent is true.

Write the contrapositive of each sentence and compare its truth value to that of the original conditional.

26. If $x < 3$, then $x < 4$.
27. If $x > 3$, then $x > 4$.

28. If $a > 0$, then $1/a > 0$.
29. If $x = 0$, then $xy = 0$.
30. If an integer is divisible by 12, it is divisible by 6.

For the exercises to follow, p, q, and r are sentences—that is, variables or place holders for sentences.

31. Find the converse of $p \rightarrow q$.
32. Find the contrapositive of $p \rightarrow q$.
33. Find the contrapositive of $(p \;\&\; r) \rightarrow q$.
34. Suppose in some instance that $p \rightarrow q$ is true and that p is true. What can be said of the truth value of q?
35. Suppose in some instance that $p \rightarrow q$ is true and that q is true. What can be said of the truth value of p?
36. Suppose that $p \leftrightarrow q$ is true and p is false. What can be said of the truth value of q?
37. If $p \rightarrow q$ is true, what can be said of the truth value of $\sim q \rightarrow \sim p$?
38. Is $p \rightarrow q$ equivalent to $q \rightarrow p$? Justify your answer.

1.11 Synonyms

It is of fundamental importance to be able to determine the antecedent and the consequent of each conditional sentence. In the examples appearing previously, the antecedent has usually occurred after the "if" in the first part of the sentence, while the consequent usually occurred in the second part of the sentence after the word "then." Many variations occur in the writing of conditionals both in the position of the antecedent and consequent, and in the words used for the connective. Most of the forms in common usage today are presented in this section.

The conditional sentence

$$\forall x, \sin x = 0 \rightarrow x \neq \pi/2$$

can be correctly written in each of the following ways:

$\forall x$, if $\sin x = 0$, then $x \neq \pi/2$,

$\forall x$, $\sin x = 0$ only if $x \neq \pi/2$,

$\forall x$, only if $x \neq \pi/2$, $\sin x = 0$.

The conditional

A number is even only if its double is even

is written symbolically as

$\forall x$, (x is even) $\rightarrow$ ($2x$ is even).

These examples show that the "only if" part of the sentence is the consequent of the conditional, regardless of where it appears in the sentence.

Other connective words frequently used are "necessary" and "sufficient." Sentence structure varies considerably with their usage. Care should be taken to observe which components the words apply to rather than which components they may occur *next* to.

In the conditional sentence

A *necessary* condition for x to be positive is that it is not negative,

the "necessary condition" relates to the sentence, "x is not negative," which is the consequent of the conditional. Symbolically, the conditional would appear as

$\forall x$, (x is positive) $\rightarrow$ [$\sim$ (x is negative)].

Using the connective involving "sufficient," this may be written

A *sufficient* condition for x not to be negative is that it is positive,

or, perhaps more appropriately,

For x not to be negative, it is sufficient that it is positive.

In either case, the sufficient condition is "x is positive," the antecedent of the conditional.

The conditional

$\forall x, x^3 > 0 \rightarrow x > 2$

could be correctly written in each of the following ways:

If $x^3 > 0$, then $x > 2$;

$x^3 > 0$ only if $x > 2$;

For x^3 to be greater than 0, it is necessary that $x > 2$;

A sufficient condition for x to be greater than 2 is that $x^3 > 0$;

$x^3 > 0$ is sufficient for $x > 2$.

Using the "necessary and sufficient" terminology, the biconditional

$\forall x\ \forall y,\ x < y \leftrightarrow y > x$

can be written

For $x < y$, it is necessary and sufficient that $y > x$.

EXERCISE SET 1.9

Write each sentence symbolically. (Include quantifiers which are implicitly understood.) List the truth value for each sentence.

1. x is less than 5 only if x is less than 4.
2. Only if x is less than 5 is x less than 4.
3. For x to be less than 5, it is necessary that it be less than 4.
4. A sufficient condition for x to be less than 5 is that it be less than 4.
5. x is divisible by 6 only if x is divisible by 2.
6. For x to be divisible by 6, it is necessary that it be divisible by 2.
7. Each x is divisible by 6 if and only if it is divisible by 2.
8. For xy to be 0, it is necessary that x be 0.
9. For xy to be 0, it is sufficient that x be 0.
10. $xy = 0$ only if $x = 0$.
11. $xy = 0$ if $x = 0$.
12. A necessary and sufficient condition for $x = 0$ is that $xy = 0$.
13. A necessary condition for a triangle to be isosceles is that it be either equiangular or equilateral.
14. In order that a triangle be isosceles, it is sufficient that it be equiangular or equilateral.
15. A triangle is equiangular if it is equilateral, and conversely.
16. $x + 2$ is greater than 2 if x is greater than 0.
17. $x + 2$ is greater than 2 only if x is greater than 0.
18. For $x + 2$ to be greater than 2, it is necessary and sufficient that x be positive.
19. A triangle T is a right triangle if its two acute angles are complementary.
20. A sufficient condition for triangle T to be a right triangle is that its two acute angles be complementary.

Write each conditional using each of the four connective combinations: if . . . then, only if, sufficient, and necessary.

21. $\forall x, (x > 0) \rightarrow (x^2 > 0)$.
22. $\forall x$, (x is a natural number), (x is not positive) $\rightarrow$ (x is zero).
23. $(x + a = b) \rightarrow (x = b - a)$.
24. $p \rightarrow q$ (where p and q are sentences).

1.12 Denials of Generalizations

The *denial* of a sentence is formed by prefixing "it is not the case that" or "it is false that" to the sentence. It is often desirable to substitute equivalent sentences of a more suitable form for such sentences. The following discussion illustrates some of the sentences commonly substituted for denials of generalizations.

The denial of the universal generalization

$$\forall x, x < 2$$

is

It is not the case that $\forall x, x < 2$.

The statement that

$$\forall x, x < 2$$

is false means that there must be at least one number x such that x is not less than 2. In place of the denial, one can write

$\exists x$, it is not the case that $x < 2$,

or, using the more familiar symbolism,

$$\exists x, x \nless 2.$$

Each universal generalization asserts that a statement is true for each number, line, triangle, or whatever; the denial of such a generalization implies that "there is at least one" number, line, triangle, or whatever, for which the statement is *not* true.

EXAMPLE 1.6 For each x, $x^2 > 0$.

Denial: It is false that for each x, $x^2 > 0$.

Statement equivalent to the denial: For some x, $x^2 \ngtr 0$.

EXAMPLE 1.7 For every x, $x < 3$ or $x > 3$.

Equivalent of the denial: For some x, it is not the case that [$x < 3$ or $x > 3$].

The denial of the existential generalization

For some x, $x = x + 1$

is

It is not the case that for some x, $x = x + 1$.

This denial implies that no number is equal to itself plus 1, or equivalently each number is unequal to itself plus 1. This denial then is equivalent to

For each x, it is not the case that $x = x + 1$

or, using the usual denial of equality,

For each x, $x \neq x + 1$.

Each existential generalization asserts that a statement is true for "at least one" number, line, or whatever; the denial of such a generalization implies that there is no number, line, or whatever such that the statement is true. To say that there is "no" number, line, or whatever for which the statement is true is to say that for *each* number, line, or whatever, the statement is false.

EXAMPLE 1.8 For some x, $|x| < x$.

Denial: It is not the case that for some x, $|x| < x$.

Equivalent of the denial: For each x, $\sim (|x| < x)$ (or, "For each x, $|x| \nless x$").

EXAMPLE 1.9 Some numbers have a negative square.

Equivalent to the denial: Each number has a nonnegative square.

EXAMPLE 1.10 $\exists x$, $x > 3$ and $x < 3$.

Equivalent to the denial: $\forall x$, it is not the case that $[x > 3$ and $x < 3]$.

The procedure above can be extended to generalizations involving more than one quantifier. How this may be done is illustrated step by step in the first of the examples below.

EXAMPLE 1.11 $\forall x \, \forall y,\ x \cdot y = x + y$.

Denial: It is false that $\forall x \, \forall y,\ x \cdot y = x + y$.

As a universal generalization in x, this is equivalent to

$\exists x$, it is false that $[\forall y,\ x \cdot y = x + y]$.

As a universal generalization in y, this in turn is equivalent to

$\exists x \, \exists y$, it is false that $x \cdot y = x + y$

or, in more familiar language,

$\exists x \, \exists y,\ x \cdot y \neq x + y$.

EXAMPLE 1.12 $\exists x \, \exists y,\ x + y \neq y + x$.

Equivalent of the Denial: $\forall x \, \forall y,\ x + y = y + x$. (Note that "it is false that $x + y \neq y + x$" means "$x + y = y + x$.")

EXAMPLE 1.13 There is an x such that each number y is less than x.

Equivalent of the denial: $\forall x \, \exists y,\ y \nless x$, or, in words, "For each x, there is a number y which is not less than x."

EXAMPLE 1.14 $\forall x \, \forall y \, \exists z,\ x + y = z$.

Equivalent of the denial: $\exists x \, \exists y \, \forall z,\ x + y \neq z$.

In general, it is possible and most desirable to rephrase the denial of a quantified sentence in such a way that the "not" connective words do not apply to the part of the sentence containing the quantifier. It is further possible to restrict the use of the "not" connective so that it applies only to single components rather than to compound statements. How this is accomplished is explored at this time.

The denial of

For each x, $x < 2$ or $x > 2$

is equivalent to

For some x, $\sim [x < 2 \text{ or } x > 2]$.

The "not" connective applies to the disjunction

$x < 2$ or $x > 2$.

The sentence asserts that for some x, $x < 2$ or $x > 2$ is false. That is, there is an x such that x *is not* less than 2 *and* x *is not* greater than 2 (otherwise the disjunction would be true).

With this consideration, the denial is equivalent to

$\exists x$, $x \not< 2$ *and* $x \not> 2$.

In this form, the sentence uses the "not" connective only on the individual components $x < 2$, $x > 2$. Other examples where this property is maintained in restatements of denials are:

EXAMPLE 1.15 $\forall x$, $x < 2$ *or* $x > 3$.

Equivalent of denial: $\exists x$, $x \not< 2$ *and* $x \not> 3$.

EXAMPLE 1.16 *Some* triangles are isosceles *or* equilateral.

Equivalent of denial: All triangles are *not* isosceles *and not* equilateral.

EXAMPLE 1.17 Each angle has a complement *or* is greater than $\pi/2$.

Equivalent of denial: Some angle has *no* complement *and* is *not* greater than $\pi/2$.

For denials involving conjunctions, the procedure is similar. To deny

For some x, $x > 0$ and $x = 0$

it may be asserted that

For each x, $\sim [x > 0 \text{ and } x = 0]$.

That is, for each x, the resulting instance of $x > 0$ and $x = 0$ is false. For this to be the case, each x must be such that it is not greater than 0 *or* else it is not equal to 0 (or both). That is,

For each x, $x \not> 0$ or $x \neq 0$.

Other examples follow.

EXAMPLE 1.18 $\forall x$, x is even *and* x is positive.

Equivalent of denial: $\exists x$, x is *not* even *or* x is *not* positive.

EXAMPLE 1.19 Some triangle is isosceles *and* equilateral.

Equivalent of denial: Each triangle is *non*isosceles *or* is *non*equilateral.

EXERCISE SET 1.10

Write denials of each of the following sentences. Then write a sentence equivalent to the denial so that each occurrence of the connective "not" applies to only one component. Label the denial *true* or *false*. (Symbolize the sentence if necessary to aid in writing the denial.)

1. Each number is less than 3.
2. Some numbers are perfect squares.
3. For each x, $x + x = 2x$.
4. Some number is not positive.
5. Each triangle has three sides.
6. Some parallelograms are not squares.
7. For each x, $x = 2$ or $x \neq 2$.
8. Each number is positive or negative.
9. Each integer is even or is odd.
10. For each x, x is positive or x is negative or x is not an integer.
11. There is a parallelogram which is a square and is a rectangle.
12. For each x, x is positive and is even.
13. There is an x which is divisible by 6 but is not divisible by 3.
14. It is false that each x is positive or negative.
15. There is a number which is less than or equal to 0 and has a positive square.
16. Each number is less than 0, greater than 0, or equal to 0.

17. Each number is divisible by 2 and divisible by 3, or is not divisible by 6.
18. $\exists x\, \exists y,\ x + y = x$ and $x - y = x$.
19. $\forall x\, \exists y,\ y > x$ and $y < 0$, or $x > 0$ or $x = 0$.
20. $\forall x\, [\sim (\exists y,\ x = 2y)]$.
21. Each x is greater than 0 or else there is a y larger than x and less than 0.
22. Some x is positive and less than each y which is positive.

Write the denial of each sentence and then rewrite it in proper form, i.e., with each "$\sim$" symbol occurring only in single sentences. The variables p, q, and r are for sentences.

23. $p \lor q$.
24. $p \lor \sim q$.
25. $p \,\&\, q$.
26. $(p \,\&\, q) \lor r$.
27. $(p \lor q) \,\&\, r$.
28. $\forall x,\ (p \,\&\, \sim q)$.

1.13 Denials of Conditionals; Denials of Biconditionals

In a previous lesson, a very careful look was taken at mathematical conditionals to determine exactly what they did and did not assert. The principles learned at that time should be recalled in order to understand the writing of equivalent sentences for denials of conditionals.

The conditional

If x is divisible by 2, then it is divisible by 4

is a false statement. As proof of this, since it is a universal generalization (although the universal quantifier is not explicitly stated), a counterexample is offered. In order for a number to be a counterexample, the resulting instance must have a true antecedent and a false consequent. The number 6 is a counterexample, since the resulting instance

If 6 is divisible by 2, then it is divisible by 4

is false. Indeed, 6 is divisible by 2, but 6 is not divisible by 4. In other words, to assert that the conditional is not so is to assert that

There is a number x such that x is divisible by 2, *and* x is *not* divisible by 4.

To deny the conditional

If $r \times r = r, r = 0$

is equivalent to asserting that

There is an r such that $r \times r = r$, but $r \neq 0$.

That is,

$$\exists r, (r \times r = r) \,\&\, (r \neq 0).$$

(Can you find such a number r?)

Other examples are:

EXAMPLE 1.20 $\forall x, (x > 3) \rightarrow (x > 4)$.

Equivalent of denial: $\exists x, (x > 3) \,\&\, (x \not> 4)$.

EXAMPLE 1.21 $\forall x, x > 4 \rightarrow x > 0$.

Equivalent of denial: $\exists x, (x > 4) \,\&\, (x \not> 0)$.

EXAMPLE 1.22 If a triangle is isosceles, it is equilateral.

Equivalent of denial: There is a triangle which is isosceles *and* is *not* equilateral.

EXAMPLE 1.23 If the radius of a circle is greater than 1, then its circumference is greater than 4.

Equivalent of denial: There is a circle which has radius greater than 1 *and* has a circumference *not* greater than 4.

The most suitable form equivalent to the denial of a conditional is the (existentially quantified) *conjunction* of the antecedent with the denial of the consequent. However, students frequently forget this fact and insist, incorrectly, that various forms of conditionals are equivalent to the denial of a conditional. The most common offense in attempting to write a sentence equivalent to the denial of a conditional is merely denying the antecedent and the consequent, without changing the connective. Thus, in a futile attempt to deny

If x is even, then $-x$ is odd,

the sentence

If x is not even, $-x$ is not odd

is presented. The latter could hardly be equivalent to the denial of the original sentence since both it and the original are false. A sentence equivalent to the denial, of course, is

For some x, x is even and $-x$ is not odd.

A sentence equivalent to the denial of a biconditional can be obtained by first writing the sentence as the conjunction of two conditionals. The biconditional

For each x, $x^2 > 0$ if and only if $x > 0$

would appear as

If $x^2 > 0$, then $x > 0$ and if $x > 0$, then $x^2 > 0$.

A statement equivalent to the denial is

There is an x such that $x^2 > 0$ and $x \ngtr 0$, or $x > 0$ and $x^2 \ngtr 0$.

(Can you find an instance of proof of this sentence?)

(There are other, much shorter forms that are equivalent to the denial of a biconditional, but none aids in understanding as does this rather lengthy version.)

EXERCISE SET 1.11

Write an equivalent to the denial of each of the following conditionals and biconditionals using the connective "not" only on the individual components. Recall that each conditional and biconditional is universally quantified unless otherwise stated. Classify your answer as *true* or *false*.

1. If x is less than 5, then x is less than 4.
2. If x is divisible by 14, then x is divisible by 7.
3. If x is divisible by 7, then x is divisible by 14.
4. If $x = 0$, then $(x - 2)x = 0$.
5. If $x(x - 2) = 0$, then $x = 0$.
6. If $\sin A = \frac{1}{2}$, then $A = 30°$.
7. For each number, if the number is even or odd, then 1 added to the number is odd or even.
8. A parallelogram is a square only if it is a rectangle.
9. A pentagon is regular only if its angles are each 180° and each side is 1 cm in length.
10. A necessary condition for an integer to be positive is that it is not negative.
11. A sufficient condition for an integer to be positive is that it be not negative.
12. A sufficient condition for a number to be negative is that it be not positive and not 0.
13. Two lines are parallel if they are on the same plane and do not have a point in common.
14. For each angle A, the sine of that angle is positive if the angle is in quadrant I or quadrant IV.
15. If $xy = 0$, then $x = 0$.
16. $xy = 0$ only if $x = 0$ and $y = 0$.
17. In order that $x^2 = 4$, it is sufficient that $x = 2$.
18. If $x^2 = 4$ and x is positive, then x is 2.
19. For each number x, $|x| = x$ only if $x > 0$.
20. $x = 3$ if and only if $x^2 = 9$. (*Hint*: Write as the conjunction of two conditionals.)
21. If x is even then $x - 1$ is odd, and conversely.
22. $x > 0$ or $x < 0$ if and only if $x \neq 0$.
23. A parallelogram is a square if and only if it is a rectangle and has equal diagonals.
24. If $x < y$, then for some z, $xz < yz$.
25. There is a triangle that has two equal sides only if it has two equal angles.

Write the denial of each sentence and then rewrite it in proper form. The variables p, q, r, and so on are for sentences.

26. $\forall x, p \rightarrow q$.
27. $p \rightarrow (q \vee r)$.
28. $(p \;\&\; q) \rightarrow r$.
29. $(p \;\&\; q) \leftrightarrow r$.
30. $(\sim p \vee q) \leftrightarrow (r \;\&\; s)$.

Sets

CHAPTER TWO

2.1 Introduction

One of the problems of mathematics is that of finding an adequate language for expressing ideas. In the previous chapters the ambiguity of everyday speech showed itself frequently; in fact, one of the reasons for studying logic is to remove as much of the ambiguity as possible from the use of the sentential connectives in mathematics. In this chapter a simple but extremely useful idea for stating precisely what is intended is introduced—the notion of a set.

At first the language and notation may seem to be both bothersome and cumbersome. However, after becoming moderately familiar with the new terminology, you will wonder how you were able to say things clearly without it.

The notion of a set is by no means new to you; you have worked with the set of whole numbers and the set of fractions, and in algebra you learned the arithmetic of another set of numbers—the set of real numbers. The rules for addition of real numbers differed depending upon whether the numbers chosen were from the set of positive numbers, the set of negative numbers, or from both sets.

The entities of geometry, too, are usually viewed as sets of points. Thus, a circle is a set of points each of which is the same distance from a fixed point, the center; a triangle is a set of points (viewed in another way, a triangle is a set of three line segments). Furthermore, to find the locus of points equidistant from two parallel lines is simply to find the set of points equidistant from the two lines.

2.2 Notation

The most critical problem in the use of sets is making clear which things (elements) belong to a given set and which do not. A standard notation used by mathematicians to describe a set in terms of its elements is the *set-selector* notation. The use of this notation is illustrated by the following examples.

EXAMPLE 2.1 $\{x: x < 7\}$ denotes the set of all real numbers smaller than 7, and is read, "the set of all real numbers x such that x is less than 7." 4.1 is an element of the set since $4.1 < 7$ is a true statement. 7 is not an element of the set since $7 < 7$ is a false statement.

EXAMPLE 2.2 $\{x: x \text{ is even}\}$ denotes the set of all even numbers and is read, "the set of all real numbers x such that x is even."

EXAMPLE 2.3 $\{L\colon L$ is parallel to the line "$y = 3x - 2$"$\}$ denotes the set of all lines of the plane parallel to the line "$y = 3x - 2$" and is read, "the set of all L such that L is parallel to the line '$y = 3x - 2$.'"

EXAMPLE 2.4 $\{x\colon 3 < x < 4\}$ denotes the set of all real numbers between 3 and 4, and is read,

The set of all x such that 3 is less than x and x is less than 4.

In the examples where the selector statement involved numbers, the "selection" of elements was made from the set of *real numbers*. Where lines were involved, it was presumed that the lines were on the plane (instead of in space, for example).

The statement

6 is an element of $\{x\colon x < 7\}$

is written symbolically as

$$6 \in \{x\colon x < 7\}.$$

The entire sentence would be read

6 is an element of the set of all x where x is less than 7.

To indicate that an object is not an element of a set, the symbol "$\notin$" is used. Thus

$$8 \notin \{x\colon x < 7\}$$

reads, "8 is not an element of the set of all x where x is less than 7." Several sentences about elements of sets are given below with their respective truth values.

EXAMPLE 2.5 (a) $1 \in \{x\colon x > 2\}$. (False)

(b) $1 \notin \{x\colon x > 2\}$. (True)

(c) $\pi \in \{x\colon 0 < x < 3\}$. (False)

(d) $7.2 \in \{x\colon x^2 > 45\}$. (True)

(e) $5 \in \{x\colon x < 2 \text{ or } x > 4\}$. (True)

EXERCISE SET 2.1

Express each set in Exercises 1–18 in set-selector notation. Use standard mathematical abbreviations where suitable.

1. The set of all real numbers less than 2.
2. The set of all real numbers greater than 2.
3. The set of all numbers less than 2 and greater than 0.
4. The set of all numbers greater than -2 or equal to -2.
5. The set of positive numbers.
6. The set of all nonzero numbers.
7. The set of all numbers which are not negative.
8. The set of all numbers between 2 and 4 not including 2 or 4.
9. The set of all numbers between 2 and 4 including both 2 and 4.
10. The set of all even integers.
11. The set of all x where $x^2 + 2x + 1 = 0$.
12. The set of all solutions to the equation $x^2 + 5x - 8 = 0$.
13. The set of all numbers which are not solutions to $x^2 - 3x + 2 = 0$.
14. The set of all angles A where $\sin A = \frac{1}{2}$.
15. The set of all angles where $\sin A = \cos A$.
16. The set of all points on the circle $x^2 + y^2 = 4$.
17. The set of all points on the x-axis.
18. The set of all numbers greater than 2 and less than 0.

In Exercises 19–24, write the words indicating how the set notation is read. Use "real number," "line," "angle," and so forth in the reading as needed for clarity. Then express each exercise in words without using a variable.

19. $\{x: x > 3 \text{ and } x < 5\}$.
20. $\{x: x \text{ is even}\}$.
21. $\{A: \tan A = 1\}$.
22. $\{L: L \text{ is parallel to the } x\text{-axis}\}$.
23. $\{x: \text{if } x > 3, x > 4\}$.
24. $\{x: 3 < x^2 < 4\}$.

Classify each sentence in Exercises 25–40 as true or false, appropriately.

25. $2 \in \{x: x \geq 2\}$.
26. $2 \notin \{x: x \geq 2\}$.
27. $2.5 \in \{x: x \geq 2\}$.
28. $0.43 \in \{x: 0 < x < 1\}$.
29. $7 \notin \{x: 0 < x < 1\}$.

30. $7 \notin \{x: 0 < x \text{ or } x > 1\}$.
31. $\pi \in \{x: x > 3 \text{ or } x < 4\}$.
32. -2 is in the set of all x where x is an odd positive integer or x is an even negative integer.
33. $\sqrt{5}$ is in the set of positive numbers.
34. 3 is in the set of prime numbers.
35. $6 \in \{y: y \text{ is even and positive, and divisible by } 3\}$.
36. $10 \in \{y: y \text{ is even and } y \text{ is positive, and } y \text{ is divisible by } 3\}$.
37. $8 \in \{z: z > 0 \text{ or } z < 0\}$.
38. $\pi \in \{x: x \text{ is a natural number}\}$.
39. "$x + y = 3$" $\in \{L: L$ is parallel to "$2x + 3y = 4$"$\}$.
40. "$x - 2y = 0$" $\in \{L: L$ is parallel to "$x - 2y = 6$"$\}$.

2.3 The Roster Notation

For sets consisting of only a few elements, and for sets which can be written sequentially, the *roster notation* is of great convenience. In this notation the elements of the set are displayed between the braces. Thus the set which has elements 1, 2, and 5 is denoted by

$$\{1, 2, 5\}.$$

The set of all counting numbers can be written as

$$\{1, 2, 3, 4, 5, \ldots, n, \ldots\}$$

where the first three dots, . . . , mean to continue on as the sequence started; the n refers to the nth number in the sequence (here the number n itself); and the last three dots mean to continue the sequence "forever."

The set of all positive even integers is written

$$\{2, 4, 6, 8, \ldots, 2n, \ldots\}.$$

Notice that the nth term in this instance is $2n$. The tenth term is then $2 \cdot 10$ or 20, and the 88th term is $2 \cdot 88$ or 176.

EXAMPLE 2.6 $5 \in \{2, 4, 5\}$ is true, but $5 \in \{3, 6, 9, \ldots, 3n, \ldots\}$ is false.

EXAMPLE 2.7 $\pi \in \{1, 2, 3, \ldots, n, \ldots\}$ is false, but $-76 \in \{-1, -2, -3, \ldots, -n, \ldots\}$ is true.

The sets

$$\{1, 2, 3\}, \qquad \{3, 2, 1\}, \qquad \{1, 2, 3, 3, 2\}$$

are the same since each has the elements 1, 2, 3 and no others. Although the last set has the elements 2 and 3 listed twice, this does not mean that it has any more elements. The elements, regardless of how many times they are listed, are still only the three numbers, 1, 2, 3. In practice, a multiple listing of elements as in the last set is not desirable.

The first and second sets are the same, even though the elements are listed in a different order. The order in which the elements of a set are listed is not a property of the set.

2.4 Intervals, Half Lines, Rays

The set of real numbers each of which is greater than the real number a and less than the real number b is called the *open interval from a to b.* It is denoted by

$$]a, b[.$$

In set-selector notation,

$$]a, b[\; = \{x: a < x < b\}.$$

a is called the *left endpoint* of the interval and b the *right endpoint* of the interval. Note that an open interval does not contain its endpoints.

An open interval $]a, b[$ along with both of its endpoints is called the *closed interval from a to b*, and is denoted by

$$[a, b].$$

In set-selector notation,

$$[a, b] = \{x: a \leq x \leq b\}.$$

An open interval $]a, b[$ along with its left endpoint is called the *left closed interval from a to b* (or *right open interval from a to b*) and is denoted by

$$[a, b[.$$

A similar definition is given for the *right closed* (or *left open*) *interval from a to b* which is denoted by

$$]a, b].$$

EXAMPLE 2.8 $]2, 4[$, the open interval from 2 to 4, is the set of all numbers larger than 2 but less than 4. Numbers such as 2.01, 3, and 3.999 are in this interval, but neither 2 nor 4 is in the interval. In set-selector notation,

$$]2, 4[= \{x: 2 < x < 4\}.$$

EXAMPLE 2.9 $]-\sqrt{2}, \sqrt{2}]$, the right closed interval from $-\sqrt{2}$ to $\sqrt{2}$, is the set of all numbers larger than $-\sqrt{2}$ and less than or equal to $\sqrt{2}$. This interval contains the endpoint $\sqrt{2}$ but not the endpoint $-\sqrt{2}$. Some elements of the set are -1.4, -1, 0, 1.2, and 1.41. In set-selector notation,

$$]-\sqrt{2}, \sqrt{2}] = \{x: -\sqrt{2} < x \leq \sqrt{2}\}.$$

The set of all numbers which are larger (or smaller) than some number a is called a *half line* and is denoted by

$$]a, \infty) \qquad (\text{or } (-\infty, a[).$$

a is called the *endpoint* of the half line and does not belong to the half line. In no case should the two symbols ∞ and $-\infty$ be taken to be real numbers. In set-selector notation,

$$]a, \infty) = \{x: a < x\}$$

and

$$(-\infty, a[= \{x: x < a\}.$$

A half line $]a, \infty)$ (or $(-\infty, a[$) along with its endpoint is called a *ray* and is denoted by

$$[a, \infty) \qquad (\text{or } (-\infty, a]).$$

a is called the *endpoint* of the ray and, of course, belongs to the ray. In set-selector notation,

$$[a, \infty) = \{x: a \leq x\}$$

and

$$(-\infty, a] = \{x: x \leq a\}.$$

EXAMPLE 2.10 $(-\infty, 2[$, one of the two half lines with endpoint 2, is the set of all numbers less than 2. -3 and 1 belong to this half line, but 2 and 5 do not. In set-selector notation

$$(-\infty, 2[= \{x: x < 2\}.$$

EXAMPLE 2.11 $[6, \infty)$, one of the two rays with endpoint 6, is the set of all numbers greater than or equal to 6. In set-selector notation,

$$[6, \infty) = \{x: 6 \leq x\}.$$

[NOTE: Consistent with this notation, $(-\infty, \infty)$ is often used to designate the set of all real numbers.]

2.5 Graphs of Sets of Real Numbers

The real numbers belonging to an interval or other set can be pictured as points on the real number line. The examples below indicate how this is done. Notice the position of the brackets ([,]) in determining whether or not a boundary number is in the interval. Individual numbers are pictured as an enlarged dot on the line.

EXAMPLE 2.12 The graph of $\{1, -1, 0\}$ is

-4 -3 -2 -1 0 1 2 3 4

EXAMPLE 2.13 The graph of $[-1, 1]$ is

-3 -2 -1 0 1 2 3

EXAMPLE 2.14 The graph of $]2, 4[$ is

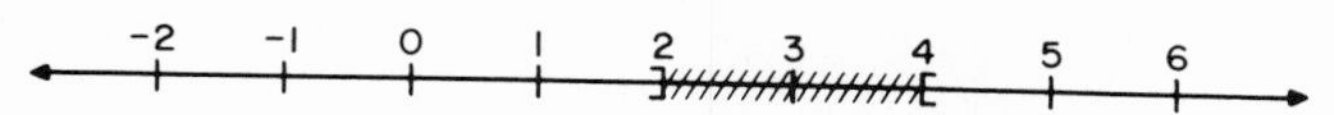

Notice that 2 and 4 *are not* elements of the set.

EXAMPLE 2.15 The graph of $[1, \infty)$ is

Notice that 1 *is* an element of the set.

The difference between the set $\{4, 6\}$ and the set $]4, 6[$ is portrayed by the graphs of the two sets: The graph of $\{4, 6\}$:

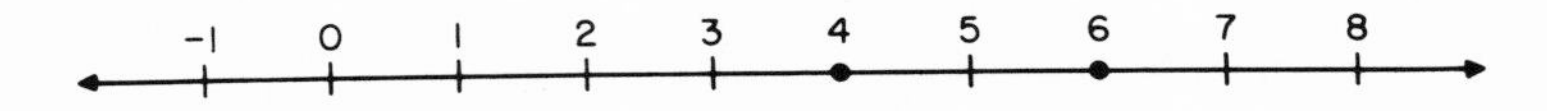

The graph of $]4, 6[$:

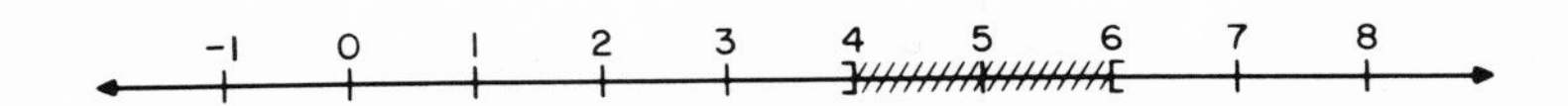

EXERCISE SET 2.2

Classify each sentence in Excercises 1–20 as true or false, appropriately.

1. $2 \in \{x: x \geq 2\}$.
2. $2.5 \in \{x: x \leq 2\}$.
3. $2.5 \in \{x: x \geq 2\}$.
4. $\frac{1}{2} \in [0, 1]$.
5. $\frac{1}{2} \in [0, 1[$.
6. $1.4 \in [1, \infty)$.
7. $4 \in [2, 4]$.
8. $4 \in]2, 4[$.
9. $\pi \in \{x: x > 0 \text{ and } x < 2\}$.
10. $\pi \in \{x: x > 0 \text{ or } x < 0\}$.
11. $0 \in (-\infty, -1]$.
12. $7 \in (-\infty, \infty)$.
13. $-7 \in \{x: x \in (-\infty, 0[\text{ and } x \text{ is an integer}\}$.
14. $4 \in \{x: x \in [1, 3[\text{ or } x \in [-2, 4[\}$.
15. $\sqrt{10} \in [2.7, \pi]$.
16. $\pi \in [\sqrt{7}, \sqrt{10}]$.
17. $-7 \in \{x: \text{if } x \in [0, \infty), \text{ then } x > 0\}$.
18. $3 \in \{1, 2, 3, \ldots, n, \ldots\}$.
19. $10 \notin \{1, 2, 3, \ldots, n, \ldots\}$.
20. $10 \in \{x: x < 4 \rightarrow x < 0\}$.

In Exercises 21–33 write each set using interval, ray, or half-line notation. Graph each set on a number line.

21. $\{x: 2 < x < 4\}$.
22. $\{x: 0 \leq x \text{ and } x \leq 1\}$. (This set is called the *closed unit interval*).
23. $\{x: x > 0 \text{ and } x \leq 1\}$.
24. $\{x: x > 1\}$.
25. $\{x: x > 1 \text{ or } x = 1\}$.
26. $\{x: x < 4 \text{ or } x < 5\}$.
27. $\{x: x < 4 \text{ and } x < 5\}$.
28. $\{x: x > -1 \text{ and } x < 1\}$.
29. The set of all numbers between 2 and 4, not including 2 or 4.
30. The set of all real numbers larger than 5.
31. The set of all negative numbers.
32. The set of all nonnegative numbers.
33. The set of all nonpositive numbers which are larger than -3.

In Exercises 34–45 write each set using set-selector or roster notation.

34. $[0, 2]$.
35. $]-1, 3[$.
36. $[4, +\infty)$.
37. $]-3, 4]$.
38. $(-\infty, -3]$.
39. $(-\infty, \infty)$.
40. $]-2, 3]$.
41. $]3, 3[$.
42. $]\pi, \infty)$.
43. The set of all positive integers greater than 2.
44. The set of all natural numbers between 2 and 7 (not including 2 or 7).
45. The set of all integers which are multiples of 3 and are not positive.

2.6 Subsets

Each of the elements of the open interval $]0, 1[$ is an element of the closed interval $[0, 1]$. That is, the open interval consists entirely of elements of the closed interval. The set $]0, 1[$ is said to be a *subset* of $[0, 1]$. The sets

$$[0, \tfrac{1}{2}], \qquad [\tfrac{1}{2}, 1[, \qquad \{1\}$$

are also subsets of $[0, 1]$ because each element from each of these sets is an element of $[0, 1]$. In fact, any set that can be formed from elements of $[0, 1]$ is a subset of $[0, 1]$. (How many such subsets are there?) Any set which contains an element which is not in $[0, 1]$ is not a subset of $[0, 1]$.

The above remarks may be extended to sets generally. The subsets of a set A are those sets which may be formed from the elements of A. To determine whether a set is a subset of a second set, it is more convenient to formulate the definition of subset in the following manner: a set B is a subset of a set A provided the generalization.

$$\forall x, \text{ if } x \in B, \text{ then } x \in A$$

is a true sentence. (Of course, this wording is in agreement with the notion of subset suggested above).

Is $[0, 1]$ a subset of $]0, 1[$? That is, is the set $[0, 1]$ composed entirely of numbers that are in $]0, 1[$? It can be proved that $[0, 1]$ is not a subset of $]0, 1[$ by proving that

$$\text{If } x \in [0, 1], \text{ then } x \in \,]0, 1[$$

is a false sentence. This is done by showing that

There is some number x such that $x \in [0, 1]$ and $x \notin \,]0, 1[$.

0 is such a number. (Can you find another counterexample?)

The interval $[0, 1]$ is not a subset of $\{x: x < 1\}$ since $1 \in [0, 1]$ and $1 \notin \{x: x < 1\}$. The set $\{x: x < 1\}$ is not a subset of the interval $[0, 1]$ either, since $-1 \in \{x: x < 1\}$, but $-1 \notin [0, 1]$.

To indicate the subset relationship between two sets, the symbol "$\subset$" is used.

$$]1, 3[\,\subset [1, 4]$$

is read

$]1, 3[$ is a subset of $[1, 4]$,

or

$]1, 3[$ is contained in $[1, 4]$.

The symbol "$\not\subset$" is read "is not a subset of" or "is not contained in." It was proved above that

$$[0, 1] \not\subset \,]0, 1[.$$

An interesting exercise concerning subsets is to find all of the subsets of a given set. The subsets of the set $\{1, 4, 7\}$ include

$$\{1\}, \quad \{4\}, \quad \{7\}, \quad \{1, 4\}, \quad \{1, 7\}, \quad \{4, 7\}.$$

Two other subsets that are often overlooked are the set itself, $\{1, 4, 7\}$, and the set with no elements, $\{\quad\}$. Check in each of these cases to see if each element of these sets is also an element of the set $\{1, 4, 7\}$.

The set with no elements, denoted "$\{\quad\}$" above, is usually represented by "$\emptyset$," and read "the empty set." Note that $\emptyset$ is a subset of $\{1, 4, 7\}$ since if it were not, then there must be an x such that $x \in \emptyset$ and $x \notin \{1, 4, 7\}$. But there cannot be an x such that $x \in \emptyset$ since $\emptyset$ has no elements.

EXERCISE SET 2.3

Determine whether each sentence (Exercises 1–20) is true or false. Disprove each false sentence.

1. $[0, 1] \subset [0, 2]$.
2. $[-2, 3] \subset]-4, \sqrt{6}[$.
3. $[-\sqrt{3}, \sqrt{3}] \subset]-\sqrt{3}, \sqrt{3}]$.
4. $\{x: x \text{ is rational and } x > 0\} \subset]0, \infty)$.
5. $\{1, 2, 3, \ldots\} \subset \{1, 2, 3, 4\}$.
6. $\{1, 2, 3\} \subset \{2, 4, 6, \ldots\}$.
7. $\{x: x > 2 \text{ and } x < 5\} \subset \{x: x > 2\}$.
8. $[0, 1] \subset \{0, 1, 2\}$.
9. $\{x: x > 2\} \not\subset \{x: x > 2 \text{ or } x < 0\}$.
10. $\{x: x > 2 \text{ or } x < 0\} \not\subset \{x: x > 2\}$.
11. $\{x: 0 < x < 1\} \not\subset [0, 1]$.
12. $\{1, 2, 3\} \subset \{1, 2, 4\}$.
13. $\{1, 2, 4\} \not\subset \{1, 2, 3\}$.
14. $\{x: x > 0 \text{ and } x < 5\} \subset \{y: y > 0\}$.
15. $\{x: x > 0\} \subset \{y: y > 0 \text{ and } y < 5\}$.
16. π is in the set of all positive numbers which are less than 3.1416.
17. $\sqrt{7}$ is in the set of all numbers between 2 and 3.
18. If x is in the set of numbers between -1 and $+1$, then $x + 1$ is in the set of numbers between -1 and $+3$.
19. $\{x: x > 0 \rightarrow x = 1\} \subset \{x: x > 0 \rightarrow x \geq 1\}$.
20. $\{y: \text{If } y > 0, y > 1\} \subset (-\infty, 0]$.

Rewrite each sentence (Exercises 21–27) using symbols for the sets and the subset relation. Record whether true or false.

21. The set of all numbers less than 4 is a subset of the set of all numbers less than 3.
22. The set of even numbers contains the set of positive even numbers.
23. The set of positive numbers is contained in the set of nonnegative numbers.
24. The set of positive numbers contains the set of nonnegative numbers.
25. If x is a member of the set of all prime numbers, then $\{x\}$ is a subset of the set of prime numbers.
26. If y is in the set of positive numbers or in the set of negative integers, then y is in the set of integers.
27. If z is in the set of integers, then z is in the set of positive numbers or in the set of negative integers.

Find all the subsets of each set (Exercises 28–34).

28. $\{0, 1\}$.
29. $\{1, 2, 4, 8\}$.
30. $\{0\}$.
31. $\{0, 1, 2\}$.
32. $\emptyset$.
33. $\{1, 2, 5, 7, 9\}$.
34. $[0, 1]$.

For each exercise below, assuming the sentence is true, which of the statements

$$A \subset B, \quad A \not\subset B, \quad B \subset A, \quad B \not\subset A$$

must necessarily be true? Explain.

35. If $x \in A$, then $x \in B$.
36. $\forall x, x \in A$ or $x \in B$.
37. $x \in A$ is necessary for $x \in B$.
38. $\exists x, x \in A$ and $x \notin B$.
39. $\forall x, x \notin A$ or $x \in B$.
40. $\exists x, x \in A$ and $x \in B$.
41. If $y \notin A$, then $y \notin B$.
42. $y \in A$ if $y \in B$.
43. $x \in A$ only if $x \in B$.
44. $x \in A$ is sufficient for $x \in B$.
45. $x \in A$ if and only if $x \in B$.
46. $\forall x, x \notin A$.
47. $\forall x, x \in A$.
48. $\forall x, x \in A$ or $x \notin B$.

2.7 Set Intersection

The statement that a number is less than 3 and greater than 1 can be interpreted in the following two ways using set language: first, the number is in the half line $(-\infty, 3[$, since the number is less than 3, and it is also in the half line $]1, \infty)$, since it is greater than 1; second, the number is in the interval $]1, 3[$. In the first case, the number was thought of as belonging to each of the two sets,

$$(-\infty, 3[\quad \text{and} \quad]1, \infty)$$

In the second case, only one set, the interval $]1, 3[$, was considered. The set of all elements common to two given sets is said to be the *intersection* of the two sets. In the example above, the intersection of the half lines

$$(-\infty, 3[\quad \text{and} \quad]1, \infty)$$

is the interval $]1, 3[$. As another example, the intersection of two lines L and M that meet in the single point P is the set consisting of the single point P.

The intersection of two sets is indicated by writing the symbol "$\cap$" between names for the sets. Thus the intersection of the half lines $(-\infty, 3[$ and $]1, \infty)$ can be written as

$$(-\infty, 3[\cap]1, \infty).$$

The sets $(-\infty, 3[$ and $]1, \infty)$ are graphed on the first line below, and the resulting intersection, $]1, 3[$, is graphed on the second line.

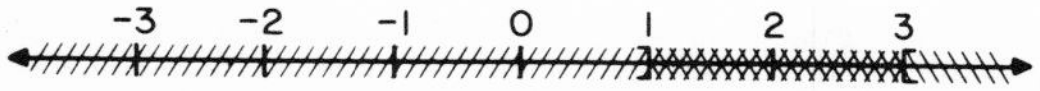

-3 -2 -1 0 1 2 3

Graphs of $(-\infty, 3[$ and $]1, \infty)$

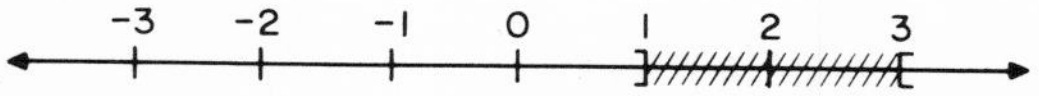

-3 -2 -1 0 1 2 3

Graph of $(-\infty, 3[\cap]1, \infty) =]1, 3[$

EXAMPLE 2.16 "$[4, 7] \cap [5, 11] = [5, 7]$" is read, "The intersection of $[4, 7]$ and $[5, 11]$ is $[5, 7]$."

Graphs of $[4, 7]$ and $[5, 11]$

Graph of $[4, 7] \cap [5, 11]$

EXAMPLE 2.17 $\{2, 3, 4, 5, 6\} \cap \{2, 4, 6, 8\} = \{2, 4, 6\}$.

Graphs of $\{2, 3, 4, 5, 6\}$ and $\{2, 4, 6, 8\}$

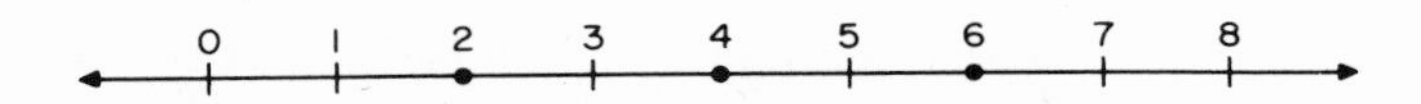

Graph of $\{2, 3, 4, 5, 6\} \cap \{2, 4, 6, 8\}$

EXAMPLE 2.18 $(-\infty, 2] \cap]2, \infty) = \emptyset$.

Graphs of $(-\infty, 2]$ and $]2, \infty)$

Graph of $(-\infty, 2] \cap]2, \infty)$

Formally, the intersection of any pair of sets is the set of all elements common to both of the sets. For the sets A and B,

$$A \cap B = \{x : x \in A \text{ and } x \in B\}.$$

The intersection, $A \cap B$, is always a set regardless of what sets A and B are chosen, although this intersection may be the set without any elements (the empty set).

2.8 Set Union

The set of all elements which are less than 4 or greater than 7 can be expressed as $\{x: x < 4 \text{ or } x > 7\}$. Another way to think of the same set is to think of each x such that x is in the set of all numbers less than 4 or x is in the set of all numbers greater than 7. That is, the set is $\{x: x \in (-\infty, 4[\text{ or } x \in]7, \infty)\}$. This set, then, consists of all those points which are either in the half line $(-\infty, 4[$ or in $]7, \infty)$, or both. It is called the *union* of those two sets; expressed with symbols,

$$\{x: x \in (-\infty, 4[\text{ or } x \in]7, \infty)\} = (-\infty, 4[\cup]7, \infty).$$

The union of two sets is the set which consists of all the elements that belong to at least one of the sets. For the sets A and B,

$$A \cup B = \{x: x \in A \text{ or } x \in B\}.$$

EXAMPLE 2.19 "$[0, 2] \cup [1, 3] = [0, 3]$" is read, "The union of $[0, 2]$ and $[1, 3]$ is $[0, 3]$."

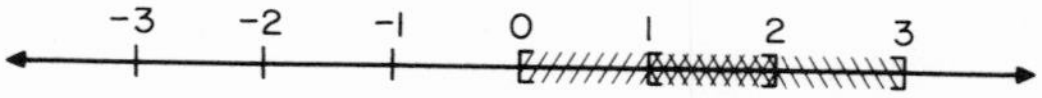

-3 -2 -1 0 1 2 3

Graphs of $[0, 2]$ and $[1, 3]$

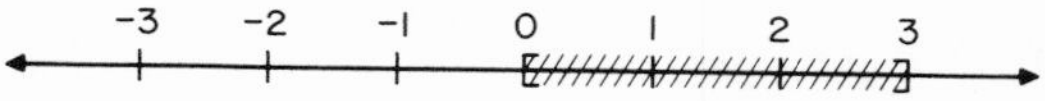

-3 -2 -1 0 1 2 3

Graph of $[0, 2] \cup [1, 3]$

EXAMPLE 2.20 $[0, 1] \cup]1, 2[= [0, 2[$.

EXAMPLE 2.21 $\emptyset \cup \{x: x > 2\} = \{x: x > 2\}$.

EXAMPLE 2.22 $\{1, 2\} \cup \{2, 3\} = \{1, 2, 3\}$.

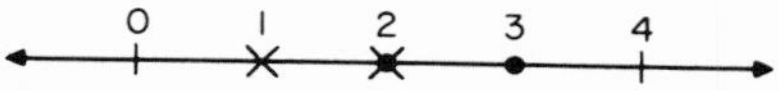

0 1 2 3 4

Graphs of $\{1, 2\}$ and $\{2, 3\}$

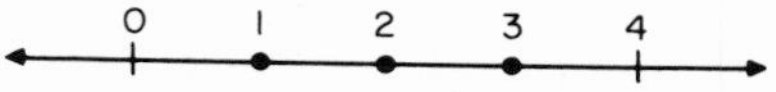

0 1 2 3 4

Graph of $\{1, 2\} \cup \{2, 3\}$

EXERCISE SET 2.4

Express each set (Exercises 1–11) in terms of intervals, half lines, or rays in simplest form. Graph each set of the union or intersection on one graph; then graph the resulting union or intersection on a graph immediately below.

1. $[0, 1] \cup [-1, 0]$.
2. $]-2, 3[\cup]2, 4[$.
3. $[7, \infty) \cup [8, \infty)$.
4. $]1, 2[\cup]2, 3[$.
5. $[1, 2] \cup]2, 3[\cup]\pi/2, \pi[$.
6. $(-\infty, -2] \cup]1, 4] \cup]2, \infty)$.
7. $]0, \pi] \cap]-\pi, \pi[$.
8. $(-\infty, 1[\cap]-1, \infty)$.
9. $]2, 3] \cap [3, \infty)$.
10. $]\sqrt{2}, \infty) \cap (-\infty, -\sqrt{2}[$.
11. $]1, 2[\cap]1, 3[\cap]0, \sqrt{2}[$.

Express each set (Exercises 12–26) in terms of intervals, half lines, or rays in simplest form.

12. $\{x: x < 2 \text{ or } x \geq 3\}$.
13. $\{x: x < \pi \text{ or } x < 3\}$.
14. $\{x: x \leq \sqrt{5} \text{ or } x > 2.2\}$.
15. $\{x: x \leq \sqrt{2}\} \cup \left\{x: x \geq \dfrac{\sqrt{10} + 1}{3}\right\}$.
16. $[0, 2] \cup]-1, 1[$.
17. $\{x: x \geq 2 \text{ and } x \leq 5\}$.
18. $\{x: x \geq \sqrt{2}\} \cap \{x \leq \sqrt{5}\}$.
19. $\{x: x \text{ is positive and } x < \pi\}$.
20. $\left\{x: x \geq \dfrac{\sqrt{5} + \sqrt{2}}{2}\right\} \cap \left\{x: x \geq \dfrac{\sqrt{3} + 2}{2}\right\}$.
21. $([0, 1] \cap [-1, \frac{1}{2}]) \cup]2, 3[$.
22. $[0, 1] \cap ([-1, \frac{1}{2}] \cup]2, 3[)$.
23. $(]3, \infty) \cup (-\infty, -2[) \cap (]4, \infty) \cup (-\infty, -3[)$.
24. $\{x: x < \sqrt{2} \text{ and } x > -\sqrt{2}\} \cup \{x: x < \sqrt{3} \text{ and } x > 0\}$.
25. $\{x: x^2 < 2 \text{ or } x \text{ is between } -1 \text{ and } 3\}$.
26. $\{x: x \text{ is not in } [0, \infty)\}$.

Simplify and write as one set (Exercises 27–32).

27. $\{1, 3\} \cup \{3, 4\}$.
28. $\{1, 2, 3\} \cap \{1, 2, 4\}$.
29. $\{x: x \text{ is an integer}, x > 10\} \cap \{x: x \text{ is an integer}, x \text{ is prime}\}$.
30. $\{1, 2\} \cap [1, 2]$.
31. $\{2, 3, 4\} \cap ([0, \infty) \cup \{x: x \text{ is an integer}, x \text{ is prime}\})$.
32. $\{x: x \text{ is an even integer or } x = 1\} \cap \{x: x \text{ is an odd integer or } x = 0\}$.

Consider each statement (Exercises 33–39) as universally quantified in A, B. Classify as true or false appropriately, providing a counterexample for each false statement.

33. $A \subset B$.
34. $A \cap B \subset A$.
35. $A \subset A \cap B$.
36. $A \cup B \subset A$.
37. $A \subset A \cup B$.
38. $A \cap B = B \cap A$.
39. If $A \subset B$, then $A \cap B = A$.
40. Write an informal proof of each sentence of Exercises 33–39 which is true.

2.9 The Universal Set, Complements of Sets

The statement

$$\forall x, x > 0$$

can be considered true or false depending upon the kind of numbers one is talking about. If the statement is restricted to the set of counting numbers, then it is true to say that each (counting) number is greater than 0. But if the set of all real numbers is considered (which would be the case if no restrictions were made), then it is not true to say that each number is greater than 0.

The set from which all numbers (or whatever) of a particular discussion are to come is called the *universe* of the discussion. To avoid confusion, the universe for sets of numbers in this text has been and always will be the set of real numbers unless specifically stated otherwise. (In geometric examples, the universe is often all the points on the plane or all the lines on the plane, and so forth.) The statement above, then, would mean,

$$\forall x \ (x \text{ is a real number}),\ x > 0.$$

The sentence

$$\exists x,\ x < 5 \quad \text{and} \quad x > 4$$

means

$$\exists x \ (x \text{ is a real number}),\ x < 5 \quad \text{and} \quad x > 4.$$

In the event that a different universe is intended, it will be stated with the problem. To restrict the first statement to the set of counting numbers, one can write

$$\forall x \ (x \text{ is a counting number}),\ x > 0.$$

The *complement* of a set A is the set of all elements of the universe which are not in A. That is, letting $\overline{A}$ represent the complement of A,

$$\overline{A} = \{x\colon x \notin A\}.$$

EXAMPLE 2.23 The complement of $[0, \infty)$ is $\overline{[0, \infty)}$, and

$$\overline{[0, \infty)} = \{x\colon x \notin [0, \infty)\} = (-\infty, 0[.$$

EXAMPLE 2.24 The complement of $[0, 1]$ is $\overline{[0, 1]}$, and

$$\overline{[0, 1]} = \{x\colon x \notin [0, 1]\} = (-\infty, 0[\cup]1, \infty).$$

EXAMPLE 2.25 $\overline{\{x\colon x < 3\}} = \{x\colon x \nless 3\} = [3, \infty).$

Care must be taken to distinguish between the *complement of the intersection* of two sets, such as

$$\overline{[-3, 1] \cap [0, 4]},$$

and the *intersection of two complements of sets*, such as

$$\overline{[-3, 1]} \cap \overline{[0, 4]}.$$

The complement of the intersection can be simplified as follows:

$$\begin{aligned}\overline{[-3, 1] \cap [0, 4]} &= \{x : x \notin ([-3, 1] \cap [0, 4])\}\\ &= \{x : x \notin [0, 1]\}\\ &= (-\infty, 0[\cup]1, \infty).\end{aligned}$$

Whereas, for the intersection of the two complements,

$$\begin{aligned}\overline{[-3, 1]} \cap \overline{[0, 4]} &= \{x : x \notin [-3, 1] \cap \{x : x \notin [0, 4]\}\\ &= ((-\infty, -3[\cup]1, \infty)) \cap ((-\infty, 0[\cup]4, \infty))\\ &= (-\infty, -3[\cup]4, \infty).\end{aligned}$$

This shows that

$$\overline{[-3, 1] \cap [0, 4]} \neq \overline{[-3, 1]} \cap \overline{[0, 4]}.$$

A similar distinction must be made regarding complementation and set union. Thus,

$$\overline{[-3, 1] \cup [0, 4]} = \overline{[-3, 4]} = (-\infty, -3[\cup]4, \infty),$$

while

$$\begin{aligned}\overline{[-3, 1]} \cup \overline{[0, 4]} &= ((-\infty, -3[\cup]1, \infty)) \cup ((-\infty, 0[\cup]4, \infty))\\ &= (-\infty, 0[\cup]1, \infty).\end{aligned}$$

Thus,

$$\overline{[-3, 1] \cup [0, 4]} \neq \overline{[-3, 1]} \cup \overline{[0, 4]}.$$

EXERCISE SET 2.5

In Exercises 1–30, express each set in terms of intervals, half lines, or rays without the use of complements.

1. The complement of $[0, \infty)$.
2. The complement of $(-\infty, \pi[$.

3. $\overline{[0, \pi]}$.
4. $\overline{(-\infty, 0[\, \cup\,]\pi, +\infty)}$.
5. $\overline{]7, \infty)}$.
6. $\overline{[-2, \pi]}$.
7. $\overline{\{x: x \leq 3\}}$.
8. $\overline{(-\infty, \frac{3}{2}]}$.
9. $\overline{[0, \infty) \cup [-1, 1]}$.
10. $\overline{[0, \infty)} \cup \overline{[-1, 1]}$.
11. $\overline{(-\infty, 1] \cup]1, \infty)}$.
12. $\overline{(-\infty, 1]} \cup \overline{]1, \infty)}$.
13. $\overline{[1, 2]} \cap \overline{[2, 3]}$.
14. $\overline{[1, 2] \cap [2, 3]}$.
15. $\overline{[1, 2]} \cup \overline{[2, 3]}$.
16. $\overline{[1, 2] \cup [2, 3]}$.
17. $\{x: x \notin [1, 2] \text{ and } x \notin [2, 3]\}$.
18. $\{x: x \notin [1, 2] \cup [2, 3]\}$.
19. $\{x: x \notin [0, 1]\}$.
20. $\overline{\{x: x \notin [0, 1]\}}$.
21. $\overline{\{x: x \in [0, 1]\}}$.
22. $\overline{\overline{[0, 1]} \cap [0, \infty)}$.
23. $\overline{[0, 1] \cap \overline{[0, \infty)}}$.
24. The complement of $(-\infty, 4] \cup [3, \infty)$.
25. The complement of the union of $(-\infty, 4]$ and $[3, \infty)$.
26. The union of the complements of $(-\infty, 4]$ and $[3, \infty)$.
27. The complement of $\overline{(-\infty, 0]}$.
28. $\overline{\overline{[\sqrt{2}, \infty)}}$.
29. $\overline{\overline{[0, 1]}}$.
30. $\overline{\overline{[-1, \sqrt{2}]}}$.

Express each set below as the complement of a single interval, half line, or ray. (If this is not possible, write "not possible" for your answer.)

31. $\{x: x < 2 \text{ or } x > 3\}$.
32. $\{x: x < 5 \text{ or } x > 7\}$.
33. $\{y: y \neq 3\}$.
34. $\{1, 2, 3, 4, 5\}$.
35. The set of all positive real numbers.
36. $(-\infty, 4] \cup]5, \infty)$.
37. $[1, +\infty) \cup (-\infty, \frac{1}{2}]$.

38. $\{x: x \notin [-\pi, \pi]\}$.
39. $[0, 1]$.
40. $\{x: x^2 > 2\}$.
41. $\{x:$ if $x > 3$, then $x > 5\}$.
42. $\{x: x < 4 \leftrightarrow x < 2\}$.
43. $\{x:$ If x is a natural number, x is a counting number$\}$.
44. $\{x:$ If $x < 0$, $x^2 < 0\}$.

Algebraic Properties of the Real Numbers

CHAPTER THREE

3.1 Introduction

In Chapter Two the universal set was assumed to be the set of real numbers. It is the purpose of this chapter to clarify what is included in the set of real numbers as well as in some of the more important subsets of the real numbers. The first order of business, therefore, is to give a description of the set of real numbers. Actually, two descriptions will be presented since at various times each will be useful.

Geometrically, the real numbers are those numbers which can be pictured on a number line. Each real number corresponds to one point on the number line, and each point on the line corresponds to one real number.

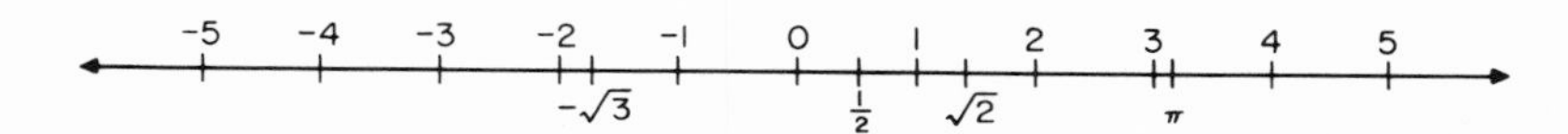

The number-line interpretation for the real numbers can be used to show the property of order; that is, if a point P is to the right of a point Q on the number line, then the real number corresponding to P is greater than the real number that corresponds to the point Q.

The numbers to the right of zero (numbers greater than zero) are called *positive* real numbers; those to the left of zero (numbers less than zero) are called *negative* real numbers; zero is neither positive nor negative. Designating the set of positive numbers by R^+, the set of negatives by R^-, and the set of real numbers by R, it follows that

$$R = R^+ \cup \{0\} \cup R^-.$$

The numbers that are not negative (the nonnegatives) are the numbers greater than or equal to zero. In set notation, the set of nonnegative real numbers is the set $\{x: x \geq 0\}$. Similarly, the set of nonpositive reals is $\{x: x \leq 0\}$.

Before giving the second description of the real numbers (section 3.3), some of the more common subsets of the reals will be considered. The set of *natural* numbers has the elements 0, 1, 2, 3, 4, 5, 6, . . . , and is denoted by N.

$$N = \{0, 1, 2, 3, 4, \ldots, n, \ldots\}.$$

(Some mathematicians exclude the number zero from this set, but in this text 0 is considered to be a natural number.)

Extending the natural numbers by including the negative whole numbers, $-1, -2, -3, \ldots$, gives a subset of the reals called the *integers*. The set of integers is denoted by I.

$$I = \{\ldots, -5, -4, -3, -2, -1, 0, 1, 2, 3, 4, 5, \ldots\}.$$

Since each natural number is an integer, $N \subset I$. The set of positive integers, or *counting numbers*, is designated by I^+;

$$I^+ = \{1, 2, 3, 4, \ldots, n, \ldots\}.$$

The integers can be divided into two subsets, the even and the odd integers. By definition,

An integer is *even* if and only if it is a whole number multiple of 2.

This means that if k is an even integer, then $k = 2m$ for some integer m. An integer is said to be *odd* if it is not even. In other words, if k is an odd integer, then k divided by 2 has a remainder of 1; or $k = 2m + 1$ for some integer m.

The set of all numbers which can be represented as fractions of integers is another subset of the real numbers. This set is called the set of rational numbers (from the notion of ratio) and is denoted by Q.

$$Q = \{r : \exists p, q \in I, q \neq 0, \text{ so that } r = p/q\}.$$

The denominator q is not to be chosen as zero since division by zero has no meaning. Since each integer n can be written as the fraction $n/1$, each integer is also a rational number. In set notation, $I \subset Q$. More generally,

$$N \subset I \subset Q \subset R.$$

EXAMPLE 3.1 Show that if n is an even integer, then $3n$ is also an even integer.

Suppose that n is an even integer. Then for some $m \in I$, $n = 2m$. (Recall the definition of an even integer.) Then

$$3n = 3(2m) = 2(3m).$$

Therefore $3n$ is an even integer since it is expressed as 2 times the integer $3m$.

EXERCISE SET 3.1

Describe each set (Exercises 1–13) in terms of its elements.

1. The intersection of the set of nonnegative and the set of nonpositive reals.
2. The complement of the set of nonpositive reals.
3. The complement of the set of positive reals.
4. The union of the set of positive reals and the set of nonpositive reals.
5. The union of the set of positive reals and the set of negative reals.
6. The set of integers intersected with the set of positive reals.
7. $I \cap Q$.
8. $N \cap I^+$.
9. $N \cup I$.
10. The intersection of the set of odd integers and the positive rationals.
11. The union of the odd integers and the even integers.
12. The intersection of the odd integers and the even integers.
13. The union of the positive odd integers and the nonnegative even integers.
14. Show that if x is even, then $x + 2$ is even.
15. Show that if x is odd, then $4x$ is even.
16. Show that if x is odd, then $x + 3$ is even.
17. Show that the product of two even numbers is an even number.
18. Show that the product of an odd number and an even number is an even number.

3.2 Real Numbers That Are Not Fractions

If all the rational numbers (fractions of integers) were pictured on the number line, it would seem that each point of the line would have a rational number paired with it. (After all, there are 99 fractions with denominator 100 between each pair of integers, 999 with denominator 1000, and so on.) Nevertheless, it will be proved (informally) that there is a real number which is not rational (that is, irrational), and hence a point on the number line with no rational number paired with it. The number chosen is that real number which corresponds to the length of the diagonal of a unit square—that is, $\sqrt{2}$. (See Figure 3.1.)

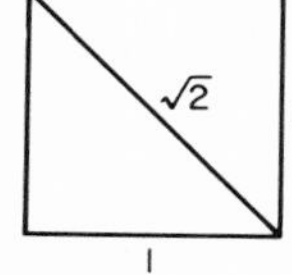

Figure 3.1

As a first step, it is shown that

For each integer p, if p is even then p^2 is even.

Proof:
Let p be any even integer. Then $p = 2m$ for some integer m, and $p^2 = (2m)^2 = 2(2m^2)$. Hence p^2 is even.
Next

For each integer p, if p^2 is even then p is even.

Proof:
Since any statement is equivalent to its contrapositive (see section 1.10), it suffices to show that

For each integer p, if p is not even then p^2 is not even.

In view of this, let p be any odd (not even) integer. Then $p - 1$ is even, $p - 1 = 2m$, and $p = 2m + 1$ for some integer m. It follows that

$$\begin{aligned} p^2 &= (2m + 1)^2 \\ &= 4m^2 + 4m + 1 \\ &= 2(2m^2 + 2m) + 1 \end{aligned}$$

and

$$p^2 - 1 = 2(2m^2 + 2m),$$

where $2m^2 + 2m$ is an integer.

Hence $p^2 - 1$ is even and p^2 is odd (not even).

The two statements just proved will be used in the proof that $\sqrt{2}$ is irrational.

Proof:
To show that $\sqrt{2}$ is not rational, assume that it is rational. (This assumption will lead to a contradictory statement about the fraction representing $\sqrt{2}$. Since the contradictory statement cannot be accepted, the assumption that $\sqrt{2}$ is a rational must be wrong. Therefore, $\sqrt{2}$ must not be rational.)
Suppose $\sqrt{2}$ is a rational number. Then there are integers p and q such that $\sqrt{2} = p/q$, and such that the fraction p/q is reduced to lowest terms. (That is, no integer other than 1 or -1 divides both p and q.) Squaring both sides of $\sqrt{2} = p/q$,

$$2 = \frac{p^2}{q^2}$$

is obtained, which is equivalent to

(1) $2q^2 = p^2$.

But $2q^2$ is an even integer, which means p^2 is an even integer (they are the same). By the previous discussion, since p^2 is an even integer, p is an even integer. That is, there is some integer s such that

$$p = 2s.$$

Then

$$p^2 = 4s^2,$$

and, by substituting in equation (1),

$$2q^2 = 4s^2$$

which is equivalent to

$$q^2 = 2s^2.$$

But $2s^2$ is an even number, which means that q^2 is an even number. But then q is even (why?); hence there is some integer r such that

$$q = 2r.$$

Since $p = 2s$ and $q = 2r$, it follows that the fraction p/q reduces to the fraction s/r. This contradicts the statement that p/q was reduced to lowest terms to begin with. The assumption that $\sqrt{2}$ is a rational number is not correct since it leads to contradictory statements. One concludes, therefore, that $\sqrt{2}$ is not a rational number (i.e., $\sqrt{2}$ is an *irrational* number).

$\sqrt{3}$ is also irrational, as are $\sqrt{5}$, $\sqrt{6}$, $\sqrt{7}$, and $\sqrt{8}$, while $\sqrt{4}$ and $\sqrt{9}$ are rational. In general, for each natural number n, $\sqrt{n}$ is irrational or else n is a perfect square.

Later in this chapter it will be shown how to distinguish rational from irrational numbers in an entirely different way. A somewhat surprising fact is that there are at least as many irrational numbers as there are rational; in fact, there are more irrationals!

EXERCISE SET 3.2

1. Prove that if x^2 is an odd integer and x is an integer, then x is an odd integer.
2. Prove that if x^2 is an even integer and x is an integer, then x is an even integer.

3. Prove that if 3 divides A^2 and A is an integer, then 3 divides A.
4. Prove that $\sqrt{3}$ is not a rational number.
5. Prove that $\sqrt{5}$ is not a rational number.
6. Prove that $\sqrt[3]{2}$ is an irrational number.
7. Show where the method used to prove that $\sqrt{2}$ is not rational fails in trying to prove that $\sqrt{4}$ is not rational.
8. For which natural numbers n is "if n divides A^2 and A is an integer, then n divides A" a true statement? Justify your answer.

3.3 Representation of Real Numbers by Infinite Decimals

Each real number can be represented in the Hindu-Arabic decimal notation as an infinite sequence of digits. Thus,

$$2 = 2.000\ldots,$$

$$\tfrac{1}{3} = 0.3333333\ldots,$$

$$5\tfrac{1}{2} = 5.5000000\ldots,$$

where the three dots indicate that the decimal continues on in the same manner forever. This means that there is no "last" digit. In some cases, it is a cycle of several digits which repeats *ad infinitum*, as in

$$\tfrac{41}{333} = 0.123123123123123\ldots,$$

where the cycle "123" is repeated. Other repeating infinite decimals are

$$17.22551225512255122551\ldots,$$

$$0.00357893578935789\ldots,$$

and

$$1004.72335116111611116111611161116\ldots.$$

Does every infinite decimal repeat sooner or later? Consider the decimal

$$0.1010010001000010000010000001\ldots,$$

in which the three dots do not mean to repeat the last digit over and over, but rather mean to continue the *pattern established* forever. Thus the last "1" written down is to be followed by 00000001000000001. . . . This infinite decimal never does repeat, nor do the decimals

$$0.123456789101112131415\ldots,$$

$$0.0102030405060708091001 1012\ldots,$$

and

$$0.1211211121111211111211111 12\ldots.$$

(Can you detect the pattern in each case?)

A convenient notation for *repeating* infinite decimals is to place a bar over the cycle of repetition in its first occurrence in the expansion. Thus,

$$0.1234123412341234\ldots$$

is represented by

$$0.\overline{1234}.$$

Further examples are

$$13.24\overline{1135} = 13.241135113511 35\ldots,$$

$$0.00257\overline{3} = 0.002573333333\ldots.$$

Each repeating decimal can be shown to represent a rational number by the procedure used in the following example.

EXAMPLE 3.2 4.321321321321. . . is a repeating decimal. Letting

$$x = 4.321321321\ldots$$

and multiplying both sides by 10^3 (3 happens to be the length of the cycle that repeats), another number is obtained which has the same repeating cycle as the original number. Furthermore, when the two numbers are "lined up" by their decimal points, the cycles also "line up."

$$1000x = 4321.321321321321\ldots,$$

$$x = \quad 4.321321321321\ldots.$$

Subtracting,

$$999x = 4317.000000\ldots,$$

so that

$$x = \tfrac{4317}{999} = \tfrac{1439}{333}.$$

The decimal expansion of each rational number can be found by long division. The rational number $\frac{2}{7}$ has the decimal expansion $0.\overline{285714}$ since

$$\begin{array}{r}
0.285714285714 \\
7\overline{)2.000000000000\ldots} \\
1\ 4 \\
\hline
60 \\
56 \\
\hline
40 \\
35 \\
\hline
50 \\
49 \\
\hline
10 \\
7 \\
\hline
30 \\
28 \\
\hline
2
\end{array}$$

In this instance, since the last remainder obtained was 2, a remainder which occurred before, the quotient will be merely a repetition of "285714" over and over.

EXAMPLE 3.3 The fraction $\frac{1}{3}$ is the repeating decimal $0.33333\ldots$, while $\frac{8}{4}$ is the repeating decimal $2.000000\ldots$.

Each positive number which has as its repeating decimal cycle only the number 0 can also be written using a repeating 9. The number 2.0 is identically $1.\overline{9}$. To write $1.\overline{9}$ as a fraction of integers, let $x = 1.\overline{9}$. Then, multiplying by 10,

$$\begin{aligned} 10x &= 19.9999999\ldots \\ -x &= -1.9999999\ldots \\ \hline 9x &= 18.0000000\ldots \end{aligned}$$

so, $x = \frac{18}{9} = 2$.

In a like manner, $213.43999999\ldots$ represents the same number as 213.44, and -17.3 is the number $-17.2\overline{9}$.

EXERCISE SET 3.3

Write each repeating decimal as a fraction of integers.

1. 1.414.
2. $2.31313\ldots$.
3. 198.888.
4. $-24.4343\ldots$.
5. $1.142142142\ldots$.
6. $135.213112111311112111113\ldots$.
7. $0.00\overline{3322}$.
8. 673.673.
9. $0.432172\overline{3}$.
10. $0.1\overline{9}$.
11. $17.37\overline{95}$.

Express each fraction of integers (Exercises 12–21) as a repeating decimal.

12.	$\frac{1}{18}$.	17.	$\frac{1}{100}$.
13.	$\frac{3}{7}$.	18.	$\frac{11}{23}$.
14.	$\frac{2}{27}$.	19.	$\frac{143}{2}$.
15.	$\frac{17}{7}$.	20.	$\frac{22}{3}$.
16.	$\frac{23}{1}$.	21.	$\frac{3}{22}$.

22. List three nonrepeating decimals that are not listed in the text.
23. Show that the sum of two repeating decimals is a repeating decimal.
24. Show that the product of two repeating decimals is a repeating decimal.
25. Find the sum of $6.\overline{234}$ and $1.\overline{567}$.
26. Find the product of $6.\overline{234}$ and $1.\overline{567}$.

3.4 Operations

In your previous study of real numbers, besides describing the real numbers and identifying certain subsets of them, considerable time was spent in learning the properties of operations with real numbers. The principal operations studied were addition, multiplication, subtraction, and division. One purpose of this chapter is to review the properties of these operations and to extend your understanding of them.

EXERCISE SET 3.4

Rewrite each sentence symbolizing the quantifiers and employing set notation where suitable; classify as true or false. Provide an instance of proof for each true generalization having only existential quantifiers, and a counterexample for each false generalization having only universal quantifiers.

EXAMPLE 3.4 The sum of two real numbers is a real number.

$\forall x \, \forall y, \ (x + y) \in R$; True.

1. The sum of two positive real numbers is a positive real number.
2. The product of two integers m, n is an integer.
3. The quotient of two natural numbers is a natural number.
4. The quotient of two real numbers is a real number.
5. The difference of any two integers is an integer.
6. The difference of any two natural numbers is a natural number.
7. The sum of a positive integer and a negative integer is a positive integer.
8. The sum and product of two rational numbers are rational numbers.
9. The quotient of two rational numbers is a rational number.
10. For each three real numbers x, y, z,

    $$(x + y) + z = x + (y + z).$$

11. For each triple of integers m, n, q, $(mn)q = m(nq)$.
12. For each triple of rationals p, q, r,

    $$p - (q - r) = (p - q) - r.$$

13. For each triple of real numbers x, y, z,

    $$x \div (y \div z) = (x \div y) \div z.$$

14. For each pair of real numbers x, y, $x - y = y - x$.
15. For each pair of integers n, m, $n + m = m + n$.
16. For each pair of rational numbers p, q, $p \div q = q \div p$.
17. For any three real numbers x, y, z,

$$x + y + z = z + y + x.$$

18. There is a number y such that for each x, $x + y = x$.
19. There is a real number y such that for each x, $x + y = y$.
20. There is a real number x such that for each y, $xy = y$.
21. For each real number x, there is a real number y such that $xy = 0$.
22. For each real number x, there is a real number y such that $x + y = x$.
23. For each real number x, there is a real number y such that $x + y = 0$.
24. There is a real number x such that for each number y, $x + y = 0$.
25. For each rational number p, there is a rational q such that $p + q = 0$.
26. For each integer m, there is an integer n such that $m + n = m$.
27. For each integer m, there is an integer n such that $m + n = 0$.
28. There is an integer m such that for each integer n, $m + n = 0$.
29. There is a natural number n such that for each integer m, $nm = m$.
30. For each natural number n, there is a natural number m such that $nm = m$.
31. For each x, y, z, $x + (yz) = (x + y)(x + z)$.
32. For each x, y, z, $x(y + z) = (xy) + (xz)$.
33. For each x, y, z, $(x + y) \div z = (x \div z) + (y \div z)$.
34. For each x, y, z, $(x + y) - z = (x - z) + (y - z)$.

3.5 Closure

When two even integers are added, the sum is again an even integer. However, when two odd integers are added, the sum is not an odd integer. In the case of addition of even integers, where the sum is *always* in the original set, the set is said to be *closed* under the operation addition. In the case of the addition of odd integers, where the sum is not always in the original set (in fact, it is never in the original set), the set is said to be *not closed* under addition.

It should be kept in mind that both a set and an operation are involved in closure. To make a closure assertion meaningful, one should include both the set and the operation in the statement. For instance,

The set of even integers is closed under addition, {*even integers*} *is closed under* $+$.

The set of odd integers is not closed under addition, {odd integers} is not closed under $+$.

Another way of stating this same information is to say that the pair consisting of the set together with the operation is *closed* or is *a closed system*. The above examples, stated in this manner, are

$(\{\text{even integers}\}, +)$ is closed,

$(\{\text{odd integers}\}, +)$ is not closed.

Which of the following systems are closed and which are not?

(a) $(R, +)$.

(b) $(Q, \times)$.

(c) $(I, \div)$.

The first pair, $(R, +)$, is closed since for each pair of real numbers, the sum is always a real number. The second pair, $(Q, \times)$, is closed also since for each pair of rational numbers, the product is always a rational number. The last pair is not closed. The statement that $(I, \div)$ is closed can be written as

$$\forall n \in I, \forall m \in I, (n \div m) \in I.$$

The denial of this statement is equivalent to

$$\exists n \in I, \exists m \in I, (n \div m) \notin I.$$

The numbers 1, 2 provide an instance of proof for this denial, since $(1 \div 2)$ is not an integer and therefore a counterexample to "$(I, \div)$ is closed."

In finding a counterexample to the statement that $(I, \div)$ is closed, an example was selected where the quotient, $p \div q$, was a number which was not an integer. Another counterexample (which illustrates an important general class of counterexamples) is one in which the indicated quotient, $p \div q$, is not even a number! $2 \div 0$ is such an example. The student should be aware of this in considering whether or not Q is closed under division. All quotients $p \div q$ in which $q \neq 0$ are rationals. But $(Q, \div)$ is not closed since $(p \div 0) \notin Q$ (for any rational number p).

In addition to the operations of addition, multiplication, and so forth, other operations with pairs of real numbers can be invented using combinations of these operations. For example, define the operation $*$ (read "star") by the sentence

$$\forall x \, \forall y, \; x * y = \frac{x + y}{2}.$$

(This operation gives the *arithmetic average* of the two numbers.) The set N is not closed under this operation since

$$1 * 2 = \frac{1 + 2}{2} = \frac{3}{2},$$

and $\frac{3}{2} \notin N$. The set Q is closed under this operation. For if $a, b \in Q$, then for some integers m, n, p, q, where $n \neq 0$, $q \neq 0$,

$$a = \frac{m}{n}, \; b = \frac{p}{q}.$$

Then

$$a * b = \frac{a + b}{2} = \frac{m/n + p/q}{2} = \frac{mq + np}{2nq}.$$

But $(mq + np) \in I$, $2nq \in I$, and $2nq \neq 0$. This means $(a * b) \in Q$ since it is represented as a fraction of integers. (Are Q^+ and I closed under $*$?)

EXERCISE SET 3.5

In Exercises 1–32, tell whether the set is closed or not closed under the given operation. If your answer is "not closed," give a proof of your answer.

1. $(R, +)$.
2. $(R^+, +)$. (R^+ is the set of all positive reals, R^- the set of all negative reals, Q^+ the set of all positive rationals, and so forth.)
3. $(R^-, +)$.
4. $(R^-, -)$.
5. The nonnegative reals under addition.
6. The nonnegative reals under subtraction.
7. The nonpositive reals under addition.
8. The reals under division.
9. $(\{\text{odd integers}\}, +)$.

10. ({even integers}, $+$).
11. ($\{\ldots, -5, -3, -1, 1, 3, 5, \ldots\}, \times$).
12. ($\{\ldots, -4, -2, 0, 2, 4, \ldots\}, \times$).
13. $(I, +)$.
14. $(I, -)$.
15. The integers under division.
16. The set of counting numbers under addition.
17. The set of counting numbers under subtraction.
18. $(N, \times)$.
19. $(N, \div)$.
20. $(Q^+, +)$.
21. $(Q, -)$.
22. $(Q, \times)$.
23. $(Q, \div)$.
24. $(\{x: x \text{ is prime}, x \in N\}, +)$.
25. $(\{0, 4, 8, \ldots\}, +)$.
26. $(\{0, 4, 8, \ldots\}, \times)$.
27. $(\{0, 4, 8, \ldots\}, \div)$.
28. $(\{-1, 0, 1\}, +)$.
29. $(\{-1, 0, 1\}, \times)$.
30. $(R, *)$, where the operation $*$ is defined by

$$\forall x\ \forall y,\ x * y = x - 2y.$$

31. $(Q, *)$, where the operation $*$ is defined by

$$\forall x\ \forall y,\ x * y = 2(x + y).$$

32. $(I, *)$, where $\forall x \in I, \forall y \in I, x * y = x^2 + y^2$.
33. Define an operation $*$ on the set $\{0, 1, 2, 3\}$ which is closed. Is $\{0, 1, 2\}$ closed under your operation $*$? Is $\{0\}$ closed under your operation $*$?
34. Given that the set X is closed under the operation $*$, is it necessary that a subset A of X is closed under the operation?
35. If a, b are rational numbers, then there are integers m, n, p, q, where $n \neq 0$, $q \neq 0$, such that

$$a = \frac{m}{n}, \qquad b = \frac{p}{q}.$$

Define $a + b$, $a - b$, $a \times b$, and $a \div b$ in terms of the integers m, n, p, q. Discuss closure of Q under each of these operations in terms of the definitions given.

36. If both subsets A and B of R are closed under an operation $*$, is it necessary that $A \cup B$ is closed under $*$? Is it necessary that $A \cap B$ is closed under $*$?

3.6 The Associative and Commutative Principles

A familiar concept from the study of algebra and of real numbers is that in the addition of three (or more) numbers, the process can be carried out in any order. For example, to find the sum

$$3 + 9 + 7,$$

one could add 3 to 9 and then add 12, the sum of 3 and 9, to 7. This would be indicated by

$$(3 + 9) + 7,$$

where one adds from left to right in general. Another way to add the numbers is to add 9 to 7, obtaining 16, and then add 3 to 16. This is indicated by

$$3 + (9 + 7).$$

Still another way is to add the 3 to the 7, obtaining 10, and then add it to 9 or 9 to it. This is represented by

$$(3 + 7) + 9 \quad \text{and} \quad 9 + (3 + 7).$$

Are there other ways in which the addition could be carried out?

After extensive consideration of this "principle of rearranging," mathematicians generally consider two principles which together permit the "rearranging principle"; they are the *associative* and *commutative* principles.

The *commutative principle* for addition of real numbers is

$$\forall x\, \forall y,\ x + y = y + x.$$

Briefly, this principle states that the result is the same whether x is added to y or y is added to x. Thus,

$$\pi + 3 = 3 + \pi, \quad \sqrt{2} + 7 = 7 + \sqrt{2}, \quad (18 - 7) + \tfrac{1}{3} = \tfrac{1}{3} + (18 - 7).$$

Not all operations have a corresponding principle. For example, subtraction is not generally commutative, as shown by the instance $2 - 3 = 3 - 2$.

The second principle for the "rearranging property" is that of *associativity*. This principle for addition of real numbers is defined as

$$\forall x \, \forall y \, \forall z, \ (x + y) + z = x + (y + z).$$

In the addition of three numbers, this principle assures that addition of the sum of the first two numbers to the third gives the same result as the addition of the first number to the sum of the second and third. It is important to realize that in both cases, the ordering of the addends *is the same*!

To illustrate how these two principles permit rearranging more generally, it will be shown that

$$a + b + c = c + b + a.$$

Since, without any parenthetic notation, addition (and other operations) will be carried out in order from left to right, the problem is to show that

$$(a + b) + c = (c + b) + a.$$

Beginning with the expression $(a + b) + c$, by the commutative principle,

$$(a + b) + c = c + (a + b).$$

(Which two numbers were "commuted"?)

Then

$$c + (a + b) = c + (b + a)$$

again by the commutative principle. (Which two numbers were "commuted"?)

Continuing,

$$c + (b + a) = (c + b) + a$$

by the associative principle. Thus, by the chain of equalities,

$$(a + b) + c = (c + b) + a$$

or

$$a + b + c = c + b + a.$$

Other rearrangements will be considered in the examples.

The above two principles are also valid for multiplication of real numbers. Thus,

$$\forall x\, \forall y,\; x \cdot y = y \cdot x \qquad \textit{(commutative principle, multiplication)}$$

and

$$\forall x\, \forall y\, \forall z,\; (x \cdot y) \cdot z = x \cdot (y \cdot z). \qquad \textit{(associative principle, multiplication)}$$

EXAMPLE 3.5 Show that $2 \times 7 \times 3 = 3 \times 7 \times 2$ by using the associative and commutative principles of multiplication (and not merely multiplication facts of arithmetic). List the principles used for each step of the proof.

$$\begin{aligned} 2 \times 7 \times 3 &= (2 \times 7) \times 3 && \text{(definition)} \\ &= 3 \times (2 \times 7) && \text{(commutative principle, mult.)} \\ &= 3 \times (7 \times 2) && \text{(commutative principle, mult.)} \\ &= (3 \times 7) \times 2 && \text{(associative principle, mult.)} \\ &= 3 \times 7 \times 2. && \text{(definition)} \end{aligned}$$

EXAMPLE 3.6 If the operation $*$ is defined for real numbers by $a * b = (a + b)/3$, prove that the commutative principle holds for $*$ over the reals. (That is, show that $\forall a\, \forall b,\; a * b = b * a$.)

$$\begin{aligned} a * b &= \frac{a + b}{3} && \text{(definition of } *) \\ &= \frac{b + a}{3} && \text{(commutative principle, addition)} \\ &= b * a. && \text{(definition of } *) \end{aligned}$$

EXERCISE SET 3.6

Identify the principle, associative for addition or commutative for addition, associative for multiplication or commutative for multiplication, which each statement of Exercises 1–12 illustrates.

1. $7 + 3 = 3 + 7.$
2. $8 + (4 \times 3) = (4 \times 3) + 8.$
3. $8 + (4 \times 3) = 8 + (3 \times 4).$

4. $8 + (4 + 3) = (8 + 4) + 3.$
5. $7 - 11 + 3 = 3 + (7 - 11).$
6. $(7 + 11) \times (8 + 4) = (8 + 4) \times (7 + 11).$
7. $(7 + 11) + (8 + 4) = [(7 + 11) + 8] + 4.$
8. $6 + 8 + 14 = 8 + 6 + 14.$
9. $(5 + 5) + 5 = 5 + (5 + 5).$
10. $8\pi(6 + a) = (6 + a)(8\pi).$
11. $a(b + c) = a(c + b).$
12. $(a + b) + (c + d) = [a + (b + c)] + d.$

In Exercises 13–25, show by using the associative or commutative principles (and not facts of arithmetic) that the equations are true. (Sentences containing variables are assumed to be universally quantified.)

13. $(7 + 4) + 2 = 2 + (4 + 7).$
14. $4 + 7 + 3 = 4 + 3 + 7.$
15. $a + b + c = a + c + b.$
16. $a + b + c = c + a + b.$
17. $3 \times (8 \times 7) = (7 \times 8) \times 3.$
18. $8 \times 9 \times 4 = 8 \times 4 \times 9.$
19. $a \times b \times c = a \times c \times b.$
20. $a \times b \times c = b \times a \times c.$
21. $(a \times b) \times (c \times d) = (a \times c) \times (b \times d).$
22. $(a + bc)d = d(cb + a).$
23. $(x + x) + x = x + (x + x).$
24. $a + b + c + d + e = (a + b) + [(c + d) + e].$
25. $abcde = (ab)[(cd)e].$

In Exercises 26–40, tell whether associativity or commutativity holds for the operation over the given set. In each case where a principle is not generally valid, provide a counterexample.

26. Addition over the rationals.
27. Multiplication over the rationals.
28. Subtraction over the integers.
29. Subtraction over the reals.
30. Division over the reals.
31. Division over the natural numbers.
32. Addition over A, where $A \subset R$.
33. Operation $*$ over R where $\forall x\ \forall y,\ x * y = 2(x + y).$
34. Operation $*$ over R where $\forall x\ \forall y,\ x * y = x - 2y.$
35. Operation $*$ over R where $\forall x\ \forall y,\ x * y = x - y.$
36. Operation $*$ over R where $\forall x\ \forall y,\ x * y = xy.$

37. Addition over $\{0\}$.
38. Subtraction over $\{0\}$.
39. Addition over $\{0, 1\}$.
40. Division over $\{1\}$.
41. Prove that the commutative and associative principles hold for addition over the rationals from the assumption that they hold for addition and multiplication over the integers. Show all steps in your proof. (Refer to Exercise 35, Exercise Set 3.5.)

3.7 Identities

The number 0 behaves in a very special way. No matter which real number x is chosen,

$$x + 0 = 0 + x = x.$$

That is, 0 added to any number x (and any number x added to 0) yields *identically* the number x. Appropriately, 0 is called the *identity of addition.*

By definition, a number e is an identity for addition if

$$\forall x, x + e = e + x = x.$$

From your knowledge of the real numbers, you can verify that the identity must be 0 and 0 alone.

Similarly for e to be an identity element for multiplication, the following statement must be true:

$$\forall x, x \cdot e = e \cdot x = x.$$

It is evident that e must be the number 1.

If there is a number e which is an identity element for subtraction, it must be true that

$$\forall x, x - e = e - x = x.$$

The number zero satisfies

$$x - e = x, \text{ for each } x,$$

but 0 does not satisfy

$$e - x = x, \text{ for each } x.$$

By further consideration of the equations involved, you should convince yourself that no such real number e exists which works for each real number x. This means that there is no identity element for the operation of subtraction over the real numbers.

3.8 Inverse Elements

The inverse of an operation is that operation that "undoes" the original operation. Since subtracting 5 undoes what adding 5 does, and in general, subtracting x undoes what adding x does, subtraction is regarded as the inverse of addition (and addition is the inverse of subtraction). Multiplication and division are inverse to each other in a like manner.

The notion of an inverse element is related to the notion of inverse operations. The element y that is *inverse* to the element x with respect to addition is the number (if there is such a number) such that

$$x + y = y + x = 0.$$

The number $-x$ is such a number since

$$x + (-x) = (-x) + x = 0, \text{ for each } x.$$

Since adding $-x$ undoes what adding x does, as in

$$(a + x) + (-x) = a + (x + (-x)) = a + ((-x) + x) = a + 0 = a,$$

it is natural to call $-x$ the *additive inverse* of x.

The formal statement that additive inverses exist for a given set, S, is

$$\forall x \in S\, \exists y \in S,\, x + y = y + x = 0.$$

This is a universal generalization; in order to say that a given set has additive inverses, there must be such an inverse in the set for each member of the set. The formal requirement demands that each inverse commute with the given number. This universal generalization is true for the set of real numbers since, as was shown above, for each real number x, $-x$ exists and

$$\forall x,\, x + (-x) = -x + x = 0.$$

It is not true, however, for the set of natural numbers, since the number 1 (and others) has no inverse from the natural numbers.

Extending the concept of inverse to multiplication, the statement that inverses for multiplication (*multiplicative inverses*) exist for each real number is

$$\forall x\, \exists y,\ x \cdot y = y \cdot x = 1.$$

For a given number x, it is necessary to find a number y that "undoes" the multiplication by x. The reciprocal of x, $1/x$, is such a number since

$$x \cdot \frac{1}{x} = \frac{1}{x} \cdot x = 1.$$

A reciprocal does exist for every number except 0, but there is no number y such that

$$0 \cdot y = y \cdot 0 = 1.$$

For every nonzero real number x, however, the reciprocal of that number, $1/x$, does exist and is the multiplicative inverse. The statement

$$\forall x \neq 0\, \exists y \neq 0,\ x \cdot y = y \cdot x = 1$$

is true.

In general, a given set S has inverses for the operation $*$ if

$$\forall x \in S\, \exists y \in S,\ x * y = y * x = e,$$

where e is the identity of the operation.

Inverses do not exist for subtraction or division for the set of real numbers since there is no identity e for either operation upon which to base the concept of inverse!

EXAMPLE 3.7 Find an identity for the operation $*$ given by

$$x * y = x + y - 3$$

(over the reals).
A number e is wanted such that for each x,

$$x * e = e * x = x.$$

Since $x * e = e * x$, let $x * e = x$. Then

$$x + e - 3 = x, \qquad \text{(definition of } *)$$

so

$$e = 3.$$

The identity for the operation $*$ is 3.

(Verify that $3 * x = x$ for each x.)

EXAMPLE 3.8 Find the inverse of a number n for the operation $*$ defined by $x * y = x + y - 3$.
The identity for $*$ is 3 (see Example 3.7). For p to be the inverse of n, the equations

$$n * p = p * n = 3$$

must hold. Suppose (since $n * p = p * n$)

$$n * p = 3.$$

Then

$$n + p - 3 = 3. \qquad \text{(definition of } *)$$

Therefore,

$$p = 6 - n.$$

The inverse of n is then $6 - n$.

(Verify that $(6 - n) * n = 3$.)

EXERCISE SET 3.7

1. Which of the following sets have an identity for addition? Which have an identity for multiplication?
   (a) I.
   (b) Q.
   (c) N.
   (d) Q^-.

(e) R.
(f) R^+.
(g) R_0 (set of all nonzero reals).
(h) The nonnegative rationals.

2. For each set listed, state whether or not it contains additive inverses for all elements. For those sets which do not have inverses, explain.
   (a) N.
   (b) I.
   (c) The set of nonnegative integers.
   (d) Q.
   (e) R.
   (f) R^+.
   (g) R_0.
   (h) The set of odd integers.
   (i) The set of even integers.
3. For each set listed, state whether or not it contains multiplicative inverses for all elements. For those sets which have elements which do not have inverses, explain why.
   (a) N.
   (b) I.
   (c) Q.
   (d) R.
   (e) Q^+.
   (f) R^+.
   (g) R_0.
   (h) The set of all nonzero rationals (Q_0).
   (i) Q^-.
   (j) R^-.

For each operation $*$ over the reals (Exercises 4–6), determine whether or not an identity element exists and whether or not inverses exist.

4. $\forall a\, \forall b,\ a * b = (a + b)/2$.
5. $\forall a\, \forall b,\ a * b = a + b - 2$.
6. $\forall a\, \forall b,\ a * b = ab/2$.
7. The statement

$$\forall x\, \exists y,\ x - y = y - x = 0$$

is true. Does this mean that inverses exist for subtraction?

8. Show that for each nonzero integer k, $0/k$ is an identity for addition of fractions of integers.
9. Show that both $(-m)/n$ and $m/-n$ are additive inverses of the fraction m/n, $n \neq 0$.

3.9 The Distributive Principle

The *distributive principle* for multiplication over addition is

(1) $\forall x \, \forall y \, \forall z, \; x(y + z) = (xy) + (xz).$

This property involves both of the operations addition and multiplication (rather than only one operation as in associativity, commutativity, and so forth). The word "distributive" comes from the concept of distributing the multiplier x over the individual addends, y and z, in the right member. You have used this principle in elementary algebra not only to find the product of a monomial and a binomial, but also to factor out a common monomial factor.

The commutative principle for multiplication and the distributive principle together imply

(2) $\forall x \, \forall y \, \forall z, \; (y + z)x = (yx) + (zx).$

The distributive principle (2) is sometimes referred to as the "right distributive principle," while that of (1) is referred to as the "left distributive principle." From time to time, either of these will be used in dealing with real numbers and in each case will be called the "distributive principle."

The distributive principle is utilized in the ordinary multiplication algorithm involving two-place numbers (or larger). In the multiplication of 72 by 3, 72 is viewed as 70 + 2, and the multiplier, 3, is "distributed over" the addends 70 and 2 as indicated by the running equalities

$$72 \times 3 = (70 + 2) \times 3 = (70 \times 3) + (2 \times 3) = 210 + 6 = 216.$$

EXERCISE SET 3.8

Identify the principle which each statement illustrates (Exercises 1–5). Follow the usual convention of performing multiplication first in expressions where both multiplication and addition occur, if not indicated otherwise by parentheses.

1. $3(4 + 5) = 12 + 15.$
2. $(37 \times 91) + (63 \times 91) = 100 \times 91.$
3. $3 + (7 + 2) = (3 + 7) + 2.$
4. $2 + (3 \times 95 + 7 \times 95) = 2 + (10 \times 95).$
5. $6 \times (\frac{1}{3} + \frac{1}{2}) = 2 + 3.$

Show using associative, commutative, distributive principles, etc. (and not facts of arithmetic alone) that each equation (Exercises 6–10) is true.

6. $4 + 7 \times 3 = 4 + 3 \times 7$.
7. $(5 \times 31) + 6 + (2 \times 31) = 6 + (5 + 2) \times 31$.
8. $\frac{1}{2} \times 350 \times 200 = 100 \times 350$.
9. $25 \times 9 = 20 \times 9 + 5 \times 9$.
10. $19 \times 870 + \frac{7}{8} \times 870 + 19\frac{1}{2} \times 130 + \frac{3}{8} \times 130 = 1000 \times 19\frac{7}{8}$.
11. For each pair of operations, tell whether the first operation distributes over the second. (Assume that the numbers involved are real numbers.)
    (a) $(+, \times)$.
    (b) $(\times, +)$.
    (c) $(+, \div)$.
    (d) $(\div, +)$.
    (e) $(\times, -)$.
    (f) $(\div, -)$.
    (g) $(+, -)$.
    (h) $(+, +)$.
    (i) $(\times, \div)$.
    (j) $(\times, \times)$.
    (k) $(-, \times)$.
12. For each answer of Exercise 11 for which there is a distributive law, write the law as a universal generalization using variables.
13. Sometimes an operation distributes "on the right" but not "on the left" (or vice versa). For example, division where defined distributes over addition on the right but not on the left. Thus

$$\forall x\, \forall y\, \forall z \neq 0,\ (x + y) \div z = (x \div z) + (y \div z)$$

is true, while

$$\forall x \neq 0\ \forall y \neq 0 \text{ and } y \neq -x\ \forall z,\ z \div (x + y) = (z \div x) + (z \div y)$$

is not true. (Find a counterexample.)
Tell which of parts (a)–(k) of Exercise 11 distribute on one side but not the other, and write the law as a universal generalization using variables.
14. Show how the distributive law can be used to verify

$$(a + b)(c + d) = (ac + ad) + (bc + bd).$$

Order Properties of the Real Numbers

CHAPTER FOUR

4.1 Introduction

The algebraic properties of the real numbers (e.g., commutative and associative principles of addition) were studied in Chapter Three. A knowledge of these properties is helpful in solving equations. In solving inequalities, the general order properties of the real numbers are needed as well as the algebraic properties.

4.2 Solution Sets

To "solve an equation" is to find all of the numbers which provide true instances of the equation. The set of all numbers which provide true instances is called the *solution set* of the equation. Each of the numbers of the solution set is said to *satisfy* the equation and is called a *root* or a *solution* of the equation. One must realize that in solving an equation one is not viewing the equation as a generalization that is true for all numbers or even true for some numbers; rather, one is attempting to *determine* those numbers for which the equation is true.

The solution set of an equation may be a set with one number such as in

$$3x + 1 = 4,$$

where the solution set is $\{1\}$. ($3 \cdot 1 + 1 = 4$ is a true instance.) It may have more than one number, such as in

$$x^2 = 4,$$

where the solution set is $\{2, -2\}$, or it may be an infinite set such as in

$$x + x = 2x,$$

where the solution set is $(-\infty, \infty)$. Indeed, the solution set may have no members, such as in

$$x + 1 = x,$$

where the solution set is empty.

The above remarks can be extended directly to other open sentences, and, in particular, to inequalities. The solution set of

$$2x < 6$$

is the set of all numbers which give true instances—that is, the set of all numbers which are less than 3. The solution set is the half line $(-\infty, 3[$, and the graph of the solution set is

Viewed graphically, it is natural to speak of the solution set of $2x < 6$ as the set of numbers *to the left of* 3.

The solution set of the sentence

x is an even integer and $x \in [0, 10]$,

is the set

$\{0, 2, 4, 6, 8, 10\}$

since each of these elements (and no others) gives a true instance of the sentence in question.

Some general methods of solving inequalities are illustrated in the examples to follow. More sophisticated algebraic methods for simplification of the inequalities will be given in later sections.

EXAMPLE 4.1 Find the solution set of the sentence $4 < 2x < 7$.

[NOTE: $4 < 2x < 7$ means $4 < 2x$ and $2x < 7$.]

To find the set of solutions, it is helpful to first find individual solutions to the sentence. 3 is a solution since the resulting instance,

$4 < 2 \cdot 3 < 7$,

is true (since $4 < 2 \cdot 3$ and $2 \cdot 3 < 7$). Likewise, $3\frac{1}{4}$ is a solution, but $3\frac{1}{2}$ and 4 are not. (Why not?) Continued investigation shows that all numbers larger than 2 but less than $3\frac{1}{2}$, and only those numbers, are solutions. The solution set is the open interval

$]2, 3\frac{1}{2}[$,

or graphically,

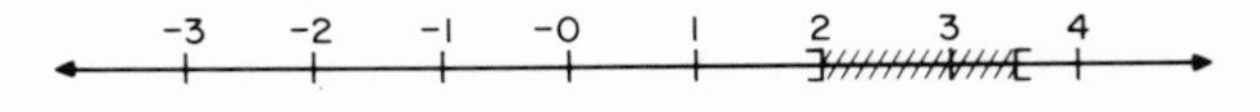

Solution set of $4 < 2x < 7$

Notice that the endpoints of the interval, 2 and $3\frac{1}{2}$, are respective solutions to the equations

$$4 = 2x \quad \text{and} \quad 2x = 7$$

obtained by replacing the inequality signs with the sign of equality.

EXAMPLE 4.2 Solve $3x + 4 > 7$.
To find the solution set of a given inequality, it is often helpful to find the solution of the equation obtained by replacing the inequality sign with the sign of equality. The equation

$$3x + 4 = 7$$

has only one solution, 1. (This is not a solution for the inequality!) If a number larger than 1 were chosen for x, then $3x + 4$ would be larger than 7; while if a number smaller than 1 were chosen, $3x + 4$ would be less than 7. The solution set, then, is the set of all numbers larger than 1; that is,

$$]1, +\infty).$$

Notice that the solution to the equation $3x + 4 = 7$ is the endpoint of the solution set.

EXAMPLE 4.3 Solve $\dfrac{1}{x+2} \leq 0$.

In this case, the solutions are those numbers which will make $1/(x + 2)$ a negative number or zero. $1/(x + 2)$ can never be 0, and it will be negative only when $x + 2$ is negative. But $x + 2$ is negative for all numbers x which are less than -2. The solution set is $(-\infty, -2[$, or, graphically,

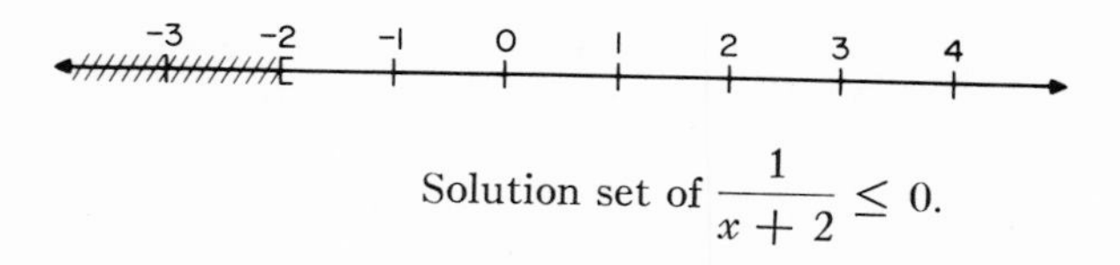

Solution set of $\dfrac{1}{x+2} \leq 0$.

EXAMPLE 4.4 Find the solution set of the following sentence:

The distance from x to 3 is less than 5.

Distance problems are often solved by considering the graph.

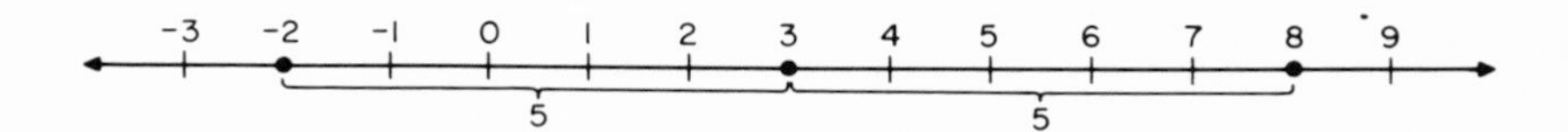

Distance from x to 3 is less than 5

The distance from x to 3 is equal to 5 at the two points -2 and 8. The points to the right of -2 but to the left of 8 are closer to 3 than are -2 and 8: their distance from 3 is less than 5. The numbers in this interval are the solutions to the statement given. The solution set is $]-2, 8[$, and the graph of the solution set is

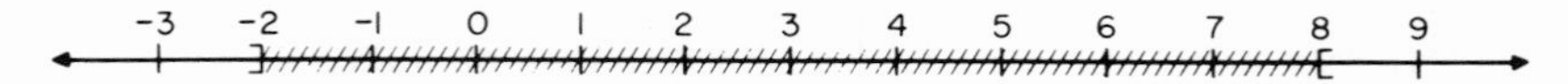

Solution set of "The distance from x to 3 is less than 5"

EXERCISE SET 4.1

Find and graph the solution set for the given equation, inequality or other open sentence.

1. $2x < 4.$
2. $3x \leq 4.$
3. $-2 < x < 3.$
4. $-2 > x > -3.$
5. $x < 2$ or $x > 3.$
6. $-2 > x > 3.$
7. $x > 3.$
8. $3x + 1 = x + 5.$
9. $3x + 1 < x + 5.$
10. $3 - 5x > 0.$
11. $(3x - 7)/2 \leq 0.$
12. $3x/4 - \frac{1}{2} < 0.$
13. $7 - 2x > 4 + x.$
14. $0.1x - 2.32 > 0.$
15. $1/x < \frac{2}{3}.$
16. $x + 1 > 0$ and $x - 3 < 0.$
17. $x - 1 < 0$ and $3x + 2 > -4.$
18. $-7 \leq x + 3 \leq 7.$
19. $-2 < (5 - 2x)/4 < 2.$

20. $2x + 1 < 0$ and $2x - 1 > 0$.
21. $3x + 5 < 8$ and $3x - 5 < -8$.
22. $2x + 3 < 0$ or $2x - 3 \geq 0$.
23. $x - 1 < 0$ or $x + 1 > 0$.
24. $1/(x + 3) < 0$.
25. $1/(2x - 5) \geq 0$.
26. The distance from x to 0 is less than 4.
27. The distance from x to 0 is more than 4.
28. The distance from x to 0 is 4.
29. The distance from x to -2 is less than 6.
30. The distance from x to -2 is greater than 6.
31. The distance from $x + 2$ to 0 is greater than 6.
32. The distance from $2x$ to 0 is less than or equal to 8. (Hint: Solve first for values for $2x$.)
33. The distance from x to 0 is less than or equal to 4.
34. The distance from $2x$ to 5 is less than or equal to 8.
35. The distance from $3x$ to -4 is greater than or equal to 2.
36. The distance from $5x$ to 7 is less than 3.
37. The distance from x to 4 is greater than 2 and less than 3.
38. The distance from $2x$ to 3 is less than $\frac{3}{2}$ but greater than or equal to $\sqrt{2}/2$.
39. The distance from x to $2x$ is equal to 3.
40. The distance from x to $2x$ is more than 3.

4.3 Properties of Order

One inequality that has the solution set $(-\infty, 5[$ is $x < 5$. There are other inequalities with the same solution set however:

$$2x < 10,$$

$$x + 3 < 8,$$

and

$$5x - 1 < x + 19,$$

to name a few. Inequalities such as these which have exactly the same solution set are said to be *equivalent inequalities*. Similarly, two equations that have the same solution set are said to be *equivalent equations*, and in general, two open sentences which have the same solution set are said to be *equivalent sentences*. In equation solving, use is made of the fact that there are basic principles regarding the transformation of an equation into another which is equivalent to it. One such principle is the *addition transformation principle*:

$$\forall x\ \forall y\ \forall z,\ x = y \quad \text{if and only if} \quad x + z = y + z.$$

Another is the *multiplication transformation principle*:

$$\forall x\ \forall y\ \forall z \neq 0,\ x = y \quad \text{if and only if} \quad xz = yz.$$

The idea is to use the transformation principles to obtain an equation which is equivalent to the original but easier to solve. To solve

$$3x + 5 = x - 1,$$

one can apply the addition transformation principle to obtain the equivalent equation

$$(3x + 5) + (-5) = (x - 1) + (-5)$$

or, more simply,

$$3x = x - 6.$$

The addition transformation principle is applied again to obtain the equivalent equation

$$3x + (-x) = x - 6 + (-x)$$

or

$$2x = -6.$$

Even though it is now apparent that the solution is -3, one usually applies the multiplication transformation principle to obtain the equivalent equation

$$2x \cdot \tfrac{1}{2} = -6 \cdot \tfrac{1}{2}$$

or

$$x = -3.$$

The solution set of the last equation is $\{-3\}$; this must be the solution set of the original equation, $3x + 5 = x - 1$. (Is it?)

There are similar transformation principles that can be used to obtain equivalent inequalities. Your experience in solving inequalities may be sufficient for you to accept the generalization

$$\forall x\ \forall y\ \forall z,\ x < y \quad \text{if and only if} \quad x + z < y + z$$

as a principle for inequalities. However, a geometric interpretation may help to firm your acceptance of this rule.

To say that x is less than y is to say that the graph of x on the number line is to the left of the graph of y, as in the illustration.

The graph of $x + z$ is a point at distance $|z|$ from x, to the right of x if z is positive and to the left of x if z is negative. Similarly, $y + z$ is a point at distance $|z|$ from y, to the right or left as z is positive or negative. In the case in which z is a positive number, the picture is

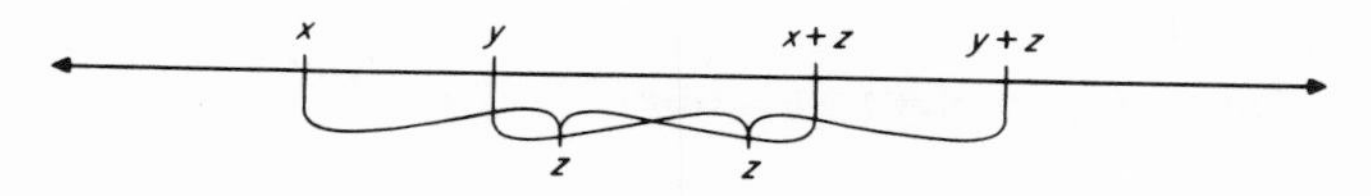

Since $x + z$ is the same distance to the right of x as $y + z$ is to the right of y, the same relative position that exists between x and y also exists between $x + z$ and $y + z$. Therefore, since $x < y$,

$$x + z < y + z.$$

The other cases (when z is negative and when z is 0) can be pictured in a similar manner.

This principle can be used to help solve an inequality such as

$$3x - 7 < 3 + 2x.$$

The addition of $-2x$ to both sides yields the equivalent inequality,

$$(3x - 7) + (-2x) < (3 + 2x) + (-2x)$$

or

$$x - 7 < 3.$$

(Which algebraic principles were used to simplify each side of the inequality?)

Adding 7 to both sides gives

$$x < 10.$$

Therefore $3x - 7 < 3 + 2x$ and $x < 10$ are equivalent and must have the same solution set. The solution set of $x < 10$ is the half line

$$(-\infty, 10[.$$

The solution set of $3x - 7 < 3 + 2x$ is also $(-\infty, 10]$. One is encouraged to check one's work by testing some numbers from $(-\infty, 10[$ to see that they are solutions and also by testing some numbers in the complement of $(-\infty, 10[$ to see that they are not solutions. The check is not done to determine whether or not the procedure was theoretically correct, but to help catch careless mistakes in computation. Another assurance that the solution set is feasible is that 10, the endpoint of the half line, is the solution to the equation $3x - 7 = 3 + 2x$.

4.4 Solution of Polynomial Inequalities

Using the addition transformation principle, inequalities involving a polynomial form can often be solved. Adding $-8x + 3$ to both sides of the inequality

$$3x^2 - 2x < 8x - 3$$

results in the following equivalent inequality

$$3x^2 - 10x + 3 < 0.$$

You may recall that a similar transformation was made to solve the corresponding quadratic equation. As in the solution of the quadratic equation, the polynomial may be factored, giving

$$(3x - 1)(x - 3) < 0.$$

For the open sentence $(3x - 1)(x - 3) = 0$ to be true, x is either $\frac{1}{3}$ or 3. The graphs of these two numbers separate the line into three sections as shown below. Each of these sections is considered in finding the solutions of the inequality.

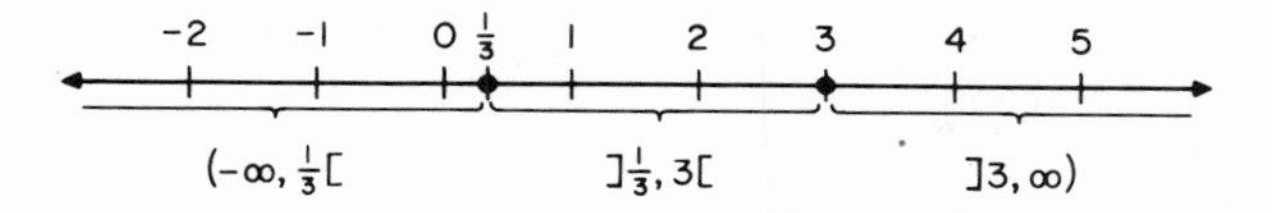

If x is in the first section, $(-\infty, \frac{1}{3}[$, then

$$(3x - 1) < 0 \quad \text{and} \quad (x - 3) < 0.$$

Since the product of two negative numbers is positive,

$$(3x - 1)(x - 3) > 0.$$

This means that no number of $(-\infty, \frac{1}{3}[$ is a solution. (Why?)

If $x \in]\frac{1}{3}, 3[$, then $(3x - 1) > 0$ and $(x - 3) < 0$, which means

$$(3x - 1)(x - 3) < 0,$$

as desired. The solution set contains all numbers in the interval $]\frac{1}{3}, 3[$.

If x is in the last section, $]3, \infty)$, then

$$(3x - 1) > 0 \quad \text{and} \quad (x - 3) > 0,$$

and

$$(3x - 1)(x - 3) > 0.$$

No number of $]3, \infty)$ is a solution. Since all numbers of the real line have been considered, the solution set is the interval $]\frac{1}{3}, 3[$ as graphed below.

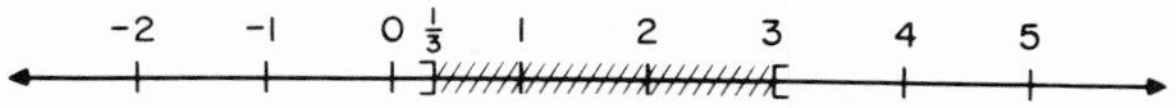

Solution set of $3x^2 - 2x < 8x - 3$.

EXAMPLE 4.5 Solve $3x - 2 < x + 4$.
Adding $-x + 2$ to both sides, the equivalent inequality,

$$2x < 6,$$

is obtained. This inequality has the solution set

$$(-\infty, 3[,$$

which is the solution set of the original sentence.

EXAMPLE 4.6 Solve $x^2 > x + 2$.
Adding $-(x + 2)$ to both sides, the equivalent inequality

$$x^2 - x - 2 > 0$$

is obtained. Factoring yields

$$(x - 2)(x + 1) > 0.$$

Solutions to the equation $(x - 2)(x + 1) = 0$ are 2 and -1. The graphs of these numbers separate the line into three sections as shown below.

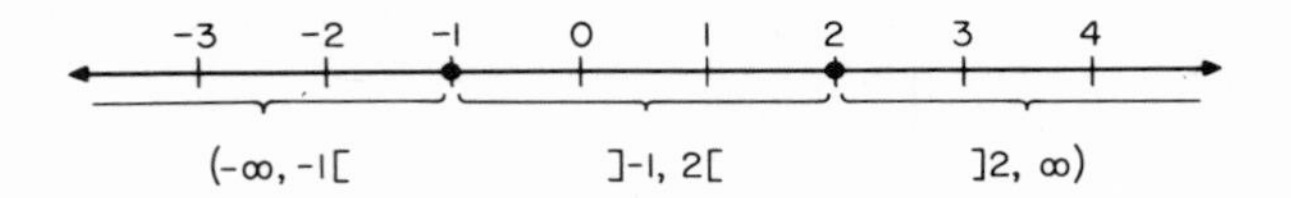

If x is in the first set, $(-\infty, -1[$, then $(x - 2) < 0$ and $(x + 1) < 0$. Therefore

$$(x - 2)(x + 1) > 0,$$

and all numbers of $(-\infty, -1[$ are solutions.
If x is in the interval $]-1, 2[$, then $(x - 2) < 0$, but $(x + 1) > 0$, and

$$(x - 2)(x + 1) < 0.$$

No numbers in the interval $]-1, 2[$ are solutions.
If x is in the set $]2, \infty)$, then $(x - 2) > 0$ and $(x + 1) > 0$, and $]2, \infty)$ is contained in the solution set. The solution set for the original inequality, then, is

$$(-\infty, -1[\cup]2, \infty),$$

or, graphically,

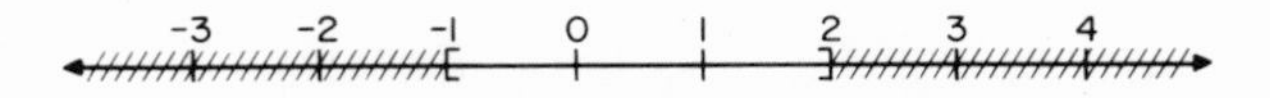

Solution set of $x^2 > x + 2$

EXERCISE SET 4.2

Find and graph the solution set of each open sentence. Employ the addition transformation principle where needed to simplify the inequalities.

1. $x + 7 \leq 4.$
2. $2 + x < 2x.$
3. $x + 3 < 8.$
4. $x + 3 \leq 8.$
5. $7 - 3x > 2x + 12.$
6. $(x + 1)(x - 2) < 0.$
7. $(x + 1)(x - 2) = 0.$
8. $(x + 1)(x - 2) > 0.$
9. $(2x + 3)(x - 2) < 0.$
10. $x^2 - 6x + 9 > 0.$
11. $x^2 - 25 < 0.$
12. $x^2 + 25 \leq 0.$
13. $x^2 + 2x < -1.$
14. $2x^2 + 3x + 5 < x^2 + 7x + 1.$
15. $x^2 - 3x + 4 \geq 2(1 - x).$
16. $3x^2 + 4x \geq 6x - 5x^2 + 1.$
17. $(x^2 - 4x + 3)(x + 2) \leq 0.$
18. $(x - 2)^2(x + 4) > 0.$
19. $x^2 + 2x + 1 < 4.$
20. $2x^2 + 3x < 0.$
21. $(x + 4)(2x - 3) \leq (3x - 4)(x + 3).$
22. $(x + 1)(x - 2) < 0$ and x is positive.
23. $x^2 > 0$ and $x + 4 < 5.$
24. $x + 1 > 0$ or $x^2 + 2x > 0.$
25. $x^2 + 3x + 2 \leq 0$ and $2x + 3 \leq 0.$

For each inequality (Exercises 26–29), find an equivalent inequality where x alone is related to expressions involving other variables. (For instance, $a < x - b < c$ is equivalent to $a + b < x < c + b$.)

26. $2x + 3a < b + x.$
27. $(x + 2)a < ax + (b - x).$
28. $x^2 - a \leq 0$, where $a \in R^+$.
29. $ax^2 + bx + c \leq 0$, where $b^2 - 4ac \geq 0.$
30. Show that $a < b$ if and only if $(b - a) \in R^+$.
31. Using the result of Exercise 30 (and the fact that R^+ is closed under addition), show that if $a < b$ and $b < c$, then $a < c$.

4.5 The Multiplication Transformation Principle

One equation transformation principle which is not paralleled for inequalities is the *multiplication transformation principle*,

$$\forall x\ \forall y\ \forall z \neq 0,\ x = y \quad \text{if and only if} \quad xz = yz.$$

To show that $x < y$ if and only if $xz < yz$ is *not* generally true, one need only give a counterexample. Choosing $x = -2$, $y = 3$, and $z = -1$, we have $-2 < 3$, but $(-2)(-1) \not< 3(-1)$.

The above rule can be modified to apply to inequalities by requiring that $z > 0$. The principle is,

$$\forall x\ \forall y\ \forall z > 0,\ x < y \quad \text{if and only if} \quad xz < yz.$$

One should pay particular attention to the fact that z is restricted to being a *positive* number. This principle may be proved with the aid of the addition transformation principle. For, by the addition transformation principle,

$$x < y \quad \text{if and only if} \quad x - y < 0.$$

Now, the product of two numbers is negative if and only if one of the numbers is positive and the other is negative. So, since $z > 0$, $x - y < 0$ if and only if $(x - y)z < 0$ (or $xz - yz < 0$). Therefore,

$$x < y \quad \text{if and only if} \quad xz < yz, \text{ for } z > 0.$$

In a similar manner, for $z < 0$, since $x < y$ if an only if $x - y < 0$, the product $(x - y)z$ is positive if and only if both $x - y$ and z are negative. Thus $(x - y)z > 0$ and $xz > yz$. This means

$$\forall x\ \forall y\ \forall z < 0,\ x < y \quad \text{if and only if} \quad xz > yz.$$

These principles may be used as an aid in solving inequalities as illustrated by the following examples.

EXAMPLE 4.7 $5x + 1 < 7$.
First, by adding -1 to each side,

$$5x < 6$$

is obtained. Then, since $\frac{1}{5}$ is positive, multiplying both sides by $\frac{1}{5}$ (or dividing by 5) gives

$$x < \tfrac{6}{5}.$$

The solution set to this and the original inequality is

$$(-\infty, \tfrac{6}{5}[.$$

EXAMPLE 4.8 $\dfrac{2}{x+1} < 1.$

It is to be noted first of all that $x + 1 \neq 0$, that is, $x \neq -1$ (why?). In order to remove $x + 1$ from the denominator, there is a temptation to multiply both sides by $(x + 1)$; however, since $x + 1$ may be positive or negative, one would not know whether the resulting equivalent inequality should be

$$2 < x + 1 \text{ (if } x + 1 \text{ were positive)}$$

or

$$2 > x + 1 \text{ (if } x + 1 \text{ were negative).}$$

One solution is to consider the cases $x + 1 < 0$ and $x + 1 > 0$ separately (remember $x + 1$ may not equal 0!).
If $x + 1 > 0$, then the inequality

$$2 < (x + 1)$$

is equivalent to the original, or, simplified further,

$$x > 1.$$

The solution set contains all numbers which satisfy the original condition, $x + 1 > 0$, and the derived inequality, $x > 1$. That set is

$$\{x: x + 1 > 0 \text{ and } x > 1\} =]1, \infty).$$

If $x + 1 < 0$, multiplication of both sides of the original inequality by $x + 1$ yields

$$2 > (x + 1) \quad \text{or} \quad x < 1.$$

The solution set from this part includes all numbers satisfying the original condition, $x + 1 < 0$, and the derived inequality, $x < 1$. This set is

$$\{x: x + 1 < 0 \text{ and } x < 1\} = (-\infty, -1[\cap (-\infty, 1[= (-\infty, -1[.$$

The solution set for the original inequality,

$$\frac{2}{x + 1} < 1,$$

is then the set of all solutions from both cases, namely,

$$(-\infty, -1[\cup]1, \infty).$$

An alternate method of solving similar inequalities is shown in the next example.

EXAMPLE 4.9 $\dfrac{x + 1}{x - 1} > 0.$

Here again, $x - 1$ cannot be 0—that is, $x \neq 1$. But $x - 1$ may be positive or negative. However, whatever $x - 1$ may be, $(x - 1)^2$ will always be positive (since it is not 0).
Multiplying by $(x - 1)^2$, the equivalent inequality

$$\frac{(x + 1)(x - 1)^2}{x - 1} > 0$$

or

$$(x + 1)(x - 1) > 0$$

is obtained. The solution set and graph are:

$$(-\infty, -1[\cup]1, \infty).$$

Solution set of $\dfrac{x + 1}{x - 1} > 0.$

EXAMPLE 4.10 $\dfrac{(x + 1)}{(x - 4)} \geq 2.$

First it is noted that $x - 4 \neq 0$, so $x \neq 4$.

Multiplying by $(x - 4)^2$ and simplifying, one obtains

$$\frac{(x + 1)(x - 4)^2}{x - 4} \geq 2(x - 4)^2,$$

$$(x + 1)(x - 4) \geq 2(x - 4)^2 \qquad (\text{and } x \neq 4),$$

$$x^2 - 3x - 4 \geq 2x^2 - 16x + 32,$$

$$x^2 - 13x + 36 \leq 0,$$

$$(x - 9)(x - 4) \leq 0.$$

The solution set to this last inequality is $[4, 9]$.
However, in the original inequality it is necessary that x *not* be 4. This means the solution set to the original inequality is the interval $]4, 9]$. (The extraneous solution 4 was obtained by canceling $(x - 4)$ from the numerator and denominator of the left-hand side of the inequality after multiplying both sides by $(x - 4)$. You may recall similar extraneous solutions while solving fractional equations.)

EXERCISE SET 4.3

Find and graph the solution set of each inequality. Use transformation principles when doing so will simplify the inequality.

1. $3x < 1$.
2. $-3x < -1$.
3. $2x - 4 > 7 - x$.
4. $7 - x < 2x - 4$.
5. $2(x + 2) \leq 3(2x - 3)$.
6. $7x^2 + 2x < 7(x + 3)(x - 2)$.
7. $\dfrac{x + 2}{3} < \dfrac{2x - 3}{5}$.
8. $\dfrac{x + 1}{-2} \geq \dfrac{2x + 1}{-4}$.
9. $\dfrac{x + 4}{x + 1} < 0$.
10. $\dfrac{x + 4}{x + 1} \geq 0$.
11. $\dfrac{x + 1}{x + 4} < 0$.

12. $\dfrac{2x - 3}{2x + 3} > 0.$

13. $\dfrac{x + 1}{x + 4} < \dfrac{1}{x + 4}.$

14. $\dfrac{2x}{x - 3} > \dfrac{x}{x - 3}.$

15. $x(x + 2) < x(x - 3).$

16. $\dfrac{x^2 + 2x - 3}{x + 2} > 0.$

17. $\dfrac{x + 2}{x - 3} < 1.$

18. $\dfrac{2}{x - 4} \geq 3.$

19. $\dfrac{3}{2x + 3} < 1.$

20. $\dfrac{7}{x - 2} \geq \dfrac{7}{x + 2}.$

21. $\dfrac{x^2 + 3x + 2}{x - 2} < \dfrac{x - 2}{x + 2}.$

For each inequality (Exercises 22–25), find the solution set for x in terms of the other variables.

22. $ax > b,\ a < 0.$
23. $a(x + 1) > b(x - 2),\ a < b.$
24. $x/a \leq b,\ a > 0.$
25. $\dfrac{a(x + 2)}{b} < \dfrac{b(3 - x)}{a};\ a > 0,\ b < 0.$
26. Show that if $0 < a < b$, then $0 < a^2 < b^2$. (*Hint*: if $0 < a < b$, then by multiplying by a, $0 < a^2 < ab$.)
27. Show that if $a < b < 0$, then $a^2 > b^2 > 0$.

4.6 Absolute Value

The absolute value of a real number x, written $|x|$, is the length of the segment of the real line from x to 0. This length is positive if $x \neq 0$

and is 0 if $x = 0$. Indeed, if x is nonnegative, then this length is equal to x;

$$|x| = x \quad \text{if} \quad x \geq 0.$$

If x is negative, this length is equal to $-x$, the additive inverse of x,

$$|x| = -x \quad \text{if} \quad x < 0. \qquad \text{(See Figure 4.1.)}$$

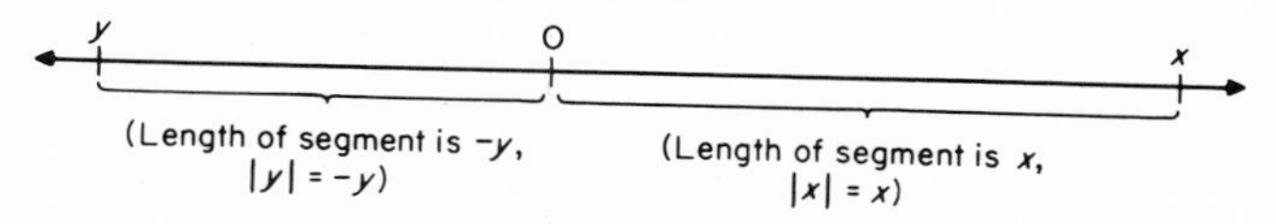

Figure 4.1

The absolute values of several numbers are given in the following example.

EXAMPLE 4.11 (a) $|2| = 2$.

(b) $|-2| = 2$.

(c) $|1.4| = 1.4$.

(d) $|-1.3| = 1.3$

(e) $|x + 2| = \begin{cases} x + 2, & \text{if } x + 2 \geq 0, \\ -(x + 2), & \text{if } x + 2 < 0. \end{cases}$

Since for any real number x, $x^2 \geq 0$, the absolute value of x^2 is x^2; that is,

$$|x^2| = x^2.$$

Since $x^2 = (-x)^2$, it follows that $|(-x)^2| = x^2$. For each real number x, then

$$|x|^2 = |x^2| = x^2.$$

4.7 Inequalities Involving Absolute Value

The distance concept is helpful in solving open sentences involving absolute value. Thus x is a solution to $|x - 3| < 2$ if and only if the distance from $(x - 3)$ to 0 is less than 2.

Set of all numbers whose distance from 0 is less than 2.

This means that

$$(x - 3) < 2 \quad \textit{and} \quad (x - 3) > -2,$$

which can be written more briefly as

$$-2 < x - 3 < 2.$$

An equivalent expression obtained by adding 3 to both sides is

$$1 < x < 5.$$

Set of all x where $|x - 3| < 2$

Notice, however, that this set,]1, 5[, is the set of all numbers whose distance from 3 is less than 2. This means an alternate interpretation of $|x - 3| < 2$ is possible—namely, that

The distance from x to 3 is less than 2.

$|7 - 3|$, then, may be interpreted as "the distance from 7 to 3," which is 4, or "the distance from $(7 - 3)$ to 0," again 4. $|-8 + 5|$ interpreted as the distance from $(-8 + 5)$ to 0 is 3, and, interpreted as the distance from -8 to -5, is also 3. [The distance is taken from -8 to -5 since $(-8 + 5)$ is $(-8 - (-5))$.]

EXAMPLE 4.12 Solve $|x - 5| < 5$.
Geometrically, $|x - 5| < 5$ says that "the distance from x to 5 is less than 5."

Set of numbers whose distance from 5 is less than 5

The graph above shows the solution set is]0, 10[.

As an alternate solution, to say that the distance from $x - 5$ to 0 is less than 5 is to say

$$-5 < x - 5 < 5.$$

Simplifying this, one obtains

$$0 < x < 10,$$

which has the solution set $]0, 10[$.

EXAMPLE 4.13 Solve $|x + 2| > 3$.
Interpreting this to be

The distance from x to -2 is greater than 3,

the solution is described graphically as

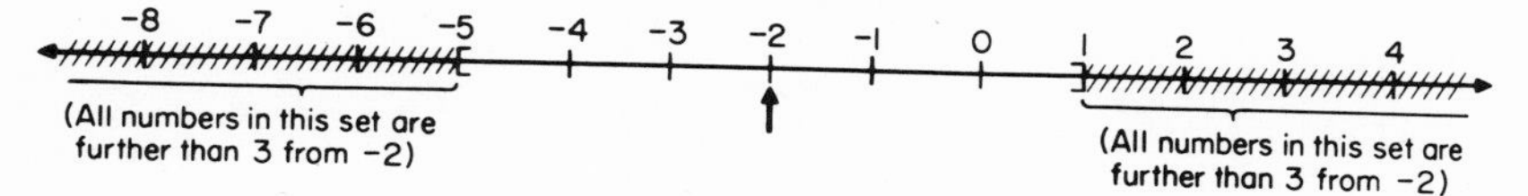

The solution set is $(-\infty, -5[\cup]1, \infty)$.

Notice that each number in $[-5, 1]$ would not be a solution since its distance from -2 is less than or equal to 3, not greater than 3.
As an alternate solution, $|x + 2| > 3$ if and only if the distance from $x + 2$ to 0 is *greater than* 3. That is, $x + 2 > 3$ or $x + 2 < -3$. Simplifying this sentence by adding -2 to each side of each inequality gives

$$x > 1 \quad \text{or} \quad x < -5.$$

Its solution set is $(-\infty, -5[\cup]1, +\infty)$.

EXAMPLE 4.14 Solve $\left|\dfrac{x + 3}{x + 1}\right| \leq 1$.

Interpreting this sentence as "the distance from $(x + 3)/(x + 1)$ to 0 is less than or equal to 1," one obtains

$$-1 \leq \frac{x + 3}{x + 1} \leq 1.$$

Multiplying by $(x + 1)^2$, being careful to note that $x + 1 \neq 0$, so $x \neq -1$,

$$(1) \quad -(x + 1)^2 \leq (x + 3)(x + 1) \leq (x + 1)^2,$$

$$(-x^2 - 2x - 1) \leq (x^2 + 4x + 3) \leq (x^2 + 2x + 1).$$

To solve this more complicated inequality, it is helpful to separate the two inequalities and write the sentence as the conjunction

$$-x^2 - 2x - 1 \leq x^2 + 4x + 3 \quad \text{and} \quad x^2 + 4x + 3 \leq x^2 + 2x + 1.$$

By simplifying each side,

$$2x^2 + 6x + 4 \geq 0 \quad \text{and} \quad 2x + 2 \leq 0,$$

$$x^2 + 3x + 2 \geq 0 \quad \text{and} \quad x \leq -1,$$

$$(x + 2)(x + 1) \geq 0 \quad \text{and} \quad x \leq -1.$$

The solution sets of the last inequalities are

$$(-\infty, -2] \cup [-1, +\infty) \quad \text{and} \quad (-\infty, -1],$$

respectively.
The solution for the inequality (1) is the *intersection* of these two sets,

$$((-\infty, -2] \cup [-1, +\infty)) \cap (-\infty, -1] = (-\infty, -2] \cup \{-1\}.$$

Since the restriction that $x + 1 \neq 0$ does not allow -1 as a solution, the solution set for the original inequality is $(-\infty, -2]$.

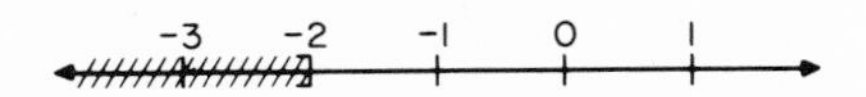

Graph of solution set of $\left|\dfrac{x+3}{x+1}\right| \leq 1$

EXERCISE SET 4.4

In Exercises 1–10, rewrite each distance statement using absolute value signs. Find and graph the solution set.

1. The distance from x to 0 is less than 4.
2. The distance from x to 0 is greater than 4.
3. The distance from x to 0 is 4.
4. The distance from $(x - 2)$ to 0 is less than 5.
5. The distance from x to 2 is less than 5.
6. The distance from x to 3 is less than 2 and greater than 1.
7. The distance from $2x$ to 5 is greater than or equal to 3.
8. The distance from $3x$ to 4 is $\sqrt{2}$ or less.

9. The distance from $2x$ to 7 is positive.
10. The distance from x to 3 is less than 5, and the distance from $2x$ to -3 is less than 3.

Find and graph the solution set for each open sentence of Exercises 11–26.

11. $|x - 3| < 2.$
12. $|x + 4| > 3.$
13. $|2x - 3| \leq 7.$
14. $|x - 5| \leq 1.$
15. $|x^2| > 3.$
16. $|2x - 7| \geq 4.$
17. $|3 - 4x| \geq 8.$
18. $|x^2| \leq 2.$
19. $\left|\dfrac{x - 1}{x - 3}\right| < 1.$
20. $\dfrac{2}{|x + 1|} > 1.$
21. $|x^2 + x - 4| < 2.$
22. $|x^2 + x| > 2.$
23. $\left|\dfrac{x + 1}{x + 3}\right| \geq 1.$
24. $|(x - 2)^2| < 1.$
25. $|x + \pi| \leq 0.$
26. $|x + \pi| \geq 0.$

Solve for x in terms of the other variables (Exercises 27–29).

27. $|x - a| < b, b > 0.$
28. $|x - a| > b.$
29. $|x - h|^2 < a^2.$
30. Show that $\sqrt{x^2} = x$ is not generally true for $x \in R$.
31. Prove the triangle inequality, $|a + b| \leq |a| + |b|$. (*Hint*: Show that $|a + b|^2 \leq (|a| + |b|)^2$ using the equation $|x^2| = |x|^2$.)

Subsets of the Plane; An Introduction to Analytic Geometry

CHAPTER FIVE

5.1 Introduction

In the previous chapters, solution sets of open sentences such as $2x + 3 = 5$ or $2x < 7$ were graphed on a number line. For each number which was a solution, there was a corresponding point on the graph, and vice versa. This beginning of analytic geometry will be extended in this chapter to sentences with two variables whose solutions will be graphed as points on the plane.

5.2 Rectangular Coordinates

By means of two coordinate axes, each ordered pair of numbers determines a point on the plane called its *graph*, and, conversely each point on the plane determines an ordered pair of numbers called its *coordinates*. The *coordinate axes* are real number lines, each with uniform scales and a common unit of distance, which are placed perpendicular to each other. The *first component axis* (or *x-axis*) lies horizontally, with the positive numbers to the right; the *second component axis* (or *y-axis*) lies vertically, with the positive numbers upward. The two axes meet at their 0 points; this point of intersection is called the *origin*, and is designated by O (see Figure 5.1).

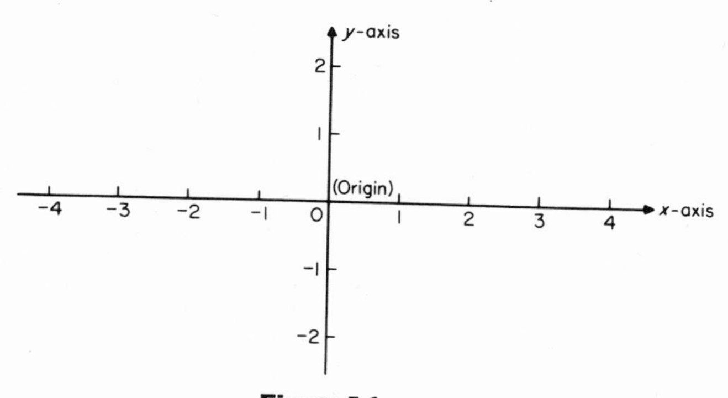

Figure 5.1

For a given ordered pair of numbers (a, b), its graph P is the point of intersection of the vertical line passing through the point a on the x-axis and the horizontal line passing through the point b on the y-axis. Conversely, for a given point S in the plane, the first number c of its pair of coordinates (c, d) is the point of the x-axis on the vertical line through S; the second number d is the point of the y-axis on the horizontal line through S (see Figure 5.2).

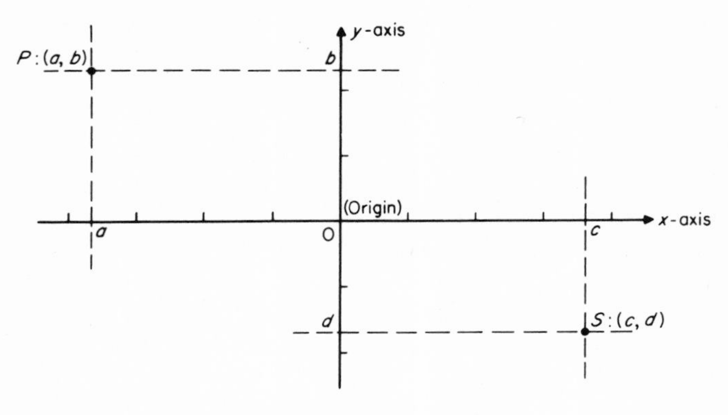

Figure 5.2

Because of the correspondence between points and their pairs of coordinates, a point may be designated by its pair of coordinates. Thus $(1, 0)$, $(17, -3)$, $(5, -\frac{1}{2})$, and $(\sqrt{2}, -\pi)$ are points on the plane. The process of locating and marking these points on a graph is called *graphing* or *plotting* the points.

For each real number a, $(a, 0)$ is a point on the x-axis and $(0, a)$ is a point on the y-axis. The set of all points on the x-axis is

$$\{(x, y) : y = 0 \text{ and } x \in R\}$$

or, more simply,

$$\{(x, 0) : x \in R\}.$$

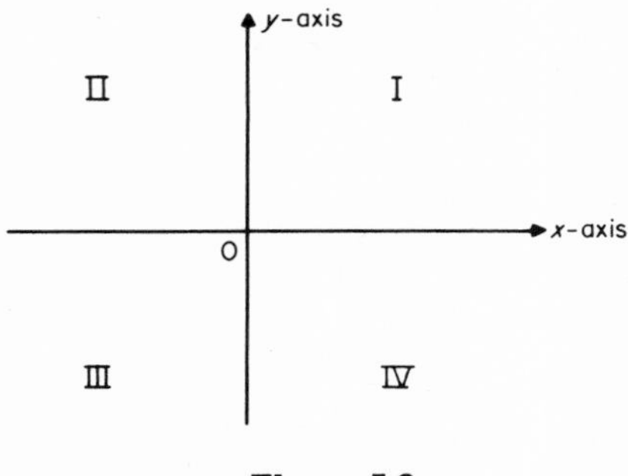

Figure 5.3

The coordinate lines divide the plane into four quarters or *quadrants*. To identify these regions of the plane, the quadrants are numbered I, II, III, and IV, counterclockwise, as shown in Figure 5.3. Since each of the points in quadrant I is to the right of the y-axis, its first component (x-value) is positive. Since each point in quadrant I is above the x-axis, its second component (y-value) is also positive. The set of all points in this quadrant is then

$$\{(x, y) : x > 0 \;\&\; y > 0\}.$$

The sets of points in the four quadrants are:

Quadrant I : $\{(x, y) : x > 0 \,\&\, y > 0\}$,
Quadrant II : $\{(x, y) : x < 0 \,\&\, y > 0\}$,
Quadrant III: $\{(x, y) : x < 0 \,\&\, y < 0\}$,
Quadrant IV : $\{(x, y) : x > 0 \,\&\, y < 0\}$.

The plane is denoted by R^2 and is the union of the four quadrants and the two axes.

EXERCISE SET 5.1

1. Plot the following points on one graph. Label each point.

   $(0, 1)$, $(2, \sqrt{2})$,
   $(1, 2)$, $(-7, \frac{3}{4})$,
   $(2, 0)$, $(-3, 1)$,
   $(\sqrt{3}, -2)$, $(2, 2)$.

2. Name the quadrant or axis which contains each point.

   (a) $(0, 1)$.
   (b) $(-1, -2)$.
   (c) $(-2, 3)$.
   (d) $(0, -4)$.
   (e) $(-4, 0)$.
   (f) $(1, 3)$.
   (g) $(\sqrt{7}, |-3|)$.
   (h) (x, y) if $x > y > 0$.
   (i) (x, y) if $x < y < 0$.
   (j) (x, y) if $x \in I^+$, $y \in I^+$.
   (k) (x, y) if $x^2 + y^2 = 0$.
   (l) (x, y) if $x > 0$, $y = 2$.
   (m) (x, y) if $x - y = 1$, $x < 0$.
   (n) (x, y) if $x = y^2$, $y < 0$.
   (o) $(0, 0)$.

5.3 Graphing Solution Sets

A *solution* to an open sentence containing the two variables x and y, such as

$$2x + y = 5,$$

consists of an ordered pair of numbers such that if the first number is substituted for x and the second for y, the resulting sentence is true. $(3, -1)$ is a solution for $2x + y = 5$, since $(2)(3) + (-1) = 5$. Similarly $(2, 1)$, $(-5, 15)$, $(\frac{1}{2}, 4)$, $(\pi, 5 - 2\pi)$ are solutions while $(0, 0)$, $(-1, 3)$, $(1, 2)$, $(\sqrt{2}, 4)$ are not. The solution set of

$$2x + y = 5$$

is

$$\{(x, y) : 2x + y = 5\}.$$

The *graph of an open sentence* is the graph of all ordered pairs in the solution set of the sentence. The graph of the sentence $2x + y = 5$ is the graph of all points of $\{(x, y) : 2x + y = 5\}$, which is a line of points as pictured below (Figure 5.4). Is each of the points indicated on the graph a solution to the sentence, and does each solution appear on the graph?

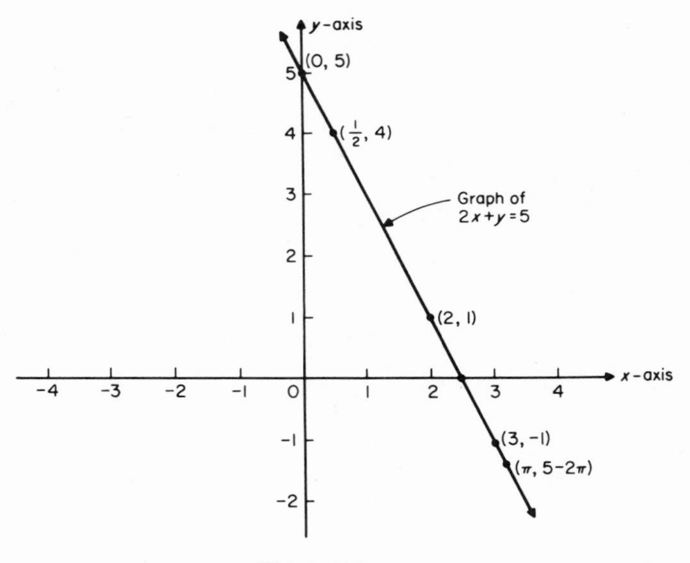

Figure 5.4

To plot the graph of a sentence, such as $2x + y = 5$, one may find several solutions to the sentence, plot the corresponding points, and try to guess what the entire graph is from the result. This procedure is perhaps the most important single method for graphing an arbitrary sentence. There are a number of special techniques that are very helpful, but this "plot and guess" method is the most general. Since the result is partly speculation, care must be taken to ensure that enough points are plotted to make the guess a reasonable one.

When graphing an inequality such as

$$x - 2y > 0,$$

it is helpful to first graph the statement obtained by replacing the inequality sign with an equal sign, i.e.,

$$x - 2y = 0.$$

The graph of this sentence is the dashed line of Figure 5.5 that bounds the shaded region; it is dashed to indicate that it is *not* part of the solution set.

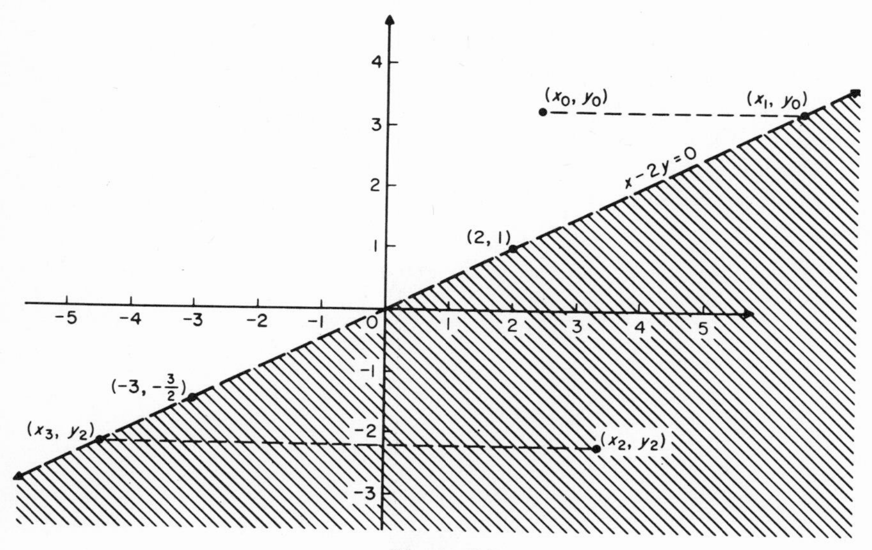

Figure 5.5

Consider a point (x_0, y_0) above or to the left of the line $x - 2y = 0$. The value x_0 is less than x_1, where (x_1, y_0) is on the line; hence,

$$x_0 - 2y_0 < x_1 - 2y_0 = 0.$$

This means $(x_0, y_0) \notin \{(x, y) : x - 2y > 0\}$. Since (x_0, y_0) was arbitrary, no point above or to the left of the line can be in the solution set. Choosing (x_2, y_2) below or to the right of the line, then $x_2 > x_3$ where (x_3, y_2) is on the line. Thus

$$x_2 - 2y_2 > x_3 - 2y_2 = 0.$$

This means $(x_2, y_2) \in \{(x, y) : x - 2y > 0\}$. All points below or to the right of the line are in the solution set.

The *extent of* x in the graph of a sentence is the set of x-values which occur in some solution of the sentence. The *extent of* x in the graph of $y = x^2$ is the entire real line, $(-\infty, \infty)$. However, the extent of x in the graph of $x = y^2$ is the ray $[0, \infty)$, since only the nonnegative values of x occur in solutions. The *extent of* y in the graph of a sentence is, similarly, the set of all y-values which occur in some solution of the sentence. The *extent of* y in $x = \sqrt{y+1}$ is $[-1, \infty)$; the extent of y in $xy = 1$ is $(-\infty, 0[\cup]0, \infty)$, since no solution $(x, 0)$ occurs.

EXAMPLE 5.1 Plot the graph of $x + y = 1$. Find the extent of x and the extent of y.

The procedure used is to find and plot several points of the solution set $\{(x, y) : x + y = 1\}$. By arbitrarily choosing values for x, such as -1, 0, 1, 3, and solving $x + y = 1$ for y, the points $(-1, 2)$, $(0, 1)$, $(1, 0)$, $(3, -2)$ are found and plotted. Since all four points lie on a line, this line is the "guess" for the graph. By checking several other solutions, one becomes more firmly convinced that this is the graph of the solution set.

The extent of x is $(-\infty, \infty)$; the extent of y is $(-\infty, \infty)$ (Figure 5.6).

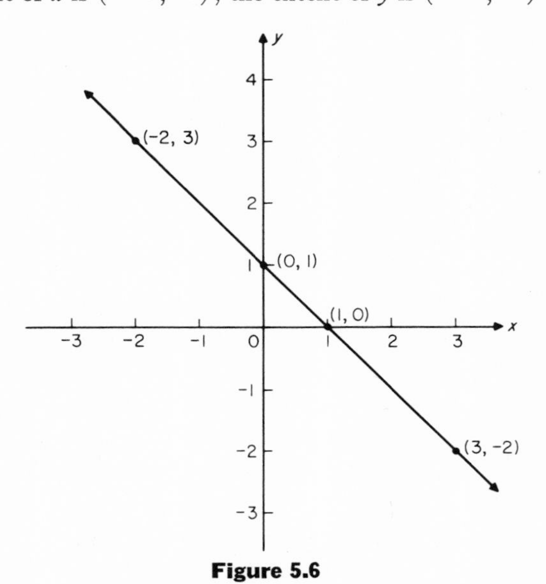

Figure 5.6

EXAMPLE 5.2 Plot the graph of $x + y < 1$. Find the extent of x and the extent of y.

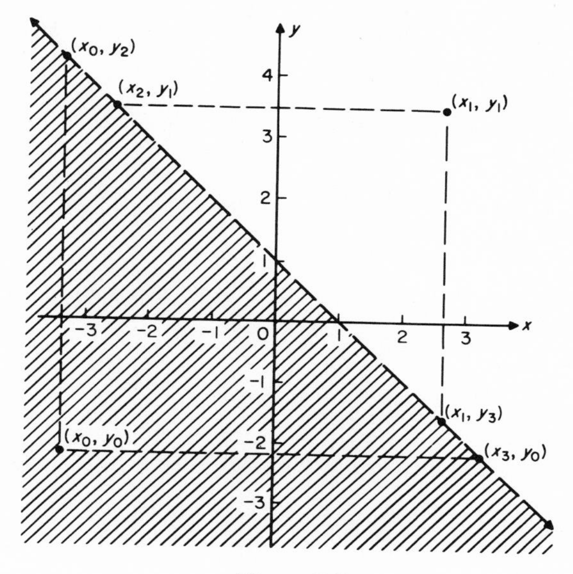

Figure 5.7

The graph of $x + y = 1$ (Example 5.1) is sketched as a dashed line to indicate that it is *not* a part of the solution set, $\{(x, y) : x + y < 1\}$. For any point (x_0, y_0) below or to the left of the line, $x_0 + y_0 < 1$. Why? All such points are in the solution set. Similarly, for any point (x_1, y_1) above or to the right of the line, $x_1 + y_1 > 1$. No such points are in the solution set. The extent of x is $(-\infty, \infty)$; the extent of y is $(-\infty, \infty)$ (Figure 5.7).

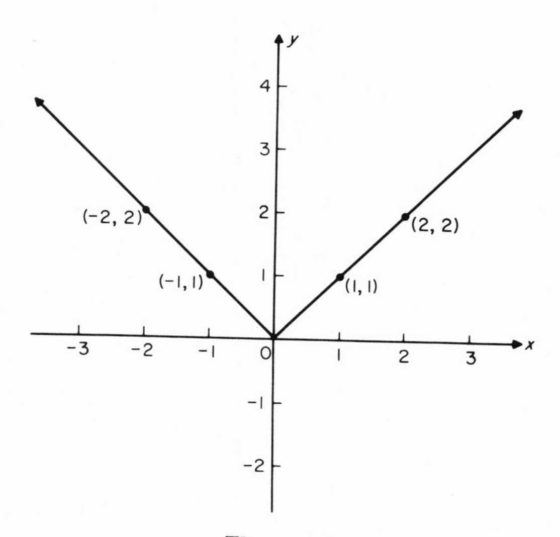

Figure 5.8

EXAMPLE 5.3 Plot the graph of $\{(x, y) : |x| = y\}$. Find the extent of x and the extent of y.

The graph of the solution set is the graph of the sentence $|x| = y$. Since $|1| = |-1| = 1$, each of the pairs $(1, 1)$, $(-1, 1)$ is a solution. In general, since $|x| = |-x|$, the entire solution set consists of two rays, one originating at $(0, 0)$ and passing through $(1, 1)$, the other originating at $(0, 0)$ and passing through $(-1, 1)$.

The extent of x is $(-\infty, \infty)$; the extent of y is $[0, +\infty)$ (Figure 5.8).

EXERCISE SET 5.2

Find four solutions (if possible) to each sentence (Exercises 1–15).

1. $2x + y = 3$.
2. $2x + y < 3$.
3. $2x + y > 3$.
4. $x^2 < 4y$.
5. $x/y = 5$.
6. $y = \sqrt{x}$.
7. $x = \sqrt{y}$.
8. $x^2 + y^2 > 0$.
9. $y = x$ or $y = -x$.
10. $x \geq 0$ and $y < 0$.
11. $x \in [0, 1]$ and $y = 0$.
12. $y = x^2 + 2x + 1$.
13. $(x - 1)^2 = (y + 3)^2$.
14. If $x > 0$, $y > 0$.
15. $y = |x|$.

Plot the graph of the solution set of each sentence, labeling at least four solutions of each graph. Find the extent of x and the extent of y. Describe the graph of the solution set in *geometric terms* [e.g., "a circle with center O, radius 3" or "a line through points $(0, 1)$ and $(2, -1)$"].

16. $y = 3 - 5x$.
17. $y > 3 - 5x$.
18. $y < 3 - 5x$.
19. $x = -2y + 3$.
20. $x < -2y + 3$.
21. $x \leq -2y + 3$.
22. $x/y = 5$.

23. $y = x$.
24. $x^2 = y^2$.
25. $y = 4$. (*Hint*: Solution set is $\{(x, y) : x \in R, y = 4\}$.
26. $x^2 + y^2 = 4$.
27. $x^2 + y^2 < 4$.
28. $x^2 + y^2 > 4$.
29. $x^2 + y^2 \leq 4$.
30. $y = -\sqrt{x}$.
31. $y < -\sqrt{x}$.
32. $y > -\sqrt{x}$.
33. $x = 1$ and $y < 1$.
34. $x = 1$ or $y < 1$.
35. If $x = 1$, then $y < 1$.
36. $x = 1$ or $y > 1$.
37. $y = x$ or $y = -x$.
38. $y = x^2 + 3x - 4$.
39. $y > (x + 4)(x - 1)$.
40. $xy = 0$.
41. $xy \neq 0$.
42. $x/y = 0$.

5.4 Symmetry

The graph of $y = x^2$ is *symmetric with respect to the y-axis* (see Figure 5.9); that is, the parts on either side of the axis are mirror images or

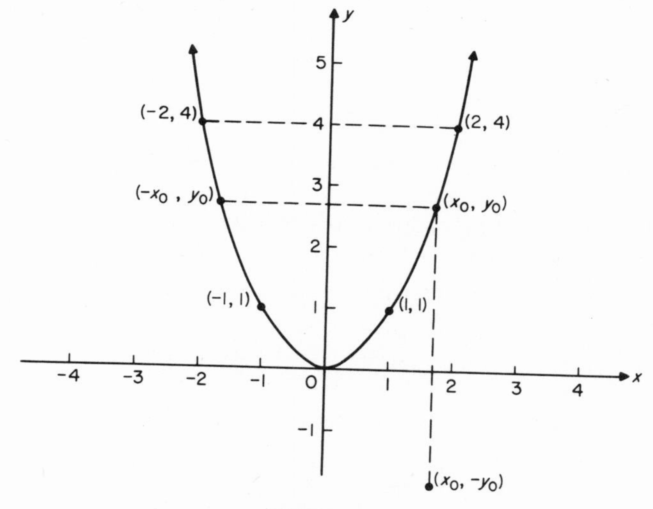

Figure 5.9

reflections of each other. For the y-axis to be a *line of symmetry* of the graph, each point (x_0, y_0) must have a reflection point $(-x_0, y_0)$ directly opposite it. This is the case for $y = x^2$ since the solution set of $y = x^2$ is the same as the solution set of $y = (-x)^2$, where $(-x)$ has been substituted for x. In set notation, the graph of $y = x^2$ is symmetric to the y-axis since

$$\{(x, y) : y = x^2\} = \{(x, y) : y = (-x)^2\}.$$

These two sets are the same since $x^2 = (-x)^2$ for each x.

The graph of $y = x^2$ is *not* symmetric to the x-axis since for any solution (x_0, y_0), other than (0, 0), its reflection with respect to this axis, $(x_0, -y_0)$, is *not* a solution. The solution sets of $y = x^2$ and of the equation obtained by substituting $(-y)$ for y, $(-y) = x^2$, are *not* the same.

The x-axis is a *line of symmetry* of $x^2 - 2x + y^2 = 0$, since each point (x_0, y_0) of its graph has its reflection point $(x_0, -y_0)$ on the graph also (see Figure 5.10). In other words, the solutions of $x^2 - 2x + y^2 = 0$ and the equation obtained by substituting $(-y)$ for y, $x^2 - 2x + (-y)^2 = 0$, are the same.

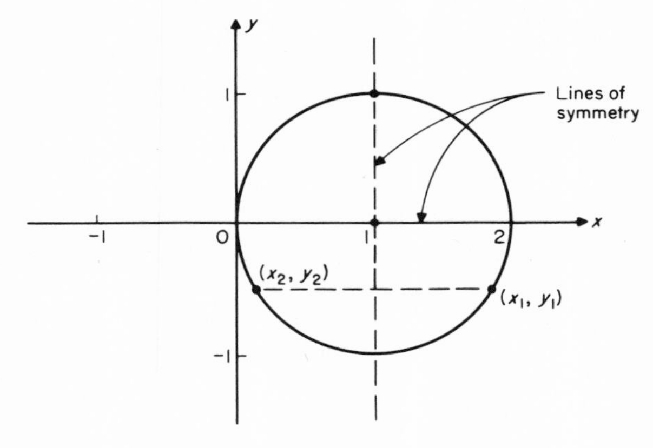

Figure 5.10

The graph is not symmetric to the y-axis. This is recognized from the equation (as well as from Figure 5.10) since substitution of $(-x)$ for x in the equation yields a different solution set. That is,

$$\{(x, y) : x^2 - 2x + y^2 = 0\} \neq \{(x, y) : (-x)^2 - 2(-x) + y^2 = 0\}.$$

Although symmetry to the y-axis does not exist for each point (x_1, y_1) on the graph, there is a reflection point (x_2, y_1) on the graph *with respect to the vertical line through* (1, 0). This being the case, the graph is said to be symmetric *with respect to* this vertical line through (1, 0). In a similar

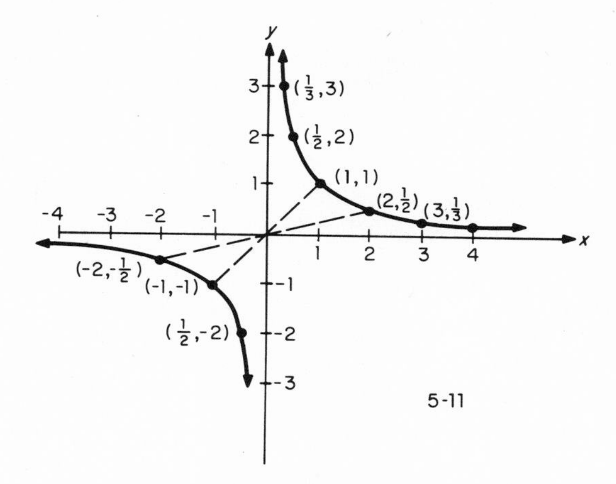

Figure 5.11

manner, symmetry to vertical and horizontal lines in general can be considered.

The reflection of a point (x_0, y_0) with respect to the origin is the point $(-x_0, -y_0)$. A graph is symmetric with respect to the origin if for each point on it, its reflection point through the origin is also on the graph. The graph of $xy = 1$ possesses such symmetry (see Figure 5.11). This is verified by the equality of the solution sets of $xy = 1$ and the equation obtained by substituting $(-x)$ for x, and $(-y)$ for y, $(-x)(-y) = 1$. That is to say,

$$\{(x, y) : xy = 1\} = \{(x, y) : (-x)(-y) = 1\}.$$

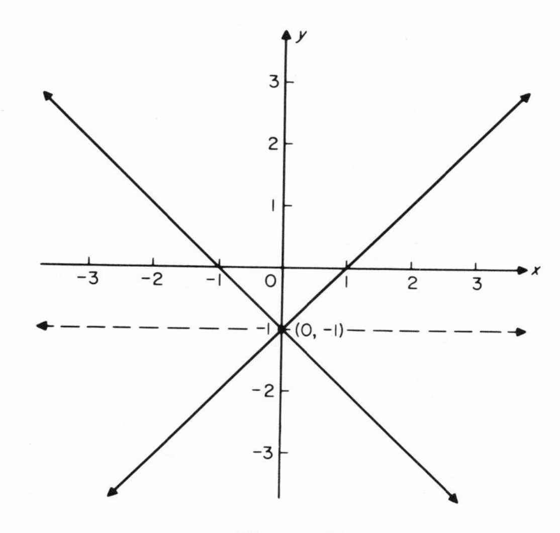

Figure 5.12

The concept of symmetry with respect to the origin can be generalized to the concept of symmetry to any point. Thus a circle is always symmetric to its center point; a line is symmetric to any point upon it.

EXAMPLE 5.4 Plot the graph of $|x| = |y + 1|$; discuss its symmetry with respect to vertical or horizontal lines, and with respect to points.

The graph is symmetric to the y-axis, to the horizontal line through $(0, -1)$, and to the point $(0, -1)$ (Figure 5.12).

EXAMPLE 5.5 Discuss the symmetry of the graph of $y = x^3$ with respect to horizontal or vertical lines and with respect to points. Plot the graph.

Plotting the graph (Figure 5.13) reveals no symmetry to horizontal or vertical lines. The figure appears to be symmetric to the origin.

Since the solution sets of $y = x^3$ and $(-y) = (-x)^3$ are identical, the graph is, indeed, symmetric to the origin.

The graph is not symmetric to either axis since the solution sets of $y = x^3$ and $y = (-x)^3$ are not the same, and the solution sets of $y = x^3$ and $(-y) = x^3$ are not the same.

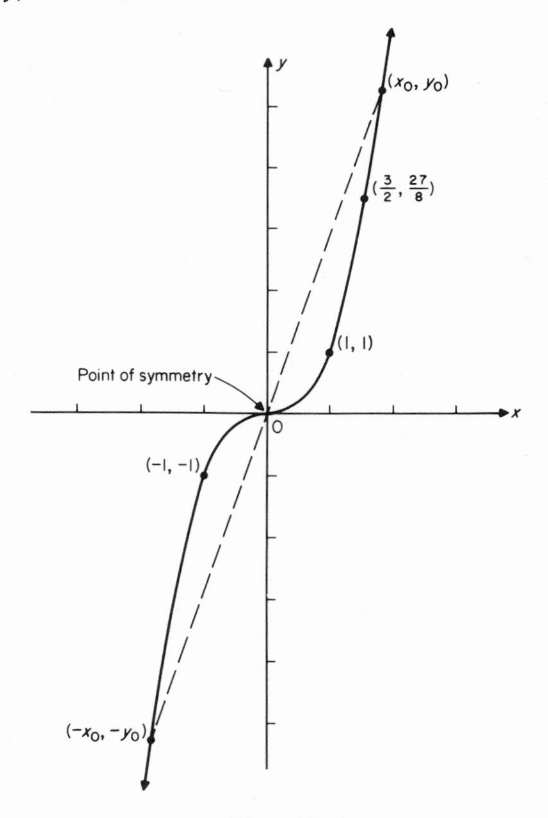

Figure 5.13

EXAMPLE 5.6 Find all points of symmetry and all vertical or horizontal lines of symmetry of the graph of $\{(x, y) : x + 2 > 0\}$. Graph the set, labeling these points and lines.

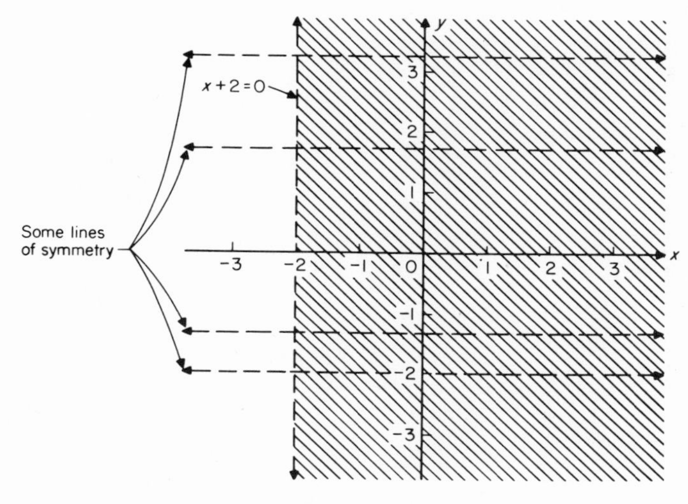

Figure 5.14

The graph is given in Figure 5.14. The graph is symmetric to any horizontal line, but to no vertical line and to no point.

EXERCISE SET 5.3

Determine whether or not the graph of each sentence or set will be symmetric to the x-axis, the y-axis, or the origin.

1. $x^2 + 2y = 0$.
2. $x^2 + 4y^2 = 4$.
3. $2x - 4y = 3$.
4. $x^2 + y^2 < 4$.
5. $\{(x, y) : y = 4\}$.
6. $\{(x, y) : x = 3\}$.
7. $\{(x, y) : x > 0 \ \& \ y > 0\}$.
8. $\{(x, y) : x = 1 \text{ or } y = 1\}$.
9. $x/y - 2 = 0$.
10. $(x + 1)^2 - (y + 2)^2 = 0$.
11. $x^2 - 4x + y^2 + 4y = 0$.
12. $x < 0$ or $y > 0$.

Plot the graph of the solution set of each sentence (Exercises 13–30). Discuss its symmetry with respect to the vertical or horizontal lines, and with respect to points. Find the extent in x and in y.

13. $y = 2x + 3$.
14. $y > 2x + 3$.
15. $x/y = 1$.
16. $x^2 + 2x = y$.
17. $y^2 + 2x = 0$.
18. $(x - 1)/(y - 2) = \frac{2}{3}$.
19. $y > 3x^2$.
20. $x > 3y^2$.
21. $x = 5$.
22. $y = 5$.
23. $y = |x|$.
24. $y = |x^2|$.
25. $|y| = |x|$.
26. $|x - 2| = y$.
27. $y = |x^3|$.
28. $y < x^3$.
29. $y > x^3$.
30. $y = x^4$.
31. Consider the equation $x^2 + 2x + y^2 - 4y = 0$. By completing the square in x and in y, the equation can be written as

$$(x + 1)^2 + (y - 2)^2 = 5.$$

Plot the graph to show that the vertical line through -1 on the x-axis, where $(x + 1) = 0$, and the horizontal line through 2 on the y-axis, where $(y - 2) = 0$, are lines of symmetry of the graph of the equation. Explain why this is so.

32. Complete the square of the equation

$$x^2 - 3x = y,$$

and plot the graph to show that the vertical line through $+\frac{3}{2}$ on the x-axis [where $(x - \frac{3}{2}) = 0$] is a line of symmetry.

In Exercises 33–38, complete the square in x and in y (where possible) to determine horizontal and vertical lines of symmetry. (See Exercises 31 and 32.) Plot each graph, labeling these lines.

33. $x^2 + 2x + y^2 + 2y = 0$.
34. $x^2 + y^2 + 6y = 7$.
35. $x = y^2 - y$.
36. $x^2 + 8x = y^2 - 8y$.
37. $2x^2 + 4x + y^2 = 4$.
38. $3y^2 - 6y - x^2 = 0$.

5.5 Distance

The *distance* between two points P and Q can be expressed in terms of their coordinates by the theorem of Pythagoras. Let P be the graph of (x_1, y_1) and let Q be the graph of (x_2, y_2). In Figure 5.15, point M is the

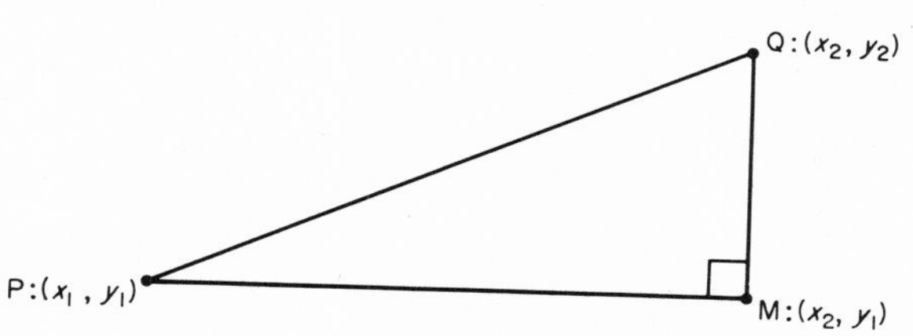

Figure 5.15

graph of (x_2, y_1). By the Pythagorean theorem, the distance between P and Q is the square root of the sum of the squares of the distances from P to M and M to Q. The distance from P to M is $|x_2 - x_1|$ (or $\sqrt{(x_2 - x_1)^2}$) and the distance from M to Q is $|y_2 - y_1|$ (or $\sqrt{(y_2 - y_1)^2}$). The distance from P to Q, $d(P, Q)$, is therefore given by

$$d(P, Q) = \sqrt{(x_2 - x_1)^2 + (y_2 - y_1)^2}.$$

EXAMPLE 5.7 Find the distance between $(-2, 5)$ and $(1, 3)$.

$$\begin{aligned} d[(-2, 5), (1, 3)] &= \sqrt{(1 - (-2))^2 + (3 - 5)^2} \\ &= \sqrt{3^2 + (-2)^2} \\ &= \sqrt{13}. \end{aligned}$$

EXAMPLE 5.8 Find $d[(1, 0), (5, 0)]$.

$$\begin{aligned} d[(1, 0), (5, 0)] &= \sqrt{(5 - 1)^2 + (0 - 0)^2} \\ &= \sqrt{4^2} \\ &= 4. \end{aligned}$$

EXAMPLE 5.9 Find the distance between $(a + 2, b)$ and $(a - 1, b + 3)$.

$$\begin{aligned} &d[(a + 2, b), (a - 1, b + 3)] \\ &\qquad = \sqrt{(a + 2 - a + 1)^2 + (b - b - 3)^2} \\ &\qquad = \sqrt{3^2 + (-3)^2} \\ &\qquad = 3\sqrt{2}. \end{aligned}$$

The *distance* (or perpendicular distance) from a point (x_0, y_0) to a line L is the length of the perpendicular segment between the point and the line. (The distance from a point on a line to the line itself is 0.) The distance from $(1, -3)$ to the vertical line through $(7, 0)$ is then 6. The distance from $(-2, 2)$ to the horizontal line through $(0, 4)$ is 2 (see Figure 5.16).

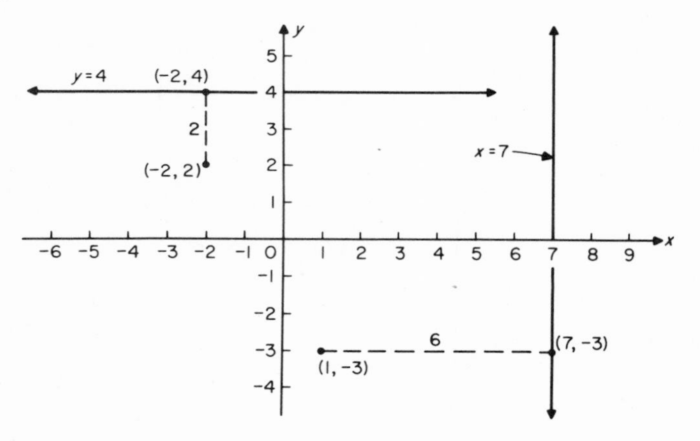

Figure 5.16

EXERCISE SET 5.4

Find the distance between each pair of points. Plot the pairs of points of Exercises 1–5 on one graph, joining each pair with a line segment.

1. $(-5, 0)$, $(7, 0)$.
2. $(0, 1)$, $(0, 3)$.
3. $(0, 1)$, $(3, 0)$.
4. $(-7, 0)$, $(0, -3)$.
5. $(2, 4)$, $(5, 8)$.
6. $(4, -7)$, $(-1, 5)$.
7. $(3, -18)$, $(-4, 6)$.
8. $(1, 1)$, $(2, 2)$.
9. (a, b), $(2a, 2b)$.
10. (a, b), $(a + 2, b + 2)$.
11. $(3, 2\sqrt{3})$, $(4, \sqrt{3})$.
12. $(x, 3)$, $(y, 4)$.
13. (x, y), $(3, 4)$.
14. (s, a), (y, a).
15. $(a, 0)$, $(b, 0)$.
16. $(x - 3, y - 2)$, $(0, 0)$.
17. (a, a), (b, b).

18. $(a, 0)$, $(0, b)$.
19. $(-9, 0)$, $(0, -b)$.
20. $(x - 1, y + 2)$, $(x + 3, y - 1)$.

Plot the graph of the point and line of each exercise (21–30). Find the distance from the point to the line.

21. $(0, 0)$; vertical line through $(2, 2)$.
22. $(-1, 2)$; vertical line through $(-3, 1)$.
23. $(3, 2)$; horizontal line through $(1, 1)$.
24. $(7, 4)$; the x-axis.
25. $(3, 3)$; horizontal line through $(3, -2)$.
26. $(a, 4)$; horizontal line through $(3, -1)$.
27. $(2, a)$; vertical line through $(0, b)$.
28. (a, b); vertical line through (c, d).
29. (a, b); horizontal line through (c, d).
30. $(2, 2)$; line through $(1, 0)$ and $(0, 1)$.
31. Show that $(2, 3)$ is equidistant from $(1, -2)$ and $(3, 8)$. Graph to show that $(2, 3)$ is the midpoint of the segment from $(1, -2)$ to $(3, 8)$.
32. Use the distance formula to show that

$$P = \left(\frac{a+b}{2}, \frac{c+d}{2}\right)$$

is equidistant from (a, c) and (b, d). Graph, and show that P is the midpoint of the segment from (a, c) to (b, d).
33. Find the midpoint of the segment from $(6, 4)$ to $(2, 1)$.
34. Find the midpoint of the segment from $(2, 3)$ to $(-1, 4)$.
35. Find the set of all points equidistant from $(1, 2)$ and $(-3, -4)$.
36. Find the set of all points equidistant from $(2, 1)$ and $(-2, -1)$.

5.6 Using Distance to Obtain Analytic Descriptions of Sets of Points

In describing a set of points, the notion of distance is often used. A circle is described as a set of points each of which is a given distance, called the *radius*, from a fixed point called the *center*. The interior of a circle of radius r and center (a, b) may be described as the set of points each of which is a distance *less than* r from the center (a, b).

For a given set of points, it is often possible by means of the distance formula to write an *analytic description* of the set; that is, it is possible to find an equation or inequality whose solution set is the given set. For a circle of radius 4 with center at the origin, the set can be described by

$$\{(x, y) : d[(x, y), (0, 0)] = 4\}.$$

Using the distance formula, the sentence $d[(x, y), (0, 0)] = 4$ may be written as:

$$\sqrt{(x - 0)^2 + (y - 0)^2} = 4,$$
$$\sqrt{x^2 + y^2} = 4,$$
$$x^2 + y^2 = 16.$$

The circle then is described as the solution set to the equation

$$x^2 + y^2 = 16.$$

This equation is the analytic description of the circle.

EXAMPLE 5.10 Find an analytic description for the set of all points each of which is distance 2 from the point $(1, -1)$.
This set may be written as:

$$\{(x, y) : d[(x, y), (1, -1)] = 2\}.$$

The sentence $d[(x, y), (1, -1)] = 2$, can be expressed by means of the distance formula as

$$\sqrt{(x - 1)^2 + (y + 1)^2} = 2$$

or, by squaring both sides,

$$(x - 1)^2 + (y + 1)^2 = 4.$$

The equation is an analytic description of the circle shown in Figure 5.17.

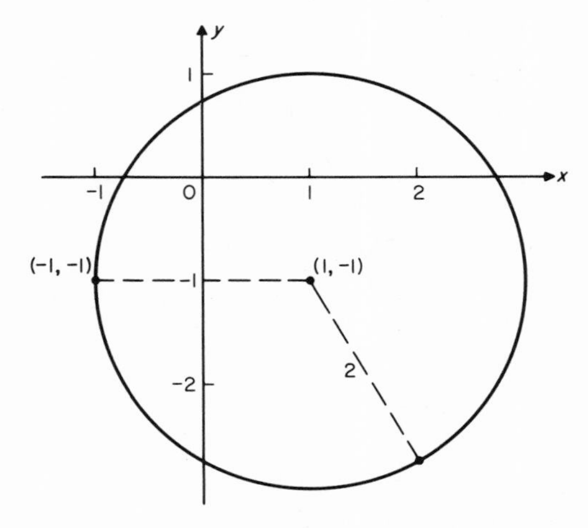

Figure 5.17

EXAMPLE 5.11 Give an analytic description of the set of all points each of which is at a distance greater than 2 and less than 3 from the point $(-1, 2)$. (See Figure 5.18.)

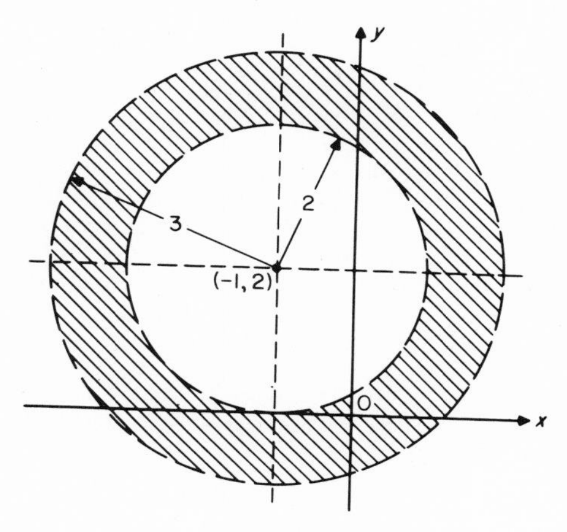

Figure 5.18

This set may be written as:

$$\{(x, y) : 2 < d[(x, y), (-1, 2)] < 3\},$$

or

$$\{(x, y) : 2 < \sqrt{(x+1)^2 + (y-2)^2} < 3\}.$$

The analytic description can be simplified to be

$$-1 < x^2 + 2x + y^2 - 4y < 4.$$

EXAMPLE 5.12 Describe analytically the set of all points equidistant from the line $y = 2$ and the point $(0, -2)$.
From Figure 5.19, the set can be written as

$$\{(x, y) : d[(x, y), (x, 2)] = d[(x, y), (0, -2)]\}.$$

The equation

$$d[(x, y), (x, 2)] = d[(x, y), (0, -2)]$$

can be simplified to be

$$(x - x)^2 + (y - 2)^2 = (x - 0)^2 + (y + 2)^2$$

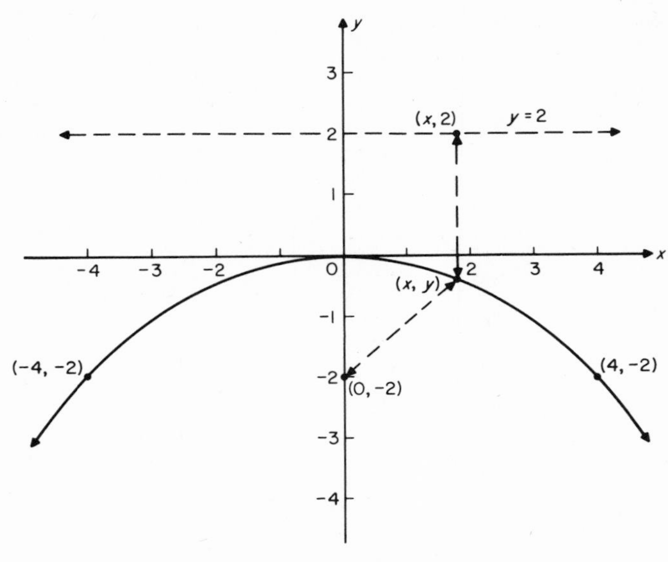

Figure 5.19

or

$$x^2 + 8y = 0.$$

This equation is an analytic description of the set.

EXAMPLE 5.13 Find an analytic description for the set of all points the sum of whose distances from $(3, 1)$ and $(-1, 1)$ is 6. Plot the graph of the set.

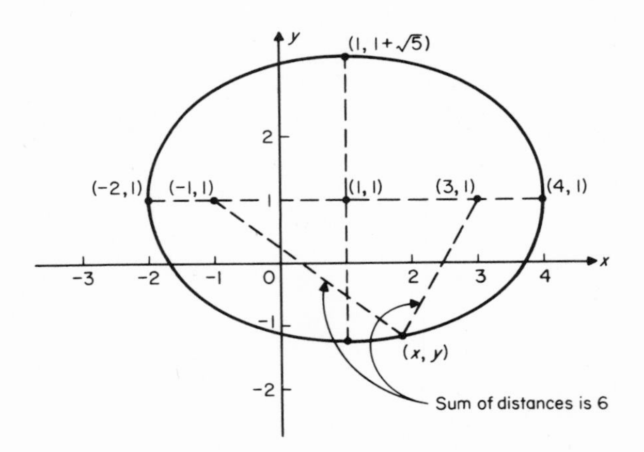

Figure 5.20

The graph is drawn in Figure 5.20. The set

$$\{(x, y) : d[(x, y), (-1, 1)] + d[(x, y), (3, 1)] = 6\}$$

is described by the equation

$$d[(x, y), (-1, 1)] + d[(x, y), (3, 1)] = 6,$$

which simplifies to

$$\sqrt{(x + 1)^2 + (y - 1)^2} + \sqrt{(x - 3)^2 + (y - 1)^2} = 6,$$

$$\sqrt{(x + 1)^2 + (y - 1)^2} = -\sqrt{(x - 3)^2 + (y - 1)^2} + 6,$$

$$(x + 1)^2 + (y - 1)^2 = (x - 3)^2 + (y - 1)^2 - 12\sqrt{(x - 3)^2 + (y - 1)^2} + 36,$$

$$2x - 11 = -3\sqrt{(x - 3)^2 + (y - 1)^2},$$

$$4x^2 - 44x + 121 = 9[(x - 3)^2 + (y - 1)^2],$$

$$5x^2 - 10x + 9y^2 - 18y = 31.$$

EXAMPLE 5.14 Write an analytic description for the set of all points each of which is closer to $(1, 2)$ than to $(-1, 0)$. Plot the graph.
The set of all such points is

$$\{(x, y) : d[(x, y), (1, 2)] < d[(x, y), (-1, 0)]\}.$$

The inequality as expanded by the distance formula is

$$(x - 1)^2 + (y - 2)^2 < (x + 1)^2 + (y - 0)^2,$$

$$x^2 - 2x + 1 + y^2 - 4y + 4 < x^2 + 2x + 1 + y^2,$$

$$-4x - 4y + 4 < 0,$$

$$x + y - 1 > 0.$$

The line $x + y - 1 = 0$ is graphed in Figure 5.21. The solution set is the shaded region to the right of this line.

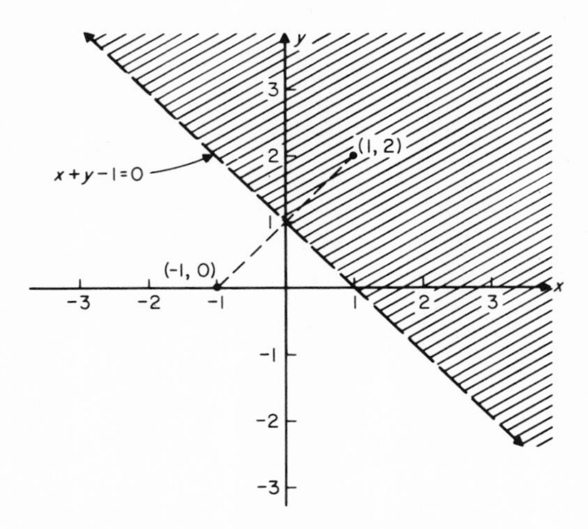

Figure 5.21

EXERCISE SET 5.5

Write an analytic description for each set of points. Plot the graph.

1. $\{(x, y) : d[(x, y), (0, 0)] = 1\}$.
2. The set of all points each of which is a distance 2 from the origin.
3. The set of all points each of which is a distance 2 from $(1, -1)$.
4. The set of all points each of which is a distance 3 from the point $(2, 4)$.
5. $\{(x, y) : d[(x, y), (2, 4)] > 3\}$.
6. The set of points of the circle with center $(-2, 3)$, radius 4.
7. The set of all points each of which is a distance 2 from the line $x = 3$. (*Hint*: Plot the graph.)
8. The set of all points each of which is at a distance 1 from the line $\{(x, y) : x = y\}$.
9. The set of all points each of which is a distance less than 2 from $\{(x, y) : x + y = 2\}$.
10. The set of all points equidistant from $(1, 6)$ and $(-3, -2)$.
11. The set of all points equidistant from $(2, 4)$ and $(-1, -2)$.
12. The set of all points equidistant from the origin and $(2, 2)$.
13. The set of all points nearer to the origin than to $(2, 2)$ (see Exercise 12).
14. The set of all points farther from $(-2, -1)$ than from $(4, 2)$.
15. The set of all points each of which is a distance 2 from the line $x = y$ and also equidistant from $(2, 3)$ and $(1, 7)$.
16. The set of all points equidistant from the y-axis and the point $(2, 0)$.
17. The set of all points equidistant from $(1, 2)$ and the line $x = 3$.

18. The set of all points whose distance from $(1, 2)$ is greater than its distance from the line $x = -1$.
19. $\{(x, y) : 3 \leq d[(x, y), (0, 2)] \leq 4\}$.
20. The set of points at a distance greater than 3 or less than 2 from the point $(-1, 2)$.
21. The set of all points (x, y) each of which is distance x from $(1, 0)$.
22. The set of all points (x, y) each of which is distance less than y from $(0, 2)$.
23. The set of all points each of which is distance 1 from the line $x = y$ and distance 3 from the line $x + y = 0$.
24. The set of all points the sum of whose distances from $(0, 2)$ and $(0, -2)$ is 5.
25. The set of all points the sum of whose distances from $(3, 1)$ and $(-1, 1)$ is 4.
26. $\{(x, y) : d[(x, y), (-3, 0)] - d[(x, y), (3, 0)] = 2\}$.
27. The set of all points the difference of whose distances from $(0, 1)$ and $(6, 1)$ is 2.
28. The set of all points the difference of whose distances from $(1, 1)$ and $(-1, -1)$ is 1.
29. $\{P: P$ is twice as far from $(0, 2)$ as from $(4, 2)\}$.
30. The set of all points which are twice as far from the line $x = 2$ as from the point $(-2, 1)$.

5.7 Slope and Intercepts

Let P: (x_0, y_0) and Q: (x_1, y_1) be two distinct points. *Δy from P to Q* is the number $y_1 - y_0$. The symbol Δy is read "delta-y" and is called the *change in y from P to Q*. Likewise, *Δx from P to Q* is $x_1 - x_0$.

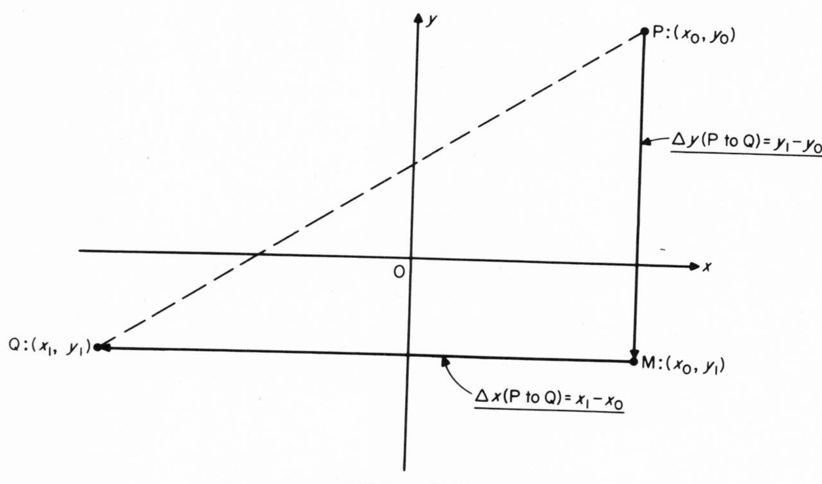

Figure 5.22

Figure 5.22 shows the segments whose lengths are Δy and Δx: arrows are used to indicate that Δy and Δx are from P to Q. By the direction of the arrow, the signs of Δy and Δx can be determined. (Both are negative in this illustration.)

The ratio $\Delta y/\Delta x$, read "delta-y over delta-x" or "the change in y over the change in x," is called the *slope* of the segment PQ. If Δx is 0, then the slope is undefined. For delta-x to be 0, the segment PQ must be vertical; such a segment is sometimes said to have a *vertical slope*.

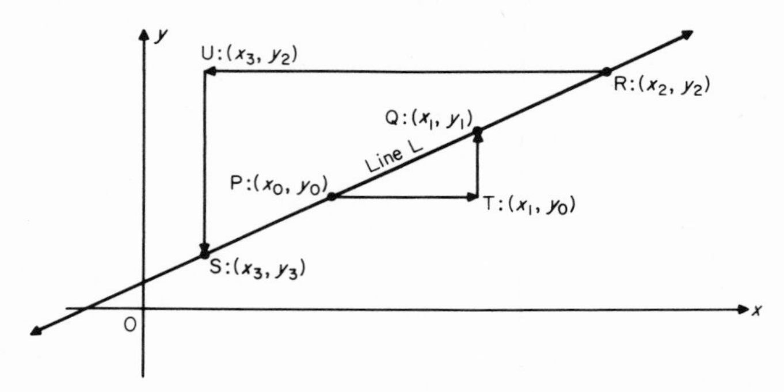

Figure 5.23

For a given line L, the slopes obtained from points P to Q and from R to S ($P \neq Q$, $R \neq S$), where P, Q, R, S are all on line L, are the same regardless of which points are chosen. In Figure 5.23, it is seen that triangles PTQ and SUR are similar right triangles. This means that the ratio of the lengths of the legs of one is equal to the ratio of the lengths of the corresponding legs of the other. The slopes have the same algebraic signs, for if the line slopes upward from left to right the slope will be positive (why?), and if it slopes downward from left to right the slope will be negative. Other cases to consider are where the lines are horizontal or vertical.

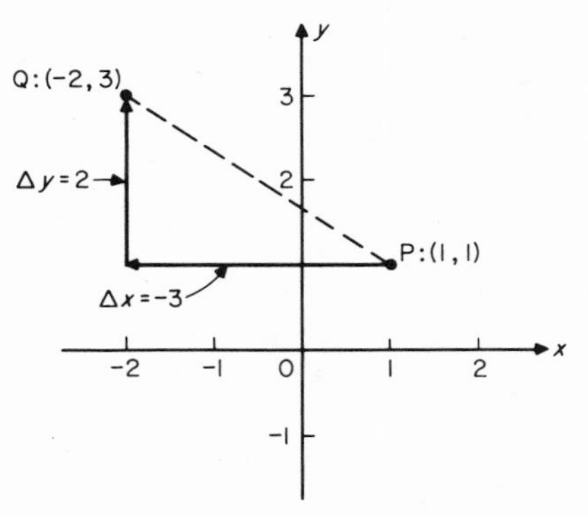

Figure 5.24

EXAMPLE 5.15 Find Δy, Δx and the slope from P: (1, 1) to Q: (−2, 3). Show Δy and Δx graphically (Figure 5.24).
By definition,

$$\Delta y\ (P \text{ to } Q) = 3 - 1 = 2,$$

$$\Delta x\ (P \text{ to } Q) = -2 - 1 = -3.$$

The slope from P to Q is given by

$$\frac{\Delta y}{\Delta x} = \frac{2}{-3} = -\frac{2}{3}.$$

EXAMPLE 5.16 Find the slope of the line $3x + 2y = 12$ (Figure 5.25).

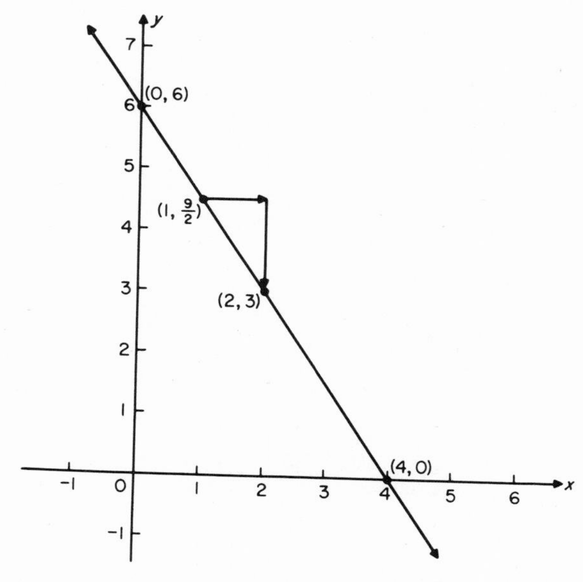

Figure 5.25

Two points are selected on the line, say $(1, \frac{9}{2})$ and $(2, 3)$. Then

$$\frac{\Delta y}{\Delta x} = \frac{3 - \frac{9}{2}}{2 - 1} = \frac{-\frac{3}{2}}{1} = -\frac{3}{2}.$$

(Select two other points on the line and see if the slope from one to the other is $-\frac{3}{2}$ also.)

For a given curve (or other set), the points which are both on the curve and the y-axis are called the *y-intercepts* of the curve. The set of *y-intercepts* is then the intersection of the curve and the *y-axis*. Those points which are both on the curve and the x-axis are called the *x-intercepts* of the curve.

Since each point on the y-axis is of the form $(0, y)$, the y-intercepts for the curve

$$\{(x, y) : x^2 + y^2 = 4\}$$

are found by solving the equation $x^2 + y^2 = 4$, where $x = 0$, i.e.,

$$0^2 + y^2 = 4.$$

The solutions, 2, -2, show that $(0, 2)$ and $(0, -2)$ are the y-intercepts.

The x-intercepts are obtained by solving

$$x^2 + 0^2 = 4,$$

since $y = 0$ for each point on the x-axis. The solutions 2, -2 give $(2, 0)$ and $(-2, 0)$ as x-intercepts (see Figure 5.26).

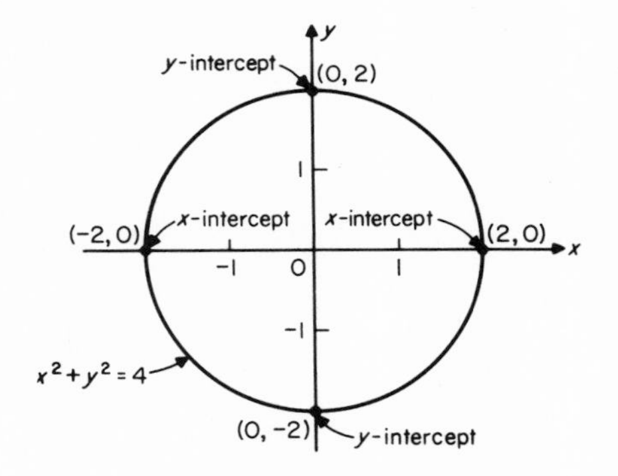

Figure 5.26

EXAMPLE 5.17 Find the slope, the x-intercepts, and the y-intercepts of the line $3x - 4y = 6$. Graph (Figure 5.27).

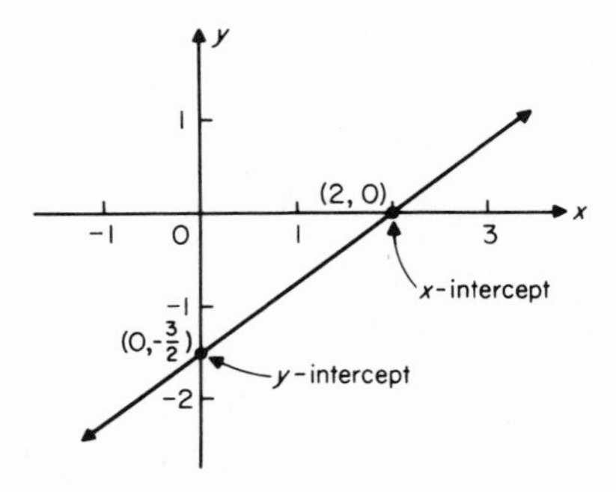

Figure 5.27

The x-intercept is $(2, 0)$ and the y-intercept is $(0, -\frac{3}{2})$. From these two points, the slope is calculated:

$$\frac{\Delta y}{\Delta x} = \frac{0 - (-\frac{3}{2})}{2 - 0} = \frac{\frac{3}{2}}{2} = \frac{3}{4}.$$

EXERCISE SET 5.6

Find Δy and Δx *from P to Q* and show graphically. Find $\Delta y/\Delta x$ for the line segment between the points.

1. $P: (1, 2), Q: (4, 1)$.
2. $P: (4, 1), Q: (1, 2)$.
3. $P: (4, 1), Q: (-2, 3)$.
4. $P: (-2, -4), Q: (3, 0)$.
5. $P: (3, 0), Q: (-2, -4)$.
6. $P: (-2, -4), Q: (-7, -8)$.
7. $P: (-7, -8), Q: (8, 4)$.
8. $P: (8, 4), Q: (-7, -8)$.
9. $P: (x_1, y_1), Q: (x_2, y_2)$.
10. $P: (x_2, y_2), Q: (x_1, y_1)$.
11. $P: (x, y), Q: (x_1, y_1)$.
12. $P: (x_1, y_1), Q: (x, y)$.
13. $P: (0, 0), Q: (x, x)$.
14. $P: (1, 1), Q: (3, 1)$.
15. $P: (1, 1), Q: (1, 3)$.

In Exercises 16–38, find the x- and y-intercepts of each set listed and of the solution set of each open sentence listed. Graph. For each line, find the slope.

16. $\{(x, y) : x + y = 1\}$.
17. $\{(x, y) : y = 2x - 3\}$.
18. $\{(x, y) : 2x - y = 4\}$.
19. $3x + 5y = 7$.
20. $-x + 3y = 7$.
21. $y = 4$.
22. $x = 1$.
23. $\dfrac{y - 2}{x + 1} = 3$.
24. $x^2 + y^2 = 4$.

25. $y/x = -2.$

26. $\dfrac{x - 1}{2y} = 1.$

27. $\dfrac{x + 3}{y - 1} = 5.$

28. $x + 3 = 5(y - 1).$

29. $y = \frac{1}{3}(x - 1).$

30. $y - 3 = -2(x + 1).$

31. $\dfrac{x}{2} - \dfrac{y}{3} = 1.$

32. $\dfrac{1}{x} + \dfrac{2}{y} = \dfrac{1}{xy}.$

33. $2x + 3y = 0.$

34. $2x + 3y < 0.$

35. $2x + 3y \geq 0.$

36. $|x - y| = 1.$

37. $|2x - y| = 3.$

38. $x/y = 0.$

39. Show that the slope of the line $ax + by + c = 0$ is $-a/b$ $(b \neq 0)$, and therefore, when the equation is written in the form

$$y = \frac{-a}{b}x + \left(\frac{-c}{b}\right),$$

the coefficient of x is the slope of the line of the equation. Show that the constant $-c/b$ is the y-value of the y-intercept. This form of the equation is called the *slope-intercept* form.

40. Convert each equation below into the *slope-intercept* form (see Exercise 39), and from this form determine the slope and the y-intercept. Graph.

   (a) $x + 3y - 2 = 0.$

   (b) $3x - 2y = 4.$

   (c) $x = 4y - 3.$

   (d) $y = 4x - 3.$

41. Prove by means of plane geometry that two parallel lines (non-vertical) have the same slope.

42. Show that if line L_1: $ax + by + c = 0$ has the same slope as L_2, then the equation for L_2 can be written as $ax + by + d = 0$, for some number d.

43. Find the line parallel to $3x - 2y + 4 = 0$ on $(3, 2)$. (*Hint*: Use Exercises 41 and 42.)

44. Prove that if line L_1 is perpendicular to line L_2 (and neither is vertical), then the slope of L_1 is the negative reciprocal of the slope of L_2; i.e., if m_1 is the slope of L_1 and m_2 is the slope of L_2, then $m_1 = -1/m_2$. (Prove by use of plane geometry; assume both m_1 and m_2 exist.)
45. Find an equation of the line perpendicular to $3x + 4y = 0$ on $(-2, 1)$. (See Exercise 44.)
46. Find an equation of the line perpendicular to $2x - y = 4$ on $(1, 1)$. (See Exercise 44.)

5.8 Writing Linear Equations

A particular line can be designated in several ways other than by its equation. For example, if two points (distinct) of the line were given, the line could be determined. If only the slope of the line were known, this would not be enough information since many lines have a given slope. However, if in addition to the slope, one point on the line were known, then the line could be determined.

To find an equation of the line with slope 2 on $(1, 6)$, let (x, y) be any other point on the line. Since the slope of the segment from $(1, 6)$ to (x, y) is 2,

$$\frac{y - 6}{x - 1} = 2.$$

Since the point $(1, 6)$ is not a solution of the equation in this form (why not?), but it is a point on the line, this equation does not describe the entire line. The equation

$$y - 6 = 2(x - 1)$$

does have all of the solutions of the line including $(1, 6)$. Rewriting in *standard form*, $ax + by + c = 0$, the equation is

$$2x - y + 4 = 0.$$

To find an equation of a line through two given points, the slope can be calculated first, and the same procedure as above can be used. This is illustrated in Example 5.18 below.

EXAMPLE 5.18 Find an equation for the line which passes through $(1, 1)$ and $(-3, 7)$.

The slope of the line is

$$\frac{\Delta y}{\Delta x}((-3, 7) \quad \text{to} \quad (1, 1)) = \frac{1 - 7}{1 - (-3)} = \frac{-6}{4} = -\frac{3}{2}.$$

For each point (x, y) on the line other than the point $(1, 1)$, the slope of the segment from $(1, 1)$ to (x, y) must be $-\frac{3}{2}$ also. Thus

$$\frac{y - 1}{x - 1} = \frac{-3}{2}.$$

In standard form, the equation is

$$3x + 2y - 5 = 0.$$

(Since the line passes through $(-3, 7)$ also, the slope of each segment from $(-3, 7)$ to (x, y) must be $-\frac{3}{2}$. Do you get the same equation as above by using this fact?) (See Figure 5.28.)

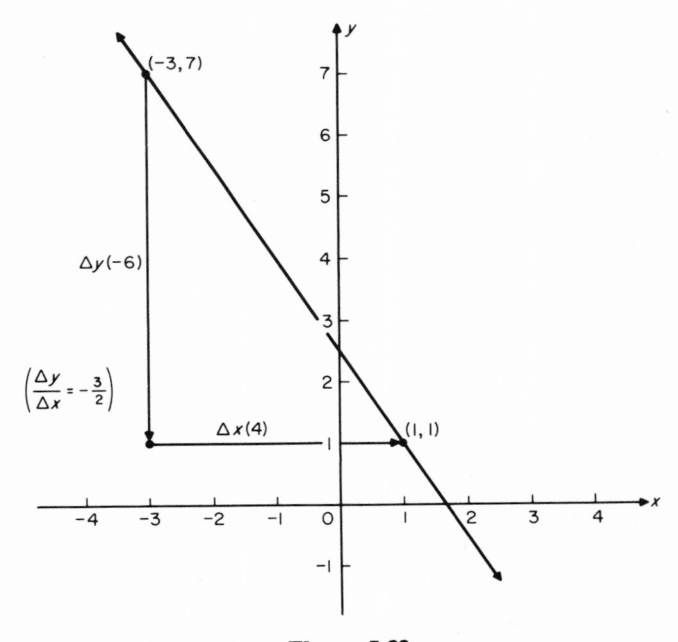

Figure 5.28

EXAMPLE 5.19 Find an equation for the line on $(-2, 1)$ parallel to the line $2x - 3y = 5$ (Figure 5.29).

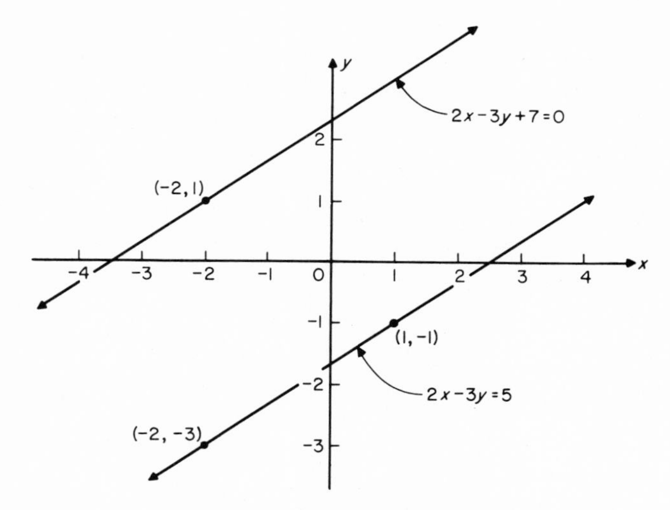

Figure 5.29

The slope of the line $2x - 3y = 5$ is $\frac{2}{3}$. Since the required line is parallel to this line, it also has slope $\frac{2}{3}$. (See Exercise 41, Exercise Set 5.6.) Using this slope and the point $(-2, 1)$,

$$\frac{y - 1}{x + 2} = \frac{2}{3},$$

which gives the equation

$$2x - 3y + 7 = 0.$$

EXERCISE SET 5.7

Write an equation of each line, expressed in the standard form $ax + by + c = 0$.

1. The line with slope -2 and x-intercept $(3, 0)$.
2. The line with slope -3 and x-intercept $(4, 0)$.
3. The line with slope 5 on $(-2, 1)$.
4. The line with slope -2 on $(-1, 3)$.
5. The line with x-intercept $(2, 0)$, y-intercept $(0, -3)$.
6. The line with slope 0 on $(2, -3)$.
7. The line on $(0, 3)$ and $(-2, 0)$.
8. The line on $(1, 1)$ and $(-1, 4)$.
9. The line on $(2, 3)$ and $(2, 4)$.

10. The line on $(-1, -2)$ and $(1, -2)$.
11. The line on $(-2, 1)$ parallel to the line $3 - 4x = 2y$.
12. The line on $(-3, 3)$ parallel to the line $x = 4$.
13. The line parallel to $2x + y = 3$ which passes through the origin.
14. The line on $(3, 7)$ parallel to the x-axis.
15. The line on $(3, 7)$ parallel to the y-axis.
16. The line on $(1, -3)$ perpendicular to the line $2x - y = 7$. (See Exercise 44, Exercise Set 5.6).
17. The line on $(2, -5)$ perpendicular to the line $2x - 5y = 0$.
18. The line on $(-2, 1)$ perpendicular to the line $x = 5$.
19. The line on $(-2, 4)$ perpendicular to the line $y = 2$.
20. The perpendicular bisector of the line segment between $(-2, 3)$ and $(2, -1)$.
21. The perpendicular bisector of the line segment between $(3, 1)$ and $(-4, -2)$.
22. The perpendicular bisector of the line segment between $(3, 2)$ and $(-2, 2)$.
23. The line tangent to the circle $x^2 + y^2 = 4$ at $(\sqrt{2}, \sqrt{2})$. (*Hint*: Graph the line.)
24. The lines passing through $(2, 0)$ which are tangent to the circle $x^2 + y^2 + 4x = 0$.
25. The line which passes through the points common to $x^2 + y^2 = 4$ and $x^2 = 3y$.
26. The line which passes through points common to $x^2 + y^2 - 4x = 0$ and $2x^2 + y^2 = 0$.
27. The lines which bisect the angles formed by the x-axis and the line $x = 0$.
28. The line on $(-3, 3)$ and the point of intersection of the lines $y - 2x = 0$ and $2y + x = 5$.
29. The line which passes through the points common to $x^2 + y^2 = 4$ and $x^2 + y^2 = 2x$.
30. The line with slope m and y-intercept $(0, b)$.

5.9 Circles

A *circle* is a set of points each of which is the same distance from some specified point. The specified point is the *center* of the circle, and the distance from the center to any point of the circle is the *radius* of the circle. As thus defined, the radius of a circle is a number. Any segment which contains the center of the circle and whose endpoints lie on the circle is a *diameter* of the circle. The number which is the length of a diameter of a circle is sometimes referred to as the diameter of the circle, also. A line that passes through an endpoint of a diameter of a circle which is also perpendicular to that diameter is a *tangent* to the circle. Each circle has a unique tangent at each of its points.

Since three noncollinear points determine a unique triangle, and each triangle has a unique *circumcenter* (a point equidistant from the three vertices of the triangle), three noncollinear points determine uniquely the circle which contains the three points.

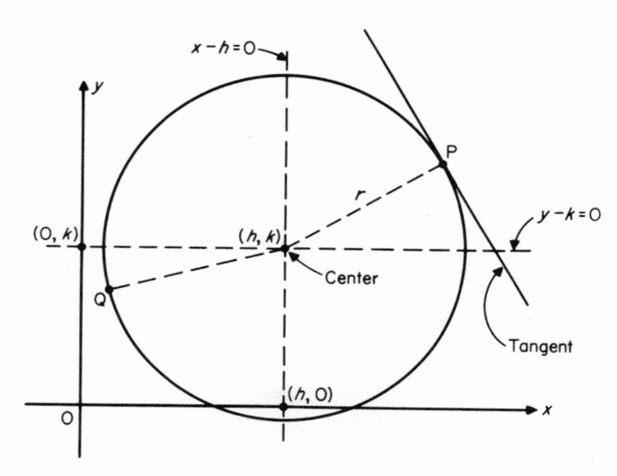

Figure 5.30

Circles are most often described either in terms of their center and radius or by an equation. For a circle of radius r, center (h, k), the equation can be found by use of the distance formula. For each point (x, y) on the circle (Figure 5.30),

$$d[(x, y), (h, k)] = r,$$

$$\sqrt{(x - h)^2 + (y - k)^2} = r,$$

$$(x - h)^2 + (y - k)^2 = r^2.$$

Conversely, if the equation of the circle were given, the center and radius could be found by converting the equation to the form above. This is done by completing the square in x and y. Notice that the lines $x - h = 0$ and $y - k = 0$ are the vertical and horizontal lines of symmetry, respectively.

EXAMPLE 5.20 Find an equation (analytic description) of the circle with center $(0, 0)$ and radius 5 (Figure 5.31).

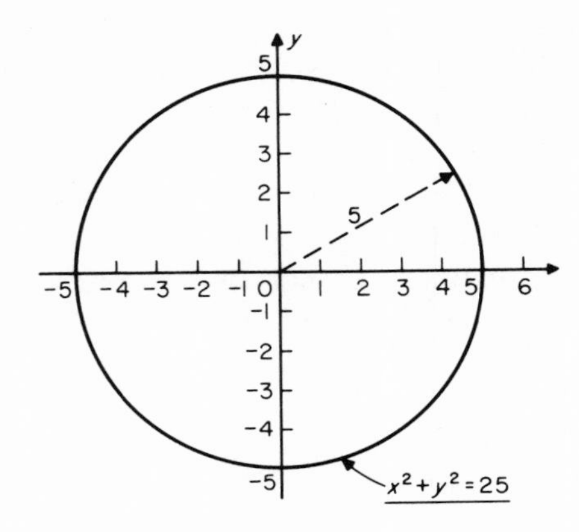

Figure 5.31

The circle is

$$\{(x, y) : d[(x, y), (0, 0)] = 5\}.$$

The equation can be simplified as

$$\begin{aligned} d[(x, y), (0, 0)] &= 5, \\ \sqrt{(x - 0)^2 + (y - 0)^2} &= 5, \\ (x - 0)^2 + (y - 0)^2 &= 25, \\ x^2 + y^2 &= 25. \end{aligned}$$

EXAMPLE 5.21 Find an equation of the circle with center (1, 2) and radius $\sqrt{17}$.

$$\begin{aligned} d[(x, y), (1, 2)] &= \sqrt{17}, \\ \sqrt{(x - 1)^2 + (y - 2)^2} &= \sqrt{17}, \\ (x - 1)^2 + (y - 2)^2 &= 17, \\ x^2 + y^2 - 2x - 4y - 12 &= 0. \end{aligned}$$

EXAMPLE 5.22 Find the center and radius of the circle

$$x^2 + y^2 + 4x - 6y = 0.$$

Plot the graph.
Rewriting the equation as

$$x^2 + 4x + y^2 - 6y = 0$$

and completing the square for $x^2 + 4x$ and $y^2 - 6y$ by adding 4 and 9, respectively,

$$(x^2 + 4x + 4) + (y^2 - 6y + 9) = 4 + 9,$$
$$(x + 2)^2 + (y - 3)^2 = 13,$$
$$(x + 2)^2 + (y - 3)^2 = (\sqrt{13})^2.$$

The radius is $\sqrt{13}$, center $(-2, 3)$ (Figure 5.32).

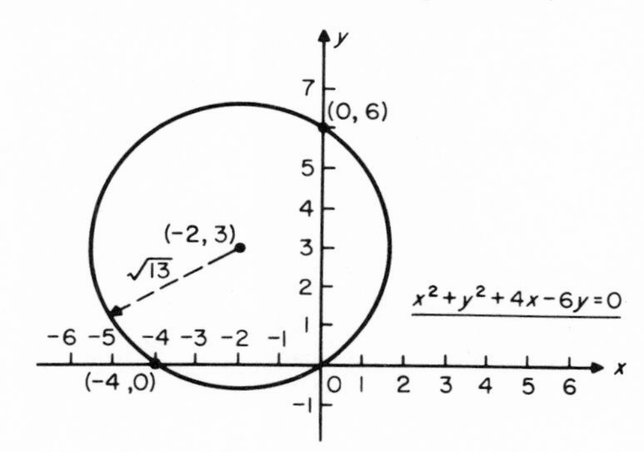

Figure 5.32

EXERCISE SET 5.8

Find an equation for each circle. Graph Exercises 8–12.

1. Center (0, 0), radius 2.
2. Center (0, 0), radius $\sqrt{2}$.
3. Center (1, 2), radius $\sqrt{3}$.
4. Center $(2, -1)$, radius 1.
5. Center $(0, -9)$, radius 9.
6. Center $(3, -2)$, radius 3.
7. Center (a, b), radius c.
8. The circle which has as a diameter the segment with endpoints $(-2, 3)$ and $(3, -1)$.
9. The circle which has as a diameter the segment with endpoints $(3, -2)$ and $(-1, 3)$.
10. The circle, center $(-12, -1)$, tangent to $12x - 5y - 30 = 0$.
11. The circle, center (1, 3), tangent to $x + 2y + 2 = 0$.
12. The circle passing through (2, 3), $(-1, 7)$, and (1, 5). (*Hint*: Find the intersection of the perpendicular bisector to the sides of the triangle formed by their three points. This is the circumcenter of the triangle, and is equidistant from each of the points.)
13. The circle passing through $(-3, 1)$, $(7, 1)$, and $(-7, 5)$.

14. The circle passing through (6, 2), (2, 4), and (3, −1).
15. The circle passing through (−11, 3), (2, −10), and (14, 8).

For each sentence whose solution set is a circle, graph, determining its center and radius.

16. $x^2 + y^2 = 3^2$.
17. $x^2 + y^2 = 4^2$.
18. $\frac{x^2}{2^2} + \frac{y^2}{2^2} = 1$.
19. $x^2 + y^2 = 4$.
20. $(x - 1)^2 + y^2 = 4$.
21. $x^2 + (y + 2)^2 = 16$.
22. $(x + 3)^2 + (y - 1)^2 = 1$.
23. $(2x - 1)^2 + (2y)^2 = 1$.
24. $x^2 - 2x + 1 + y^2 = 1$.
25. $x^2 + y^2 + 4y + 4 = 9$.
26. $x^2 + 2x + y^2 = 0$.
27. $x^2 - 4x + y^2 = 5$.
28. $x^2 + y^2 - 2x = 3$.
29. $x^2 + y^2 - 6y + 5 = 0$.
30. $x^2 + y^2 + 4x - 6y + 13 = 0$.
31. $x^2 + y^2 + 2x - 4y + 1 = 0$.
32. $x^2 + y^2 - 8x + 4y = 0$.
33. $x^2 + y^2 - 4x + 2y - 2 = 0$.
34. $2x^2 + 2y^2 + 3x - 5y + 7 = 0$.
35. $(x + 1)^2 + (y - 2)^2 + 4x - 2y = 0$.
36. $x^2 + y^2 - 15x + 6 = 0$.
37. $x^2 + y^2 + 8x + 5y - 23 = 0$.
38. $2x^2 + 2y^2 + 15x + 2 = 0$.
39. $x^2 + y^2 - 10x + 2y = 10$.
40. $x^2 + y^2 + 18x + 24y + 225 = 0$.

Graph the solution set of each inequality. Describe the graph in geometric terms.

41. $x^2 + y^2 < 4$.
42. $x^2 + y^2 \geq 4$.
43. $x^2 + y^2 \leq 2x + 2y$.
44. $x^2 + y^2 \geq 2x + 2y$.
45. $x^2 + y^2 > 4x - 6y - 13$.

Graph each set.

46. $\{(x, y) : x^2 + y^2 - 4x < 0 \;\&\; x - y < 0\}$.
47. $\{(x, y) : x^2 + y^2 - 4x < 0 \;\&\; x - y \geq 0\}$.

48. $\{(x, y) : x + y = 0 \mathbin{\&} x^2 + y^2 - 4x - 2y < 4\}$.
49. $\{(x, y) : x^2 + y^2 < 8 \mathbin{\&} x^2 + y^2 + y \leq 0\}$.
50. $\{(x, y) : x^2 + y^2 - 2x < 2 \mathbin{\&} x^2 + y^2 + 2x < 2\}$.

5.10 The Ellipse

An *ellipse* is a set of points each of which is located such that the sum of its distances from two fixed points, called *foci* (singular: *focus*), is constant. A representative ellipse where the fixed distance is $2a$ is sketched in Figure 5.33, which shows the lines of symmetry, foci, and vertices.

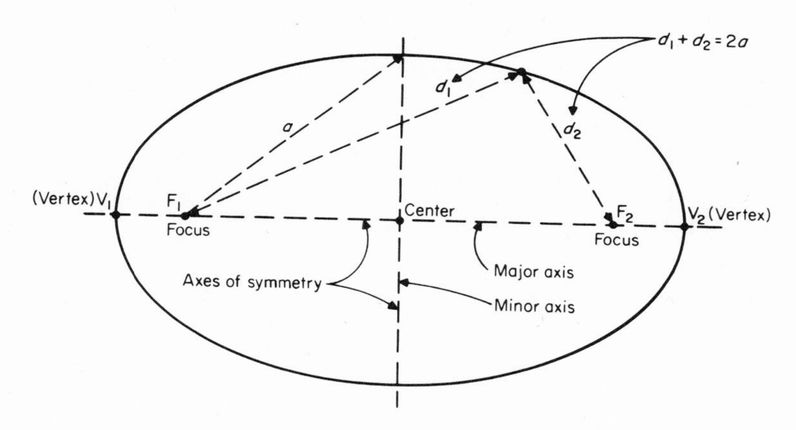

Figure 5.33

The two examples to follow show (1) how to obtain the analytic description of an ellipse by use of the distance formula and (2) how to graph the ellipse, find its vertices, etc., from the analytic description.

EXAMPLE 5.23 Find the analytic description of the ellipse whose distances from $(1, 0)$ and $(-1, 0)$ sum to 4.

$$d[(x, y), (1, 0)] + d[(x, y), (-1, 0)] = 4,$$

$$\sqrt{(x - 1)^2 + y^2} + \sqrt{(x + 1)^2 + y^2} = 4,$$

$$\sqrt{(x - 1)^2 + y^2} = 4 - \sqrt{(x + 1)^2 + y^2},$$

$$(x - 1)^2 + y^2 = 16 - 8\sqrt{(x + 1)^2 + y^2} + (x + 1)^2 + y^2,$$

$$-4x - 16 = -8\sqrt{(x + 1)^2 + y^2},$$

$$x + 4 = 2\sqrt{(x + 1)^2 + y^2},$$

$$x^2 + 8x + 16 = 4[x^2 + 2x + 1 + y^2],$$

$$3x^2 + 4y^2 - 12 = 0.$$

Writing this equation in the form

$$\frac{x^2}{4} + \frac{y^2}{3} = 1$$

makes it easier to identify it with the graph. The axes intercepts are seen to be $(2, 0)$, $(-2, 0)$, $(0, \sqrt{3})$, and $(0, -\sqrt{3})$ (Figure 5.34).

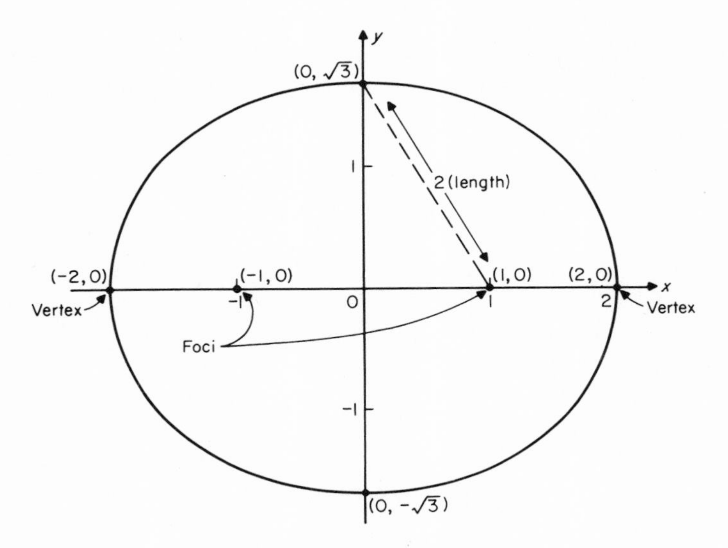

Figure 5.34

EXAMPLE 5.24 Graph, determining center, lines of symmetry, and vertices,

$$4x^2 + 9y^2 - 8x + 18y + 9 = 0.$$

To find the center and lines (axes) of symmetry, the squares in x and y are completed,

$$4(x^2 - 2x + 1) + 9(y^2 + 2y + 1) = 4.$$

Then, dividing through by the constant on the right, 4,

$$\frac{(x-1)^2}{1} + \frac{(y+1)^2}{\frac{4}{9}} = 1.$$

The lines of symmetry are $x - 1 = 0$, $y + 1 = 0$.

To find the points where the ellipse intercepts the vertical axis, let $x - 1 = 0$. Then

$$(y + 1)^2 = \tfrac{4}{9},$$

$$y + 1 = \pm\tfrac{2}{3},$$

$$y = -\tfrac{1}{3}, -\tfrac{5}{3}.$$

The resulting points are $(1, -\frac{1}{3})$, $(1, -\frac{5}{3})$.
Likewise, to find the points where the ellipse intercepts the horizontal axis, let $y + 1 = 0$. Then

$$(x - 1)^2 = 1,$$

$$x - 1 = \pm 1,$$

$$x = 2, 0.$$

This gives the points $(0, -1)$, $(2, -1)$. The graph is given below (Figure 5.35).

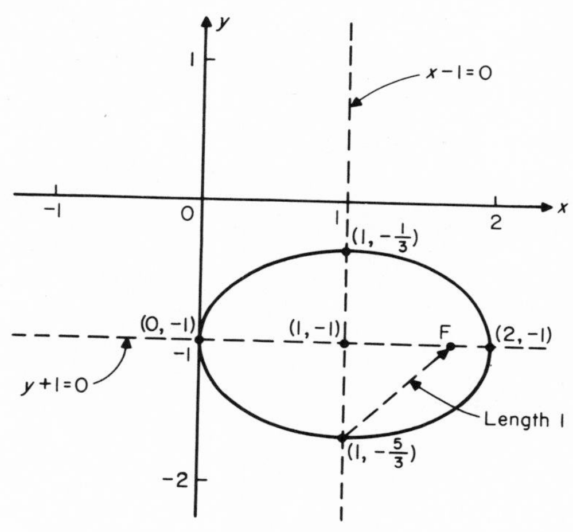

Figure 5.35

EXERCISE SET 5.9

Find an analytic description for each ellipse (or other set).

1. The ellipse with foci $(0, 2)$, $(0, -2)$, where the sum of distances to the foci is 6.

2. The ellipse with foci (1, 2), (3, 2), where the sum of distances to the foci is 4.
3. The ellipse with foci (−1, 2), (3, 2), where (4, 2) is a vertex. (*Hint*: Find the sum of distances by use of the vertex.)
4. The ellipse with foci (−1, −2), (−1, −3), where one vertex is (−1, 3).
5. The ellipse with vertices (0, 2), (0, −2), (1, 0), and (−1, 0).
6. The ellipse with horizontal and vertical axes, with vertices (−1, −2), (1, 5), and foci on $x = 1$.
7. The *interior* of the ellipse with center (1, 1), focus (1, 3), vertex (1, 4).
8. The *interior* of an ellipse which intercepts its lines of symmetry (axes) at (−1, 4), (7, 4), (3, 6), and (3, 2).

For each sentence, graph, determining the center, axes of symmetry, and vertices for each ellipse.

9. $\left(\frac{x}{3}\right)^2 + \left(\frac{y}{2}\right)^2 = 1.$
10. $\frac{x^2}{25} + \frac{y^2}{16} = 1.$
11. $x^2 + \left(\frac{y}{3}\right)^2 = 1.$
12. $\frac{x^2}{2} + \frac{y^2}{3} = 1.$
13. $\frac{x^2}{16} + \frac{y^2}{16} = 1.$
14. $\left(\frac{x-1}{2}\right)^2 + \left(\frac{y-2}{3}\right)^2 = 1.$
15. $\left(\frac{x+3}{3}\right)^2 + \left(\frac{y+5}{2}\right)^2 = 1.$
16. $4(x + 1)^2 + (y - 2)^2 = 4.$
17. $9(x - 2)^2 + 4(y + 1)^2 = 36.$
18. $x^2 + 2x + 1 + 4y^2 - 8y + 4 = 4.$
19. $9x^2 - 18x + 9 + 4y^2 + 8y + 4 = 36.$
20. $x^2 - 2x + 4y^2 + 8y + 1 = 0.$
21. $x^2 + y^2 + 4x - 2y - 4 = 0.$
22. $16x^2 + 25y^2 - 32x + 50y + 25 = 0.$
23. $4x^2 + 4x + y^2 = 0.$
24. $x^2 + 9y^2 - 16 < 0.$
25. $4x^2 + 4x + 16y^2 - 8y - 7 > 0.$
26. $\frac{(x+1)^2}{4} + \frac{(y-3)^2}{1} \leq 1.$

5.11 Hyperbolas

A set of points each of which is such that the *difference* between its distances from two specified points, called *foci*, is constant is a *hyperbola*.

EXAMPLE 5.25 Find an equation of the set of points each of which is such that its distances from (1, 1) and (−1, −1) differ by 2. Graph.

$$|d[(x, y), (1, 1)] - d[(x, y), (-1, -1)]| = 2,$$

$$|\sqrt{(x-1)^2 + (y-1)^2} - \sqrt{(x+1)^2 + (y+1)^2}| = 2.$$

Squaring and simplifying, and squaring again,

$$x^2 + y^2 + 2xy + 2x + 2y + 1 = x^2 + 2x + 1 + y^2 + 2y + 1,$$

or

$$xy = \tfrac{1}{2}.$$

The graph is shown in Figure 5.36.

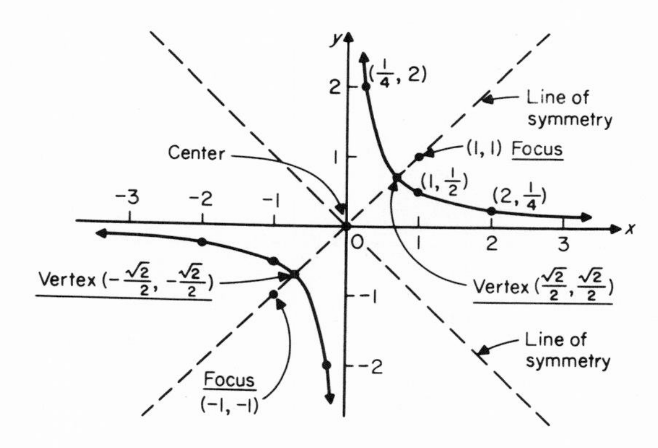

Figure 5.36

The hyperbola of Example 5.25 illustrates several characteristics of hyperbolas. The curve consists of two branches, each of which approaches the coordinate axes *asymptotically*.† The axes in this case are said to be *asymptotes* of the hyperbola. The point where the asymptotes cross is the *center* of the hyperbola. The further a point of the hyperbola is from the center, the closer it is to one of the asymptotes. The center is a point of symmetry for the curve, and each of the bisectors of the angles formed by

† *Approaches* and *asymptotic* are defined more precisely in the calculus, along with the notion of tangent.

the asymptotes are the *axes* of the curve. The intersections of the lines with the curve are the *vertices* of the hyperbola.

EXAMPLE 5.26 Locate the center and vertices of the hyperbola

$$2x^2 - 3y^2 - 4x + 12y - 28 = 0.$$

Graph.
Completing the square in x and in y,

$$\left(\frac{x-1}{3}\right)^2 - \left(\frac{y-2}{\sqrt{6}}\right)^2 = 1$$

is obtained. In this form, the lines $x - 1 = 0$, $y - 2 = 0$ are seen to be lines of symmetry. The center is at $(1, 2)$, vertices $(-2, 2)$, $(4, 2)$.

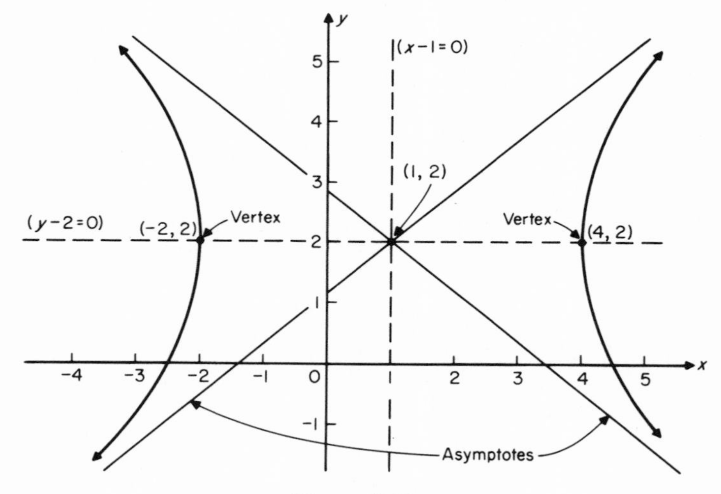

Figure 5.37

EXERCISE SET 5.10

Graph the hyperbolas of Exercises 1–4 on the same graph.

1. $xy = 10$.
2. $xy = 6$.
3. $xy = 2$.
4. $xy = -1$.
5. Graph $xy < -\frac{1}{2}$.

6. Graph $xy < +1$.
7. For what values of k is $xy = k$ an equation for the asymptotes of Exercises 1–4?
8. For what values of k is $(x - a)(y - b) = k$ an equation for the asymptotes of any hyperbola $(x - a)(y - b) = c$?
9. What lines are asymptotes of $(x - 3)y = 2$?

Graph the following hyperbolas by first drawing in the asymptotes.

10. $(x - 3)y = 4$.
11. $x(y - 3) = 2$.
12. $(x + 4)(y - 1) = 4$.
13. $x(y + 5) = -1$.

Plot the graphs of Exercises 14–18 on the same graph.

14. $x^2 - y^2 = 4$.
15. $x^2 - y^2 = 1$.
16. $x^2 - y^2 = \frac{1}{4}$.
17. $x^2 - y^2 = 0$.
18. $x^2 - y^2 = -1$.

Graph, labeling axes of symmetry, asymptotes, and vertices.

19. $\left(\frac{x}{3}\right)^2 - \left(\frac{y}{2}\right)^2 = 1$. (*Hint*: one asymptote is $\frac{x}{3} - \frac{y}{2} = 0$.)

20. $\left(\frac{x}{3}\right)^2 - \left(\frac{y}{2}\right)^2 = -1$.

21. $\frac{x^2}{25} - \frac{y^2}{16} = 1$.

22. $x^2 - \left(\frac{y}{3}\right)^2 = 1$.

23. $\frac{x^2}{2} - \frac{y^2}{3} = 1$.

24. $\frac{y^2}{3} - \frac{x^2}{2} = 1$.

25. $\left(\frac{x + 3}{3}\right)^2 - \left(\frac{y + 5}{2}\right)^2 = -1$.

26. $\frac{(y + 1)^2}{9} - \frac{(x - 2)^2}{16} = 1$.

27. $4(x^2 + 6x + 9) - (y^2 - 2y + 1) = 4.$
28. $25(x^2 + 4x + 4) - 16(y^2 + 2y + 1) = -400.$
29. $x^2 + 2x + 1 - 4y^2 + 8y - 4 = 4.$
30. $9y^2 - 18y + 9 - 4x^2 - 8x - 4 = 36.$
31. $x^2 - 2x - 4y^2 - 8y = 0.$
32. $4x^2 - 9y^2 - 8x - 18y + 9 = 0.$
33. $x^2 - y^2 + 4x + 2y + 4 = 0.$
34. $9y^2 - x^2 - 6y = 0.$

5.12 Parabolas

A *parabola* is a set of points each of which is equidistant from a fixed point (the *focus*) and a fixed line (the *directrix*). The intersection of the parabola with the line through the focus perpendicular to the directrix is the *vertex* of the parabola.

EXAMPLE 5.27 Find an equation of the parabola with directrix the line $x = -1$ and focus the point $(2, 3)$ (Figure 5.38).

$$d[(x, y), (2, 3)] = d[(x, y), (-1, y)],$$
$$(x - 2)^2 + (y - 3)^2 = (x + 1)^2 + (y - y)^2,$$
$$x^2 - 4x + 4 + (y - 3)^2 = x^2 + 2x + 1,$$
$$(y - 3)^2 = 6x - 3,$$
$$(y - 3)^2 = 6(x - \tfrac{1}{2}).$$

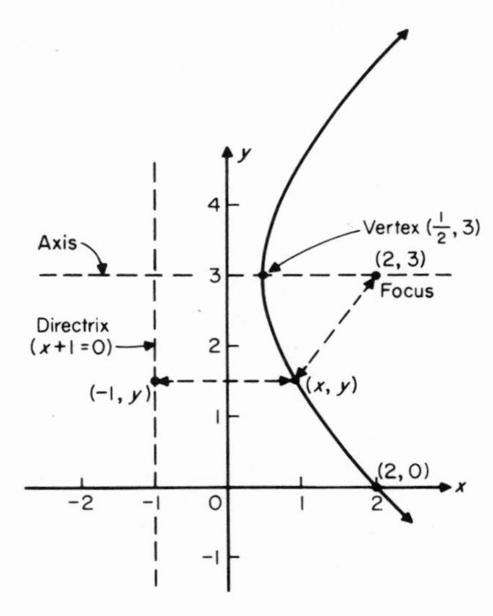

Figure 5.38

EXAMPLE 5.28 Determine the vertex and direction of opening, and then graph the parabola $4y = x^2 + 2x$ (Figure 5.39).

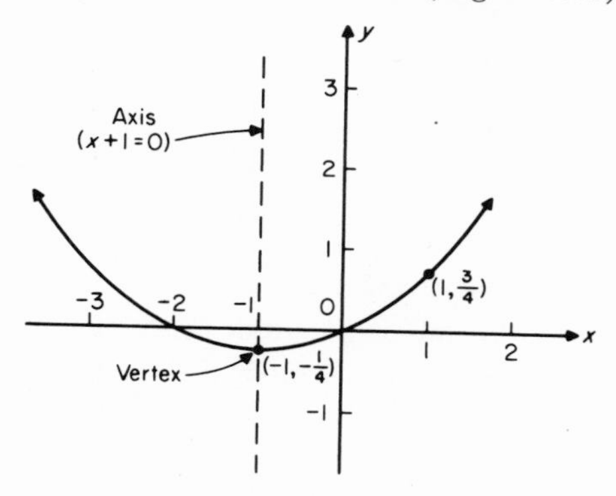

Figure 5.39

Completing the square in x, the equation is

$$(x + 1)^2 = 4y + 1.$$

Since the parabola has $x + 1 = 0$ as its line of symmetry, the vertex occurs where $x = -1$, that is, where

$$4y + 1 = 0,$$

$$y = -\tfrac{1}{4}.$$

Vertex: $(-1, -\frac{1}{4})$, opens upward. (Note extent of y.)

EXERCISE SET 5.11

Graph each sentence whose solution set is a parabola. Label the vertex and axis of symmetry. (You should be able to predict the location of the vertex as well as the direction of opening by considering symmetry and extent.)

1. $4x = y^2$
2. $8x = y^2$.
3. $-x = y^2$.
4. $4(y + 1) = x^2$.
5. $(y - 2)^2 = -8x$.
6. $(x + 1)^2 = 8 - 4y$.
7. $16y + 16 = (x - 2)^2$.
8. $4 - 4x = y^2 + 4y + 4$.
9. $y = x^2 - 2x$.
10. $y = 2 - 3x^2$.
11. $4x^2 - 4x + 2y - 6 = 0$.

12. $3x - 2y^2 + 4y + 7 = 0.$
13. $5 - 6y^2 = 4x + 3y.$
14. $x - y^2 = 2y.$
15. $(x + y)^2 + 4 = x^2 + 2xy.$

Write an analytic description of each parabola. Graph.

16. Directrix: $x = 1$. Focus: $(-1, 0)$.
17. Directrix: $y = -2$. Focus: $(0, 0)$.
18. The set of points equidistant from the x-axis and the point $(1, 1)$.
19. The set of points equidistant from the y-axis and $(1, 1)$.
20. The parabola with vertex $(0, 2)$, focus $(0, 0)$.
21. The parabola with vertex $(-3, 2)$, directrix $x = -1$.
22. The parabola with vertex $(1, 2)$ which passes through $(2, 3)$ and opens to the right.

5.13 Conics

Ellipses, circles, hyperbolas, and parabolas are classified as *conics* or *conic sections* because each is the curve of intersection of a plane and a right circular cone (Figure 5.40).

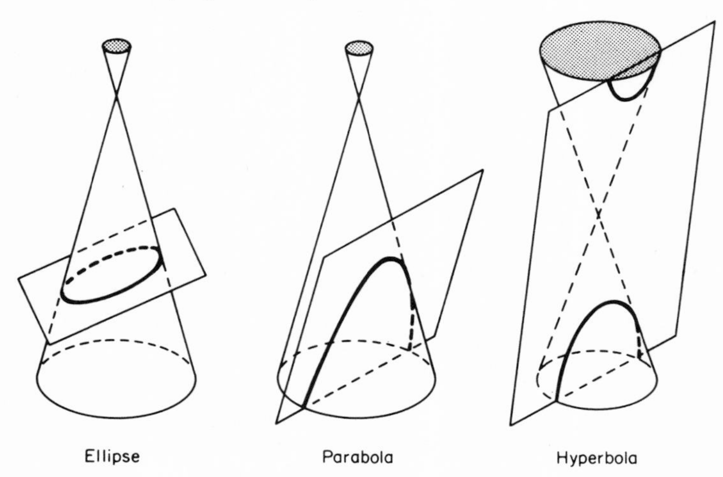

Figure 5.40

Conics frequent mathematics to such an extent that successful work in many areas demands a familiarity with their standard equations both in regard to quickly recognizing the conic and graphing it from its equation, as well as quickly writing the equation of a conic knowing its location on a graph. The following exercises involve a mixture of conics. In many cases you should be able to recognize the type of conic immediately, locating the center, radius, vertices, asymptotes, or any other descriptive features with a minimum of effort.

EXERCISE SET 5.12

Graph, labeling identifying points and lines.

1. $x^2 = y^2 - 4x$.
2. $4y - x^2 = 4y^2$.
3. $x(x + 1) = (y - 2)$.
4. $x(2 - x) - 2(y^2 + 1) = 0$.
5. $x(y - 2) \leq 4$.
6. $y^2 = 4 - x^2 + 2x$.
7. $x^2 - 4x < 3y + 2$.
8. $(y - 1)^2 = 3(x - 4)$.
9. $4x^2 + 4y^2 - 4x + 8y - 6 \leq 0$.
10. $6x - x^2 = 2y + y^2$.
11. $(x - 1)(y + 2) = 0$.
12. $2xy + 6x - y - 3 = 0$.
13. $x^2 + y^2 = 0$.
14. $2 - x = 3 + 5y$.
15. $(x - 2)(y + 3) = 4$.
16. $(y - x)^2 = 0$.
17. $y^2 = x^2 + 4x + 4$.
18. $x^2 - 2x + 1 = y^2 + 6y + 9$.
19. $(y - 2x + 1)(y + x) = 0$.
20. $y = 3/(x + 2)$.
21. $y = x + 1$.
22. $y + 2 = x - 3$.
23. $x^2 - 4 = y + 1$.
24. $x + 1 = y + 2$.

Write an equation for each of the conics in Exercises 25–29.

25. The circle centered at (3, 5) with radius 7.
26. The ellipse with vertices at (1, 5) and (7, 5) and *minor diameter* 4. (The minor diameter is the smaller of the distances between intercepts on the axes of symmetry.)
27. The hyperbola with asymptotes $x/2 = \pm y/3$ and one vertex at the point (1, 0).
28. The parabola equidistant from the line $y = 7$ and the point (2, 3).
29. The hyperbola with asymptotes $(x - 3)/4 = \pm(y + 1)/3$ that passes through the point (5, 2).
30. What points (if any) are points of symmetry of an ellipse? A parabola? A hyperbola?

Trigonometry

CHAPTER SIX

6.1 Introduction

In the study of analytic geometry a correspondence was made between points on the plane and pairs of real numbers. For a given pair of coordinate axes, each point P on the plane has a unique ordered pair of rectangular coordinates, (x, y). Another way of designating points on the plane by means of ordered pairs of real numbers is presented in this chapter. The relationships between these two ways of naming points give rise to one of the more important classes of functions in mathematics and science—the *trigonometric functions*.

6.2 Polar Coordinates

The positive ray of a given coordinate axis, called the *initial axis*, and a given unit of rotation (usually the degree, the radian, or the revolution) are used to assign coordinates to each point P on the plane. The initial axis is rotated about its origin so that in its *final position* it lies on the point P (see Figure 6.1). Letting r be the coordinate of P on the rotated axis and θ the measure (for the chosen unit of measure) of the rotation made by the axis from its initial position, the pair of real numbers (r, θ) are called *polar coordinates* of P. $\theta > 0$ if the rotation is *counterclockwise*, and $\theta < 0$ if the rotation is *clockwise*. In any case, *θ is a real number*. If the unit of rotation is the degree, then for a rotation of 30°, θ is the *real number* 30.

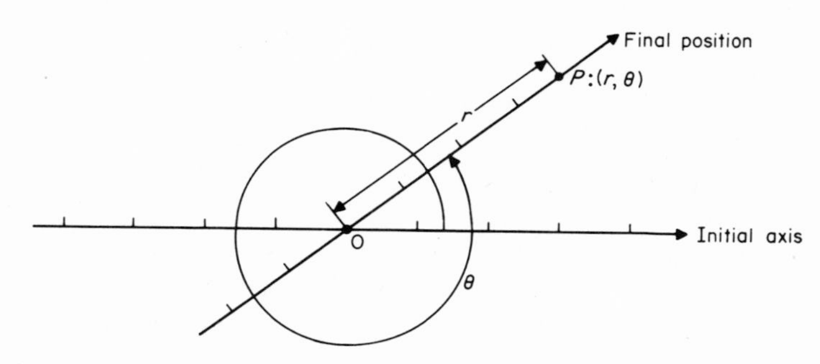

Figure 6.1

EXAMPLE 6.1 Graph the points that have the given polar coordinates where the rotations are measured in degrees (see Figure 6.2):

A: $(2, 40)$, C: $(1, 180)$,

B: $(-1, 90)$, D: $(-2, 240)$.

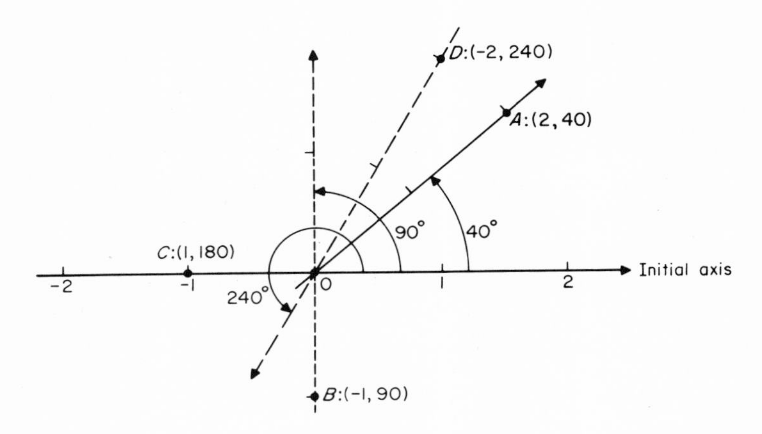

Figure 6.2

Each pair of polar coordinates for the points in Example 6.1 have positive measures of rotation. That is, the rotations have been measured *counterclockwise*. The graphs of several points which are given by negative rotations are shown in Figure 6.3.

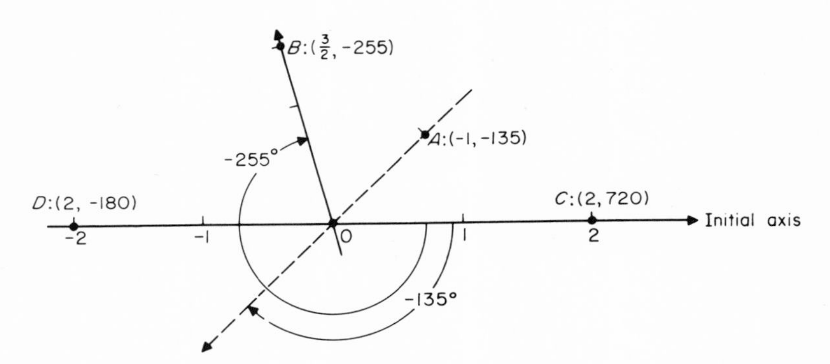

Figure 6.3

Although for a given unit of rotation and a given initial axis each pair of polar coordinates represents only one point, it is possible to have many different pairs of polar coordinates for the same point. For example, the point P, which has coordinates (3, 120), using degree measures of rotations, also has coordinates $(-3, 300)$ as well as $(-3, -60)$ and $(3, -240)$ (see Figure 6.4). Of course, there are many more coordinates with rotations greater than 360° or less than $-360°$, since if the line is rotated an additional one, two, or more revolutions (360°) beyond the rotation of 120°, it will end up in the same position. Therefore, $(3, 120 + 360)$, $(3, 120 + 2(360))$, and in general, $(3, 120 + 360n)$, $n \in I$, are all coordinates of the one point P. (Are there other coordinates of P?)

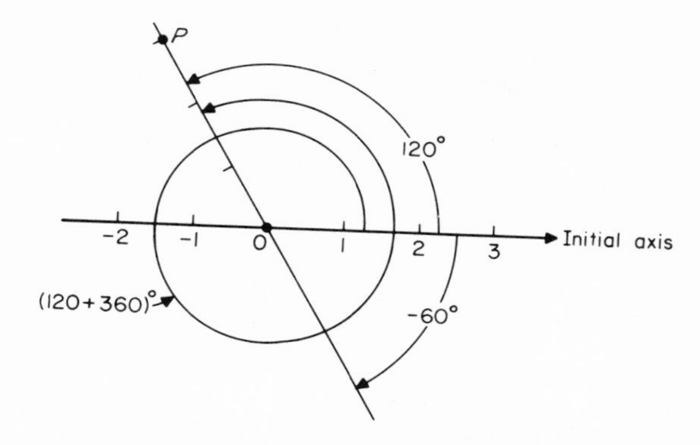

Figure 6.4

For many purposes it is convenient to work only with those coordinates for which the measure of rotation is less than one revolution, and for which r is a nonnegative real number. If these restrictions are made, each point other than the origin will have exactly one pair of polar coordinates, and each pair $(0, \theta)$ will be a pair of polar coordinates for the origin.

EXAMPLE 6.2 Find a pair of polar coordinates (r, θ) for each point where $0 \leq \theta < 360$ and $r \geq 0$, where the rotations are in degrees.

(a) $A(2, 400)$. [*Ans.* (2, 40).]

(b) $B(-3, 60)$. [*Ans.* (3, 240).]

(c) $C(-2, -50)$. [*Ans.* (2, 130).]

(d) $D(-5, 1000)$. [*Ans.* (5, 100).]

EXERCISE SET 6.1

Graph the following points on one graph, where the coordinates are polar and the rotations are measured in *degrees*.

1. (1, 30).
2. (−1, 30).
3. (1, 120).
4. (−2, 180).
5. (2, 0).
6. (4, 270).
7. (−3, −90).
8. $(\sqrt{2}, -10)$.
9. $(\frac{1}{2}, -40)$.
10. (6, 360).

Graph the following points on one graph, where the coordinates are polar and the rotations are measured in *degrees*.

11. $(3, 90)$.
12. $(-3, 270)$.
13. $(-3, -90)$.
14. $(3, -270)$.
15. $(-3, 630)$.

Find a pair of polar coordinates for each point where the first coordinate r is nonnegative and the second coordinate θ is between 0 and 360, where rotations are in *degrees*.

16. $(-2, 180)$.
17. $(-3, 90)$.
18. $(-\sqrt{2}, 10)$.
19. $(3, -120)$.
20. $(2, -315)$.
21. $(-4, -10)$.
22. $(2, 700)$.
23. $(-3, 620)$.
24. $(-2, -420)$.
25. $(\pi, -20)$.

Find all the coordinates for each point given where the rotations are measured in degrees (Exercises 26–30).

26. $(1, 0)$.
27. $(2, 30)$.
28. $(\pi, -45)$.
29. $(-3, 460)$.
30. $(-4, -120)$.
31. Find r if $(r, 30)$ is the same point as $(r, -30)$, where the rotations are measured in degrees.
32. Find θ if $(1, \theta)$ is the same point as $(1, -\theta)$, rotations in degrees.
33. Find θ if $(2, \theta)$ is the same point as $(2, n\theta)$ for $n \in I, n \neq 0$, rotations in degrees.
34. Find θ in terms of ϕ so that (r, ϕ) and $(-r, \theta)$ are the same point for each r, rotations in degrees.

6.3 Degrees, Radians, Revolutions

Rotations can be measured in several different units. The most common units are *degrees* (used thus far), *radians*, and *revolutions*. A rotation of *one revolution* is the same as a rotation of 360 *degrees*. A rotation of *one revolution* is also the same as a rotation of 2π *radians*. (See the table below.) The radian is the most important of the three units of rotation for theoretical work. *Whenever the unit of rotation is not specified, it is understood to be the radian.*

RELATIONS BETWEEN MEASURES OF ROTATIONS

1 revolution $=$ 360 degrees   1 degree $= \dfrac{1}{360}$ revolution

1 revolution $= 2\pi$ radians   1 radian $= \dfrac{1}{2\pi}$ revolution

1 radian $= \dfrac{180}{\pi}$ degrees   1 degree $= \dfrac{\pi}{180}$ radian

Figure 6.5 shows a circle of radius R drawn with center at the origin. The arc of the circle intercepted by the axis and a line rotated one radian measures R, or one radius, in length. A rotation of 2π radians intercepts an arc of length $2\pi R$, the circumference of the circle.

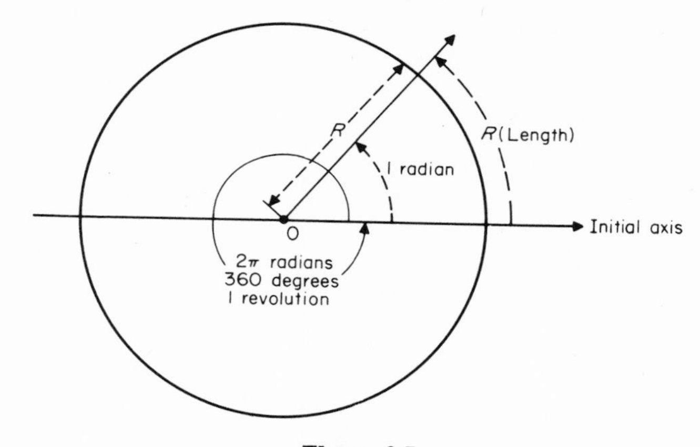

Figure 6.5

The following examples illustrate how the above relations may be used to convert the measure of a rotation from one system of units to another.

EXAMPLE 6.3 Express the rotation of 2.5 revolutions in degrees and also in radians (see Figure 6.6).

$$\begin{aligned} 2.5 \text{ revolutions} &= (2.5)\ (360) \text{ degrees} \\ &= 900 \text{ degrees.} \end{aligned}$$

$$\begin{aligned} 2.5 \text{ revolutions} &= (2.5)\ (2\pi) \text{ radians} \\ &= 5\pi \text{ radians.} \end{aligned}$$

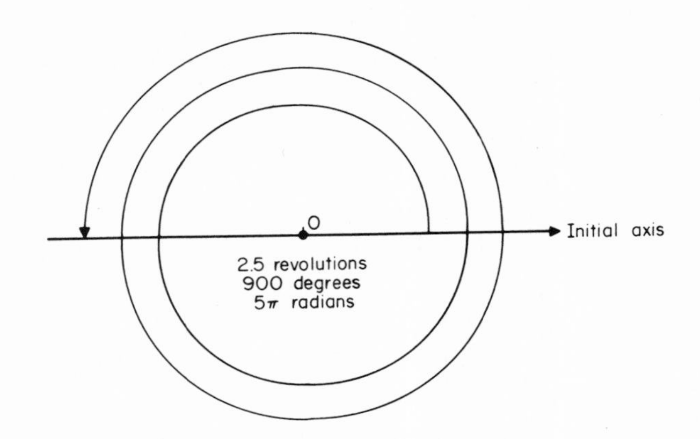

Figure 6.6

EXAMPLE 6.4 Express the rotation of -135 degrees in radians and in revolutions (see Figure 6.7).

$$-135 \text{ degrees} = (-135)\left(\frac{\pi}{180}\right) \text{ radians}$$

$$= -\tfrac{3}{4}\pi \text{ radians.}$$

$$-135 \text{ degrees} = (-135)\left(\frac{1}{360}\right) \text{ revolutions}$$

$$= -\tfrac{3}{8} \text{ revolution.}$$

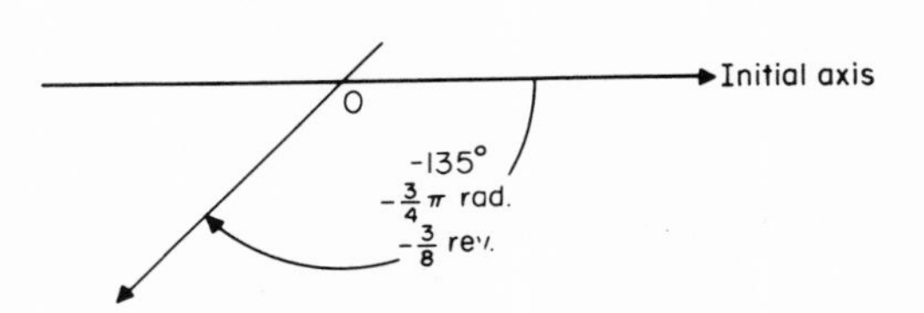

Figure 6.7

EXAMPLE 6.5 Given that coordinates of a point P are $(4, \pi/6)$, find other coordinates where the rotation is given in (a) degrees and (b) revolutions.

(a) $$\frac{\pi}{6} \text{ radians} = \frac{\pi}{6} \cdot \frac{180}{\pi} \text{ degrees}$$

$$= 30 \text{ degrees.}$$

(b) $$\frac{\pi}{6} \text{ radians} = \frac{\pi}{6} \cdot \frac{1}{2\pi} \text{ revolutions}$$

$$= \tfrac{1}{12} \text{ revolution.}$$

The point P has coordinates

$$(4, 30), \qquad \text{rotation in degrees,}$$

and

$$(4, \tfrac{1}{12}), \qquad \text{rotation in revolutions.}$$

The measure of a positive rotation of less than π radians can be interpreted as the measure of the angle which is the union of the positive rays of the initial axis and the rotated axis. Rotations of any magnitude are frequently called *generalized angles* or simply *angles*, with the word "angle" having an expanded meaning. Also, a measure of a rotation can be interpreted as an *angular measure of an arc of a circle*. In case the circle has unit radius and the unit of angular measure is the radian, then the length of the arc equals numerically the angular measure of the arc (see Figure 6.8).

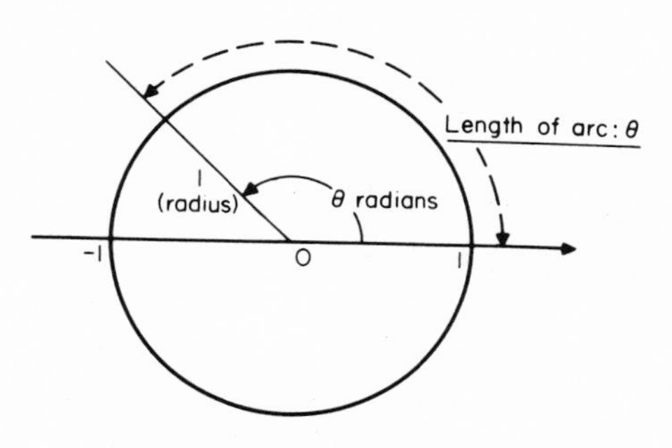

Figure 6.8

For a circle of radius r, an arc of θ radians has length S given by $S = r\theta$ (see Figure 6.9).

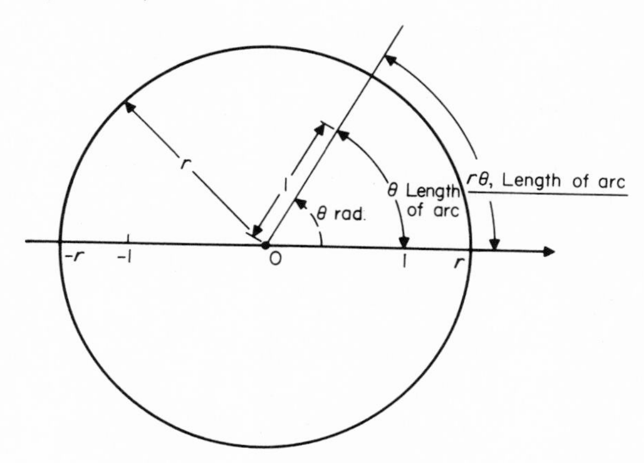

Figure 6.9

EXAMPLE 6.6 Find the length of arc of a circle of radius r traversed by a rotation of θ, when:

(a) $r = 1, \theta = 3$.

[*Ans.* $r \cdot \theta = 1 \cdot 3 = 3$. (For a unit circle, the measure of the rotation in radians and the arc length are equal.)]

(b) $r = 3, \theta = \pi$.

[*Ans.* $r \cdot \theta = 3 \cdot \pi = 3\pi$ (circumference of half-circle).]

(c) $r = 2, \theta = 45°$.

[*Ans.* $r \cdot \theta$ (in radians), $2 \cdot (45 \cdot \pi/180) = \pi/2$.]

(d) $r = 4, \theta = 3\frac{1}{2}$ revolutions.

[*Ans.* $r \cdot \theta$ (in radians), $4 \cdot (3\frac{1}{2} \cdot 2\pi) = 28\pi$.]

EXERCISE SET 6.2

Give each of the following measures of rotations in degrees and also in radians. (Do not bother to approximate answers by using decimal approximations.)

1. 2 revolutions.
2. -1.5 revolutions.
3. 0.06 revolutions.
4. 5.6 revolutions.
5. -3.4 revolutions.
6. $3/2\pi$ revolutions.
7. $\frac{7}{360}$ revolutions.

Give each of the following measures of rotations in revolutions and also in radians.

8. $180°$.
9. $-270°$.
10. $45°$.
11. $-730°$.
12. $1327°$.
13. $(130°/\pi)$.
14. $(-2°/\pi)$.

Each of the following is the radian measure of a rotation. Find the equivalent measures in revolutions and also in degrees.

15. 2π.
16. $-\pi$.

17. $\pi/3$.
18. $11\pi/6$.
19. $-23\pi/3$.
20. 2.
21. -0.5.

Graph the points which are represented by the following pairs of polar coordinates all on the same graph.

22. $(1, 0)$.
23. $(1, \pi/2)$.
24. $(0, 3)$.
25. $(-2, \pi)$.
26. $(3, 20\pi)$.
27. $(2.5, -3.2)$.
28. $(2.5, 1$ revolution$)$.
29. $(3, 2.4$ revolutions$)$.

Give three more pairs of polar coordinates for each of the points represented by the given pair, using the same measure of rotation.

30. $(2, \pi/2)$.
31. $(3, -\pi)$.
32. $(1, \pi/6)$.
33. $(2, \frac{3}{2})$.
34. $(1.5, 3)$, rotation in revolutions.
35. $(3, -24)$, rotation in revolutions.

Give a pair of polar coordinates (r, θ) with $r \geq 0$ for the point represented by each of the following pairs of polar coordinates, using the same units of measure for rotations.

36. $(-2, \pi/3)$.
37. $(-1, -\pi)$.
38. $(-3, -\pi/4)$.
39. $(-4, 0)$.
40. $(-1.5, 7\pi/2)$.
41. $(-2.5, \frac{1}{3})$, rotation in revolutions.
42. $(-3.2, -\frac{1}{12})$, rotation in revolutions.

Find the length of arc traversed by a rotation of measure θ on a circle of radius r. (θ is measured in radians unless otherwise stated.)

43. $r = 1, \theta = \pi$.
44. $r = 1, \theta = 3$.
45. $r = 1, \theta = 3\pi/4$.
46. $r = 2, \theta = \pi$.
47. $r = 2, \theta = 3$.
48. $r = 2, \theta = 180°$.
49. $r = 5, \theta = 6$ revolutions.
50. $r = 0.4, \theta = 540°$.

Graph the solution set for each open sentence where θ is measured in radians.

51. $r = 3$.
52. $r < 3$.
53. $r > 3$.
54. $\theta = \pi/6$.
55. $r = \theta, 0 \leq \theta \leq 2\pi$.
56. $r^2 = \theta, 0 \leq \theta \leq \pi$.

6.4 Sine and Cosine

The relationships between the rectangular and polar coordinates of a point in the plane are very important, especially for points on the unit circle

$$x^2 + y^2 = 1.$$

The open sentence

y is the second rectangular coordinate of the point with polar coordinates $(1, \theta)$

is abbreviated to

y is the sine of θ

or

$$y = \text{sine } \theta$$

or

$$y = \sin \theta.$$

This relationship defines the word *sine*. The "sine of θ" then means "the second rectangular coordinate of the point with polar coordinates $(1, \theta)$."

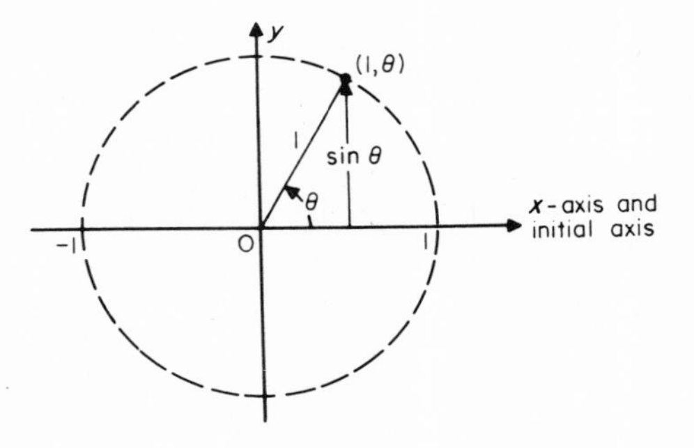

Figure 6.10

This is illustrated graphically in Figure 6.10. Similarly, the open sentence

x is the first rectangular coordinate of the point with polar coordinates $(1, \theta)$

is abbreviated to

x is the cosine of θ

or

$$x = \text{cosine } \theta$$

or

$$x = \cos \theta.$$

The "cosine of θ" means "the first rectangular coordinate of the point with polar coordinates $(1, \theta)$." (See Figure 6.11.)

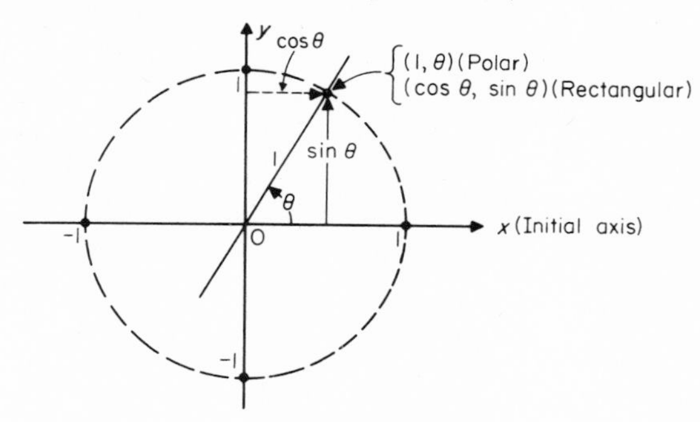

Figure 6.11

The open sentence

$$y = \sin \theta$$

defines a number y corresponding to each number θ, where θ stands for the radian measure of a rotation. The word *sine* can be considered as standing for the rule by which the number y is determined from the number θ—that is, by the rule

> Take the second rectangular coordinate of the point with polar coordinates $(1, \theta)$.

Such a rule is commonly called a *function*, and from this point on the text will refer to the *sine function*, the *cosine function*, and so on.

In case a rotation is measured in degrees, a different function is defined by the above open sentence. It will then be written "sine ( )°," and the open sentence written

$$y = \sin \theta^\circ.$$

Similarly, if the revolution is used as a measure of rotation, still a different function is defined, which is written "sine ( )^{rev}" and the open sentence written

$$y = \sin \theta^{\text{rev}}.$$

Unless otherwise specified, the sine function is the one defined using radian measure.

By considering points on the unit circle, where $r = 1$, the values for sine θ and cosine θ for certain rotations θ can be determined. If $\theta = 0$, then the coordinates of P_1 are

P_1: $(1, 0)$ (rectangular),

P_1: $(1, 0)$ (polar).

Since $x = \cos \theta$ and $y = \sin \theta$,

$$\cos 0 = 1$$

and

$$\sin 0 = 0 \qquad \text{(Figure 6.12)}.$$

Similarly for $\theta = \pi/2$, the coordinates of P_2 are

P_2: $(0, 1)$ (rectangular),

P_2: $\left(1, \dfrac{\pi}{2}\right)$ (polar).

This means

$$\cos \frac{\pi}{2} = 0$$

and

$$\sin \frac{\pi}{2} = 1.$$

These values and values for the sine and cosine of π and $3\pi/2$ appear in Figure 6.12.

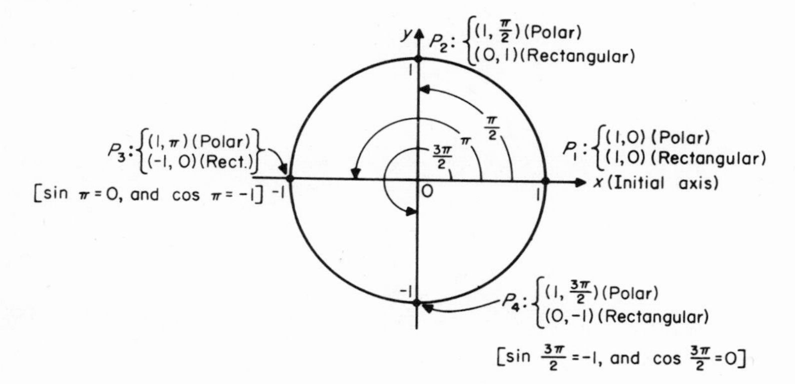

Figure 6.12

The values for sin $(\pi/6)$ and cos $(\pi/6)$ can be found from the drawing of Figure 6.13. The triangle OPQ is equilateral so that PR has length

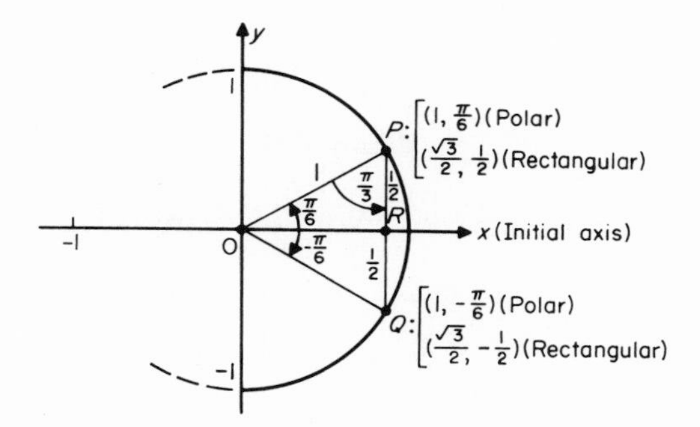

Figure 6.13

$\frac{1}{2}$, and OR has length $\sqrt{3}/2$. The rectangular coordinates of P are $(\sqrt{3}/2, \frac{1}{2})$, so that

$$\sin\frac{\pi}{6} = \frac{1}{2} \quad \text{and} \quad \cos\frac{\pi}{6} = \frac{\sqrt{3}}{2}.$$

From the coordinates of Q, it is also seen that

$$\sin\left(-\frac{\pi}{6}\right) = \sin\frac{11\pi}{6} = -\frac{1}{2},$$

$$\cos\left(-\frac{\pi}{6}\right) = \cos\frac{11\pi}{6} = \frac{\sqrt{3}}{2}.$$

Similarly, by the appropriate placement of an equilateral triangle, the values for sin and cos can be found for rotations of $\pi/3$, $2\pi/3$, $5\pi/6$, and so forth. In the case of $\pi/3$, the rectangular coordinates of P are $(\frac{1}{2}, \sqrt{3}/2)$; that is,

$$\sin\frac{\pi}{3} = \frac{\sqrt{3}}{2}, \qquad \cos\frac{\pi}{3} = \frac{1}{2}.$$

For $-\pi/3$,

$$\sin\left(-\frac{\pi}{3}\right) = -\frac{\sqrt{3}}{2}, \qquad \cos\left(-\frac{\pi}{3}\right) = \frac{1}{2}.$$

The values of $\sin(\pi/4)$, $\cos(\pi/4)$ can be found by use of the "45-45-90" triangle, as in Figure 6.14. Since the triangle OPQ is isosceles,

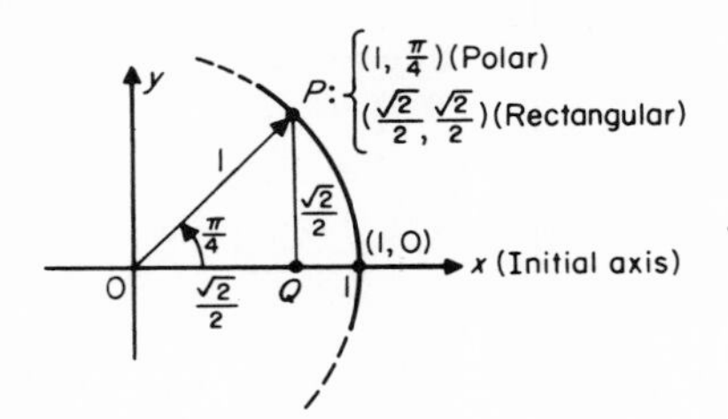

Figure 6.14

$\overline{OQ} = \overline{PQ}$. The rectangular coordinates of P are $(\sqrt{2}/2, \sqrt{2}/2)$. Therefore,

$$\sin\frac{\pi}{4} = \frac{\sqrt{2}}{2}, \qquad \cos\frac{\pi}{4} = \frac{\sqrt{2}}{2}.$$

In a similar way, sin and cos of $\pm 3\pi/4$, $\pm 5\pi/4$, and $\pm 7\pi/4$ can be found.

CHART OF VALUES FOR SIN AND COS

θ	Sin θ	Cos θ
0	0	1
$\pi/6$	$1/2$	$\sqrt{3}/2$
$\pi/4$	$\sqrt{2}/2$	$\sqrt{2}/2$
$\pi/3$	$\sqrt{3}/2$	$1/2$
$\pi/2$	1	0
$2\pi/3$	$\sqrt{3}/2$	$-1/2$
$3\pi/4$	$\sqrt{2}/2$	$-\sqrt{2}/2$
$5\pi/6$	$1/2$	$-\sqrt{3}/2$
π	0	-1

EXAMPLE 6.7 Find the values for $\sin(5\pi/4)$, $\cos(5\pi/4)$.
Using a 45-45-90 triangle, the values are calculated as in Figure 6.15.

$$\sin\frac{5\pi}{4} = -\frac{\sqrt{2}}{2}, \qquad \cos\frac{5\pi}{4} = -\frac{\sqrt{2}}{2}.$$

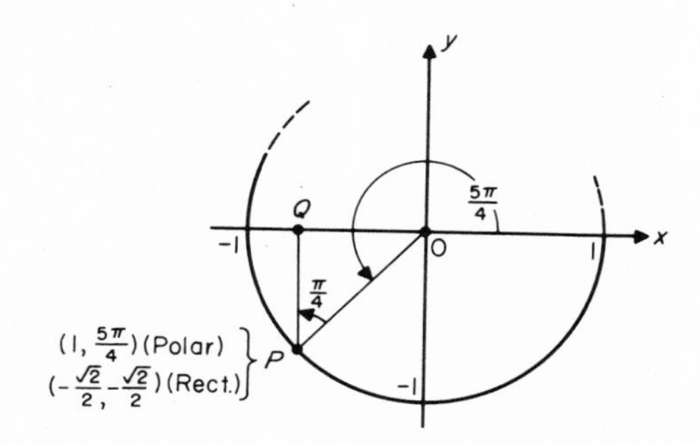

Figure 6.15

6.5 Tables of Values for Sine and Cosine

Approximate values of $\sin\theta$ and $\cos\theta$ are listed in Table 1 of the appendix for rotations measured in radians, and in Table 2 for rotations measured in degrees. The values given by these tables are 4-place decimal approximations of the real values. The following examples illustrate the use of these tables.

EXAMPLE 6.8 Find $\sin\theta$ and $\cos\theta$, where $\theta = 1.31$.
Since the unit of rotation is not specified, it is assumed to be the radian. Using Table 1,

$$\cos 1.31 = 0.2579 \text{ (approx.)},$$

$$\sin 1.31 = 0.9662 \text{ (approx.)}.$$

EXAMPLE 6.9 Find the measure of θ in radians, $0 \leq \theta \leq \pi/2$, $\sin\theta = 0.3986$.
Reading from Table 1,

$$\theta = 0.41 \text{ (radian)}.$$

EXAMPLE 6.10 If P is given by (x, y) and $(1, \theta)$, if $x = 0.8090$, and $0 \leq \theta \leq 90°$, find θ and y (Figure 6.16).

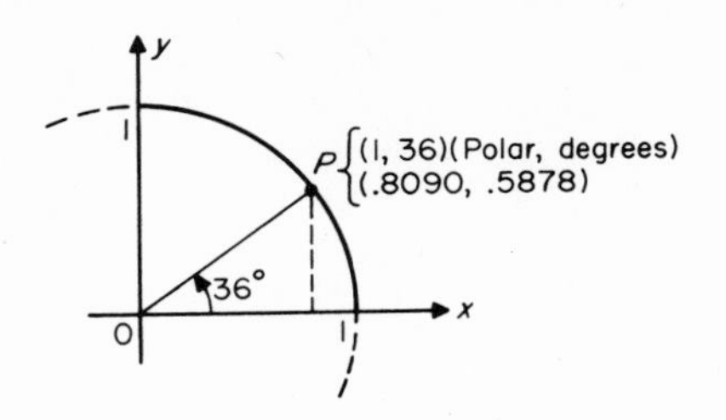

Figure 6.16

From Table 2, since

$$x = 0.8090,$$
$$\cos\theta° = 0.8090,$$
$$\theta° = 36°,$$
$$y = \sin 36°,$$
$$y = 0.5878.$$

EXAMPLE 6.11 Find the rectangular coordinates (x, y) for $P = (1, 48)$, rotation measured in degrees.
Reading Table 2,

$$x = \sin 48° = 0.7431,$$
$$y = \cos 48° = 0.6691.$$

EXERCISE SET 6.3

Find the exact value of each of the following without reference to a table.

1. $\sin 90°$.
2. $\sin 0°$.
3. $\cos 0°$.
4. $\cos 60°$.
5. $\sin 45°$.
6. $\sin 120°$.
7. $\sin -120°$.
8. $\cos -120°$.
9. $\sin 240°$.
10. $\cos -240°$.
11. $\sin (7\pi/4)$.
12. $\cos (-\pi/4)$.
13. $\sin (-2\pi/3)$.
14. $\cos (7\pi/6)$.
15. $\sin (7\pi/3)$.
16. $\cos (-3\pi/2)$.
17. $\sin (-7\pi/6)$.
18. $\cos (-5\pi/4)$.
19. $\sin (3\pi/2)$.
20. $\cos 7\pi$.

Without reference to a table, find the measures of rotation θ which satisfy the following equations, where $0 \leq \theta \leq \pi$, in radians. Give the result in both degrees and radians.

21. $\sin \theta = 0$.
22. $\cos \theta = 0$.
23. $\sin \theta = 1$.
24. $\cos \theta = 1$.
25. $\sin \theta = \frac{1}{2}$.
26. $\sin \theta = \sqrt{3}/2$.
27. $\sin \theta = \sqrt{2}/2$.
28. $\cos \theta = \sqrt{2}/2$.

Use Table 1 to find the approximate value of each of the following.

29. sin 0.31.
30. sin 1.22.
31. cos 0.03.
32. sin 0.51.
33. cos 1.32.

Use Table 2 to find the approximate value of each of the following.

34. sin 37°.
35. cos 76°.
36. sin 53°.
37. cos 22°.
38. sin 5.1°.

Find the rectangular coordinates for each point (r, θ). Use Table 1 or Table 2 where necessary.

39. (1, 45), rotation in degrees.
40. (1, 1.2).
41. (1, 37), rotation in degrees.
42. (1, 80), rotation in degrees.
43. $(1, \pi/2)$.
44. (1, 1.5), rotation in revolutions.
45. $(1, \pi/4)$.
46. (1, 0).
47. (2, 0).
48. $(2, \pi/2)$.
49. $(5, \pi/4)$.
50. $(3, \pi/6)$.

Find the polar coordinates $(1, \theta)$ for each point P on the unit circle for the given value of x or y, where the rotations are in radians. Use Table 1 where necessary.

51. $y = 0.38$, $x > 0$.
52. $x = 0.9838$, $y > 0$.
53. $y = 0.621$, $x > 0$.
54. $x = 1$.
55. $y = 0.994$, $x < 0$.
56. $x = 0.732$, $y < 0$.

A point on the unit circle has polar coordinates $(1, \theta)$. Find in which quadrant or on which axis the point lies from the information given.

57. $\cos\theta > 0$, $\sin\theta > 0$.
58. $\cos\theta < 0$, $\sin\theta > 0$.
59. $\cos\theta > 0$, $\sin\theta = 0$.
60. $\cos\theta < 0$, $\sin\theta < 0$.
61. $\cos\theta = 0$, $\sin\theta > 0$.
62. $\cos\theta > 0$, $\sin\theta < 0$.

6.6 Interpolation

For rotations whose measures do not appear in Tables 1 or 2, approximate values for sine and cosine can be found by the method of *interpolation*. To find the value of cosine 0.853, use the values for cosine 0.85 and cosine 0.86, the nearest rotations smaller and larger than 0.853 as listed in Table 1.

$$\text{cosine } 0.85 = 0.6600,$$

$$\text{cosine } 0.86 = 0.6524.$$

Since 0.853 is $\frac{3}{10}$ of the difference between 0.85 and 0.86, this same proportion of the difference between 0.6600 and 0.6524 is added to 0.6600 for the approximation. The work below illustrates this procedure.

$$\frac{3}{10} \text{ of total} \left[\begin{array}{ll} \cos 0.85 & 0.6600 \\ \cos 0.853 & ? \end{array}\right] x \qquad \text{Total difference } -0.0076$$

$$\cos 0.86 \qquad 0.6524$$

$$x = \tfrac{3}{10}(-0.0076) = -0.0023 \qquad (\textit{notice negative sign}),$$

$$\cos 0.853 = 0.6600 - 0.0023 = 0.6577.$$

EXAMPLE 6.12 Find the (approximate) value of sin 53.2°. From Table 2,

$$\frac{2}{10} \text{ of total} \left[\begin{array}{ll} \sin 53^\circ & = 0.7986 \\ \sin 53.2^\circ & = \quad ? \end{array}\right] x \qquad \text{difference } 0.0104$$

$$\sin 54^\circ = 0.8090$$

$$x = \tfrac{2}{10}(0.0104) = 0.0021,$$

$$\sin 53.2^\circ = 0.7986 + 0.0021 = 0.8007.$$

EXAMPLE 6.13 Find the rotation θ in radians and in degrees for which $\sin\theta = 0.8$.

From Table 1,

$$0.01\left[\begin{array}{l} x\left[\begin{array}{ll}\sin 0.92 &= 0.7956\\ \sin\theta &= 0.8000\end{array}\right]0.0044 \\ \\ \quad\sin 0.93 = 0.8016\end{array}\right]0.0060$$

$$x = \frac{0.0044}{0.0060}\cdot 0.01 = 0.007,$$

$$\theta = 0.927 \text{ (approx.)}.$$

From Table 2,

$$1^\circ\left[\begin{array}{l} x\left[\begin{array}{ll}\sin 53^\circ &= 0.7986\\ \sin\theta &= 0.8000\end{array}\right]0.0014 \\ \\ \quad\sin 54^\circ = 0.8090\end{array}\right]0.0104$$

$$x = \frac{0.0014}{0.0104}\cdot 1^\circ = 0.1^\circ,$$

$$\theta = 53.1^\circ \text{ (approx.)}.$$

EXERCISE SET 6.4

Find each value (approximately) by the method of interpolation.

1. $\sin 18.3^\circ$.
2. $\cos 32.6^\circ$.
3. $\sin 27.3^\circ$.
4. $\cos 87.6^\circ$.
5. $\sin 2.4^\circ$.
6. $\sin 1.172$.
7. $\sin 1.221$.
8. $\cos 0.421$.
9. $\cos 0.332$.
10. $\sin 1.431$.

Find each rotation θ in radians $(0 < \theta < \pi/2)$ in Exercises 11–14. Find each rotation θ in degrees $(0 < \theta < 90)$ in Exercises 15–18. Use interpolation where necessary.

11. $\sin\theta = 0.4924$.
12. $\sin\theta = 0.8616$.
13. $\sin\theta = 0.9945$.
14. $\cos\theta = 0.4924$.
15. $\cos\theta = 0.1223$.
16. $\cos\theta = 0.9799$.
17. $\sin\theta = 0.5520$.
18. $\cos\theta = 0.8123$.

6.7 Reduction Identities

The tables for sine and cosine of the previous section are restricted to rotations of 0 to $\pi/2$ radians. One does not need to extend these tables to find (approximate) values for sine and for cosine for other rotations since there are identities which relate the values of sine and cosine of any rotation to values of sine and of cosine of a rotation from 0 to $\pi/2$.

Since every point of the plane has a pair of polar coordinates (r, θ) with $r \geq 0$ and $0 \leq \theta \leq 2\pi$, the point $(1, \phi)$ where ϕ is not between 0 and 2π also has the coordinates $(1, \phi')$ for some ϕ' between 0 and 2π. Since sine ϕ and cosine ϕ are determined by the point rather than by any particular pair of coordinates of the point,

$$\sin \phi = \sin \phi'$$

and

$$\cos \phi = \cos \phi'.$$

Identities for this relation are

$$\sin \theta = \sin (\theta + n \cdot 2\pi), \qquad n \in I,$$

and

$$\cos \theta = \cos (\theta + n \cdot 2\pi), \qquad n \in I.$$

EXAMPLE 6.14

$$\sin 600° = \sin (600° - 360°) = \sin 240°,$$

$$\cos -\frac{\pi}{2} = \cos \left(-\frac{\pi}{2} + 2\pi\right) = \cos \frac{3\pi}{2}.$$

The following equations enable one to find the cosine and sine values for negative rotations in terms of positive rotations.

$$\cos \theta = \cos -\theta,$$

(1)

$$\sin \theta = -\sin -\theta.$$

Verification of these identities can be shown as follows. The points with polar coordinates $(1, \theta)$ and $(1, -\theta)$ have rectangular coordinates

$$(\cos \theta, \sin \theta)$$

and

$$(\cos -\theta, \sin -\theta),$$

respectively. Since these points are symmetric with respect to the x-axis, the above relations (1) hold (see Figure 6.17). (The student should sketch several other rotations to illustrate this fact.)

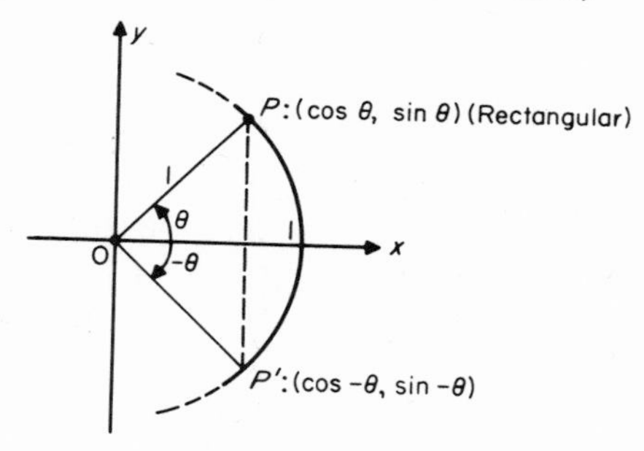

Figure 6.17

EXAMPLE 6.15 Write in terms of a rotation θ where $0 \leq \theta < 2\pi$.

(a) $\sin -\frac{\pi}{2}$.

$$\sin -\frac{\pi}{2} = -\sin -\left(-\frac{\pi}{2}\right)$$

$$= -\sin \frac{\pi}{2}.$$

(b) $\cos -3\pi$.

$$\cos -3\pi = \cos 3\pi$$

$$= \cos (3\pi - 2\pi)$$

$$= \cos \pi.$$

(c) $\sin -1.3$.

$$\sin (-1.3) = -\sin 1.3.$$

(d) $\cos -8.1$.

$$\cos -8.1 = \cos 8.1 = \cos (8.1 - 2\pi).$$

(Is $0 \leq 8.1 - 2\pi < 2\pi$?)

The identities

$$\cos\left(\theta - \frac{\pi}{2}\right) = \sin \theta$$

and

$$\sin\left(\theta - \frac{\pi}{2}\right) = -\cos \theta$$

can be used to transform sine or cosine to sine or cosine of a rotation between 0 and $\pi/2$. Geometric verification of these identities is illustrated in Figure 6.18. For a given rotation θ, let P be the point $(1, \theta)$

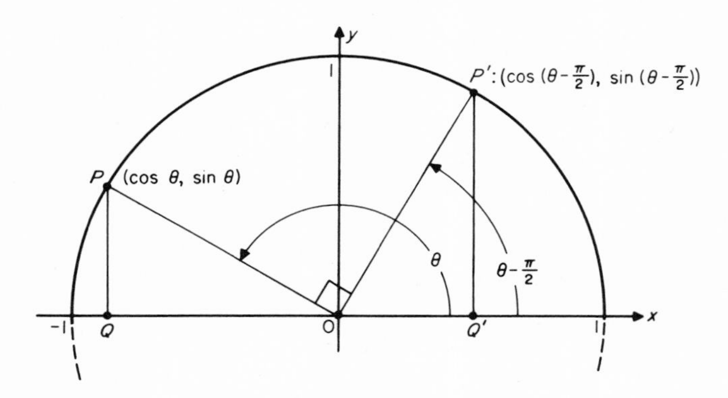

Figure 6.18

and P' be the point $(1, \theta - \pi/2)$. The rectangular coordinates for each point are

$$P\colon (\cos \theta, \sin \theta),$$

$$P'\colon \left(\cos\left(\theta - \frac{\pi}{2}\right), \sin\left(\theta - \frac{\pi}{2}\right)\right).$$

However, the triangles POQ and $Q'P'O$ are congruent. This means that

$$\overline{Q'P'} = \overline{QO},$$

or, since

$$\overline{Q'P'} = \sin\left(\theta - \frac{\pi}{2}\right) \quad \text{and} \quad \overline{QO} = -\cos\theta,$$

$$\sin\left(\theta - \frac{\pi}{2}\right) = -\cos\theta.$$

Furthermore, since $\overline{OQ'} = \overline{QP}\sin\theta = \overline{QP}$, and

$$\cos\left(\theta - \frac{\pi}{2}\right) = \overline{OQ'}, \qquad \cos\left(\theta - \frac{\pi}{2}\right) = \sin\theta.$$

Using the above identities,

$$\begin{aligned}\sin(\theta - \pi) &= \sin\left[\left(\theta - \frac{\pi}{2}\right) - \frac{\pi}{2}\right]\\ &= -\cos\left(\theta - \frac{\pi}{2}\right)\\ &= -\sin\theta\end{aligned}$$

and

$$\begin{aligned}\cos(\theta - \pi) &= \cos\left[\left(\theta - \frac{\pi}{2}\right) - \frac{\pi}{2}\right]\\ &= \sin\left(\theta - \frac{\pi}{2}\right)\\ &= -\cos\theta.\end{aligned}$$

Also,

$$\begin{aligned}\sin\left(\frac{\pi}{2} - \theta\right) &= -\sin\left(\theta - \frac{\pi}{2}\right)\\ &= -(-\cos\theta)\\ &= \cos\theta\end{aligned}$$

and

$$\begin{aligned}\cos\left(\frac{\pi}{2} - \theta\right) &= \cos\left(\theta - \frac{\pi}{2}\right)\\ &= \sin\theta.\end{aligned}$$

The identities for $\sin(\pi - \theta)$ and $\cos(\pi - \theta)$ are derived in a similar manner (see Exercise 1, Exercise Set 6.5).

A summary of the identities discussed thus far is given below:

$$
\begin{array}{ll}
\sin -\theta = -\sin \theta & \cos -\theta = \cos \theta \\
\sin\left(\theta - \frac{\pi}{2}\right) = -\cos \theta & \cos\left(\theta - \frac{\pi}{2}\right) = \sin \theta \\
\sin\left(\frac{\pi}{2} - \theta\right) = \cos \theta & \cos\left(\frac{\pi}{2} - \theta\right) = \sin \theta \\
\sin(\theta - \pi) = -\sin \theta & \cos(\theta - \pi) = -\cos \theta \\
\sin(\pi - \theta) = \sin \theta & \cos(\pi - \theta) = -\cos \theta
\end{array}
$$

EXAMPLE 6.16 Find θ so that $\cos \theta = -\sin 570°$, and $0° \leq \theta \leq 90°$.

$$
\begin{aligned}
\sin 570° &= \sin(570° - 360°) \\
&= \sin 210° \\
&= -\sin(210° - 180°) \\
&= -\sin 30° \\
&= -\cos(90° - 30°) \\
&= -\cos 60°.
\end{aligned}
$$

Hence, $\theta = 60°$.

EXAMPLE 6.17 Find sin 10.3 (approximately).
As an approximation,

$$3\pi = 3 \cdot 3.14 = 9.42,$$

$$\sin 10.3 = -\sin(10.3 - 9.42) = -\sin 0.88 = -0.7707.$$

EXAMPLE 6.18 Find the rectangular coordinates of the point with polar coordinates $(1. -3\pi/4)$.
The coordinates are

$$\left(\cos -\frac{3\pi}{4}, \sin -\frac{3\pi}{4}\right) = \left(-\frac{\sqrt{2}}{2}, -\frac{\sqrt{2}}{2}\right)$$

since

$$\cos -\frac{3\pi}{4} = -\cos\left(\pi - \frac{3\pi}{4}\right) = -\cos\frac{\pi}{4} = -\frac{\sqrt{2}}{2},$$

$$\sin -\frac{3\pi}{4} = -\sin\left(\pi - \frac{3\pi}{4}\right) = -\sin\frac{\pi}{4} = -\frac{\sqrt{2}}{2}.$$

EXAMPLE 6.19 Find the solution set for $\sin \theta = \frac{1}{2}$.
A known solution is $\pi/6$. Since $\sin \theta = \sin(\pi - \theta)$ and $\pi - \pi/6 = 5\pi/6$, $5\pi/6$ is also a solution. These are the only solutions for $0 \le \theta \le 2\pi$ (see

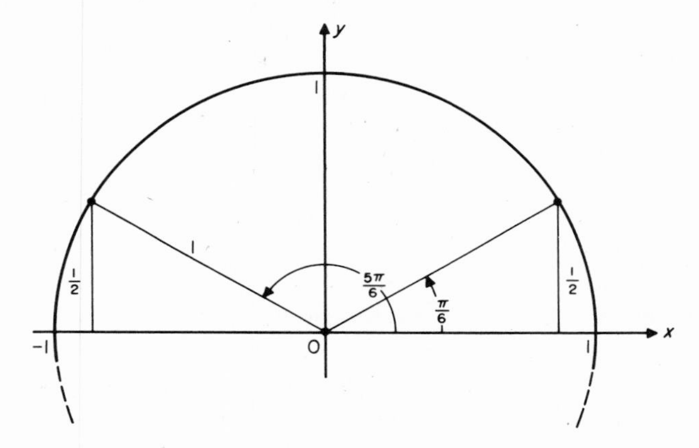

Figure 6.19

Figure 6.19). Other solutions are obtained by adding multiples of 2π to each of these angles, so that the entire solution set is

$$\left\{\theta: \theta = \frac{\pi}{6} + 2n\pi, n \in I\right\} \cup \left\{\theta: \theta = \frac{5\pi}{6} + 2n\pi, n \in I\right\}.$$

EXERCISE SET 6.5

1. Writing $\pi - \theta$ as $-(\theta - \pi)$, derive identities for $\sin(\pi - \theta)$ and $\cos(\pi - \theta)$.
2. Derive identities for $\sin(\pi/2 + \theta)$ and for $\cos(\pi/2 + \theta)$ in terms of functions of θ.

Find the exact value of each of the following using the reduction identities.

3. $\sin(-\pi/6)$.
4. $\cos(-\pi/6)$.
5. $\cos(-17\pi/6)$.
6. $\sin(5\pi/3)$.

7. $\cos (9\pi/4)$.
8. $\sin (-13\pi/4)$.
9. $\cos (11\pi/3)$.
10. $\sin 150°$.
11. $\cos 225°$.
12. $\sin -60°$.
13. $\cos -585°$.
14. $\sin 2835°$.

Find an approximate value for each of the following:

15. $\sin 3$.
16. $\cos 5.4$.
17. $\sin 6.2$.
18. $\sin -1.3$.
19. $\cos -4.2$.
20. $\sin 13.4$.
21. $\sin 122°$.
22. $\cos -23°$.
23. $\sin 733°$.
24. $\cos -1131°$.

Find all solutions to each of the following, where θ is measured in radians, $0 \leq \theta \leq 2\pi$.

25. $\sin \theta = \sqrt{3}/2$.
26. $\cos \theta = \frac{1}{2}$.
27. $\sin \theta = -\sqrt{2}/2$.
28. $\cos \theta = -\frac{1}{2}$.
29. $\sin \theta = 1$.
30. $\cos \theta = -1$.
31. $\sin \theta = 0$.
32. $\cos \theta = 0$.

Find all solutions θ for $0 \leq \theta \leq 2\pi$, where θ is given in radians.

33. $\sin \theta = 0.8$.
34. $\sin \theta = -0.631$.
35. $\cos \theta = 0.132$.
36. $\cos \theta = -0.734$.

Find the set of all solutions, θ in radians.

37. $\sin \theta = -\sqrt{2}/2$.
38. $\cos \theta = \frac{1}{2}$.
39. $\sin \theta = 0$.
40. $\cos \theta = -1$.
41. $\cos \theta = 0.3809$.
42. $\sin \theta = 0.3802$.

Find the rectangular coordinates for each point.

43. $(1, -5\pi/6)$.
44. $(1, 7\pi/2)$.
45. $(1, -120)$, rotation in degrees.
46. $(1, 410)$, rotation in degrees.
47. $(1, -638)$, rotation in degrees.
48. $(1, -8.3)$.
49. $(1, 11.4)$.
50. $(2, 810)$, rotation in degrees.
51. $(5, -270)$, rotation in degrees.

6.8 General Coordinate Relations

For an arbitrary point P with polar coordinates (r, θ), $r \geq 0$, the line through P and the origin intersects the unit circle at a point Q. Q has polar coordinates $(1, \theta)$ and rectangular coordinates $(\cos \theta, \sin \theta)$ (see Figure 6.20). By similar triangles, the pair of rectangular coordinates (x, y) of P is seen to be $(r \cos \theta, r \sin \theta)$.

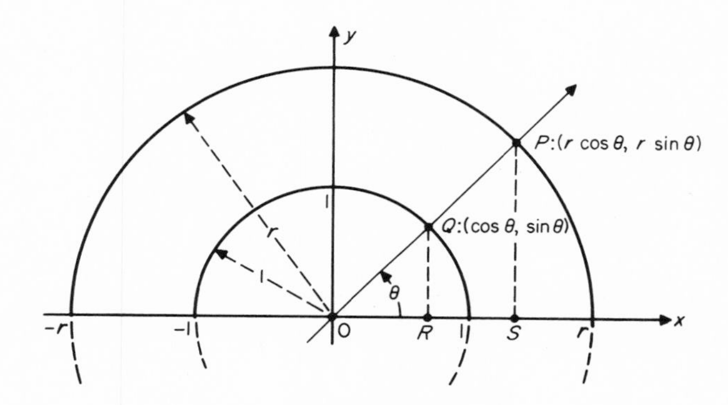

Figure 6.20

The relations between the coordinates are summarized by the following equations:

$$r = \sqrt{x^2 + y^2},$$

$$x = r \cos \theta, \qquad y = r \sin \theta,$$

$$\cos \theta = \frac{x}{r} = \frac{x}{\sqrt{x^2 + y^2}}, \qquad \sin \theta = \frac{y}{r} = \frac{y}{\sqrt{x^2 + y^2}}.$$

The following examples illustrate how to determine one set of coordinates from the other.

EXAMPLE 6.20 Find the rectangular coordinates for P which has polar coordinates $(3, 0.9)$.
Letting (x, y) be the rectangular coordinates,

$$\begin{aligned} x &= 3 \cos 0.9 \\ &= 3(0.6216) \text{ (approx.)} \\ &= 1.8648 \text{ (approx.)} \end{aligned}$$

and

$$\begin{aligned} y &= 3 \sin 0.9 \\ &= 3(0.7833) \text{ (approx.)} \\ &= 2.3499 \text{ (approx.)}. \end{aligned}$$

Rectangular coordinates of P: (1.8648, 2.3499).

EXAMPLE 6.21 Find a pair of polar coordinates (r, θ) for a point P which has rectangular coordinates (2.1, 3.2).

$$\begin{aligned} r &= \sqrt{(2.1)^2 + (3.2)^2} \\ &= \sqrt{14.65} \\ &= 3.83 \text{ (approx.)}. \end{aligned}$$

Since $\sin \theta = 3.2/3.83 = 0.8355$ (approx.), then $\theta = 0.99$ (approx.) is one solution (Table 1). Further, since P is in Quadrant I, one pair of polar coordinates of P is (3.83, 0.99). (Are there other answers?)

EXAMPLE 6.22 Find a pair of polar coordinates (r, θ) for a point P which has rectangular coordinates $(-5, -5\sqrt{3})$ (Figure 6.21).

$$\begin{aligned} r &= \sqrt{(-5)^2 + (-5\sqrt{3})^2} \\ &= \sqrt{25 + 75} \\ &= 10. \end{aligned}$$

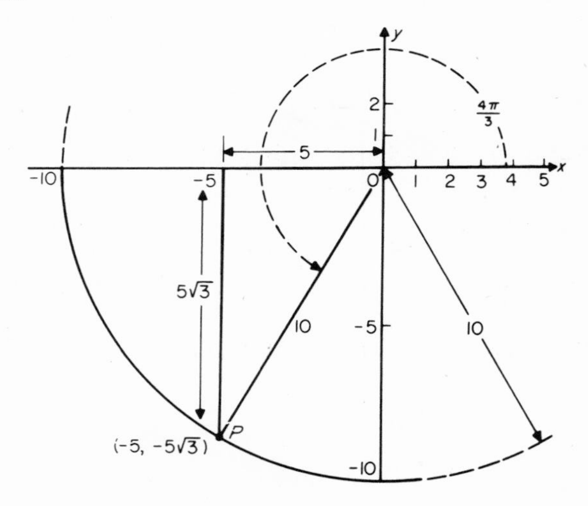

Figure 6.21

$\cos\theta = -5/10 = -\frac{1}{2}$; and since P is in Quadrant III, one solution is $\theta = 4\pi/3$. One pair of polar coordinates of P is $(10, 4\pi/3)$.

6.9 Solution of Right Triangles

The procedure of section 6.8 can be applied to the solution of right triangles. Place the vertex of one of the acute angles of the triangle at the origin, with the adjacent leg along the positive x-axis and the hypotenuse in Quadrant I. Given sufficient information about the triangle, it can now be solved using previous methods.

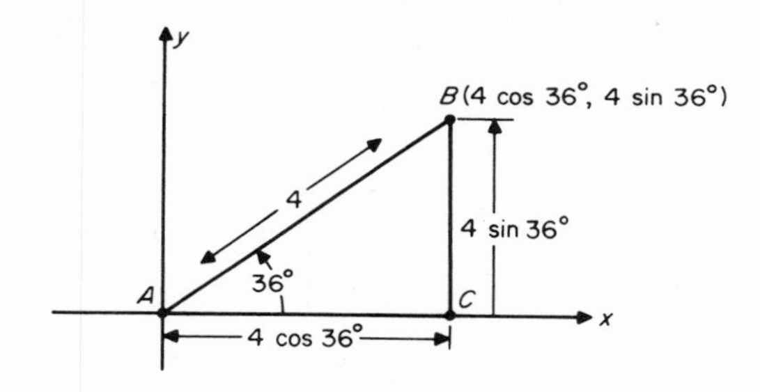

Figure 6.22

Suppose a right triangle ABC is given with angle $C = 90°$, angle $A = 36°$, and length of hypotenuse $AB = 4$. Then, placing the triangle as in Figure 6.22, the unknown angle and sides can be obtained.

$$\begin{aligned} \text{length of side } BC &= y\text{-coordinate of } B \\ &= 4 \sin 36° \\ &= 2.351 \text{ (approx.)}, \end{aligned}$$

$$\begin{aligned} \text{length of side } AC &= x\text{-coordinate of } B \\ &= 4 \cos 36° \\ &= 3.236 \text{ (approx.)}, \end{aligned}$$

$$\text{angle } B = 90° - 36° = 54°.$$

Suppose a right triangle ABC is given with angle $C = 90°$, length of side $BC = 2.13$, and length of side $AC = 1.34$ (see Figure 6.23). Then,

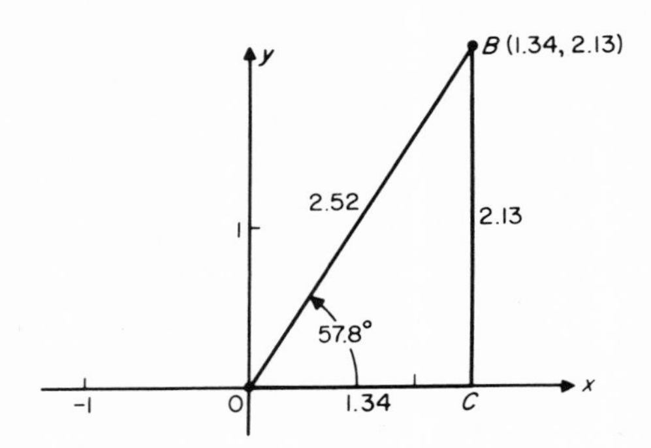

Figure 6.23

using the Pythagorean theorem, length of hypotenuse $AB = 2.52$ (approx.),

$$\sin A = \frac{2.13}{2.52}$$

$$= 0.8453,$$

$$\text{angle } A = 57.8°,$$

$$\text{angle } B = 90° - 57.8°$$

$$= 32.2°.$$

EXERCISE SET 6.6

Find the pair of polar coordinates (r, θ), $r \geq 0$ and $0 \leq \theta < 2\pi$, for each of the points represented by the following pairs of rectangular coordinates. (Give exact values when possible.)

1. $(1, 0)$.
2. $(0, 1)$.
3. $(\frac{1}{2}, \sqrt{3}/2)$.
4. $(\sqrt{2}/2, \sqrt{2}/2)$.
5. $(\frac{3}{5}, \frac{4}{5})$.
6. $(1, 1)$.
7. $(-1, \sqrt{3})$.
8. $(2\sqrt{2}, 2\sqrt{2})$.
9. $(2, -3)$.

Find the pair of rectangular coordinates (x, y) for each of the points represented by the following pairs of polar coordinates:

10. $(1, \pi/2)$.
11. $(0, 5)$.
12. $(1, -\pi/4)$.
13. $(1, \pi/3)$.
14. $(1, 7\pi/3)$.
15. $(1, -5\pi/6)$.
16. $(1, 3\pi/4)$.
17. $(1, 11\pi/2)$.
18. $(1, -15\pi/4)$
19. $(2, \pi/2)$.
20. $(2, -2\pi/3)$.
21. $(3, -7\pi/4)$.

22. $(2.5, \pi/3)$.
23. $(3.1, 13\pi/6)$.
24. $(7.2, -3\pi/4)$.
25. $(1, 60°)$.
26. $(1, -720°)$.
27. $(2, 240°)$.
28. $(3, -225°)$.
29. $(2, 3)$.
30. $(3, 67°)$.

Solve the following right triangles; that is, find the measures of the unknown angles and sides. In each case, a is the side opposite angle A, b is the side opposite angle B, and c is the side opposite angle C. C is always a right angle. (Give exact answers when possible, and use the sine and cosine rather than elementary geometry.)

31. $A = 30°, c = 1$.
32. $A = 30°, c = 3$.
33. $A = 45°, a = 2$.
34. $A = 60°, b = 2.5$.
35. $A = 37°, c = 3.2$.
36. $A = 67.5°, a = 2.4$.
37. $a = 2, c = 4$.
38. $b = \frac{1}{2}, c = 1$.
39. $a = 1, b = 3$.
40. $a = 2, b = 2$.
41. $a = 2.1, c = 1.5$.
42. $a = 5.2, b = 1.3$.

6.10 The Tangent Function

The tangent function is defined for real numbers θ in terms of the sine and cosine functions:

$$\text{tangent } \theta = \frac{\text{sine } \theta}{\text{cosine } \theta}, \qquad \text{for each } \theta \text{ such that } \cos\theta \neq 0.$$

(The usual abbreviation for "tangent θ" is "tan θ.")

For a given point $P(r, \theta)$, the rectangular coordinates will be $(r \cos\theta, r \sin\theta)$. (See Figure 6.24.) The slope of the rotated line through P is given by

$$\text{slope } OP = \frac{\Delta y}{\Delta x} = \frac{(r \sin\theta - 0)}{(r \cos\theta - 0)} = \frac{\sin\theta}{\cos\theta} = \tan\theta.$$

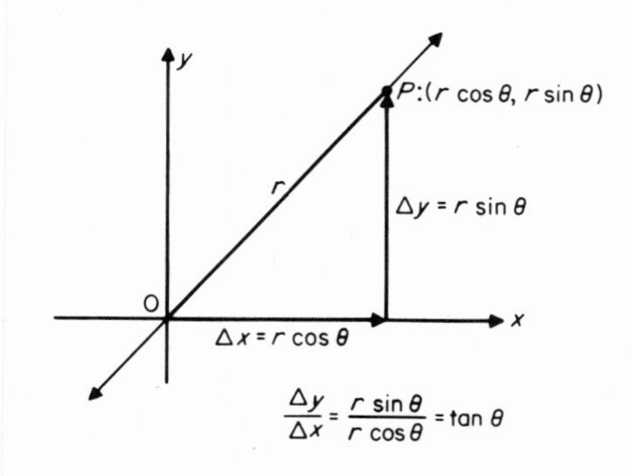

Figure 6.24

Values for the tangent are listed below in the table, together with the values of sine and cosine (rotations in radians).

θ	0	$\frac{\pi}{6}$	$\frac{\pi}{4}$	$\frac{\pi}{3}$	$\frac{\pi}{2}$	π
$\sin\theta$	0	$\frac{1}{2}$	$\frac{\sqrt{2}}{2}$	$\frac{\sqrt{3}}{2}$	1	0
$\cos\theta$	1	$\frac{\sqrt{3}}{2}$	$\frac{\sqrt{2}}{2}$	$\frac{1}{2}$	0	-1
$\tan\theta$	0	$\frac{\sqrt{3}}{3}$	1	$\sqrt{3}$	—	0

The tangent of $\pi/2$ does not exist since $\cos(\pi/2) = 0$. This is in agreement with the fact that the slope of the line through the origin and $(1, \pi/2)$ is undefined since the line is vertical.

As in the case of sine and cosine, there are three tangent functions: (1) where the rotations are in radians, (2) where the rotations are in degrees, and (3) where the rotations are in revolutions. Approximate values for tangent θ are found in Tables 1 and 2 of the appendix.

6.11 Reciprocal Functions

The reciprocal functions of the sine, cosine, and tangent are defined by

$$\text{cosecant } \theta = \frac{1}{\sin\theta},$$

$$\text{secant } \theta = \frac{1}{\cos\theta},$$

and

$$\text{cotangent } \theta = \frac{1}{\tan\theta} = \frac{\cos\theta}{\sin\theta}$$

for all values of θ for which the denominators are nonzero. A list of values for these functions are given in the table below. Values for other numbers can be found by using Tables 1 and 2 and the above identities. (The abbreviation for "cosecant" is "csc," "secant" is abbreviated to "sec," and "cotangent" to "cot" or "ctn.")

θ	0	$\frac{\pi}{6}$	$\frac{\pi}{4}$	$\frac{\pi}{3}$	$\frac{\pi}{2}$	π
$\sec\theta$	1	$\frac{2\sqrt{3}}{3}$	$\sqrt{2}$	2	—	-1
$\csc\theta$	—	2	$\sqrt{2}$	$\frac{2\sqrt{3}}{3}$	1	—
cot	—	$\sqrt{3}$	1	$\frac{\sqrt{3}}{3}$	0	—

EXAMPLE 6.23 Find cotangent $(3\pi/2)$.

$$\cot\frac{3\pi}{2} = \frac{\cos(3\pi/2)}{\sin(3\pi/2)} = \frac{0}{-1} = 0.$$

EXAMPLE 6.24 Find $\csc(7\pi/6)$, $\sec(7\pi/6)$.

$$\csc\frac{7\pi}{6} = \frac{1}{\sin(7\pi/6)} = \frac{1}{-\sin(\pi/6)} = \frac{1}{-\frac{1}{2}} = -2,$$

$$\sec\frac{7\pi}{6} = \frac{1}{\cos(7\pi/6)} = \frac{1}{-\cos(\pi/6)}$$

$$= \frac{1}{-\sqrt{3}/2} = \frac{-2}{\sqrt{3}} = \frac{-2\sqrt{3}}{3}.$$

EXAMPLE 6.25 Find cot 1.443.

$$\left.\begin{array}{l} \tan 1.44 = 7.602 \\ \tan 1.45 = 8.238 \end{array}\right] 0.636$$

$$\tan 1.443 = 7.602 + \tfrac{3}{10}(0.636) = 7.793,$$

$$\cot 1.443 = \frac{1}{7.793} = 0.1283 \text{ (approx.)}.$$

EXERCISE SET 6.7

Find the exact value.

1. $\tan(\pi/4)$.
2. $\tan \pi$.
3. $\cot(\pi/3)$.
4. $\tan(-\pi/4)$.
5. $\cot(-\pi/6)$.
6. $\cot(\pi/2)$.
7. $\tan(5\pi/6)$.
8. $\sec(\pi/4)$.
9. $\sec(-\pi/4)$.
10. $\csc(-2\pi/3)$.
11. $\csc(7\pi/4)$.
12. $\tan 60°$.
13. $\cot -45°$.
14. $\sec 390°$.
15. $\csc -420°$.

Find an approximate value.

16. $\tan 0.31$.
17. $\tan 1.23$.
18. $\cot 1.6$.
19. $\cot -0.41$.
20. $\tan 1.213$.
21. $\sec 1.21$.
22. $\csc -0.231$.

Find θ for each of the following, where $0 \leq \theta < 2\pi$, and the rotation is in radians.

23. $\tan \theta = 1$.
24. $\cot \theta = \sqrt{3}/3$.
25. $\tan \theta = -\sqrt{3}$.
26. $\cot \theta = -\frac{1}{3}$.
27. $\tan \theta = -1/\sqrt{3}$.
28. $\sec \theta = 2$.
29. $\csc \theta = -\sqrt{2}$.
30. $\tan \theta = 0$.
31. $\tan \theta = 0.54$.
32. $\sec \theta = 1.23$.
33. $\cot \theta = 3.2$.
34. $\csc \theta = 0.312$.

6.12 Graphs of Trigonometric Functions

In order to analyze the changes in $\sin \theta$ as θ changes, the equation

$$y = \sin \theta$$

can be graphed on a rectangular coordinate graph. Rewriting the equation using the usual variables, x and y, the graph is of the set

$$\{(x, y) : y = \sin x\} \qquad \text{(Figure 6.25)}.$$

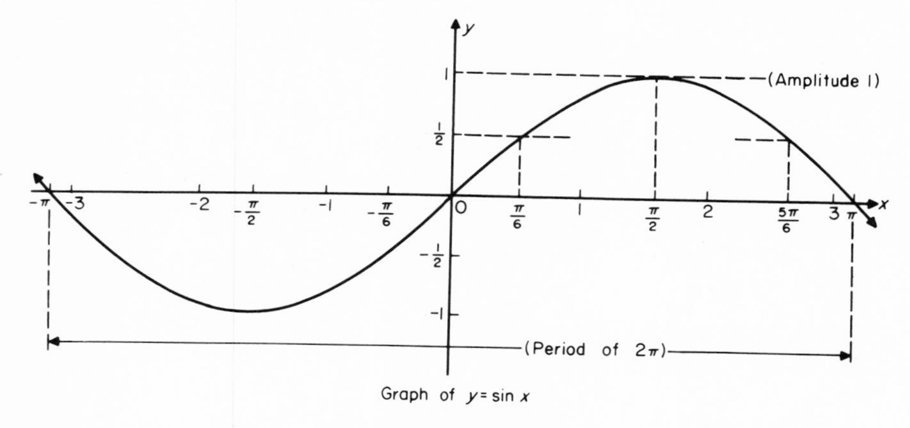

Figure 6.25

Since

$$\sin x = \sin (x + 2n\pi),$$

the graph will repeat itself at intervals of length 2π. The length of the interval in which the function does one complete *cycle* is called the *period* of the function. The *amplitude* of the "sine curve" is 1, the *amplitude* being the maximum value of $\sin x$ in a cycle. The graph is symmetric to the origin, but not symmetric to either axis. (The values of $\sin x$ are taken in reference to rotations in radians.)

[NOTE: The trigonometric functions, such as $y = \sin x$, can be considered aside from the defining notion of rotations. After all, the numbers x for which $\sin x$ is defined is the set of real numbers, and the values of $\sin x$ are real numbers. In the material to follow, reference to rotations is made only when needed.]

The graph of

$$y = a \sin bx$$

will vary in amplitude as different values for a are chosen. Since

$$-1 \leq \sin bx \leq 1,$$

the maximum of $a \sin bx$ will be $|a|$.

Since the period of the sine function is 2π, a change of 2π in bx is needed for a complete cycle. Therefore,

$$bx = 2\pi,$$

and

$$x = \frac{2\pi}{b}.$$

The period of

$$y = a \sin bx$$

is then $2\pi/|b|$. Graphs of these equations are called *sine curves*.

EXAMPLE 6.26 Find the amplitude and period of $y = 3 \sin (x/2)$. Graph (see Figure 6.26).

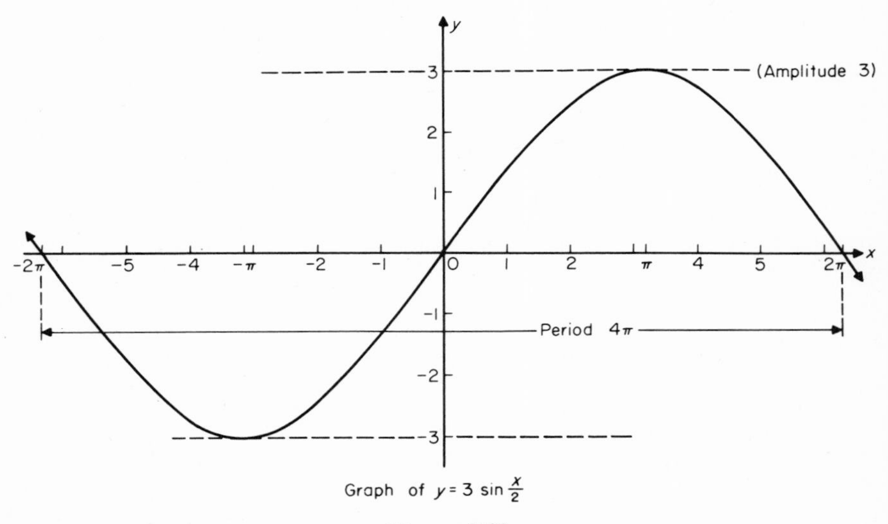

Figure 6.26

The amplitude is 3. The period is $\frac{2\pi}{\frac{1}{2}} = 4\pi$.

The graph of

$$y = \cos x \qquad \text{(Figure 6.27)}$$

shows the amplitude to be 1 and the period 2π. Since

$$\cos x = \cos(-x)$$

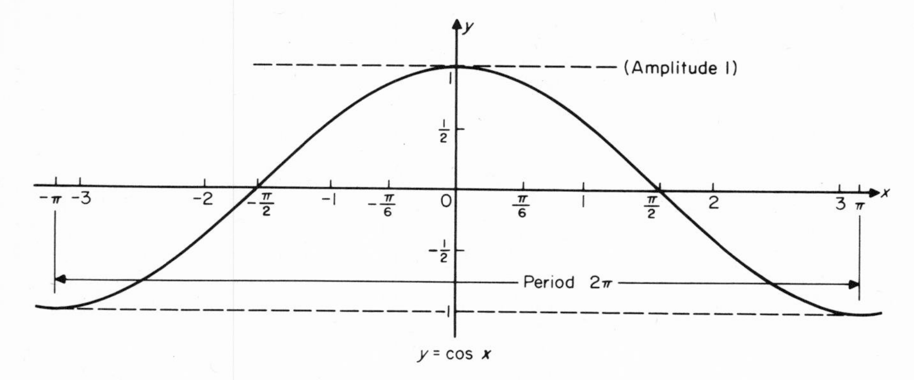

Figure 6.27

for each x, the curve is symmetric with respect to the y-axis.

When the graphs of

$$y = \sin x \quad \text{and} \quad y = \cos x$$

are superimposed, it is seen that they are similar in shape but "out of phase" by $\pi/2$ (see Figure 6.28). This is verified by the equations

$$\cos x = \sin\left(x + \frac{\pi}{2}\right)$$

$$\sin x = \cos\left(x - \frac{\pi}{2}\right).$$

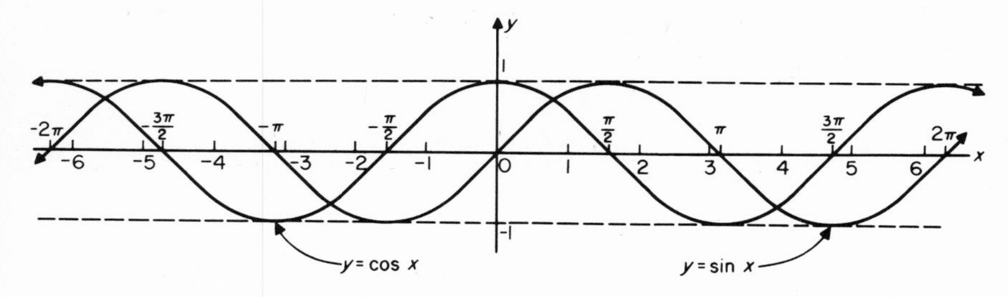

Figure 6.28

The graph of

$$y = \sin(x + k), \qquad k \geq 0.$$

is the "sine curve" moved or *translated* a distance k to the *left*. Notice that the period and the amplitude are unaffected by such a translation.

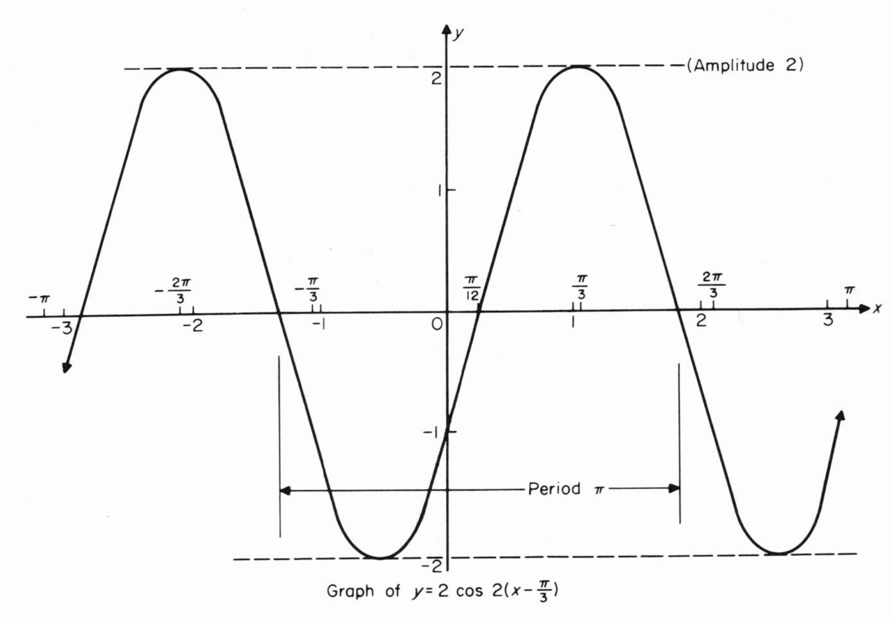

Graph of $y = 2\cos 2(x - \frac{\pi}{3})$

Figure 6.29

EXAMPLE 6.27 Find the period and amplitude of the given function. Graph (see Figure 6.29).

$$y = 2 \cos 2\left(x - \frac{\pi}{3}\right).$$

The amplitude is 2. The period is π. (The period is obtained by solving $2x = 2\pi$ for x). The graph is the graph of $y = 2 \cos 2x$ translated $\pi/3$ to the *right*.

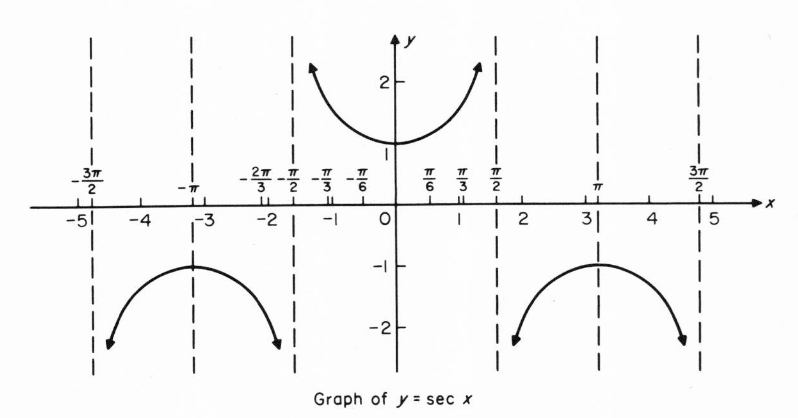

Graph of $y = \sec x$

Figure 6.30

Graphs of other trigonometric functions are found in the examples and exercises to follow.

EXAMPLE 6.28 Graph $y = \sec x$ on a rectangular coordinate graph. Recalling that $\sec x = 1/(\cos x)$, the graph is given in Figure 6.30.

EXERCISE SET 6.8

Sketch the rectangular coordinate graph of each of the following equations. Discuss the symmetry of each graph, and find its period and amplitude.

1. $y = 2 \cos x$.
2. $y = \sin 3x$.
3. $y = \cos (x/2)$.
4. $y = -2 \sin x$.
5. $y = \sin (x + \pi/4)$.
6. $y = 3 \cos (x - \pi/3)$.
7. $y = \sin 2(x - 1)$.
8. $y = 4 \cos 4x$.

Sketch the rectangular coordinate graph of each of the following.

9. $y = \tan x$.
10. $y = \cot x$.
11. $y = \sec x$.
12. $y = \tan 2x$.
13. $y = \cot (x/2)$.
14. $y = \csc (x - \pi)$.
15. $y = \sec (x + \pi)$.
16. $y = -\tan (-x)$.

6.13 Pythagorean Identities

Several of the relations between $\sin x$, $\cos x$, $\tan x$, and so forth have been given previously as definitions. For example,

$$\tan x = \frac{\sin x}{\cos x},$$

$$\sec x = \frac{1}{\cos x},$$

$$\csc x = \frac{1}{\sin x}.$$

These equations are true for each value of x for which the relations are defined. All cases where the denominator is zero are eliminated. Since the equations are universally true, save for the exceptions, they are called *trigonometric identities*. Many other fundamental identities can be derived using the Pythagorean theorem; these are called *Pythagorean identities*.

The basic Pythagorean identity is

$$(\sin x)^2 + (\cos x)^2 = 1$$

(see Figure 6.31). To avoid the use of parentheses, "$(\sin x)^2$" is written "$\sin^2 x$," and so forth. Using this notation, the above identity becomes

$$\sin^2 x + \cos^2 x = 1.$$

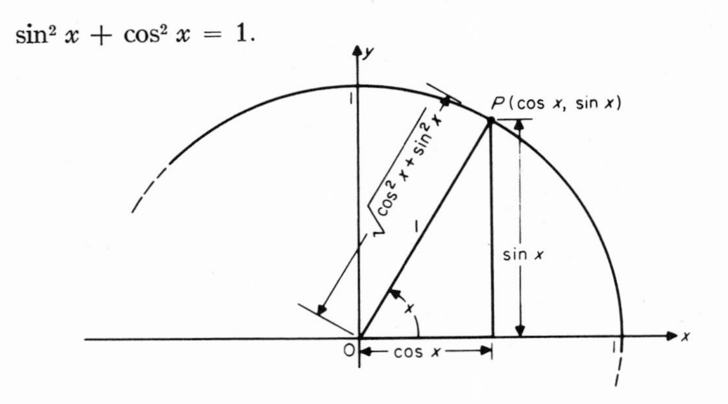

Figure 6.31

Two other identities follow directly. Dividing through by $\cos^2 x$,

$$\frac{\sin^2 x}{\cos^2 x} + \frac{\cos^2 x}{\cos^2 x} = \frac{1}{\cos^2 x} \qquad (\cos x \neq 0)$$

or

$$\tan^2 x + 1 = \sec^2 x \qquad \left(\cos x \neq 0 \text{ or } x \neq \left(\frac{\pi}{2} + n\pi\right), n \in I\right)$$

(see Figure 6.32).

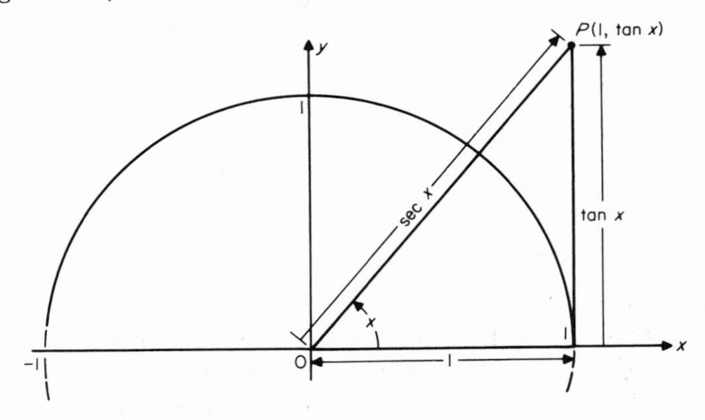

Figure 6.32

Likewise,

$$\frac{\sin^2 x}{\sin^2 x} + \frac{\cos^2 x}{\sin^2 x} = \frac{1}{\sin^2 x} \qquad (\sin x \neq 0),$$

which simplifies to

$$1 + \cot^2 x = \csc^2 x \qquad (\sin x \neq 0 \text{ or } x \neq n\pi,\ n \in I)$$

(see Figure 6.33).

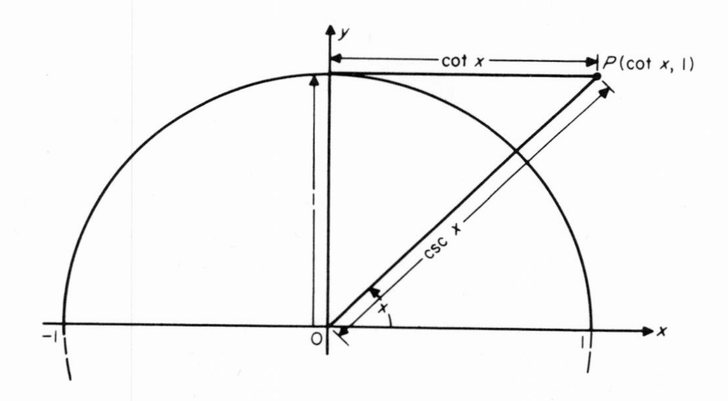

Figure 6.33

Using the Pythagorean identities along with the definitions of the trigonometric functions, sin x, cos x, and so forth can each be expressed in terms of any of the others. For example

$$\cos x = \sqrt{1 - \sin^2 x},$$

for x a measure of a rotation ending in Quadrant I or IV;

$$\cos x = -\sqrt{1 - \sin^2 x},$$

for x a measure of a rotation ending in Quadrant II or III.

Unfortunately, there is no simple way to avoid writing two equations. Sometimes these two identities are written

$$\cos x = \pm\sqrt{1 - \sin^2 x},$$

but care must be used in choosing the "+" or the "−" according to the quadrant in which the rotation of measure x ends. This identity can also be written

$$|\cos x| = \sqrt{1 - \sin^2 x},$$

which holds for all real numbers x.

This is a derivation of $\tan x$ in terms of $\sin x$:

$$\tan x = \frac{\sin x}{\cos x} = \frac{\sin x}{\sqrt{1 - \sin^2 x}},$$

for x a measure of a rotation ending in Quadrant I or IV.

$$\tan x = \frac{\sin x}{\cos x} = \frac{\sin x}{-\sqrt{1 - \sin^2 x}},$$

for x a measure of a rotation ending in Quadrant II or III.

Similarly, one identity true for all x for which $\tan x$ is defined is

$$|\tan x| = \frac{\sin x}{\sqrt{1 - \sin^2 x}}.$$

All of the functions, $\cot x$, $\sec x$, and $\csc x$, can be expressed in terms of $\sin x$.

Expressions such as

$$\sin^2 x - \frac{1}{\sec^2 x}$$

can be simplified or expressed in terms of other relations by use of the identities. The steps verifying the identity

$$\sin^2 x - \frac{1}{\sec^2 x} = 1 - 2\cos^2 x$$

are

$$\begin{aligned} \sin^2 x - \frac{1}{\sec^2 x} &= \sin^2 x - \cos^2 x \\ &= (\sin^2 x + \cos^2 x) - 2\cos^2 x \\ &= 1 - 2\cos^2 x. \end{aligned}$$

EXAMPLE 6.29 Express sec x in terms of sin x, $0 \leq x < \pi/2$.

$$\sec x = \frac{1}{\cos x} = \frac{1}{\sqrt{1 - \sin^2 x}}.$$

EXAMPLE 6.30 Find the value of tan x and sec x if $\sin x = \frac{1}{4}$ $(0 \leq x \leq \pi/2)$.

$$\tan x = \frac{\sin x}{\cos x} = \frac{\sin x}{\sqrt{1 - \sin^2 x}} = \frac{\frac{1}{4}}{\sqrt{1 - \frac{1}{16}}} = \frac{\sqrt{15}}{15},$$

$$\sec x = \frac{1}{\cos x} = \frac{1}{\sqrt{1 - \sin^2 x}} = \frac{1}{\sqrt{1 - \frac{1}{16}}} = \frac{4\sqrt{15}}{15}.$$

EXAMPLE 6.31 Verify: $\cos x\ (\tan x + \sec x) = 1 + \sin x$,

$x \neq (2n - 1)\dfrac{\pi}{2}$, $n \in I$.

$$\begin{aligned}(\cos x)\ (\tan x + \sec x) &= (\cos x)\left(\frac{\sin x}{\cos x} + \frac{1}{\cos x}\right) \\ &= (\sin x) + 1 \\ &= 1 + \sin x.\end{aligned}$$

EXERCISE SET 6.9

1. If $\sin x = \frac{3}{5}$, find cos x, tan x, cot x, sec x, and csc x by using fundamental identities $(0 \leq x \leq \pi/2)$.
2. If $\tan x = \frac{1}{3}$, find sin x, cos x, cot x, sec x, and csc x $(0 \leq x \leq \pi/2)$.
3. If $\sec x = 4$, find sin x, cos x, and tan x $(0 \leq x \leq \pi/2)$.
4. If $\cos x = 0.312$, find tan x, approximately $(0 \leq x \leq \pi/2)$.
5. Express sin x in terms of cos x.
6. Express sec x in terms of sin x (indicate any restriction on x).
7. Express $\dfrac{(\tan x) + 1}{\tan x}$ in terms of sin x (indicate any restriction on x).
8. Express $\dfrac{\sin x + 2 \tan x}{\sec x}$ in terms of cos x (indicate any restriction on x).

9. Express $\dfrac{\tan x + 1}{\tan x - 1}$ in terms of $\sin x$ $(0 \leq x < \pi/2)$.

10. Express $\dfrac{\sec^2 x + 1}{\cot x}$ in terms of $\tan x$ $(0 < x < \pi/2)$.

11. Find $\sin x$ if $\cos x = \frac{1}{3}$, $\tan x < 0$.
12. Find $\cos x$ if $\cot x = -\frac{2}{7}$, $\sin x < 0$.
13. Find $\tan x$ if $\sin x = \frac{1}{2}$, $\cos x < 0$.
14. Find $\csc y$ if $\cos y = \frac{1}{4}$, $\tan y < 0$.
15. Find $\sec z$ if $\csc z = -5$, $\cot z < 0$.
16. Find $\tan \theta$ if $\cot \theta = -2$, $\sin \theta < 0$.

Verify the following identities. In Exercises 17–21, indicate restrictions on the variables involved.

17. $\sin^2 x + 2 \cos^2 x = 1 + \cos^2 x$.

18. $\sin^2 x + \dfrac{1}{\sec^2 x} = 1$.

19. $\tan^2 x - \sec^2 x = -1$.

20. $\cos y \csc y = \cot y$.

21. $\cot \theta + \tan \theta = \sec \theta \csc \theta$.

22. $\csc^2 \phi \tan^2 \phi - 1 = \tan^2 \phi$.

23. $\tan \theta = \dfrac{\sec \theta}{\csc \theta}$.

24. $\dfrac{1 - \sin^2 x}{\sin x} = \dfrac{\cos x}{\tan x}$.

25. $\dfrac{-\tan^2 x}{1 + \cot^2 x} = \dfrac{1 - \sec^2 x}{\csc^2 x}$

26. $(1 + \sin x)(\sec x - \tan x) = \cos x$.

27. $\tan^2 x \sin^2 x - \cos^2 x = \sec^2 x - 2$.

28. $\sin^2 x + \tan^2 x = \sec^4 x - \tan^4 x$.

29. $\dfrac{\tan x}{\sec x - \cos x} = \csc x$.

30. $\dfrac{\sin z + \cot z}{\cos z} = \tan z + \csc z$.

31. $\dfrac{\sin y}{1 + \cos y} + \dfrac{1 + \cos y}{\sin y} = 2 \csc y$.

32. $\dfrac{\cot \phi}{\csc \phi - 1} = \dfrac{\csc \phi + 1}{\cot \phi}.$

33. $\dfrac{(\tan x) - 1}{1 - \cot x} = \tan x.$

34. $(1 + \tan x)(1 - \tan x) = 2 - \sec^2 x.$

35. $\tan^4 y + \sec^4 y = 2 \tan^4 y + 2 \tan^2 y + 1.$

36. $2 \cos A + 3 \sin A \cot A = 5 \sin A \cot A.$

37. $2 \cot x = \dfrac{1}{(\sec x) - 1} - \dfrac{1}{(\sec x) + 1}.$

38. $\dfrac{\sec x}{\csc x} = \dfrac{1 + \tan x}{1 + \cot x}.$

39. $\dfrac{\cot x + \csc y}{\tan y + \tan x \sec y} = \cot x \cot y.$

40. $(\sin x \cos y)^2 + (\sin x \sin y)^2 = 1 - \cos^2 x.$

41. $\dfrac{\cot x \cot y}{1 + \cot y} = \dfrac{\cos x \cos y}{\sin x \sin y + \sin x \cos y}.$

42. $\dfrac{\sin x + \sin y}{\csc x + \csc y} = \sin x \sin y.$

6.14 Addition Identities

The identity

$$\cos (x - y) = \cos x \cos y + \sin x \sin y,$$

which holds for all values of x and y, plays a central role in trigonometry. Many of the identities of the previous sections, as well as a number as yet undiscussed in this text, can be derived from this identity. This identity can be derived from the definitions that we have for sine and cosine and the notion of distance.

Referring to Figure 6.34,

$$d[A, B] = d[A', B'].$$

Therefore,

$$\sqrt{[\cos (x - y) - 1]^2 + [\sin (x - y)]^2}$$
$$= \sqrt{[\cos x - \cos y]^2 + [\sin x - \sin y]^2}.$$

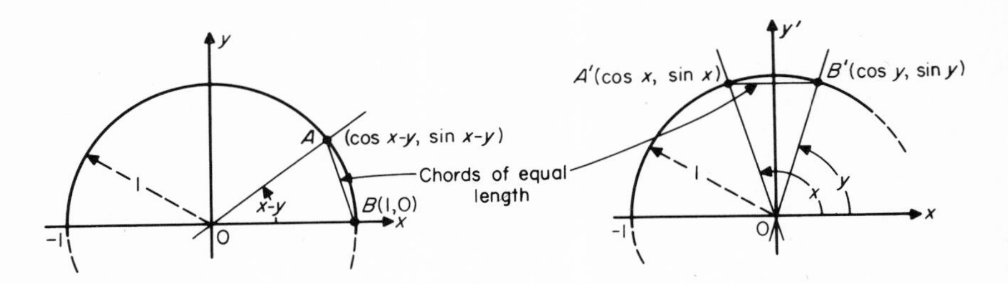

Figure 6.34

Squaring both sides and simplifying,

$$\cos^2 (x - y) - 2 \cos (x - y) + 1 + \sin^2 (x - y)$$
$$= \cos^2 x - 2 \cos x \cos y + \cos^2 y + \sin^2 x - 2 \sin x \sin y + \sin^2 y.$$

Now, $\cos^2 (x - y) + \sin^2 (x - y) = 1$, for each $x - y$, so the above equation is equivalent to

$$1 - 2 \cos (x - y) + 1 = 1 - 2 \cos x \cos y + 1 - 2 \sin x \sin y,$$

which reduces to

$$\cos (x - y) = \cos x \cos y + \sin x \sin y.$$

Related identities can be derived from this basic identity as follows:

$$\cos (x + y) = \cos (x - (-y)) = \cos x \cos (-y) + \sin x \sin (-y)$$
$$= \cos x \cos y - \sin x \sin y,$$

$$\sin (x + y) = \cos \left(\frac{\pi}{2} - (x + y)\right) = \cos \left(\left(\frac{\pi}{2} - x\right) - y\right)$$
$$= \cos \left(\frac{\pi}{2} - x\right) \cos y + \sin \left(\frac{\pi}{2} - x\right) \sin y$$
$$= \sin x \cos y + \cos x \sin y,$$

$$\sin (x - y) = \sin (x + (-y)) = \sin x \cos (-y) + \cos x \sin (-y)$$
$$= \sin x \cos y - \cos x \sin y,$$

$$\tan(x + y) = \frac{\sin(x + y)}{\cos(x + y} = \frac{\sin x \cos y + \cos x \sin y}{\cos x \cos y - \sin x \sin y}$$

$$= \left\{ \frac{\dfrac{\sin x \cos y}{\cos x \cos y} + \dfrac{\cos x \sin y}{\cos x \cos y}}{\dfrac{\cos x \cos y}{\cos x \cos y} - \dfrac{\sin x \sin y}{\cos x \cos y}} \right.$$

$$= \frac{\tan x + \tan y}{1 - \tan x \tan y},$$

for all x and y for which both sides are defined.

With these identities many additional exact values of $\sin x$, $\cos x$, and $\tan x$ can be obtained as illustrated in the examples below.

EXAMPLE 6.32 Find $\sin(5\pi/12)$, exactly.

$$\sin\frac{5\pi}{12} = \sin\left(\frac{\pi}{6} + \frac{\pi}{4}\right) = \sin\frac{\pi}{6}\cos\frac{\pi}{4} + \cos\frac{\pi}{6}\sin\frac{\pi}{4}$$

$$= \frac{1}{2}\cdot\frac{\sqrt{2}}{2} + \frac{\sqrt{3}}{2}\cdot\frac{\sqrt{2}}{2}$$

$$= \frac{\sqrt{2} + \sqrt{6}}{4}.$$

EXAMPLE 6.33 Find $\cos 15°$, exactly.

$$\cos 15° = \cos\frac{\pi}{12} = \cos\left(\frac{\pi}{3} - \frac{\pi}{4}\right) = \cos\frac{\pi}{3}\cos\frac{\pi}{4} + \sin\frac{\pi}{3}\sin\frac{\pi}{4}$$

$$= \frac{1}{2}\cdot\frac{\sqrt{2}}{2} + \frac{\sqrt{3}}{2}\cdot\frac{\sqrt{2}}{2}$$

$$= \frac{\sqrt{2} + \sqrt{6}}{4}.$$

$\cos 15°$ can also be obtained by using

$$\cos\frac{\pi}{12} = \sin\left(\frac{\pi}{2} - \frac{\pi}{12}\right)$$

and the result of Example 6.32.

Important special cases called the *double-angle identities* follow immediately from the addition identities.

$$\sin 2x = \sin (x + x) = \sin x \cos x + \cos x \sin x$$
$$= 2 \sin x \cos x,$$

$$\cos 2x = \cos (x + x) = \cos x \cos x - \sin x \sin x$$
$$= \cos^2 x - \sin^2 x,$$

$$\tan 2x = \tan (x + x) = \frac{\tan x + \tan x}{1 - \tan x \tan x}$$
$$= \frac{2 \tan x}{1 - \tan^2 x}.$$

EXERCISE SET 6.10

Using the identities of this section, simplify each of the following.

1. $\sin (\theta - \pi/2)$.
2. $\sin (\theta + \pi/2)$.
3. $\cos (\theta - \pi/2)$.
4. $\tan (\theta - \pi)$.
5. $\sin (\theta - \pi/6)$.
6. $\cos (\theta + \pi/3)$.
7. $\tan (\theta - \pi/4)$.
8. $\sin (\theta + \pi/6)$.

Derive formulas for each of the following using trigonometric functions of x or y singly and not of multiples, etc., of x or y.

9. $\tan (x - y)$.
10. $\cot (x + y)$.
11. $\cot (x - y)$.
12. $\sin 3x$.
13. $\cos 4x$.
14. $\cot 2x$.

Find the exact value for each of the following.

15. $\sin (\pi/3 + \pi/4)$.
16. $\cos (\pi/4 - \pi/6)$.
17. $\cos (7\pi/12)$.
18. $\sin (\pi/12)$.
19. $\sin (5\pi/4 - \pi/3)$.
20. $\cos 75°$.
21. $\tan (\pi/12)$.
22. $\tan 195°$.

Suppose $\sin x = \frac{1}{3}$, $\cos y = \frac{1}{5}$, where $0 \leq x \leq \pi/2$, $0 \leq y \leq \pi/2$. Find the following.

23. $\cos x$.
24. $\sin y$.
25. $\sin (x + y)$.
26. $\cos (x + y)$.
27. $\tan (x + y)$.
28. $\sin 2x$.
29. $\sin 2y$.
30. $\cos 2x$.
31. $\tan 2x$.
32. $\sin 3x$.

Verify the following identities:

33. $\cos (3\pi/2 + \phi) = \sin \phi$.
34. $\sin (x - y) \cos y + \cos (x - y) \sin y = \sin x$.
35. $\cos (x + y) \cos y + \sin (x + y) \sin y = \cos x$.
36. $\sin 4x \cos 3x + \cos 4x \sin 3x = \sin 7x$.
37. $(1 - \cos 2x)/(\sin 2x) = \tan x$.
38. $\cos 3x = 4 \cos^3 x - 3 \cos x$.
39. $\sin 3y = 3 \sin y - 4 \sin^2 y$.
40. $(2 \sin^2 2x - 1)^2 = 1 - \sin^2 4x$.

Solve each equation for x, where $0 \leq x \leq 2\pi$. (*Hint*: By the use of identities, change each equation to one involving functions of x alone.)

41. $\cot x (2 - \sec 2x) = 0$.
42. $\cos 2x = 3 \sin x + 2$.
43. $\cos 2x = \cos x$.
44. $3 \cos x - \cos 2x = 2$.

6.15 Half-angle Identities

The identities

$$\cos 2x = 2 \cos^2 x - 1$$

and

$$\cos 2x = 1 - 2 \sin^2 x$$

are obtained from the identities

$$\cos 2x = \cos^2 x - \sin^2 x$$

and

$$\sin^2 x + \cos^2 x = 1.$$

The first identity can be solved for $\cos^2 x$ to obtain

$$\cos^2 x = \frac{1 + \cos 2x}{2}.$$

Since $-1 \leq \cos 2x \leq 1$ for each x, $(1 + \cos 2x)/2$ can never be negative. On the other hand, $\cos x$ can be negative. Taking the square root of each side of the last equation gives us, therefore,

$$|\cos x| = \sqrt{\frac{1 + \cos 2x}{2}}.$$

The usual statement of the half-angle identity is obtained by substituting θ for $2x$ throughout.

$$\left|\cos \frac{\theta}{2}\right| = \sqrt{\frac{1 + \cos \theta}{2}}.$$

To find $\cos(\theta/2)$ from this identity, one need only determine whether $\cos(\theta/2) < 0$ or $\cos(\theta/2) \geq 0$, and this can be determined if it is known what quadrant $\theta/2$ ends in. Therefore, if there is an integer n such that

$$\frac{\theta}{2} \in \left](4n - 1)\frac{\pi}{2}, (4n + 1)\frac{\pi}{2}\right[,$$

then $\cos(\theta/2) > 0$ (since $\theta/2$ is of a rotation in Quadrant I or Quadrant IV).

If

$$\frac{\theta}{2} \in \left](4n + 1)\frac{\pi}{2}, (4n + 3)\frac{\pi}{2}\right[,$$

then $\cos(\theta/2) < 0$ (since $\theta/2$ is of a rotation in Quadrant II or Quadrant III). If $\theta/2$ is an odd multiple of $\pi/2$ then $\cos(\theta/2) = 0$.

Similarly, from

$$\cos 2x = 1 - 2\sin^2 x$$

the half-angle identity for sine can be derived (see Exercise 17, Exercise Set 6.11).

$$\left|\sin\frac{\theta}{2}\right| = \sqrt{\frac{1-\cos\theta}{2}}.$$

Here again, sin $(\theta/2)$ can be found by determining what quadrant $\theta/2$ is in and choosing the sign appropriately.

EXAMPLE 6.34 Find sin 15° exactly.

$$\begin{aligned}|\sin 15^\circ| &= |\sin(\tfrac{30}{2})^\circ| \\ &= \sqrt{\frac{1-\cos 30^\circ}{2}} \\ &= \sqrt{\frac{1-\sqrt{3}/2}{2}} \\ &= \tfrac{1}{2}\sqrt{2-\sqrt{3}}.\end{aligned}$$

Since 15° is a rotation into Quadrant I, sin 15° is positive. Therefore,

$$\sin 15^\circ = \tfrac{1}{2}\sqrt{2-\sqrt{3}}.$$

EXAMPLE 6.35 Find cos 105°.

$$\begin{aligned}|\cos 105^\circ| &= |\cos(\tfrac{210}{2})^\circ| \\ &= \sqrt{\frac{1+\cos 210^\circ}{2}} \\ &= \sqrt{\frac{1-\sqrt{3}/2}{2}} \\ &= \tfrac{1}{2}\sqrt{2-\sqrt{3}}.\end{aligned}$$

Since a rotation of 105° from the initial axis ends in Quadrant II, cos 105° is negative. Therefore,

$$\cos 105^\circ = -\tfrac{1}{2}\sqrt{2-\sqrt{3}}.$$

The identity for tan $(\theta/2)$ follows from the other half-angle identities.

$$\left|\tan\frac{x}{2}\right| = \left|\frac{\sin x/2}{\cos x/2}\right| = \frac{\sqrt{\tfrac{1}{2}(1-\cos x)}}{\sqrt{\tfrac{1}{2}(1+\cos x)}}.$$

Therefore,

$$\left|\tan \frac{x}{2}\right| = \sqrt{\frac{1 - \cos x}{1 + \cos x}}.$$

An improvement of this identity can be obtained as follows.

$$\tan \frac{x}{2} = \frac{\sin (x/2)}{\cos (x/2)}$$

$$= \frac{2 \sin^2 (x/2)}{2 \sin (x/2) \cos (x/2)}$$

$$= \frac{1 + \sin^2 (x/2) - \cos^2 (x/2)}{\sin x}$$

$$= \frac{1 - \cos x}{\sin x}.$$

The derived identity is

$$\tan \frac{x}{2} = \frac{1 - \cos x}{\sin x}.$$

Another similar identity is

$$\tan \frac{x}{2} = \frac{\sin x}{1 + \cos x}.$$

EXAMPLE 6.36 Find $\tan (25\pi/24)$.

$$\tan \frac{25\pi}{24} = \tan \frac{1}{2}\left(\frac{25\pi}{12}\right) = \frac{1 - \cos (25\pi/12)}{\sin (25\pi/12)}.$$

But

$$\cos \frac{25\pi}{12} = \cos \frac{1}{2}\left(\frac{25\pi}{6}\right) = \sqrt{\frac{1 + \cos (25\pi)/6}{2}}$$

$$= \sqrt{\frac{1 + \sqrt{3}/2}{2}} = \tfrac{1}{2}\sqrt{2 + \sqrt{3}}.$$

And

$$\sin\frac{25\pi}{12} = \sin\frac{1}{2}\left(\frac{25\pi}{6}\right)$$

$$= \sqrt{\frac{1 - \cos(25\pi)/6}{2}}$$

$$= \tfrac{1}{2}\sqrt{2 - \sqrt{3}}.$$

Therefore,

$$\tan\frac{25\pi}{24} = \frac{1 - \frac{1}{2}\sqrt{2 + \sqrt{3}}}{\frac{1}{2}\sqrt{2 - \sqrt{3}}}$$

$$= \frac{2 - \sqrt{2 + \sqrt{3}}}{\sqrt{2 - \sqrt{3}}}.$$

(Can you find an expression equivalent to this one that does not have a radical in the denominator?)

EXERCISE SET 6.11

Find the exact value of each of the following (Exercises 1–16):

1. $\sin(\pi/12)$.
2. $\cos(7\pi/8)$.
3. $\tan(5\pi/12)$.
4. $\sin(\pi/8)$.
5. $\cos(7\pi/12)$.
6. $\tan(9\pi/8)$.
7. $\cot(\pi/12)$.
8. $\sin(\pi/16)$.
9. $\tan(\pi/12)$.
10. $\cos(19\pi/24)$.
11. $\sin 105°$.
12. $\cos -105°$.
13. $\tan 22.5°$.
14. $\tan 7.5°$.
15. $\sec 75°$.
16. $\csc -195°$.
17. Derive the identity

$$\left|\sin\frac{x}{2}\right| = \sqrt{\frac{1 - \cos x}{2}}.$$

Give conditions on x so that $\sin(x/2)$ is positive.

18. Show that if $(\theta/2)$ is a measure of a rotation ending in Quadrant IV, then θ is a measure of a rotation ending in Quadrant III or in Quadrant IV.

19. Show that if $(\theta/2)$ is a measure of a rotation ending in Quadrant III, then θ is a measure of a rotation ending in Quadrant I or in Quadrant II.

20. Verify the identities

$$\cos 2x = 2\cos^2 x - 1 \quad \text{and} \quad \cos 2x = 1 - 2\sin^2 x.$$

Rewrite each expression using only functions of x and not of multiples of x.

21. $\sin^2 \frac{1}{2}x - \cos x$.

22. $\sin 2x + \cos 2x$.

23. $\dfrac{\sin 2x}{\sin x}$.

24. $\cos x \tan \frac{1}{2}x$.

25. $\dfrac{\cos 2x}{\cos x - \sin x}$.

26. $\dfrac{\tan \frac{1}{2}x}{\sin x}$.

27. $\csc 2x$.

28. $\csc \frac{1}{2}x$.

29. $\sec \frac{1}{2}x$.

30. $\cot 2x \cot \frac{1}{2}x$.

Verify the following identities:

31. $\cot x + \tan \dfrac{x}{2} = \csc x$.

32. $(1 + \cos y)\cos x + \sin y \sin x = 2\cos\dfrac{y}{2}\cos\left(x - \dfrac{y}{2}\right)$.

33. $\dfrac{\cos (x/2) + \sin (x/2)}{\cos (x/2) - \sin (x/2)} = \sec x + \tan x$.

34. $\dfrac{1 + \sin^2 (x/2)}{1 + \cos^2 (x/2)} = \dfrac{3 - \cos x}{3 + \cos x}$.

The following identities are used to change products to sums, and vice versa. Verify each identity.

35. $\sin x \cos y = \frac{1}{2}(\sin (x + y) + \sin (x - y))$.

36. $\cos x \sin y = \frac{1}{2}(\sin (x + y) - \sin(x - y))$.

37. $\sin x \sin y = \frac{1}{2}(\cos (x - y) - \cos (x + y))$.
38. $\cos x \cos y = \frac{1}{2}(\cos (x + y) + \cos (x - y))$.

6.16 Law of Sines and Law of Cosines

The solution of right triangles was considered in section 6.9. For the solution of an arbitrary triangle, the *law of sines* and the *law of cosines* may be employed. These laws involve the relations between the lengths of the sides and the measures of the angles of a triangle. The law of cosines is particularly important since it has many applications beyond that of solving triangles.

Suppose ABC is any triangle. Let a be the length of side BC, b be the length of side AC, and c be the length of side AB. ABC is placed with vertex A at the origin of a rectangular coordinate system with side AC along the positive x-axis. (See Figure 6.35.) Then it is placed similarly with A and C interchanged. In each position, the second coordinate (y-value) of B is the same. That is,

$$c \sin A = a \sin C,$$

$$\frac{\sin A}{a} = \frac{\sin C}{c}.$$

Following the same procedure with B and C gives the equation

$$\frac{\sin A}{a} = \frac{\sin B}{b}.$$

The law of sines follows:

$$\frac{\sin A}{a} = \frac{\sin B}{b} = \frac{\sin C}{c}.$$

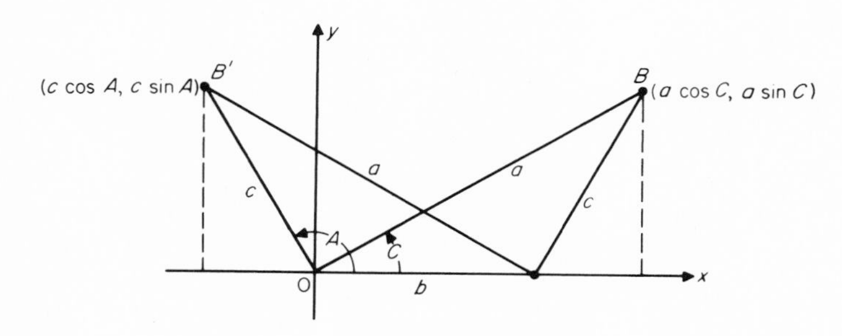

Figure 6.35

EXAMPLE 6.37 Given triangle ABC, where $A = 37°$, $a = 48$, and $b = 70$, find angles B and C.
Using the law of sines,

$$\frac{\sin 37°}{48} = \frac{\sin B}{70},$$

$$\sin B = \frac{70\ (0.6018)}{48}$$

$$= 0.8776.$$

There are two possible values for B,

$$B = 61.4°$$

or

$$B' = 180° - 61.4° = 118.6°.$$

Therefore,

$$C = 180° - (37° + 61.4°)$$
$$= 81.6°$$

or

$$C' = 180° - (37° + 118.6°)$$
$$= 24.4°.$$

A sketch of the triangles showing the ambiguity of the answers is given in Figure 6.36.

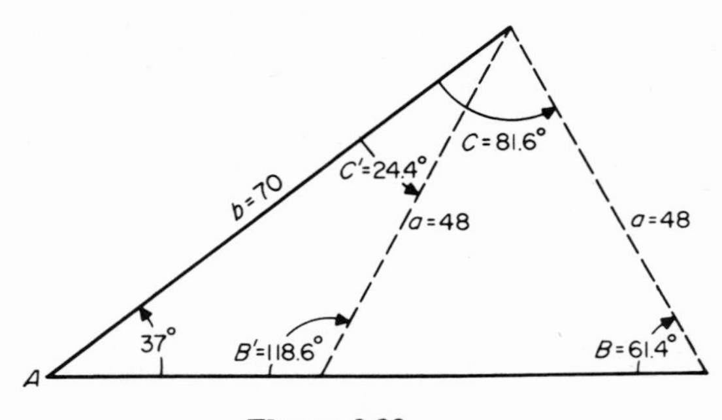

Figure 6.36

To verify the law of cosines the triangle ABC is placed as before with A at the origin and AC along the positive x-axis. The law of cosines is derived by means of the Pythagorean theorem.

$$(b - c \cos A)^2 + (c \sin A)^2 = a^2,$$

$$b^2 - 2bc \cos A + c^2 \cos^2 A + c^2 \cos^2 A = a^2,$$

$$b^2 - 2bc \cos A + c^2 = a^2.$$

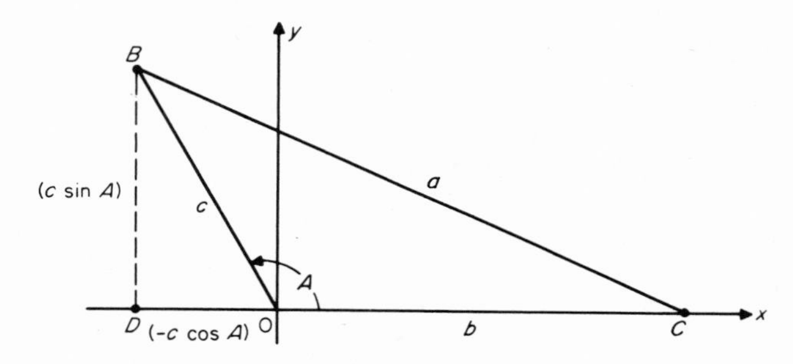

Figure 6.37

Therefore,

law of cosines: $\quad a^2 = b^2 + c^2 - 2bc \cos A.$

(Notice in the derivation that $b - c \cos A$ is the length of CD whether A is an acute or obtuse triangle.)

Interchanging the various angles yields the other forms of the law of cosines:

$$b^2 = a^2 + c^2 - 2ac \cos B,$$

$$c^2 = a^2 + b^2 - 2ab \cos C.$$

EXAMPLE 6.38 Given the triangle ABC, where $C = 23.4°$, $a = 4.21$ and $b = 2.57$, find c.
Using the law of cosines,

$$c^2 = (4.21)^2 + (2.57)^2 - 2(4.21)(2.57) \cos 23.4°,$$

$$c^2 = 4.48,$$

$$c = 2.1 \text{ (approximately)}.$$

EXERCISE SET 6.12

1. Verify the law of cosines using a figure where both A and C are acute angles.

Solve the following triangles, where A, B, C are measures of the angles and a, b, c are lengths of sides opposite the respective angles. (Solutions may not exist in some cases; in others, solutions may not be unique.)

2. $A = 46°$, $B = 84°$, $b = 3$.
3. $A = 27°$, $B = 47°$, $a = 7$.
4. $A = 32.5°$, $B = 44.6°$, $a = 12.4$.
5. $C = 27.2°$, $c = 3.41$, $b = 8.32$.
6. $B = 131°$, $a = 4.92$, $c = 1.78$.
7. $B = 75.3°$, $a = 9.6$, $b = 2.1$.
8. $a = 2.4$, $b = 3.3$, $C = 64°$.
9. $a = 11$, $c = 8.4$, $B = 60°$.
10. $a = 4$, $b = 5$, $c = 7$.
11. $a = 2.4$, $b = 3.3$, $c = 3$.
12. $a = 12.4$, $b = 18$, $c = 14$.
13. Prove that

$$\frac{a}{\sin A} = \frac{b}{\sin B} = \frac{c}{\sin C} = 2R,$$

where R is the radius of the circle circumscribing the traingle ABC.

14. The law of tangents for a triangle ABC is

$$\frac{a+b}{a-b} = \frac{\tan \frac{1}{2}(A+B)}{\tan \frac{1}{2}(A-B)}.$$

Prove this law, using a library reference if necessary.

Functions

CHAPTER SEVEN

7.1 Introduction

In mathematics as well as in each of the sciences, the concept of dependence is central. Expressions of dependence may take many forms—tables, graphs, and open sentences with two variables, to name a few.

Table 7.1, a table of squares for the first five counting numbers, illustrates a common way of describing dependence. The number a person looks for in the right-hand column depends on the number of which he wants to know the square (the number in the left-hand column).

TABLE 7.1

n	n^2
1	1
2	4
3	9
4	16
5	25

In the graph of Figure 7.1, for each value on the x-axis there is a single value on the y-axis determined by the graph in the way indicated. When viewed this way, each y-value depends on the x-value chosen.

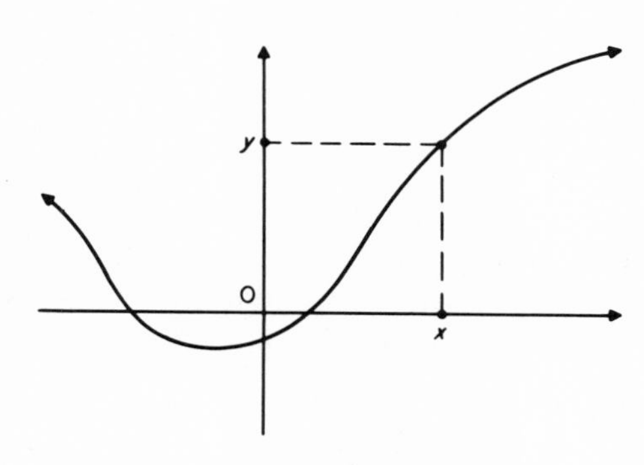

Figure 7.1

The open sentence $y = 3x$ expresses a dependence between x and y in the following way: if 2 is substituted for x, then 6 must be substituted for y to obtain a true sentence; if -4 is substituted for x, then -12 must be substituted for y for the resulting sentence to be true; each true substitution instance for y depends on the number substituted for x.

The dependence of y on values assigned to x expressed by the open sentence $y = 3x$ can also be expressed as a rule—namely, "multiply by 3."

Each of the examples given illustrates a method of showing a pairing of numbers in which the second number in each pair is the unique number that depends on the first number. That is, each example illustrates a way of describing a set of ordered pairs of numbers in which no two distinct ordered pairs have the same first component. Such sets of ordered pairs are called *functions*.

DEFINITION: A function is a set of ordered pairs no two of which have the same first component.

It is common to speak of tables, graphs, and open sentences such as those in the examples as *expressing a functional relation.*

The pairing given in Table 7.1 is the function

$$\{(1, 1), (2, 4), (3, 9), (4, 16), (5, 25)\};$$

the pairing of the graph of Figure 7.1 is the function

$$\{(x, y) : x \text{ and } y \text{ are coordinates of the points of the graph}\};$$

and the function determined by the open sentence, $y = 3x$, and also by the rule, "multiply by 3," is

$$\{(x, y) : y = 3x\}.$$

Each method of describing a function is useful, although it does not always give a complete description. A function with infinitely many pairs can be only partially represented by a table, and the graph of the function $\{(x, y) : 2y - 3x = 4\}$ can be only partially shown, as in Figure 7.2.

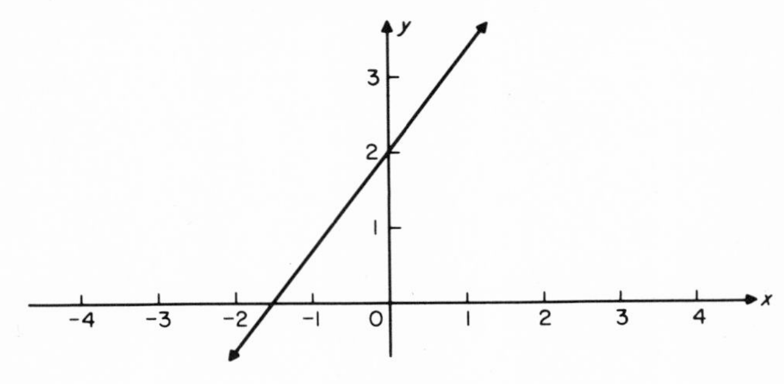

Figure 7.2

7.2 Graphs of Functions

Graphs of functions have a certain property which distinguishes them from the graphs of other sets of ordered pairs. Make a simple statement which distinguishes the graphs of Figure 7.3 from those in Figure 7.4.

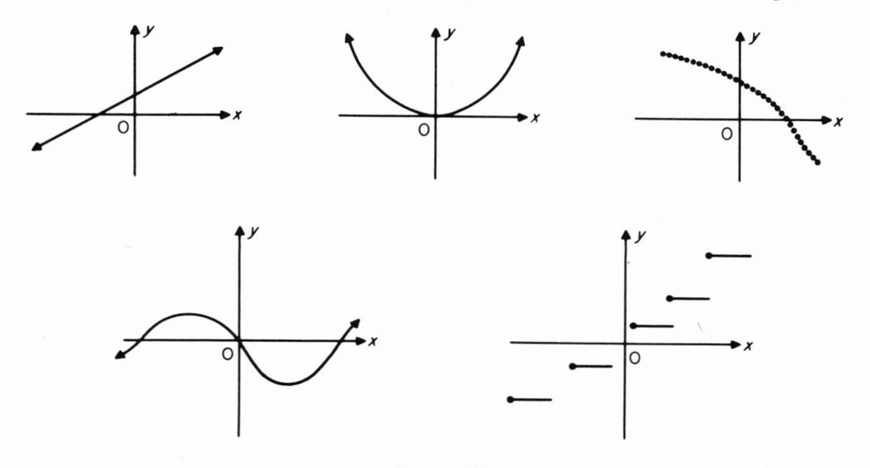

Figure 7.3

Each graph of Figure 7.3 has the property that its intersection with any vertical line cannot consist of more than one point. If the graph did meet some vertical line in two or more points, then two points of the graph would have the same first coordinate; the set of ordered pairs represented by the graph would then have two pairs with the same first component and thus would not be a function. All of the graphs of Figure 7.3 are graphs of functions.

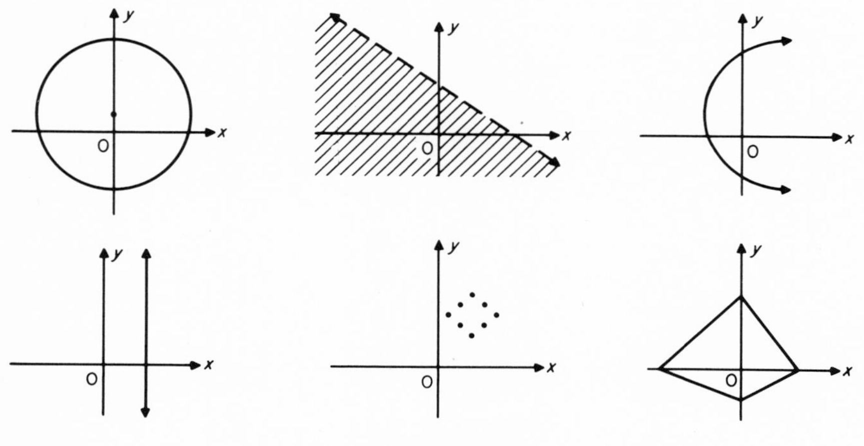

Figure 7.4

The graphs of Figure 7.4 do not pass this "vertical line test," and they are not graphs of functions. The vertical line test on the graph of a set of ordered pairs gives an alternate definition for a function.

DEFINITION: A function is a set of ordered pairs whose graph satisfies the vertical line test.

Given a set of ordered pairs which is a function, the set of all first components (x-values) of the pairs of the function is the *domain* of the function. The set of all second components (y-values) is the *range* of the function. The domain, then, is the extent in x of the graph; the range is the extent in y of the graph. If f denotes a function, its domain and range are denoted by D_f and R_f, respectively. The elements of the domain are referred to as *arguments* of the function, and the elements of the range are called *values* of the function. If $(a, b) \in f$, where f is a function, then b is the value of f at a.

EXAMPLE 7.1 Let f be the set $\{(x, y) : y = 2x - 5\}$. f is a function since f is a set of ordered pairs and its graph passes the vertical line test (see Figure 7.5). Both the domain D_f and the range R_f are the set of all real

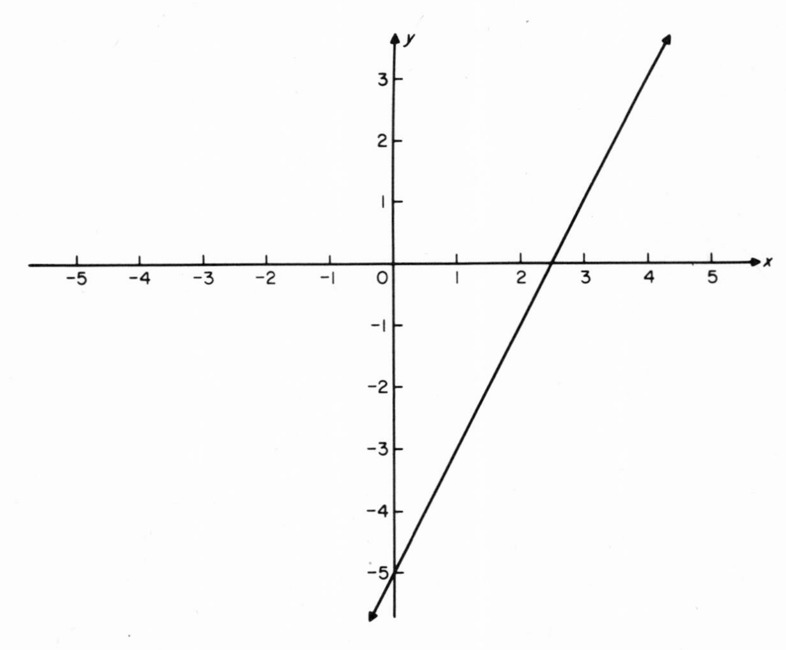

Figure 7.5

numbers. Analytically this follows from the two statements

For each x, $(x, 2x - 5) \in f$

and

For each y, there is an x such that $y = 2x - 5$.

Solving for x, $x = (y + 5)/2$, so for each y,

$$\left(\frac{y+5}{2}, y\right) \in f.$$

EXAMPLE 7.2 The set S, where $S = \{(x, y) : x^2 + y^2 = 1\}$, is not a function since, even though it is a set of ordered pairs, its graph does not pass the vertical line test. The vertical line $x = 0$ intersects the graph at the points $(0, 1)$ and $(0, -1)$ (see Figure 7.6).

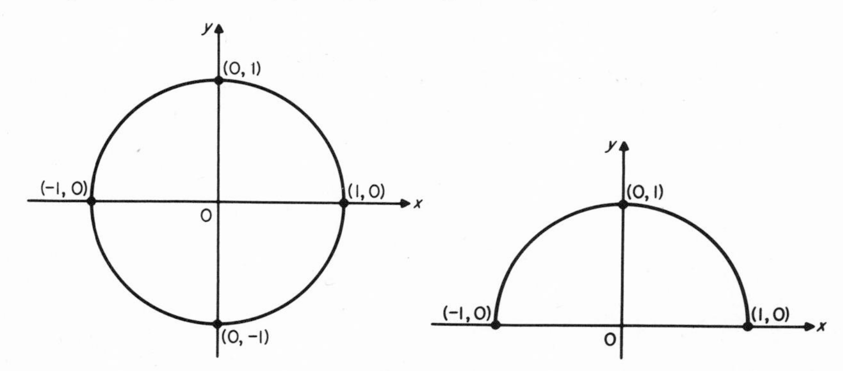

Figure 7.6 **Figure 7.7**

EXAMPLE 7.3 Let $g = \{(x, y) : x^2 + y^2 = 1 \text{ and } y \geq 0\}$. g is a function, as can be seen from its graph (Figure 7.7). The domain D_g is the interval $[-1, 1]$, and the range R_g is the interval $[0, 1]$. (Compare this with Example 7.2.) The value of g at 0 is 1.

EXAMPLE 7.4 Let $h = \{(x, y) : x = y^2\}$. Show that h is or is not a function.
Since $1^2 = (-1)^2 = 1$, both $(1, 1)$ and $(1, -1)$ are in h. Therefore, h has two ordered pairs with the same first component and is not a function.

EXAMPLE 7.5 Let $F = \{(x, y) : y = x^2\}$. Show that F is or is not a function.
Suppose that $(a, b) \in F$ and $(a, c) \in F$. Then $b = a^2$ and $c = a^2$. Therefore, $b = c$. So, $(a, b) = (a, c)$. That is, (a, b) and (a, c) are not distinct

ordered pairs with the same first component. F is a function, called the "squaring" function.

EXERCISE SET 7.1

1. A vertical line L contains the point (2, 3). Give three more points that are on L.
2. Let S be a set of ordered pairs so that (1, 5) and (1, 6) are both in S. Is S a function?
3. Show without graphing that $\{(x, y): y = x + 3\}$ is a function.
4. Show without graphing that $\{(x, y): (x - 1)^2 + (y + 3)^2 = 4\}$ is not a function.
5. Show without graphing that $\{(x, y): y = |x|\}$ is a function.
6. Show that $\{(1, 3), (2, 4), (3, 1), (2, 4), (1, 5)\}$ is not a function.

Graph each set (in Exercises 7–15) to show whether it is a function or not. For each function, give the range and domain.

7. $\{(x, y): x = y^2 + 1\}$.
8. $\{(x, y): y = x^2 + 1\}$.
9. $\{(x, y): y = x\}$.
10. $\{(x, y): |y| = x\}$.
11. $\{(x, y): y < x\}$.
12. $\{(x, y): x = y^2 \text{ and } y < -1\}$.
13. $\{(x, y): x = y \text{ and } y > 0\}$.
14. $\{(x, y): xy = 10\}$.
15. $\{(x, y): y = -\sqrt{x^2 - 2}\}$.
16. Find the value of each of the functions of Exercises 7–15 at 2.
17. For each function of Exercises 7–15, find all arguments for which the function value is 2.
18. Let f be a function such that $(x, y) \in f$ and $(x, z) \in f$. What conclusion can you make about y and z?
19. Let F be a function such that $(x, y) \in F$ and $(z, y) \in F$. What conclusion can you make about x and z?
20. Can a function that consists of a finite number of ordered pairs have more elements in its domain than in its range?
21. Can a function that consists of a finite number of ordered pairs have more values than arguments?

7.3 f(x) Notation

Let (x, y) be an element of a function f. It is customary to denote the function value y by $f(x)$. (Read $f(x)$ as you would "f of x.") Thus for each $x \in D_f$, $(x, f(x)) \in f$ (see Figure 7.8). The letter f in the symbol

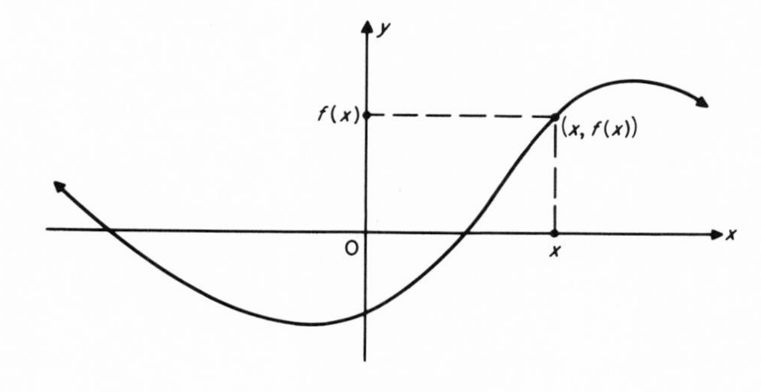

Figure 7.8

$f(x)$ can be interpreted as the rule which determines the value of the function for the given argument x.

$f(x)$ notation is frequently used to define a function. The sentence

$$f(x) = x^3 + 3, \text{ for each } x \in \text{R}$$

defines the function f where

$$f = \{(x, f(x)) : f(x) = x^3 + 3\}$$

or

$$f = \{(x, y) : y = x^3 + 3\}.$$

The equation $f(x) = x^3 + 3$ indicates what function value corresponds with a given argument (x-value). It is common practice to speak of "the function $f(x) = x^3 + 3$." Although $f(x) = x^3 + 3$ is simply an equation which defines the function (and is not the function itself), there is usually no ambiguity in identifying it with the function.

EXAMPLE 7.6 Let f be the function $\{(x, y) : y = x^2\}$. In $f(x)$ notation, the function is given by

$$f(x) = x^2, \text{ for } x \in R.$$

The function value at 2 is given by $f(2) = 2^2 = 4$. Also, $f(0) = 0$, $f(-2) = (-2)^2 = 4$, and

$$f(1 + \sqrt{2}) = (1 + \sqrt{2})^2 = 3 + 2\sqrt{2}.$$

Since the function value of f at any number is the square of that number, f can be described by a rule as "square the number."

EXAMPLE 7.7 Let $g(x) = x^2 - 5$ on $[2, 3]$. This describes the function

$$g = \{(x, y) : y = x^2 - 5, x \in [2, 3]\}.$$

Notice that $g(2) = -1$, $g(\frac{5}{2}) = \frac{5}{4}$, and $g(3) = 4$, but $g(6)$ is nonsense since 6 is not in the domain of g. If the function value is 0, i.e., $g(x) = 0$, then $x = \sqrt{5}$. (Why doesn't $x = -\sqrt{5}$ when $g(x) = 0$?)

EXAMPLE 7.8 Let $h = \{(0, 1), (1, 2), (2, 0), (3, -1)\}$. In $f(x)$ notation, h is denoted by the four equations

$$h(0) = 1, \quad h(1) = 2, \quad h(2) = 0, \quad h(3) = -1.$$

Even in this case, it is helpful to specify that the domain is the set $\{0, 1, 2, 3\}$.

EXAMPLE 7.9 Let $H = \{(x, y) : 2x^2 + 3y = 1\}$. Since the equation $2x^2 + 3y = 1$, when solved for y, is

$$y = \frac{1 - 2x^2}{3},$$

the function H is given in $f(x)$ notation by

$$H(x) = \frac{1 - 2x^2}{3}.$$

The function values at 0, 2, 4, and $2a$ are as follows:

$$H(0) = \frac{1 - 2 \cdot 0^2}{3} = \frac{1}{3}, \qquad H(2) = -\frac{7}{3},$$

$$H(4) = \frac{-31}{3}, \qquad H(2a) = \frac{1 - 8a^2}{3}.$$

If the function value is -3, then

$$H(x) = \frac{1 - 2x^2}{3} = -3$$

or

$$2x^2 = 10.$$

Thus $x = \sqrt{5}$ or $x = -\sqrt{5}$.

If x in $f(x) = 3x - 1$ is replaced by any number, then a true sentence is obtained which gives the value of f for that number. This procedure can be extended to include the replacement of x by any real number expression. To find an expression for the function value that corresponds to $7 + a$, for any a, x is replaced by $7 + a$ giving

$$f(7 + a) = 3 \cdot (7 + a) - 1 = 20 + 3a.$$

So for each a,

$$(7 + a, 20 + 3a) \in f.$$

Similarly,

$$f(b + b^2) = 3(b + b^2) - 1,$$

$$f\left(\frac{x + b}{3}\right) = 3\left(\frac{x + b}{3}\right) - 1 = x + b - 1.$$

Also,

$$f(f(2)) = 3(f(2)) - 1 = 3(3 \cdot 2 - 1) - 1 = 14$$

and

$$f(f(x^2)) = 3(f(x^2)) - 1 = 3(3x^2 - 1) - 1 = 9x^2 - 4.$$

7.4 The Trigonometric Functions

The trigonometric functions (see Chapter Six) are denoted by the names as listed in Table 7.2.

TABLE 7.2

Function name	Symbol for values
sine	$\sin x$
cosine	$\cos x$
tangent	$\tan x$
cotangent	$\cot x$
secant	$\sec x$
cosecant	$\csc x$

The sine function then is given by each of the following:

(a) $\{(x, y) : y = \sin x\}$,

(b) $f(x) = \sin x$, on R,

(c) sine (or sine function).

EXAMPLE 7.10 Let $f = \{(x, y) : y = \cos 2x\}$. In $f(x)$ notation, f is given by

$$f(x) = \cos 2x.$$

Then

$$f(0) = \cos 0 = 1, \qquad f\left(\frac{\pi}{6}\right) = \cos\frac{\pi}{3} = \frac{1}{2},$$

$$f\left(\frac{\pi}{4}\right) = 0, \qquad f\left(\frac{\pi}{2}\right) = -1.$$

To find x when $f(x) = 1$, the equation $\cos 2x = 1$ is solved. Thus $x \in \{n\pi : n \in I\}$.

EXERCISE SET 7.2

Let $f = \{(x, y): y = x - 4\}$.

1. Describe f in $f(x)$ notation.
2. Find $f(0), f(2), f(1), f(4), f(a), f(2a)$.
3. Find x if $f(x) = 4, f(x) = 2, f(x) = 8, f(x) = y$.
4. Describe f as a rule.

Let $g = \{(0, 1), (1, 2), (2, 4), (3, 0)\}$.

5. Write g in $f(x)$ notation.
6. Find $g(0)$, $g(1)$, $g(4)$, the value of g at 3.
7. Find x if $g(x) = 4$, $g(x) = 2$, $g(x) = 7$, the value of the function at x is 0.
8. Find D_g and R_g.

Let f be the function given by the rule, "Double, then add three."

9. Write f in $f(x)$ notation.
10. Find $f(2), f(-3), f(h), f(h + 2)$.
11. Find x if $f(x) = 7, f(x) = 0, f(x) = a + 3$, the value of the function at x is $h - 4$.
12. Write f as a set of ordered pairs.

Let $g(x) = x^2 + 2x$ on R.

13. Find $g(1)$, $g(3)$, $g(h + 2)$, $g(2a)$, $g(\sin t)$.
14. Find x if $g(x) = 0$, $g(x) = 8$, $g(x) = -6$, $g(x) = x$, $g(x) = x^2$.
15. Write g as a set of ordered pairs.
16. Describe g as a rule.

Let $f(x) = 2 \sin x$, on R.

17. Find $f(0), f(\pi/2), f(-\pi/6), f(\pi), f(7\pi)$.
18. For what arguments is $f(x) = 0, f(x) = 1, f(x) = -1$?
19. Find D_f and R_f.
20. Write f as a set of ordered pairs.
21. Describe f by a rule.

Write each function in $f(x)$ notation and find the indicated function values when they exist.

22. $f = \{(x, y): y = x^2\}$; find $f(1), f(-1), f(0), f(4), f(\sqrt{2} + \sqrt{3})$.
23. $g = \{(x, y): y = x\}$; find $g(1)$, $g(-7)$, $g(3)$, $g(a + b)$.
24. $h = \{(x, y): 2x + 3y = 4\}$; find $h(0)$, $h(1)$, $h(3)$, $h(\sqrt{2})$.
25. $F = \{(x, y): x^2 + y^2 = 4, y \geq 0\}$; find $F(2)$, $F(-2)$, $F(5)$.
26. $H = \{(x, y): y^2 = 2x^2 + 4x, y < 0\}$; find $H(0), H(2), H(-2), H(-1)$.
27. $S = \{(x, y): y = \cos x\}$; find $S(0)$, $S(\pi/2)$, $S(3\pi)$, $S(-\pi)$.
28. $T = \{(x, y): y = \tan x\}$; find $T(0)$, $T(\pi/2)$, $T(3\pi)$, $T(2)$.

Find all the arguments for each function value given in Exercises 29–31.

29. $f(z) = 2z + 3$ on R. $f(z) = 0, f(z) = 3, f(z) = a + 3$.
30. $f = \{(x, y): x + 2y = 1\}$. $f(x) = 0, f(x) = 4, f(x) = a$.
31. f is the "add one to the square of" function. $f(x) = 1, f(x) = 2, f(x) = 0, f(x) = \sin b$.
32. If H is a function such that $H(2x) = 3x + 2$ for each x, find $H(4)$, $H(0)$, $H(x)$, $H(3x)$.
33. If for each x, $g(x + 1) = x$, find $g(7)$, $g(x)$, $g(x^2)$.
34. If $F(3 - x) = \pi$ for each x, find $F(\pi)$, $F(3)$.
35. If $f(x^2) = \sin x$, find $f(w)$ where $w \geq 0$.

Let $f(x) = x^2 + 2$, $g(x) = 3x + 5$ for each x. Solve for x:

36. $f(x) = g(x)$.
37. $f(x - 1) = g(3x)$.
38. $f(2x) = 2f(x)$.

A function f is an *increasing* function on A if for each $x, y \in A$, $x < y$ implies $f(x) \leq f(y)$. f is *strictly increasing* on A if for each $x, y \in A$, $x < y$ implies $f(x) < f(y)$. Decreasing functions are defined similarly.

39. Prove that $f(x) = 3x + 2$ is strictly increasing on R.
40. Prove that $g(x) = 2 - x$ is strictly decreasing on R.
41. Prove that $h(x) = x^2$ is increasing on $[0, \infty)$ and decreasing on $(-\infty, 0]$.
42. Prove that x^3 is increasing on R.

A function F is *periodic* if there is a nonzero real number k so that $F(x + k) = F(x)$ for all $x \in D_F$. The smallest positive number h such that $F(x + h) = F(x)$ for each $x \in D_F$ is *the period of* F. Each of the trigonometric functions is periodic.

43. What is the period of sine? of $\sin 2x$? of $\sin \frac{1}{2}x$?
44. What is the period of cosine? of $\cos 2x$? of $\cos 11x$?
45. What is the period of tangent? of $\tan 5x$? of $\tan x/7$?
46. Show that if g is periodic with period h, then

$$g(x + 2h) = g(x) \text{ for each } x \in D_g.$$

47. Show that if $r > 0$ and if for the function g,

$$g(x - r) = g(x) \text{ for each } x \in R,$$

then

$$g(x + r) = g(x) \text{ for each } x \in R.$$

48. Is the function $f(x) = 2x + 3$ periodic? Prove your answer.

7.5 Restrictions on the Domain and Range of a Function

Strictly speaking, the domain of a function should be specified in the definition of the function. However, in the interest of simplification, the domain is understood to be the largest possible meaningful one (that is, the maximal one) whenever it is not specified. The domain of the function f, given by $f(x) = 3x - 2$, is understood to be the set of all real numbers, while the domain of the function $g(x) = \sqrt{x}$ is understood to be the set of nonnegative numbers. The domain of

$$f(x) = \sqrt{3x - 5}$$

is restricted to those numbers x such that $3x - 5 \geq 0$. Thus $D_f = [\frac{5}{3}, \infty)$.

In the definition of functions whose domain is other than the largest possible one, the restriction on the domain must be specified. In some cases, restrictions are also made on the range of a function, as in

$$f = \{(x, y): y = x^2, y > 1\},$$

where the range is restricted to the halfline $]1, \infty)$.

EXAMPLE 7.11 Find the domain and range of $f(x) = \sqrt{4 - x}$. The domain is restricted to those x for which $4 - x$ is nonnegative. This means $x \leq 4$, or $D_f = (-\infty, 4]$. The range is $[0, \infty)$ (see Figure 7.9).

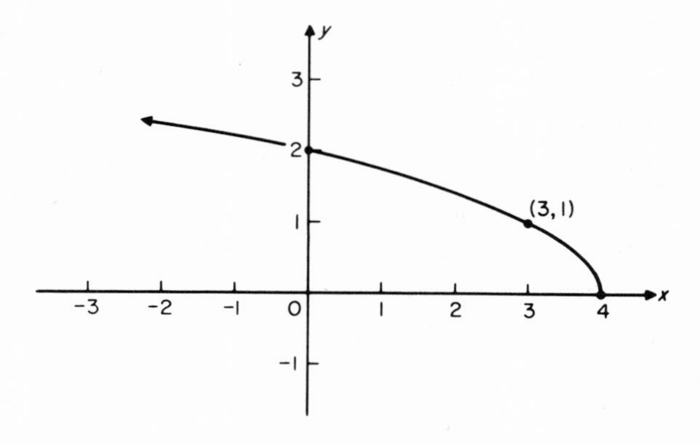

Figure 7.9

EXAMPLE 7.12 Find the range of the function $g(x) = 2x + 5$ on $[-2, 6[$.

Since $D_g = [-2, 6[$, $-2 \leq x < 6$ for each $x \in D_g$, so

$$-4 \leq 2x < 12,$$

$$-4 + 5 \leq 2x + 5 < 12 + 5,$$

or

$$1 \leq 2x + 5 < 17.$$

The range of g is $[1, 17[$.

EXAMPLE 7.13 Find the range of the function $f(x) = x^2 + 3x - 4$. By completing the square in the defining equation,

$$\begin{aligned} f(x) &= (x^2 + 3x + \tfrac{9}{4}) - \tfrac{9}{4} - 4 \\ &= (x + \tfrac{3}{2})^2 - \tfrac{25}{4}. \end{aligned}$$

Now $(x + \frac{3}{2})^2 \geq 0$, so that $f(x) \geq -\frac{25}{4}$ for all x. Therefore $R_f = [-\frac{25}{4}, \infty)$ (see Figure 7.10).

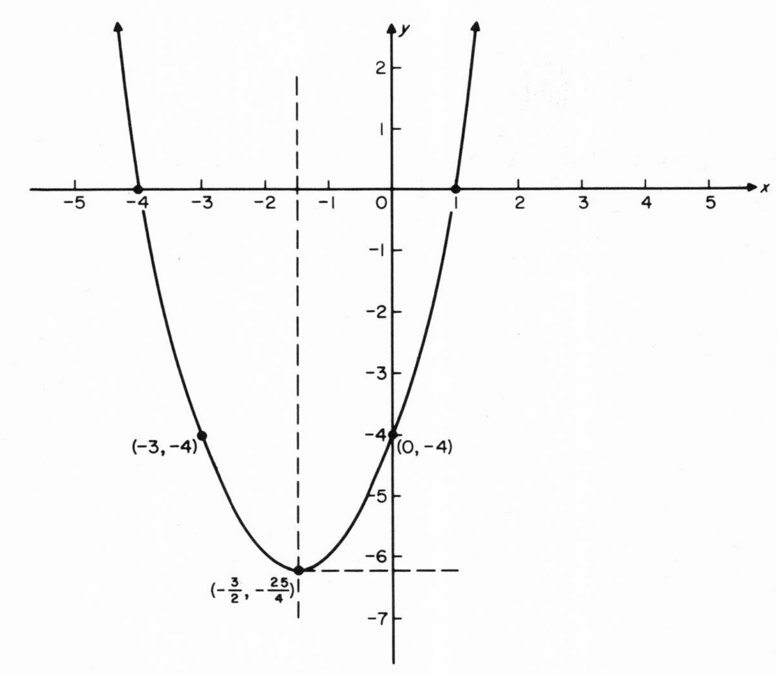

Figure 7.10

EXAMPLE 7.14 Find a restricted domain of $f(x) = x^2 - 2x$ so that the range will be the interval $[1, 4]$.

Since $R_f = [1, 4]$, $1 \leq f(x) \leq 4$. So,

$$1 \leq x^2 - 2x \leq 4.$$

By completing the square,

$$2 \leq x^2 - 2x + 1 \leq 5,$$
$$\sqrt{2} \leq |x - 1| \leq \sqrt{5}.$$

This is equivalent to

$$(x - 1 \leq -\sqrt{2} \text{ or } x - 1 \geq \sqrt{2}) \text{ and } (-\sqrt{5} \leq x - 1 \leq \sqrt{5}).$$

The domain is

$$[1 - \sqrt{5}, 1 - \sqrt{2}] \cup [1 + \sqrt{2}, 1 + \sqrt{5}].$$

EXAMPLE 7.15 Find the range and domain of $f(x) = \csc x$, $x > 0$. The domain of $\csc x$ excludes all numbers where $\sin x = 0$ since the function is defined by

$$\csc x = \frac{1}{\sin x}.$$

This means x is not a multiple of π. Since $x > 0$ also,

$$D_f = \overline{\{n\pi : n \in I\}} \cap]0, \infty).$$

The range of $\csc x$ is the set of reciprocals of numbers (except 0) in the range of $\sin x$. Since the range of $\sin x$ is $[-1, 1]$,

$$R_f = (-\infty, -1] \cup [1, \infty).$$

It is often useful to suitably restrict the extent in y of a set of ordered pairs which is not a function so that the resulting set of ordered pairs is a function. Usually the restriction is made so as to give a maximal domain.

EXAMPLE 7.16 H: $\{(x, y) : y^2 - 1 = x\}$ is not a function since both $(3, 2)$ and $(3, -2)$ are in H.
The set of ordered pairs

$$\{(x, y) : y^2 - 1 = x \text{ and } y \geq 0\}$$

that results from restricting second components to nonnegative values is a function. Other functions can be obtained by placing other restrictions on the set of second components—for example, $y \leq 0$ (see Figure 7.11).

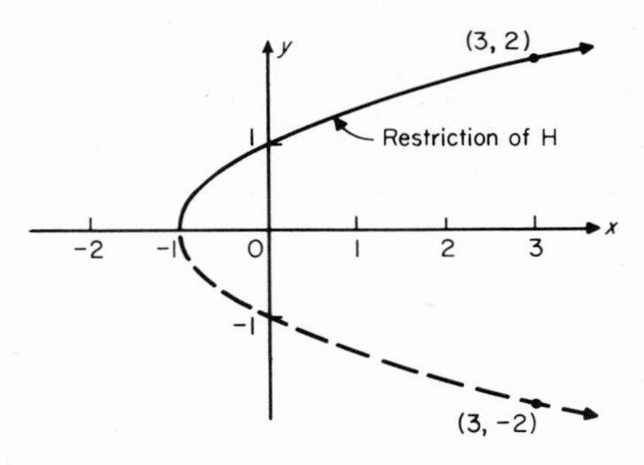

Figure 7.11

EXAMPLE 7.17 The graph of the set

$$\{(x, y) : \tan y = x, -1 \leq x \leq 1\}$$

is shown in Figure 7.12(a). If f is the restriction of this set to

$$\left\{(x, y) : \tan y = x, -1 \leq x \leq 1 \text{ and } -\frac{\pi}{4} \leq y \leq \frac{\pi}{4}\right\},$$

then f is a function [shown in Figure 7.12(b)].

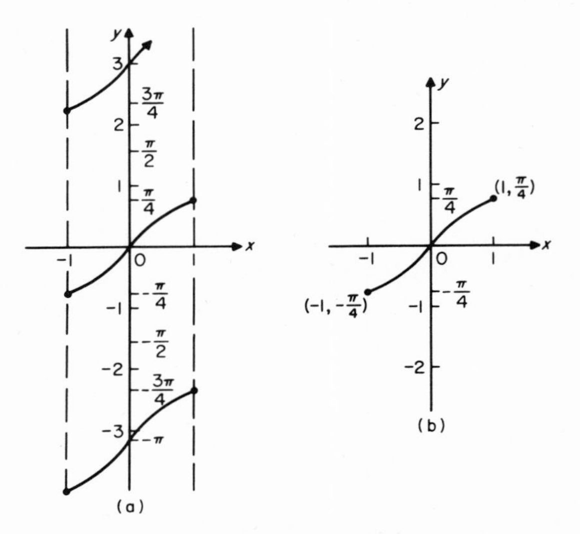

Figure 7.12

EXERCISE SET 7.3

Find a maximal domain to define a real-valued function.

1. $g(x) = \sqrt{x - 5}$.
2. $h(x) = \sqrt{x^2 + 2}$.
3. $H(x) = \sqrt{2 - x^2}$.
4. $g(x) = 1/(x - 2)$.
5. $G(x) = (x + 3)/(x^2 - 1)$.
6. $\phi(x) = \sqrt{1/(x - 1)}$.
7. $h(x) = \sec x$.
8. $\{(x, y): y = \tan(x + 1)\}$.

Determine the range of each function.

9. $f = \{(x, y): y = x + 1 \text{ for } x \in [-3, 1]\}$.
10. $g(x) = 1/(x - 1)$ on $[2, 5[$.
11. $h(x) = x^2 - 5x + 1$.
12. $A(x) = 3x - 7$ on $[-1, 1]$.
13. $F(x) = 7 - x^2$.
14. $g = \{(x, y): y = 1 + \tan x, |x| < \pi/4\}$.

Determine the domain of each function.

15. $f = \{(x, y): y = 2x - 1, -1 \leq y < 3\}$.
16. $g = \{x, y): 2y - x = 2, 0 \leq y \leq 4\}$.
17. f defined by $f(x) = (x - 2)/3$ with $R_f =]-2, 4[$.
18. $g(x) = x^2 + 2$ and $R_g = [2, 5]$.
19. $f = \{(x, y): y^2 = x, y \in [0, 2]\}$.

In Exercises 20–25, restrict the range to obtain a function on a maximal domain.

20. $\{(x, y): x^2 + y^2 = 1\}$.
21. $\{(x, y): y^2 = x\}$.
22. $\{(x, y): |y| = x\}$.
23. $\{(x, y): x^2 - y^2 = 1\}$.
24. $\{(x, y): \sin y = x\}$.
25. $\{(x, y): x = \cos y\}$.
26. Let $A(l)$ be the area of a rectangle with one side of length l and a perimeter of 10. Express A as a function of l. Give the domain and range of A.

27. Define a function V where $V(h)$ is the volume of a cube with side length h. Give the domain and range of V if the surface area of the cube is not to exceed π.
28. Define a function V where $V(r)$ is the volume of a cylinder of radius r and height 4. Give the domain and range of V if the radius cannot exceed the height.
29. Let d be the distance traveled by a belt on a pulley of radius 3 feet rotating 460 revolutions per minute. Express d as a function of t, the time measured in minutes. Give the domain and range of d.
30. Let V be the vertical distance from the tip of the hour hand on a clock to the highest point it can reach. The length of the hand is R. Express V as a function of t, the time in hours measured from 12 noon.

7.6 Mapping Notation for Functions

Instead of thinking of a function f as a single set of pairs (as in Figure 7.13), where the ordered pairs describe a matching of arguments

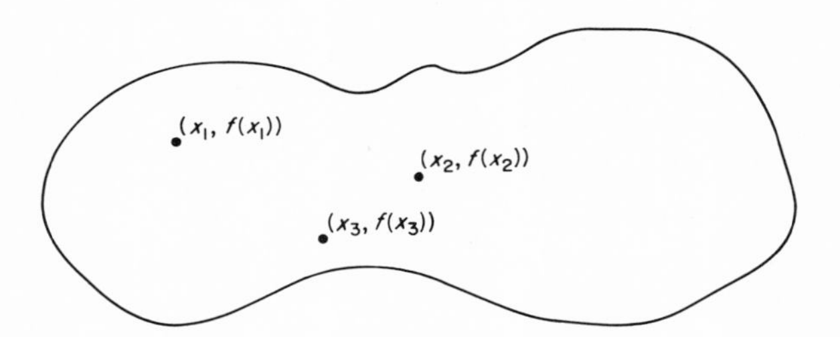

Figure 7.13

with their corresponding values, think of two separate sets, the domain of the function and the range of the function, with the matching now shown by the arrows from the domain to the range, as in Figure 7.14.

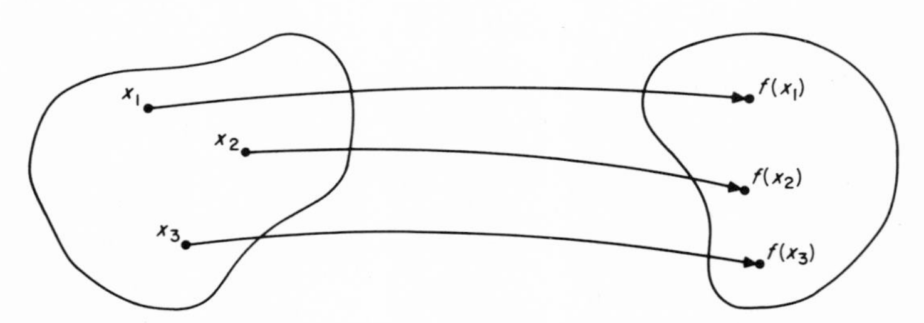

Figure 7.14

When viewed this way, a function is referred to as a *mapping of* D_f *onto* R_f. Suppose $(a, b) \in f$. The value b corresponding to the argument a is called the *image of a under the mapping f*, and one says that f *maps a into b*. The standard notation for a mapping is

$$f: a \rightarrow b,$$

read "f maps a into b" or "b is the image of a under f." (Sometimes it is read "a goes to b.")

The function $f = \{(x, y): y = x^3\}$ can be defined in mapping notation by $f: x \rightarrow x^3$ (on R). The function g defined by $g: x \rightarrow 2x - 3$ is the function

$$\{(x, y): y = 2x - 3\} \quad \text{or} \quad g(x) = 2x - 3.$$

The graph of a function is a set of points each of which represents an ordered pair of the function. A *mapping sketch* (or just *sketch*), on the other hand, pictures the domain and range as separate sets with arrows from the arguments to their images. For simple functions, fairly complete sketches of a mapping may be given. A sketch of the mapping $h: x \rightarrow x + 2$ is given in Figure 7.15. Since it is impossible to show all the arrows from

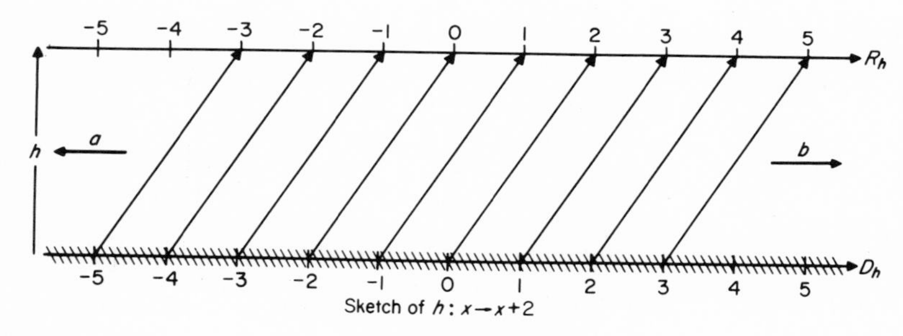

Sketch of $h: x \rightarrow x+2$

Figure 7.15

the arguments to their images, a few are shown to indicate how the mapping behaves. The shading indicates the domain, which in this instance includes all real numbers. The horizontal arrows, a and b, indicate that the mapping continues on indefinitely in the directions indicated. D_h and R_h indicate the lines containing the domain and range of h.

The graph of a function can be regarded as a mapping line of the function. A point in the domain is paired with a point in the range by mapping the point vertically to the graph and then horizontally over to the point in the range (see Figure 7.16).

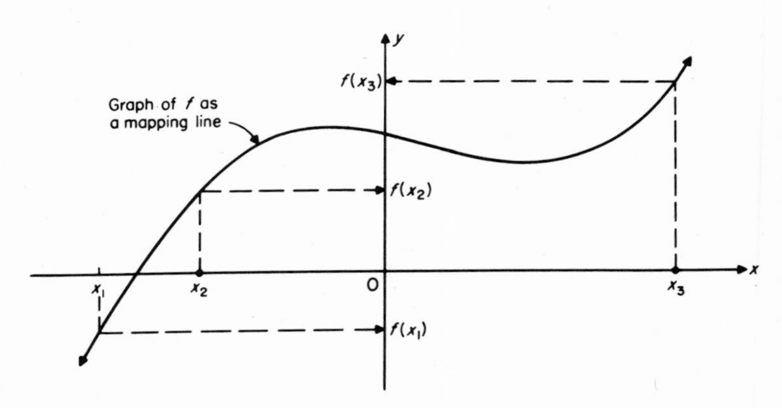

Figure 7.16

EXAMPLE 7.18 Let $f = \{(0, 1), (1, 2), (2, -2), (3, -1)\}$. f is a mapping described by

$$f: \begin{cases} 0 \rightarrow 1 \\ 1 \rightarrow 2 \\ 2 \rightarrow -2 \\ 3 \rightarrow -1 \end{cases} \quad \text{on } \{0, 1, 2, 3\}.$$

A sketch of f is shown in Figure 7.17. Compare this sketch of f with the graph of f shown in Figure 7.18.

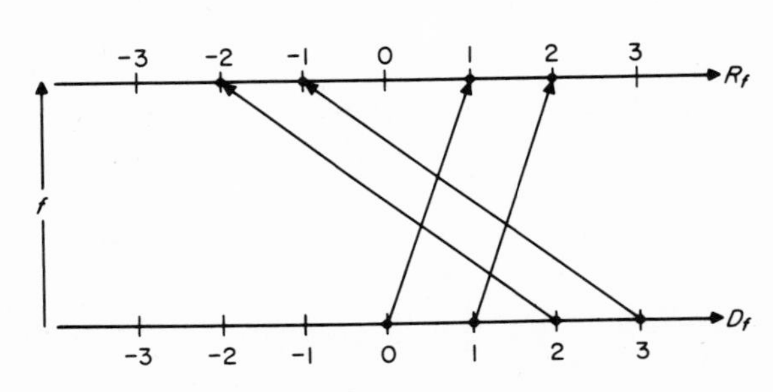

Figure 7.17

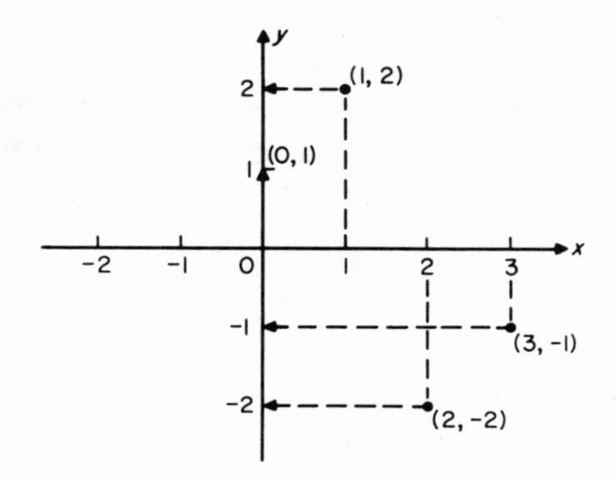

Figure 7.18

EXAMPLE 7.19 $g = \{(n, m) : m = 2n + 1, n = 1, 2, 3, \ldots\}$. As a mapping,

$$g : n \rightarrow 2n + 1 \text{ on } I^+.$$

The sketch of g is shown in Figure 7.19. The horizontal arrow on the right indicates that the mapping continues to the right following the pattern established.

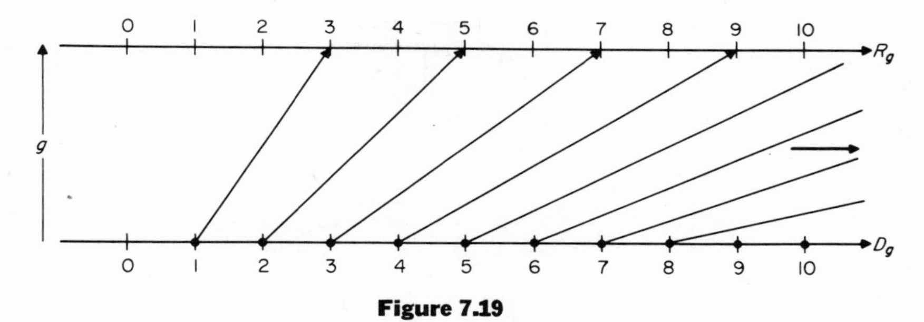

Figure 7.19

EXAMPLE 7.20 Let F be the set $\{(x, y) : y = x - 3, -1 \leq x \leq 2\}$. F is defined as a mapping by $F : x \rightarrow x - 3$ on $[-1, 2]$. Notice in the sketch of the mapping that all the arrows are parallel (see Figure 7.20).

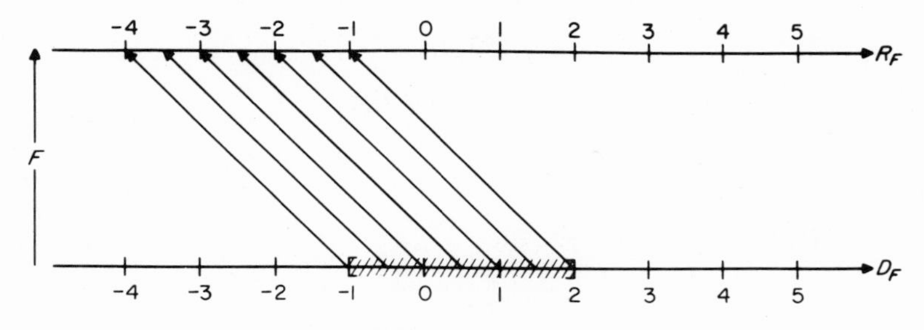

Figure 7.20

EXAMPLE 7.21 Sketch

$$F: x \longrightarrow \frac{1}{x-2} \text{ for } x \neq 2$$

and graph the function F (see Figures 7.21 and 7.22).

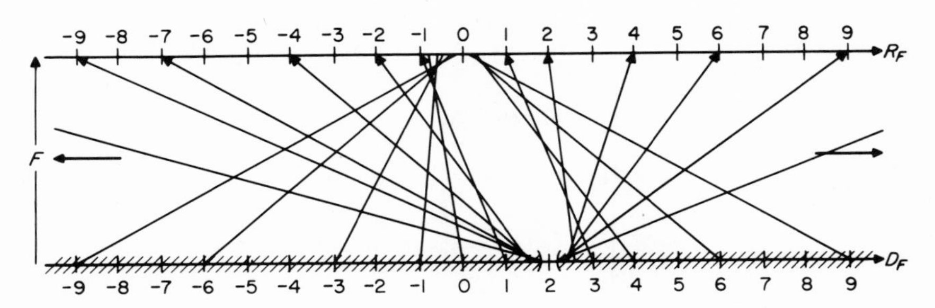

Figure 7.21

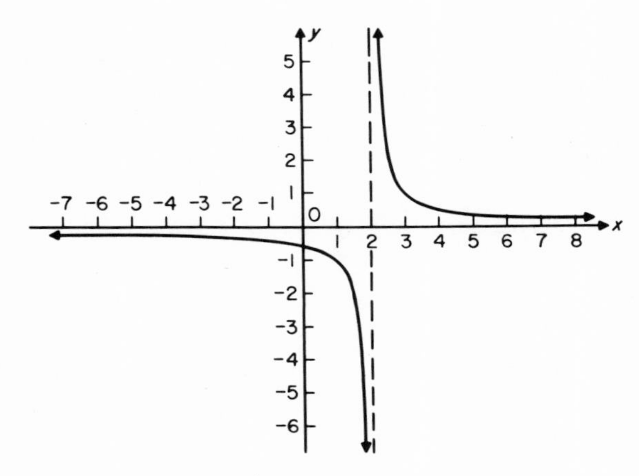

$F(x) = \frac{1}{x-2}$ on $(-\infty, 2[\ \cup\ ]2, \infty)$

Figure 7.22

EXAMPLE 7.22 g is the set

$$\{(x, y) : y = 4 \text{ for } -1 \leq x < 2,\ y = x \text{ for } 2 \leq x \leq 5\}.$$

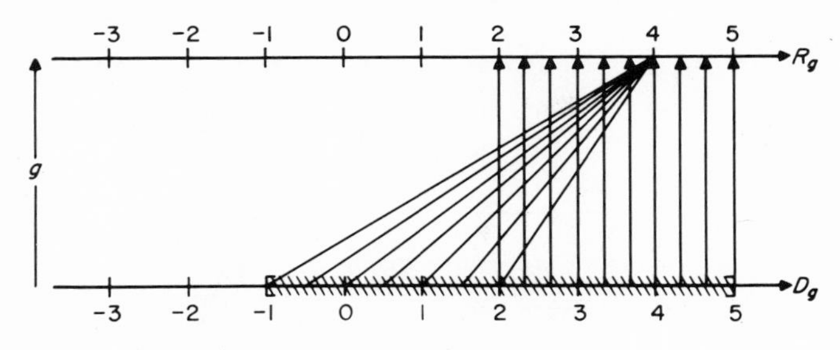

Figure 7.23

(a) Write g as a mapping, and sketch (see Figure 7.23).

$$g: \begin{cases} x \longrightarrow 4 \text{ on } [-1, 2[, \\ x \longrightarrow x \text{ on } [2, 5]. \end{cases}$$

(b) Write g in $f(x)$ notation, and graph (see Figure 7.24).

$$g(x) = \begin{cases} 4 \text{ on } [-1, 2[, \\ x \text{ on } [2, 5]. \end{cases}$$

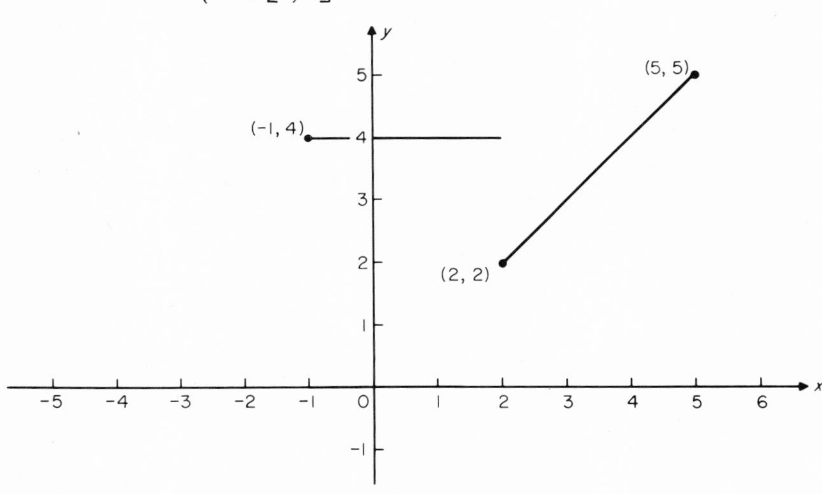

Figure 7.24

EXERCISE SET 7.4

Which of the following are sketches of functions? Justify your answer.

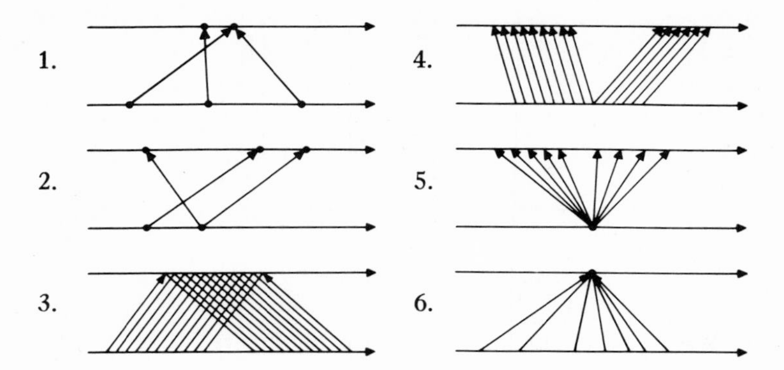

Describe the function in mapping notation and sketch (as complete a sketch as is reasonable for the given function).

7. $g = \{(-1, 2), (1, 3), (2, 2), (4, -2)\}$.
8. $H = \{(1, 1), (2, 1), (3, 1), (4, 1), (5, 1), (6, 1), (7, 1)\}$.
9. $G = \{(n, m): 3m - 2 = n, n = -2, -1, 0, 1, 2, 3, 4\}$.
10. The "square rooting" function on the domain $\{0, \frac{1}{4}, 1, 2, 4\}$.
11. $H = \{(n, m): m = 2n; n \in I^-\}$.
12. $g = \{(n, m): m = 3n + 5; n = 2, 4, 6, \ldots, 2n, \ldots\}$.
13. The "squaring" function on the nonnegative reals.
14. $f(x) = 4$ on $[-2, 5]$.
15. $F = \{(x, 3): x \in (-\infty, \infty)\}$.
16. $f = \{(x, y): 2x - y = 4\}$.
17. $f(x) = x^2$ on $[-2, 2]$.
18. $G(x) = -\sqrt{x - 2}$.
19. $g = \{(x, y): y = |x - 4|, -2 < x \leq 4\}$.
20. $F(x) = |x|$.
21. $f = \{(x, y): y = x \text{ for } x < 0, y = x^2 \text{ for } 0 \leq x\}$.
22. $F = \{(x, y): y = -x \text{ for } x < -1; y = 3 \text{ for } x = -1; y = 2x \text{ for } -1 < x\}$.
23. $F = \{(x, y): y = n \text{ for } n \leq x < n + 1, n = 1, 2, 3, 4\}$.
24. How can a function with constant slope be recognized by its graph?
25. How can a function with constant slope be recognized by its sketch?

7.7 Composition of Functions

The function f defined by

$$f(x) = x^2 + 3 \text{ on } R$$

is also defined by the rule "square, then add 3." Values of the function at a given argument are found by squaring the argument and then adding 3 to the result. That is, values of f are found by first applying the "squaring" function, and then applying the "adding 3" function to that result.

If the "squaring" function is denoted by S and the "adding 3" function by A, so that $S(x) = x^2$ and $A(x) = x + 3$, then f is "made up" of S and A in the sense that in order to find $f(x)$, A is applied to $S(x)$. That is,

$$f(x) = A(S(x)).$$

$A(S(x))$ is read, "A of S of x," which can be interpreted as "add 3 to the square of x." The function f is said to be the *composite of A with S*. One writes

$$f = A \circ S$$

(read "f equals A composed with S"). One also writes

$$f(x) = [A \circ S](x).$$

The function $g(x) = (x + 3)^2$ is "made up" of the "adding 3" function, A, and the "squaring" function, S, the same functions of which $f(x) = x^2 + 3$ is a composite. However, the order of application of A and S is reversed for g from what it is for f. f is the composite of A with S, so that

$$f(x) = [A \circ S](x) = A(S(x)) = A(x^2) = x^2 + 3,$$

while g is the composite of S with A, so that

$$g(x) = [S \circ A](x) = S(A(x)) = S(x + 3) = (x + 3)^2.$$

Since there are numbers x for which $x^2 + 3 \neq (x + 3)^2$, f and g are different functions. That is, $A \circ S \neq S \circ A$.

Viewing a function as a composite of two functions is tantamount to thinking of the function as consisting of two mappings in succession. To say that the function $f(x) = x^2 + 3$ is the composition of $A(x) = x + 3$ with $S(x) = x^2$ is to say that the mapping

$$f: x \rightarrow x^2 + 3$$

consists of the mapping

$$S: x \to x^2 \quad \text{followed by} \quad A: x \to x + 3.$$

In this sense, S takes each x into x^2, and A, in turn, takes x^2 into $x^2 + 3$.

Figure 7.25 shows partially the mappings S and A.

S				A		
1	→	1		1	→	4
3	→	9		9	→	12
-5	→	25		25	→	28
$-\sqrt{2}$	→	2		2	→	5
.4	→	.16		.16	→	3.16
	. . .				. . .	

Figure 7.25

To show the mapping S followed by the mapping A, the two lists of Figure 7.25 are merged as in Figure 7.26. This shows f as a composite of S followed by A where f maps each number of the first column into the corresponding number of the last column.

	S		A	
1	→	1	→	4
3	→	9	→	12
-5	→	25	→	28
$-\sqrt{2}$	→	2	→	5
.4	→	.16	→	3.16
		. . .		

Figure 7.26

The composition of mappings partially pictured in Figure 7.26 can be illustrated more easily with a *balloon diagram* as in Figure 7.27. In this type of diagram, one chooses an arbitrary argument, say x, and pictures

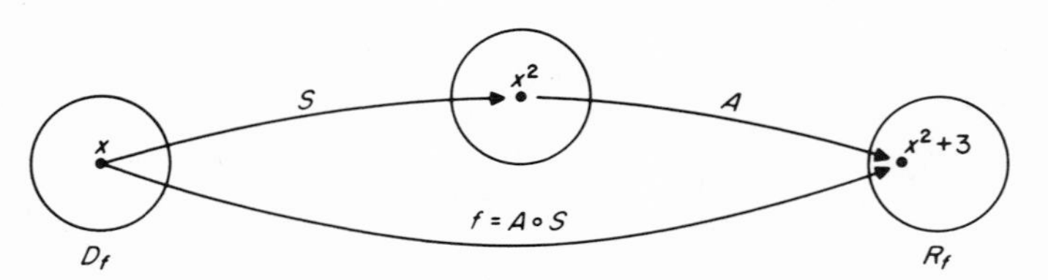

Figure 7.27

its "path" as it is "carried along" by each of the mappings of the composition.

Notice in the composition above that, although the domain of the mapping $A: x \to x + 3$ is the set of all real numbers, A is applied only to nonnegative real numbers in the composition. This happens since each value of the mapping S is the square of a number, and therefore is nonnegative. The domain of A, then, restricted to the range of S, is in this case $[0, \infty)$.

For the functions f and g given by

$$f(x) = \sqrt{x},$$

$$g(x) = 2x,$$

the composition $f \circ g$ is not defined for the negative real numbers. For example,

$$[f \circ g](-2) = f(g(-2)) = f(-4) = \sqrt{-4}$$

shows that $-2 \notin D_{f \circ g}$. In this case $D_{f \circ g} = [0, \infty)$. To find $D_{f \circ g}$, that part of the range of g which is common to the domain of f, i.e., $R_g \cap D_f$, is taken as the restricted range of g (as well as the restricted domain of f). Then the domain of $f \circ g$ is the domain of g under this restriction (see Figure 7.28).

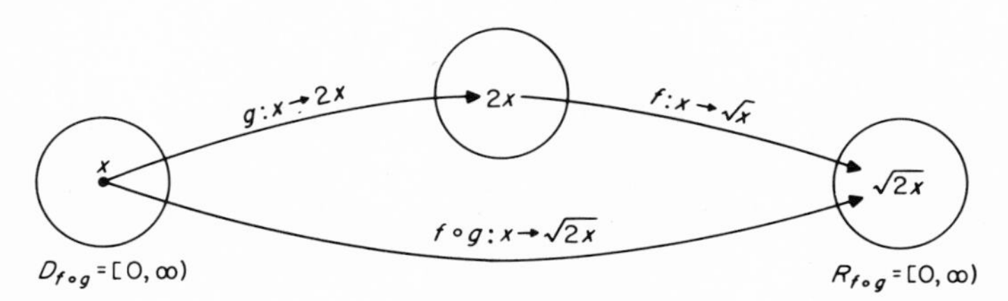

Figure 7.28

Composition can be carried out with any given pair of functions; the composite is a function. The composition of f with g, $f \circ g$, is the function that maps x onto $f(g(x))$ for each $x \in D_g$ where $g(x) \in D_f$. That is, the pairing for $f \circ g$ is given by

$$[f \circ g](x) = f(g(x)).$$

The domain of $f \circ g$ is restricted to those numbers in the domain of g where $f(g(x))$ is defined.

The composition of functions can be pictured by mapping sketches. A sketch of the composition $F \circ h$, where

$$h(x) = 2x, \qquad F(x) = x + 5,$$

$$[F \circ h](x) = F(h(x)) = F(2x) = 2x + 5,$$

is given in Figure 7.29, where the bottom line is the domain of h, the top line is the range of F, and the middle line is both the range of h and the domain of F. The dashed arrows from the bottom line to the middle show the mapping h; those from the middle to the top, the mapping F. The composite $F \circ h$ is shown by solid arrows from the bottom line to the top line. (Notice that h shows a symmetric pattern with respect to the origin while $F \circ h$ shows the same pattern centered around -5.)

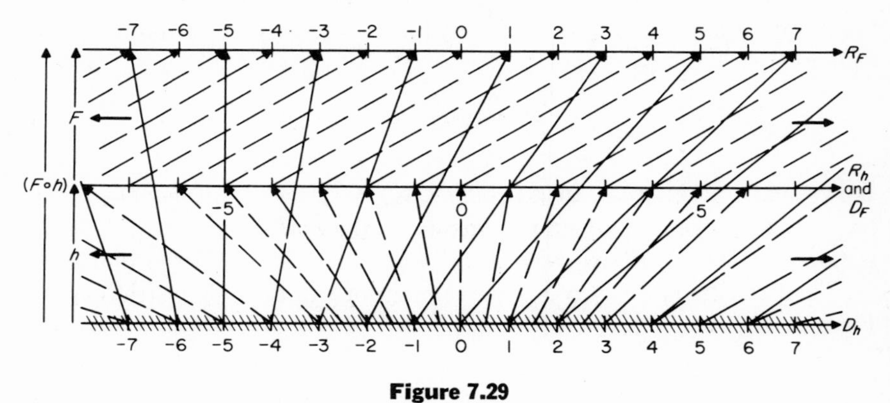

Figure 7.29

EXAMPLE 7.23 Find the composition of f with g where $f(x) = 3x - 1$ and $g(x) = x + 5$. Find the range and domain of the composition.

$$[f \circ g](x) = f(g(x)) = f(x + 5) = 3(x + 5) - 1 = 3x + 14,$$

$$D_{f \circ g} = R \quad \text{and} \quad R_{f \circ g} = R$$

(notice that $D_f \cap R_g = R$).

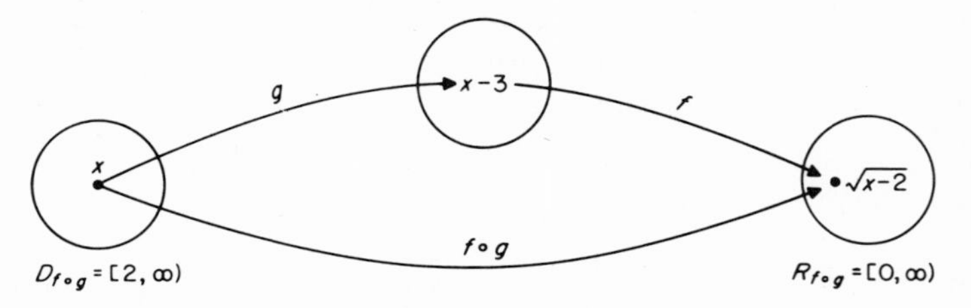

Figure 7.30

EXAMPLE 7.24 Find the composition of f with g where $f(x) = \sqrt{x+1}$ and $g(x) = x - 3$. Find the domain and range of the composition and illustrate with a balloon diagram of the mappings (see Figure 7.30).

$$[f \circ g](x) = f(g(x)) = f(x-3) = \sqrt{x-2}.$$

Since $R_g \cap D_f = R \cap [-1, \infty) = [-1, \infty)$, the domain and range of $f \circ g$ are given by

$$D_{f\circ g} = \{y\colon (y-3) \in [-1, \infty)\} = [2, \infty),$$
$$R_{f\circ g} = \{\sqrt{x-2}\colon x \in [2, \infty)\} = [0, \infty).$$

EXAMPLE 7.25 Find the composition function in mapping notation of $f\colon x \to x^2$ on $[0, 6]$ with $g\colon x \to 3x$ on R. Find the domain and range of the composition. Sketch (see Figure 7.31).

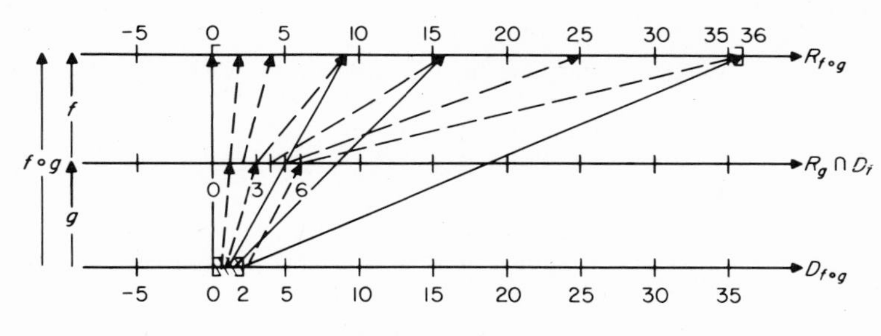

Figure 7.31

For a given x, g maps x to $3x$ and f in turn maps $3x$ to $(3x)^2$. Therefore,

$$f \circ g\colon x \to 9x^2.$$

Since $R_g = R$ and $D_f = [0, 6]$,

$$R_g \cap D_f = [0, 6].$$

Therefore,

$$D_{f\circ g} = [0, 2] \quad \text{and} \quad R_{f\circ g} = [0, 36].$$

EXAMPLE 7.26 Sketch the mappings and find $f \circ g$ for

$$f = \{(1, 2), (2, 3), (3, 1)\}$$

and

$$g = \{(1, 2), (2, 2), (3, 1)\}.$$

$f \circ g$ has the sketch shown in Figure 7.32. It follows that

$$f \circ g = \{(1, 3), (2, 3), (3, 2)\}.$$

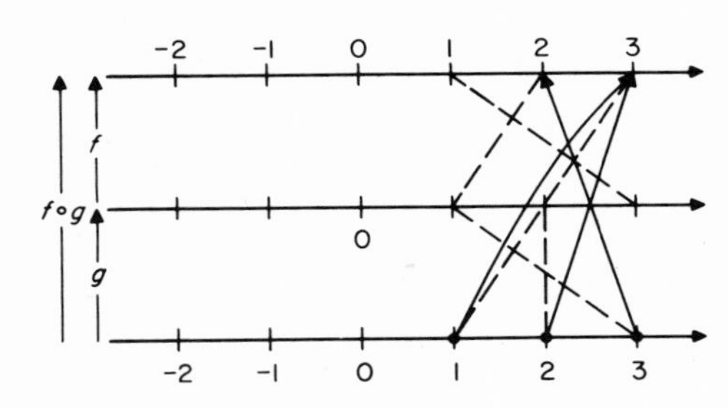

Figure 7.32

EXERCISE SET 7.5

Write the composition of the first listed function with the second as a mapping, giving the domain and range. Sketch the mappings of the composition in Exercises 1–5.

1. $f\colon x \longrightarrow 6 - x$,
   $g\colon y \longrightarrow 3y + 1$.
2. $f\colon y \longrightarrow 2y$,
   $g\colon x \longrightarrow 5x - 3$.
3. $g\colon x \longrightarrow 5x - 3$,
   $f\colon y \longrightarrow 2y$.
4. $f(x) = 2x - 3$ on $[0, 1]$;
   $g(x) = x^2$.
5. $g(x) = x^2$,
   $f(x) = 2x - 3$ on $[0, 1]$.
6. $f\colon \phi \longrightarrow \phi$ on $[0, 4]$;
   $g\colon \phi \longrightarrow 2\phi$.
7. $g\colon x \longrightarrow 2x$,
   $f\colon x \longrightarrow x$ on $[0, 4]$.
8. $f = \{(x, 3)\}$;
   $g = \{(x, y)\colon y = 2x\}$.
9. $g = \{(x, y)\colon y = 2x\}$;
   $f = \{(x, 3)\}$.
10. $f\colon a \longrightarrow 2a$, $x = 2, 4, 6$;
    $g\colon b \longrightarrow 2b$, $x = 1, 2, 3$.
11. $f = \{(1, 2), (2, 2), (3, 1)\}$;
    $F = \{(1, 2), (2, 3), (3, 1)\}$.
12. $F = \{(1, 2), (2, 3), (3, 1)\}$;
    $f = \{(1, 2), (2, 3), (3, 1)\}$.
13. $g = \{(4, 1), (5, 4), (7, 7), (9, 3), (11, 6), (12, 32)\}$;
    $h = \{(4, 1), (5, 1), (6, 9), (7, 11)\}$.

14. $f(x) = 2x$ on $[0, 1]$;
$g(x) = x + 1$ on $[0, 2]$.

15. $f(x) = x^2$ on $[-1, 1]$;
$h(x) = 6 - x$ on $[0, 1]$.

Write the composition of the first function with the second in the same notation as the functions given. Find the range and domain of the composition. Draw balloon diagrams of the composition.

16. $h: x \longrightarrow x^2$,
$j: y \longrightarrow \sqrt{y}$.

17. $j: y \longrightarrow \sqrt{y}$,
$h: x \longrightarrow x^2$.

18. $f(r) = r^2$,
$g(s) = 2s$.

19. The "squaring" function;
the "adding 4" function.

20. The "double, then add 3" function;
the "square, then subtract 1" function.

21. $\{(x, y): y = \sin x \text{ and } x \in [0, \pi]\}$;
$\{(x, 2x)\}$.

22. $\{(x, 2x)\}$;
$\{(x, \sin x): x \in [0, \pi]\}$.

23. $h: x \longrightarrow \sin x$ on $[-\pi, \pi]$;
$k: m \longrightarrow m + \pi/2,\ m \in N$.

24. $k: m \longrightarrow m + \pi/2$,
$h: x \longrightarrow \sin x$ on $[-\pi, \pi]$.

25. $f(x) = \sin x,\ x \in [0, 2\pi]$;
$g(x) = \cos x$.

26. $g(x) = \tan x,\ x \in]-\pi/2, \pi/2[$;
$h(x) = x^2 + 1$.

27. $h(x) = x^2 + 1$,
$g(x) = \tan x,\ x \in]-\pi/2, \pi/2[$.

The definition of composition is extended to more than two functions by letting

$$[f \circ f \circ f](x) = f(f(f(x))), \quad [f \circ f \circ f \circ f](x) = f(f(f(f(x)))),$$

and so on.

28. Find $[f \circ f](x)$, if $f(x) = x + 2$.

29. Find $[f \circ f \circ f](x)$, if $f(x) = x + 2$.

30. Find $\underbrace{[f \circ f \circ \ldots \circ f]}_{n}(x),\ n \in I^+,\ f(x) = x + 2$.

31. Let $g(x) = x$. Find $\underbrace{[g \circ g \circ \ldots \circ g]}_{n}(x),\ n \in I^+$.

Find $f \circ g$ and $g \circ f$ (state domains).

32. $f(x) = x$; $g(x) = \sin x$.
33. $f(x) = -x$; $g(x) = x$ on $[0, 1]$.
34. $f(x) = g(x) = 4$.
35. $f(x) = x$ on $[0, 4]$; $g(x) = x^2$ on $[1, 3]$.
36. $f(x) = 2x$; $g(x) = \frac{1}{2}x$.
37. $f(x) = x^3$; $g(x) = \sqrt[3]{x}$.
38. $f(x) = 2x + 3$; $g(x) = \frac{1}{2}(x - 3)$.

In Exercises 39–44, let

$f(x) = x + 3$, the "adding 3" function,
$g(x) = 5x$, the "multiplying by 5" function,
$h(x) = x - 3$, "the subtracting 3" function,
$i(x) = x$, the "identity" function,
$j(x) = x/5$, the "dividing by 5" function.

39. Find $[(f \circ g) \circ h]\,(0)$.
40. Find $[f \circ (g \circ h)]\,(0)$.
41. Find $[f \circ h \circ g]\,(x)$.
42. Show that $f \circ h = i = h \circ f$.
43. Is $g \circ j = j \circ g$?
44. Is $g \circ h = h \circ g$?
45. Let $G(x) = 3x - 2$. Solve for a:
$$G(a) \times G(1 - a) = G(2a).$$

7.8 Writing a Function as a Composition

It is often quite helpful (particularly in the calculus) to visualize a given (complicated) function as the composite of two or more simpler functions. For example, the function $f(x) = x^2 + 6$ can be viewed as a composite of the "squaring" and the "adding 6" functions.

Since a composition $f \circ g$ can be interpreted as the application of g followed by the application of f, one can usually write a function as a composition of simpler functions by noticing what operations are performed in what order in computing values of the function. This is illustrated in the examples below.

EXAMPLE 7.27 Write $f(x) = \sqrt{x + 5}$ as a composition of simpler functions.
The value of f at x is computed by adding 5 to x and then taking the square root of the sum; that is, the "adding 5" function is applied,

followed by the application of the "square root" function. This means that the function f is the composite of $g: x \to \sqrt{x}$ with $h: x \to x + 5$. That is,

$$f(x) = [g \circ h](x) = g(x + 5) = \sqrt{x + 5}.$$

EXAMPLE 7.28 Write $\{(x, y) : y = (x - 3)^3\}$ as a composition of simpler functions.

To obtain a function value at x, first 3 is subtracted from x and then the result is cubed. Using the basic functions $g(x) = x - 3$ and $h(x) = x^3$,

$$[h \circ g](x) = h(g(x)) = h(x - 3) = (x - 3)^3$$

or

$$f = h \circ g.$$

Balloon diagrams can be used to keep track of the mappings in a composition. Their use is illustrated in Examples 7.29 and 7.31.

EXAMPLE 7.29 Let $f(x) = x + 2$ and $g(x) = \sqrt{x}$. Find functions h and H so that $f = g \circ h$ and $f = H \circ g$. (Restrict the domain of f or of g as necessary.)

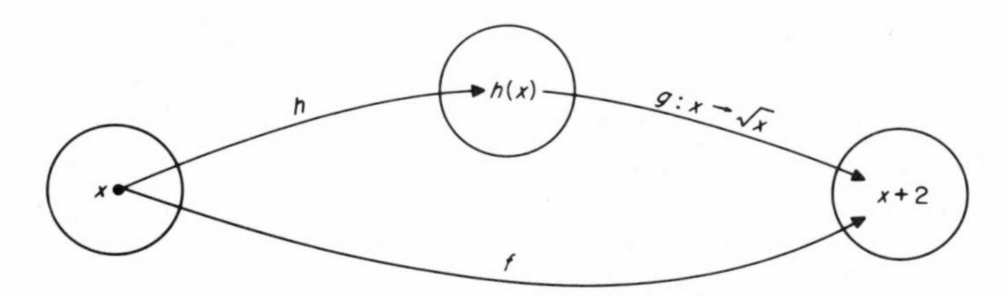

Figure 7.33

Figure 7.33 shows the proper relations between the mappings f, g, and h. From the diagram it is seen that $h(x)$ must be such that its square root is $x + 2$. Now, for each $x \geq -2$,

$$\sqrt{(x + 2)^2} = x + 2.$$

Therefore,

$$h: x \to (x + 2)^2 \text{ on } [-2, \infty).$$

f is restricted to $[-2, \infty)$.

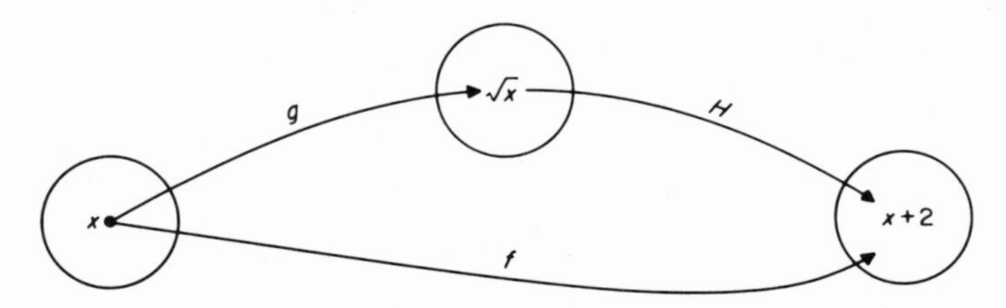

Figure 7.34

A diagram of f, g, and H is shown in Figure 7.34. From the diagram $H: \sqrt{x} \rightarrow x + 2$. But $x = (\sqrt{x})^2$ for each $x \geq 0$. So

$$H: \sqrt{x} \rightarrow (\sqrt{x})^2 + 2.$$

Therefore,

$$H: x \rightarrow x^2 + 2 \text{ on } [0, \infty).$$

f is restricted to $[0, \infty)$. (Are there other functions h and H that work?)

EXAMPLE 7.30 Let $K(x) = \sqrt{x^2 + 3}$ on R and let $f(x) = \sqrt{x}$ on $[0, \infty)$. Find a function g such that $K = f \circ g$.
The function value $f(g(x))$ must equal $K(x)$ on R. Now since f is the square root function,

$$f(g(x)) = \sqrt{g(x)} \text{ on } R.$$

But,

$$K(x) = \sqrt{x^2 + 3} \text{ on } R$$

so

$$g(x) = x^2 + 3 \text{ on } R.$$

EXAMPLE 7.31 Let $f(x) = x^2$ and $g(x) = 1 - x$. Find a function h such that $[f \circ h \circ g](x) = (6 - x)^2$.
The diagram of Figure 7.35 shows that

$$f(h(1 - x)) = (6 - x)^2.$$

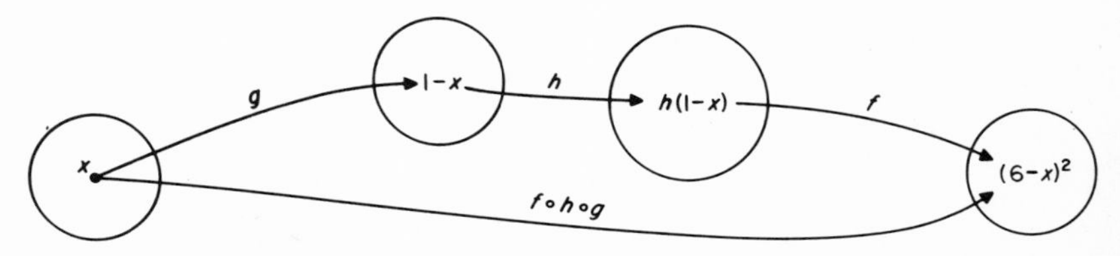

Figure 7.35

But f is the squaring function, so

$$|h(1 - x)| = |6 - x|.$$

Setting $y = 1 - x$, so that $x = 1 - y$,

$$|h(1 - x)| = |h(y)| = |6 - (1 - y)| = |5 + y|.$$

Therefore, one solution is $h(y) = y + 5$ and another is $h(y) = -y - 5$. Here is a check for h defined by $h(x) = -x - 5$.

$$f(h(g(x))) = f(h(1 - x)) = f[-5 - (1 - x)] = f(x - 6)$$
$$= (x - 6)^2 = (6 - x)^2.$$

The check for the solution $h(x) = x + 5$ is left to the student.

EXERCISE SET 7.6

For the given function f define functions g and h each different from f so that $f = g \circ h$.

1. $f(x) = 2x + 3$.
2. $f(x) = 2(x + 3)$.
3. $f(x) = 7x - 3$.
4. $f(x) = \sqrt{x - 1}$.
5. $f(z) = 2 \sin z$.
6. $f(y) = \sin 2y$.
7. $f(y) = 2 \sin y \cos y$. (*Hint*: $g(x) = 2 \sin x$, $h(x) = \cos x$ is incorrect. Change the form of $2 \sin y \cos y$.)
8. $f(x) = \cos (x + 2)$.
9. $f(x) = \tan (x - \pi)$.
10. $f(x) = 3/(x - 2)$.

Find functions f and g that satisfy the given equations. (Do not use $\{(x, y): x = y\}$ as one of the functions.)

11. $f(g(x)) = \sqrt{\sin x}$.
12. $f(g(x)) = \sin \sqrt{x}$.
13. $[f \circ g](x) = \sin (\cos x)$.
14. $[f \circ g](x) = 2^{x^2}$. [NOTE: 2^{x^2} means $2^{(x^2)}$, not $(2^x)^2$.]
15. $[f \circ g](x) = x$.
16. $f(g(x)) = x^2 + 2x + 1$. (*Hint*: change the form of $x^2 + 2x + 1$.)

17. $f(g(x)) = x^2 - x$.
18. $f(g(x)) = (1 - x)/x$.

Find functions f, g, and h that satisfy the given equation. (Do not use $\{(x, y): y = x\}$ as one of the functions.)

19. $f(g(h(x))) = \sqrt{x^2 + 2}$.
20. $f(g(h(x))) = (\sqrt{x} + 2)^3$.
21. $f(g(h(x))) = \sin(x^2 + \pi/2)$.
22. $f(g(h(x))) = 3 \cos 2x$.
23. $f(g(h(x))) = (1 - \sin x)^2$.
24. $f(g(h(x))) = \sqrt{x + 2}$.
25. $f(g(h(g(x)))) = \sin \sqrt{7 + \sqrt{x}}$.

Find all functions h that satisfy the conditions. Draw a balloon diagram for each exercise, showing all the mappings involved.

26. $[f \circ h](x) = x + 5, f(x) = x + 2$.
27. $[f \circ h](x) = 2x + 3, f(x) = 2x$.
28. $f \circ h = \{(1, 3), (2, 0), (3, 4)\}$,
    $f = \{(1, 0), (2, 3), (3, 4), (4, 3)\}$.
29. $[f \circ h](x) = 4, f(x) = x^3 + 3$.
30. $[h \circ f](x) = 6 - x^2, f(x) = x + 1$.
31. $[h \circ f](x) = \sin x$ on $[0, \pi]$, $f(x) = x/2$.
32. $[h \circ f](x) = x, f(x) = \sqrt{x + 1}$.
33. $[h \circ h](x) = x + 7$.
34. $[f \circ h](x) = x, f(x) = x^3/4 + 7$.

Let $f(x) = x + 2$. Compare the graph of g with the graphs of $g \circ f$ and of $f \circ g$ in Exercises 35–37.

35. $g(x) = x^2$.
36. $g(x) = x + 3$.
37. $g(x) = \sin x$, on $[0, 2\pi]$.
38. How does the graph of a function g compare with the graph of $g \circ f$ where $f(x) = x + 2$? where $f(x) = x + h$?
39. How does the graph of a function g compare with the graph of $f \circ g$ where $f(x) = x + 2$? where $f(x) = x + h$? (For each value h, $f(x) = x + h$ is called a *translation*.)

Let $f(x) = 2x$. In Exercise 40–42, compare the graph of g with the graphs of $g \circ f$ and $f \circ g$.

40. $g(x) = x^2$.
41. $g(x) = x + 3$.
42. $g(x) = \sin x$, on $[0, 2\pi]$.

43. How does the graph of a function g compare with the graphs of $g \circ f$ and $f \circ g$ where $f(x) = 2x$? where $f(x) = kx$? (For each value of k, the resulting function f is called a *dilation*.)
44. What is the effect of composing a function with the function I where $I(x) = x$? What is a suitable name for the function I?

Write the given function as a composition of simple functions.

45. $F(x) = 2 \cos (3x^2 + 5)$.
46. $G(x) = 2^{\sin^2(x^5-1)}$.
47. $H(x) = 1 - \tan^2 \sqrt{x^2 + x}$.

7.9 The Identity Function

The composition of the function $I(x) = x$ with any given function g gives

$$[I \circ g](x) = I(g(x)) = g(x)$$

for each $x \in D_g$. That is, $I \circ g$ is the function g itself. Likewise, the composition $g \circ I$, given by

$$[g \circ I](x) = g(I(x)) = g(x),$$

is again the function g. Since the composition of I with any function g and the composition of any function g with I are identically the function g, I is said to be the *identity function* for composition.

Algebraically speaking, with composition of functions considered as a binary operation on functions,

For each function g, $g \circ I = I \circ g = g$

shows that I is the identity for the operation $\circ$. Note the similarity to the behavior of the identities for the operations of addition and multiplication, as given in Chapter Three.

7.10 Inverse Functions; Restricted Identity

The function $f: x \rightarrow x^3$ maps each number into its cube, while the function $g: x \rightarrow \sqrt[3]{x}$ maps each number into its cube root. The composite functions $f \circ g$ and $g \circ f$ map x into x, as shown by the equations

$$[f \circ g](x) = f(g(x)) = f(\sqrt[3]{x}) = (\sqrt[3]{x})^3 = x$$

and

$$[g \circ f](x) = g(f(x)) = g(x^3) = \sqrt[3]{(x^3)} = x.$$

Therefore, as might be expected, f and g "undo" the effects of each other (see Figure 7.36).

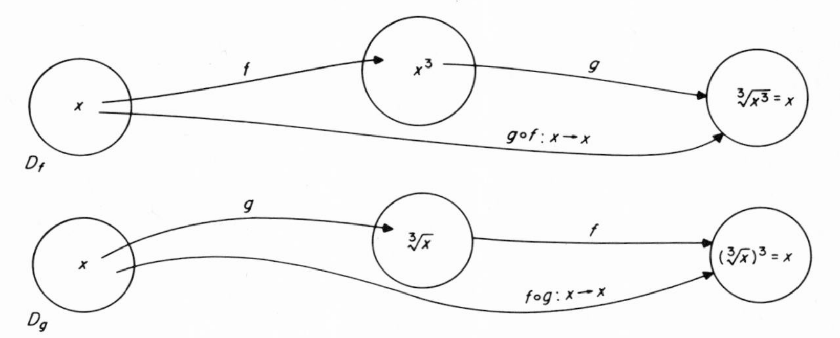

Figure 7.36

Since

$$[f \circ g]: x \to x \text{ for each } x \in R$$

and

$$[g \circ f]: x \to x \text{ for each } x \in R,$$

it follows that each of these composites is the identity function, I.

$$g \circ f = f \circ g = I.$$

The two functions f and g are said to be *inverses of each other.*

Some of the ordered pairs in f are

$$(2, 8), \quad (5, 125), \quad (1, 1), \quad (-3, -27),$$

while ordered pairs in g include

$$(8, 2), \quad (125, 5), \quad (1, 1), \quad (-27, -3).$$

For each ordered pair in f, there is a corresponding ordered pair in g which has its components reversed. That is,

$$\text{for } x \in D_f\text{, if } f\colon x \to y\text{, then } g\colon y \to x$$

and

$$\text{for } y \in D_g\text{, if } g\colon y \to x\text{, then } f\colon x \to y.$$

A pair of functions such that each "undoes" the effect of the other are inverse functions, and each is said to be the inverse of the other. If F is a function that has an inverse, then its inverse is denoted by F^{-1}, where F^{-1} is read as "F inverse."

EXAMPLE 7.32 Find the inverse function of $f\colon x \to x + 3$.
Since f maps each x into $x + 3$, f^{-1} must in turn map each $x + 3$ "back into" x (assuming f has an inverse). That is,

$$f^{-1}\colon x + 3 \to x.$$

Written in more appropriate form,

$$f^{-1}\colon x \to x - 3.$$

Notice that

$$[f \circ f^{-1}](x) = f(f^{-1}(x)) = f(x - 3) = x$$

and

$$[f^{-1} \circ f](x) = f^{-1}(f(x)) = f^{-1}(x + 3) = x.$$

$f \circ f^{-1}$ and $f^{-1} \circ f$ are sketched in Figure 7.37.

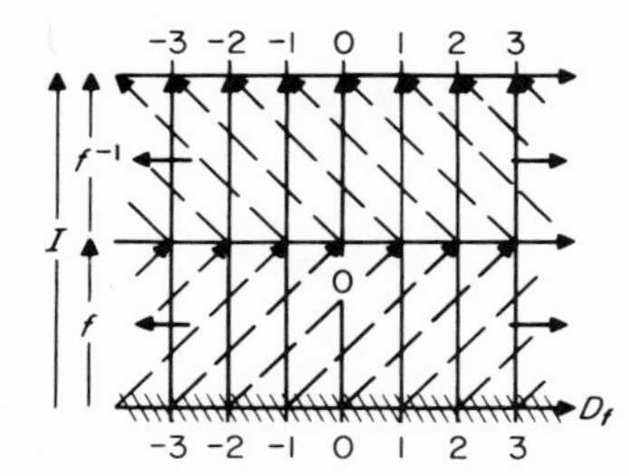

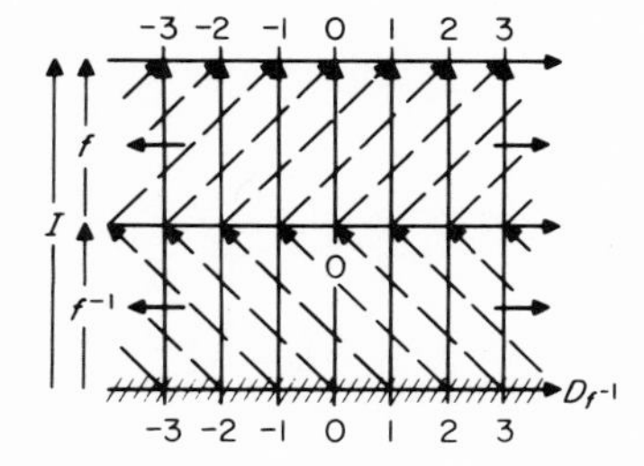

Figure 7.37

It is natural to think of "doubling" and "halving" as inverses since if you double a number, say 7, and then take half of the result, in this case half of 14, the answer is the number you started with.

Let f and g be the restrictions of the "doubling" and "halving" functions defined by

$$f(x) = 2x \text{ on } [1, 3]$$

and

$$g(x) = \frac{x}{2} \text{ on } [2, 6].$$

Suppose $a \in D_f$. Then $1 \leq a \leq 3$, so that $2 \leq 2a \leq 6$ and $f(a) \in D_g$. Now, $g(f(a)) = g(2a) = a$. Therefore,

$$[g \circ f](x) = x \text{ for each } x \in D_f .$$

Similarly, for $b \in D_g$, $2 \leq b \leq 6$, so that $1 \leq b/2 \leq 3$ and $g(b) \in D_f$. And $f(g(b)) = f(b/2) = b$. Therefore,

$$[f \circ g](x) = x \text{ for each } x \in D_g$$

Each of the compositions $g \circ f$ and $f \circ g$ maps x into x for each x in its domain. But neither of these compositions is the identity function, I; each is a restriction of the identity function.

The identity function I is often restricted to a domain A which is a subset of the real numbers. The restricted function is designated by I_A and is called the *identity function on* A. In the above composition of f with g, $f \circ g = I_{[2,6]}$, while in the composition of g with f, $g \circ f = I_{[1,3]}$.

Let $f(x) = 2x + 3$ on $[1, 4]$ and let $g(x) = (x - 3)/2$ on $[5, 11]$. Then

$$f(g(x)) = f\left(\frac{x-3}{2}\right) = 2\left(\frac{x-3}{2}\right) + 3 = x$$

for each $x \in [5, 11]$

and

$$g(f(x)) = g(2x + 3) = \frac{(2x + 3) - 3}{2} = x$$

for each $x \in [1, 4]$.

So,

$$f \circ g = I_{[5,11]} \quad \text{and} \quad g \circ f = I_{[1,4]} .$$

In this example, f and g "undo" the effects of each other, but their compositions in different orders give different restricted identities since $I_{[5,11]} \neq I_{[1,4]}$.

In general, if f and g are functions such that

$$f \circ g = I_{D_g} \quad \text{and} \quad g \circ f = I_{D_f},$$

then f is *the inverse of* g and g is *the inverse of* f. If g is the inverse of f, then g is denoted by f^{-1}.

Two things are worthy of special notice in considering inverse functions: (1) the inverse of a function (if there is one) is a *function* and (2) the proper identity functions are defined on the domains of the function and its inverse.

Let f be a function that has an inverse f^{-1}. If $(x, y) \in f$, then f must map x into y. For f^{-1} to "undo" this, f^{-1} must map y back into x. Therefore, $(y, x) \in f^{-1}$. That is,

if $(x, y) \in f$ then $(y, x) \in f^{-1}$.

And since f is the inverse of f^{-1}, it follows that

if $(x, y) \in f^{-1}$ then $(y, x) \in f$.

Putting these last two conditionals together, the relation between a function and its inverse is

$(x, y) \in f$ if, and only if, $(y, x) \in f^{-1}$.

So, if f is the set of ordered pairs $\{(x, y) : y = f(x)\}$, then f^{-1} is the set of ordered pairs $\{(y, x) : y = f(x)\}$. Now $\{(y, x) : y = f(x)\}$ is the same set as $\{(x, y) : x = f(y)\}$, where x and y have been interchanged. A summary statement is

If f is a function that has an inverse, and f is given by

$\{(x, y) : y = f(x)\}$,

then $f^{-1} = \{(x, y) : x = f(y)\}$.

EXAMPLE 7.33 Let $f = \{(x, y) : y = 3x + 2\}$. Show f^{-1} (if such a function exists) as a mapping and as a set of ordered pairs.
Since $f: x \rightarrow 3x + 2$, f^{-1} must map each $3x + 2$ into x. That is,

$$f^{-1}: 3x + 2 \rightarrow x.$$

Letting $y = 3x + 2$, and solving for x, this mapping can be rewritten as

$$f^{-1}: y \to \frac{y-2}{3}.$$

(The function f does have an inverse since f^{-1} as given is a function, and $f \circ f^{-1} = f^{-1} \circ f = I$.)
In set notation, the inverse function must be

$$f^{-1} = \{(x, y) : x = 3y + 2\},$$

where the open sentence $x = 3y + 2$ is obtained by interchanging x and y in the open sentence of the notation for f. Solving for y, the inverse is written

$$f^{-1} = \left\{(x, y) : y = \frac{x-2}{3}\right\}.$$

Not all functions have inverses. If f is a function which maps two arguments, a and b, into the same function value c [as shown in Figure 7.38(a)], then f can have no inverse, for any such inverse would map c back into a and also into b contrary to the unique value property of functions [see Figure 7.38(b)].

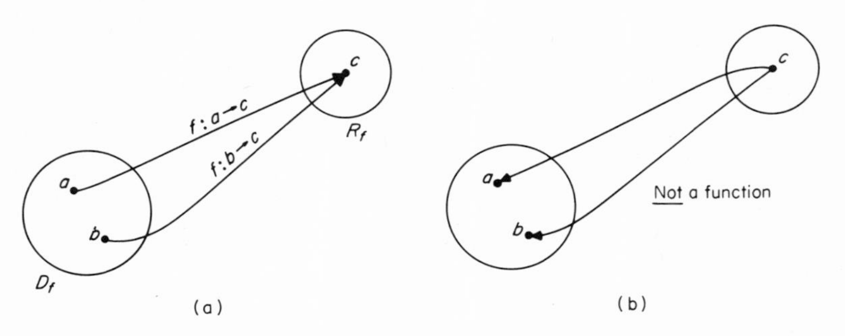

Figure 7.38

For a set of ordered pairs f to be a function, f must satisfy the condition

(1) If $(x, y) \in f$ and $(x, z) \in f$, then $y = z$.

If f also satisfies the condition

(2) If $(x, y) \in f$ and $(z, y) \in f$, then $x = z$,

f is a *one-to-one correspondence, or a one-to-one function.* The condition (1) requires that for each argument of f there is but *one* value, and the condition (2) requires that each value is the image of just *one* argument. Conditions (1) and (2) differ only in that the roles of the first and second components are interchanged. So, if f is a one-to-one function, then the set of ordered pairs obtained by interchanging the components will also be a function. This means

A function f has an inverse if and only if f is a one-to-one function.

EXAMPLE 7.34 Show that $f: x \longrightarrow 5x - 3$ does or does not have an inverse. Graph.
To show that f has an inverse, it will be shown that f is *one-to-one.* Let $(a, c) \in f$ and $(b, c) \in f$. Then $f(a) = c$, and $f(b) = c$. That is,

$$5a - 3 = c \quad \text{and} \quad 5b - 3 = c.$$

It follows that $5a - 3 = 5b - 3$, and that $a = b$. This shows that no two distinct arguments are mapped into the same value. Therefore f is *one-to-one,* and f has an inverse.
The inverse of f is f^{-1}: $(5x - 3) \longrightarrow x$, or, in appropriate form,

$$f^{-1}: x \longrightarrow \frac{x + 3}{5}.$$

The graphs are shown in Figure 7.39.

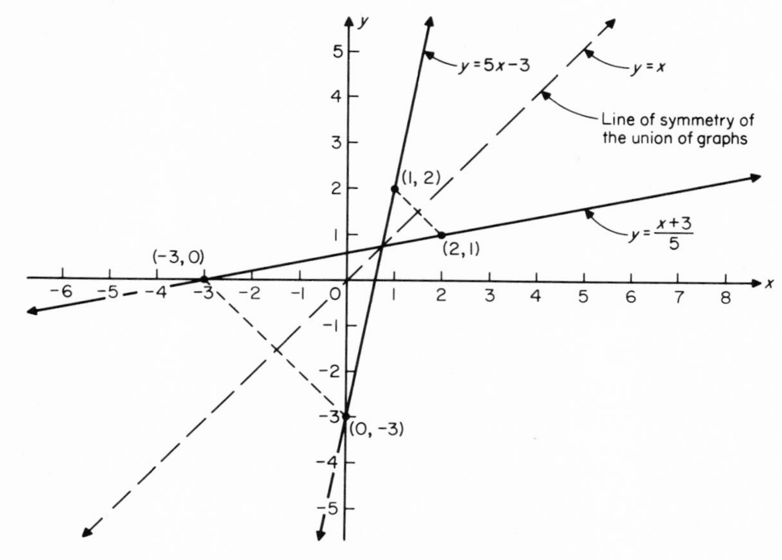

Figure 7.39

EXAMPLE 7.35 Show that $g(x) = x^2$ does or does not have an inverse. Graph.

The function g is not a one-to-one function since both $(-2, 4)$ and $(2, 4)$ are in g (and $-2 \neq 2$). This means that g does not have an inverse. The graph of g is shown in Figure 7.40(a), and the sketch of g is shown in Figure 7.40(b).

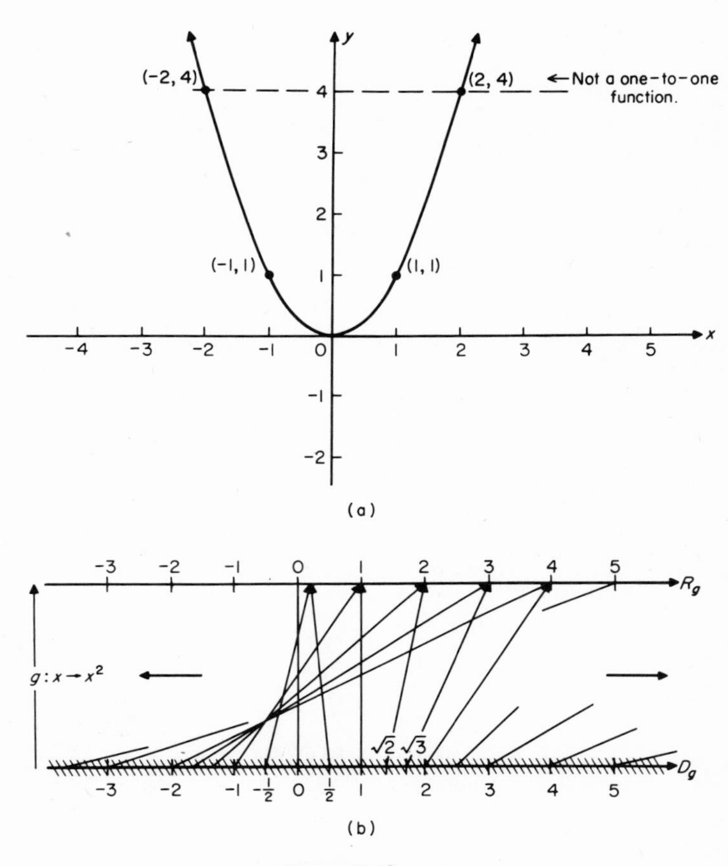

Figure 7.40

It would appear that an inverse to the "squaring" function g would be $f(x) = \sqrt{x}$, which maps each x into its square root. However,

$$[f \circ g](-2) = f(g(-2)) = f(4) = \sqrt{4} = 2.$$

So the composition fails to map -2 into -2.

Example 7.36 illustrates how $g(x) = x^2$ can be restricted so that it is the inverse of $f(x) = \sqrt{x}$.

EXAMPLE 7.36 Show that $g(x) = x^2$, $x \in [0, \infty)$ does have an inverse. Graph the function and its inverse.
To show g is one-to-one, let $(a, c) \in g$, $(b, c) \in g$. Then $g(a) = a^2 = c$ and $g(b) = b^2 = c$; so $a^2 = b^2$. By taking the square root of both sides, $|a| = |b|$. But $a \in [0, \infty)$ and $b \in [0, \infty)$; this means $a = b$. Therefore, g is one-to-one and has an inverse.
Since $g: x \longrightarrow x^2$,

$$g^{-1}: x^2 \longrightarrow x,$$

or more appropriately,

$$g^{-1}: x \longrightarrow \sqrt{x}.$$

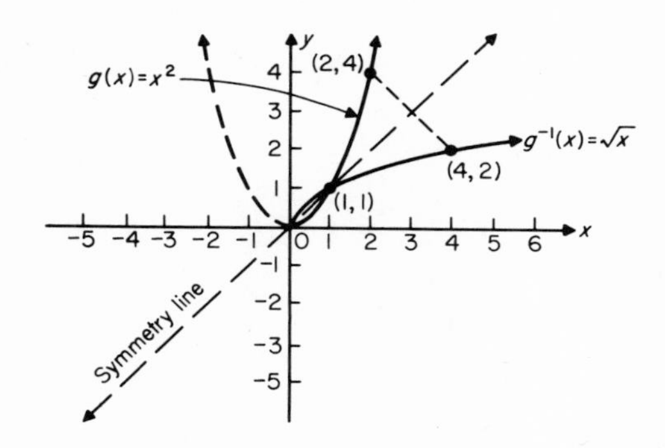

Figure 7.41

The requirement that no argument of a function have two values is given graphically by the vertical line test, which specifies that the graph of a function cannot intersect the same *vertical* line in more than one point. That no value have two arguments interchanges the roles of the first and second components. It specifies that the graph of a one-to-one function cannot intersect the same *horizontal* line in more than one point. For a set of ordered pairs to be a one-to-one function, its graph must satisfy this *horizontal line test* as well as the vertical line test.

EXAMPLE 7.37 Determine whether or not $H(x) = 7x + 2$ has an inverse.

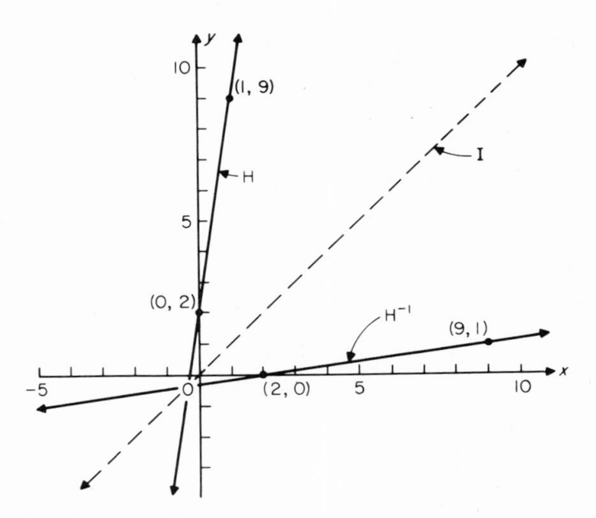

Figure 7.42

H is graphed in Figure 7.42. Notice that the graph is a line, and satisfies the horizontal line test. Therefore, H has an inverse. Since

$$H = \{(x, y) : y = 7x + 2\},$$

$$H^{-1} = \{(x, y) : x = 7y + 2\}$$

$$= \left\{(x, y) : \frac{x - 2}{7} = y\right\}.$$

So,

$$H^{-1}(x) = \frac{x - 2}{7}.$$

EXAMPLE 7.38 Determine whether $f(x) = \sin x$ has an inverse. The horizontal line test fails, as is seen in Figure 7.43. Therefore $f(x) = \sin x$ has no inverse.

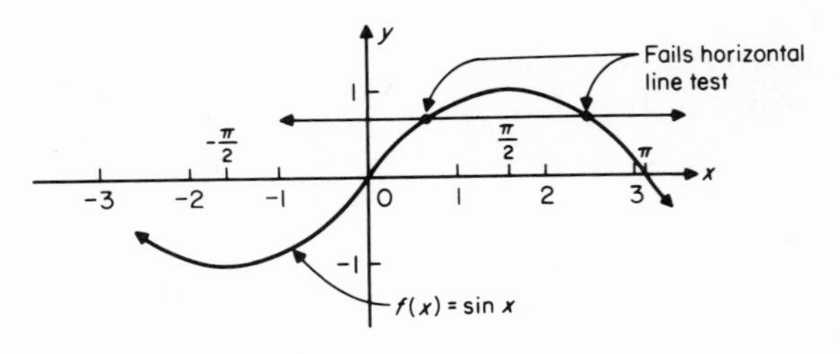

Figure 7.43

EXERCISE SET 7.7

Let $f = \{(1, 10), (2, 20), (3, 30), (4, 40)\}$.

1. Is f one-to-one?
2. Find f^{-1}.
3. Compare the ordered pairs of f with those of f^{-1}.
4. Show by a sketch that $f \circ f^{-1}(x) = x$ on R_f.
5. Is $f \circ f^{-1} = f^{-1} \circ f$?
6. How does the sketch of $f^{-1} \circ f$ differ from the sketch of $f \circ f^{-1}$?

Prove by composing in both orders that the listed functions f and g of Exercises 7–10 are inverses.

7. $f(x) = x + 7$, $g(x) = x - 7$.
8. $f(x) = 5x$, $g(x) = x/5$.
9. $f(x) = 2x + 4$ on $[1, 5]$, $g(x) = (x - 4)/2$ on $[6, 14]$.
10. $f(x) = (x + 1)^2$ on $[0, 1]$, $g(x) = \sqrt{x} - 1$ on $[1, 4]$.
11. Prove that each of the functions f in Exercises 7–10 are one-to-one functions by showing that if $(a, c) \in f$ and $(b, c) \in f$, then $a = b$.

In Exercises 12–19, find the inverse of the listed function (if it has one) by interchanging the role of x and y in the open sentence defining the function. Prove that your answer is the inverse by composing it with the given function. Graph the given function, its inverse, and the identity function $I_{D_f \cup D_{f^{-1}}}$ all on the same graph.

12. $f = \{(x, y): y = 3x + 4\}$.
13. $g = \{(x, y): y = \frac{1}{2}x - 3\}$.
14. $h = \{(x, y): y = 4 - 2x \text{ on } [-3, 2]\}$.
15. $f = \{(x, y): 3x + 2y = 5\}$.
16. $g = \{(x, y): y = x^2 + 2, x \geq 0\}$.
17. $h = \{(x, y): y = -x\}$.
18. $F = \{(x, y): y = (1 + x)/(1 - x). x \neq 1\}$.
19. $G = \{(x, y): y = 1/x, x > 0\}$.
20. Prove that each of the functions in Exercises 12–19 is one-to-one by showing that its graph passes the horizontal line test.
21. Determine a line of symmetry for the graph of $f \cup f^{-1}$ for each of Exercises 12–19.

Which graphs (Exercises 22–27) are of one-to-one functions? For those that are one-to-one, graph the inverse function. [Use the line of symmetry for a function and its inverse to graph the inverse (see Exercise 21)].

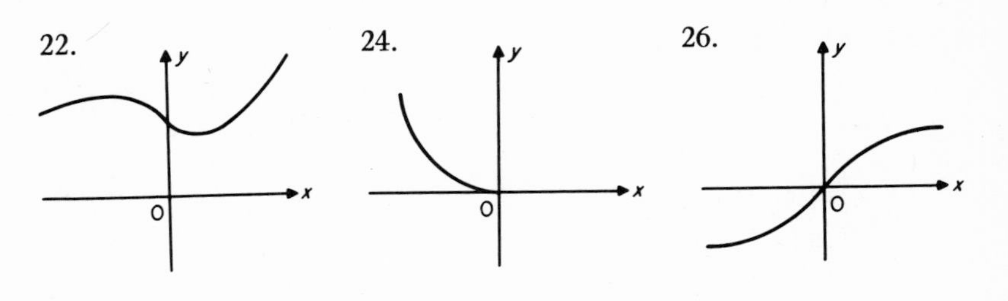

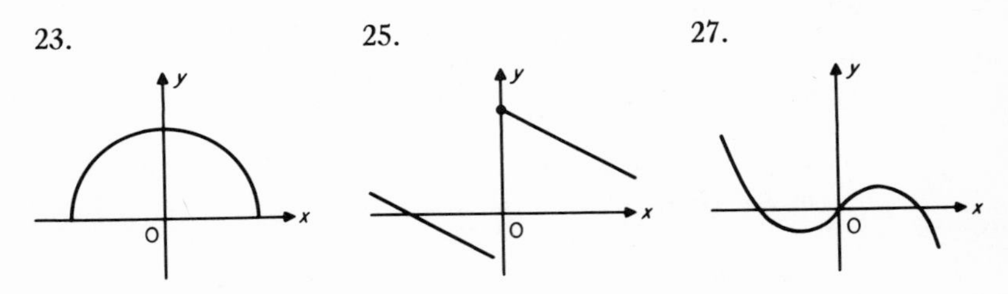

In Exercises 28–46 find the inverse for each function that has one. If the function does not have an inverse, prove this by listing two arguments that have the same value.

28. $f = \{(x, y) : y = x + 1 \text{ on } [0, 4]\}$.
29. $h(x) = (x + 4)/2$ on $[2, 6]$.
30. $f: x \longrightarrow 2x + 3$.
31. $f(x) = x^2 + 1$.
32. $f = \{(x, y) : y = 2x^2 + 4x, x > 0\}$.
33. $g(x) = x^2 + 3x - 4$.
34. $f(x) = x^2 - 2x + 1$.
35. $\{(x, y) : xy = 4\}$.
36. $f(x) = x/(x + 1), x \neq -1$.
37. $f: x \longrightarrow \sin x$.
38. $g: x \longrightarrow \cos x$.
39. $h(y) = \sec y, -\pi/2 < y < \pi/2$.
40. $f(x) = \cos x, 0 \leq x \leq \pi$.
41. $\{(x, y) : y = \sin x \cos x\}$.
42. sine on $[0, \pi]$.
43. sine on $[-\pi/2, \pi/2]$.
44. cosine on $[-\pi/2, \pi/2]$.
45. $\{(-1, -3), (0, 0), (2, 6), (3, 9)\}$.
46. $\{(-1, 3), (0, 0), (2, 3), (3, -1)\}$.
47. Describe the relations between the domains and ranges of a function and its inverse.
48. For a function that has an inverse, how can you alter a sketch of the function to get a sketch of the inverse?
49. State the condition that a set of ordered pairs is not a function.

50. State the condition that a function is not a one-to-one correspondence.
51. Given that f is a function such that

$$f^{-1}(x) = f(x) \text{ for each } x \in D_f,$$

what can you say about f?
52. Given that f is a function such that

$$f^{-1} = f,$$

what can you say about the graph of f? (Compare with Exercise 51.)
53. When a function f is given by a table, how can the table be used to find values of f^{-1}?
54. Prove that if a function f has an inverse, then

$$(f^{-1})^{-1} = f.$$

55. Prove that the composition of two one-to-one functions is a one-to-one function.
56. Prove that the composition of functions is associative.
57. Solve $[f \circ g](z) = 27$ for z, where $f(x) = x^3$ and $g(x) = 2x + 3$.

7.11 Properties of Composition

The composition of functions is associative. To show this, it will suffice to establish the following:

(1) $\{[f \circ g] \circ h\}(x) = f \circ [g \circ h](x)$ for each $x \in D_{[f \circ g] \circ h} \cap D_{f \circ [g \circ h]}$.

(2) $D_{[f \circ g] \circ h} = D_{f \circ [g \circ h]}$.

To establish (1), apply the definition of function composition:

$$\begin{aligned}[f \circ g] \circ h(x) &= [f \circ g](h(x)) = f(g(h(x))) = f([g \circ h](x)) \\ &= f \circ [g \circ h](x) \text{ for each } x \in D_{[f \circ g] \circ h} \cap D_{f \circ [g \circ h]}.\end{aligned}$$

The following establishes (2):

$$\begin{aligned}D_{[f \circ g] \circ h} &= \{x : x \in D_h \text{ and } h(x) \in D_{f \circ g}\} \\ &= \{x : x \in D_h \text{ and } h(x) \in \{z : z \in D_g \text{ and } g(z) \in D_f\}\} \\ &= \{x : x \in D_h \text{ and } [h(x) \in D_g \text{ and } g(h(x)) \in D_f]\},\end{aligned}$$

$$\begin{aligned}D_{f \circ [g \circ h]} &= \{x : x \in D_{g \circ h} \text{ and } g \circ h(x) \in D_f\} \\ &= \{x : [x \in D_h \text{ and } h(x) \in D_g] \text{ and } g(h(x)) \in D_f\}.\end{aligned}$$

By the associativity of "and,"

$$D_{[f\circ g]\circ h} = D_{f\circ [g\circ h]} \,.$$

Because function composition is associative, there is no need to insert grouping symbols in expressions indicating the composition of three or more functions. Therefore, instead of writing

$$f \circ [g \circ (f \circ h)] \quad \text{or} \quad [(F \circ F) \circ (F \circ F)] \circ F,$$

we will write

$$f \circ g \circ f \circ h \quad \text{and} \quad F \circ F \circ F \circ F \circ F.$$

We have already remarked that the composite of a pair of functions is a function, so that function composition is closed. Also, the function I such that $I(x) = x$ for each $x \in R$ is an identity for composition of functions. So we have that function composition is closed and associative, and possesses an identity. These are properties shared by addition and multiplication of real numbers (see Chapter Three). Other properties of addition and multiplication do not hold for function composition, however. It has been seen that function composition is not commutative. Also, for some functions there is no function such that their composite is the identity function. Of course, each one-to-one function has an inverse in the restricted sense, but non-one-to-one functions do not even have this type of inverse.

The preceding remarks are summarized below:

(1) For any functions f, g, h, $[f \circ g] \circ h = f \circ [g \circ h]$.

(2) For any functions f and g, $f \circ g$ is a function.

(3) For each function f, $f \circ I = I \circ f = f$.

(4) There are functions f and g, $f \circ g \neq g \circ f$.

(5) Some functions do not have inverses.

7.12 Inverse of a Composition

To find $f \circ g(x)$, first find $g(x)$ and then find the image of $g(x)$ under f. That is, the application of g is followed by the application of f. Thus it is natural to think of function composition as the operation "followed by." One can think of the function f given by $f(x) = 2x + 3$ as "doubling, followed by adding 3."

Many operations are performed in a certain order. When you dress in the morning, you put on your socks *before* you put on your shoes. When you drive downtown, you get out of your car, then lock the door (most cars are designed so that these operations cannot be reversed). To find the value of f given by $f(x) = 3x + 5$ at 2, you triple 2 first and then add 5 to that result.

How can the effect of successive operations be "undone?" Once you have your socks and shoes on your feet, you take off your shoes before you take off your socks; this is the reverse of the order in which they were put on. To get back into your locked car, you unlock the car first, then get in. Again, the operation originally done last is undone first. To find the number z such that $f(z) = 17$, first subtract 5 from 17 to get 12 and then take $\frac{1}{3}$ of 12 to get 4. So, $z = 4$. Once more, to undo the two operations, performed in order, the *last* operation is undone *first*.

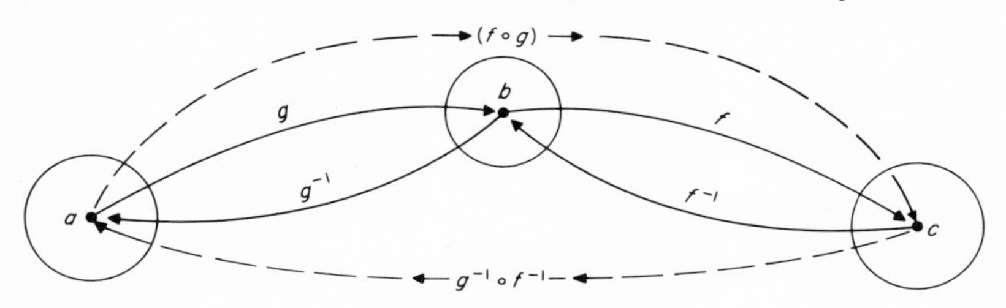

Figure 7.44

Let h be a function with an inverse and let $h = f \circ g$. The balloon diagram in Figure 7.44 shows that if g maps a into b and f maps b into c, so that $f \circ g$ maps a into c, then $g^{-1} \circ f^{-1}$ will map c into a. Thus,

$$g^{-1} \circ f^{-1}(x) = [f \circ g]^{-1}(x),$$

and since the domain of $g^{-1} \circ f^{-1}$ is the same as the domain of $[f \circ g]^{-1}$,

$$[f \circ g]^{-1} = g^{-1} \circ f^{-1}.$$

In applying the above rule to find the inverse of h where $h(x) = 6x - 11$, we first notice that h is the composite $f \circ g$ where

$$f(x) = x - 11,$$

$$g(x) = 6x.$$

Then, since

$$f^{-1}(x) = x + 11$$

and

$$g^{-1}(x) = \frac{x}{6},$$

h^{-1} is given by

$$h^{-1}(x) = [f \circ g]^{-1}(x) = g^{-1} \circ f^{-1}(x)$$
$$= g^{-1}(x + 11) = \frac{x + 11}{6}.$$

This is the inverse of h since

$$h \circ h^{-1}(x) = h\left(\frac{x + 11}{6}\right) = 6\left(\frac{x + 11}{6}\right) - 11 = x,$$

and

$$h^{-1} \circ h(x) = h^{-1}(6x - 11) = \frac{(6x - 11) + 11}{6} = x$$

(see Figure 7.45).

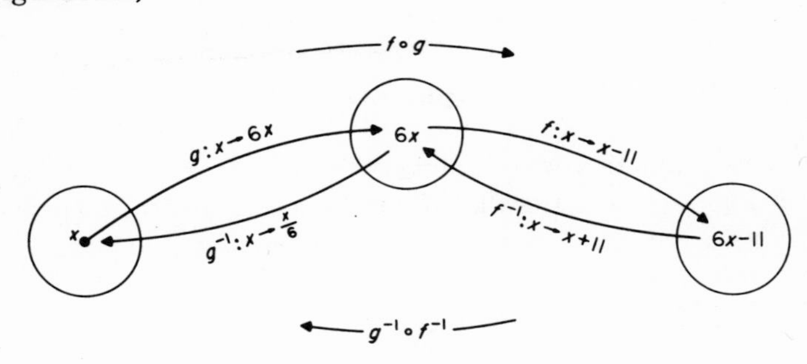

Figure 7.45

EXAMPLE 7.39 Find the inverse of $f \circ g$ where $f(x) = 2x$ and $g(x) = x + 7$.
Since $f^{-1}(x) = x/2$, $g^{-1}(x) = x - 7$,

$$[(f \circ g)^{-1}](x) = [g^{-1} \circ f^{-1}](x) = g^{-1}\left(\frac{x}{2}\right) = \frac{x}{2} - 7.$$

So,

$$[(f \circ g)^{-1}](x) = \frac{x}{2} - 7.$$

This is the inverse of $[f \circ g](x) = 2(x + 7)$ on R.

EXAMPLE 7.40 Find the inverse of $f(x) = \sqrt{x+3}$ on $[-3, \infty)$ by writing f as a composition of simpler functions and then using the inverses of these functions.

$f = g \circ h$, where $h(x) = x + 3$, and $g(x) = \sqrt{x}$. Then

$$h^{-1}(x) = x - 3 \quad \text{and} \quad g^{-1}(x) = x^2 \qquad (\text{on } [0, \infty)).$$

Hence,

$$\begin{aligned} f^{-1}(x) &= (g \circ h)^{-1}(x) = [h^{-1} \circ g^{-1}](x) \\ &= h^{-1}(x^2) = x^2 - 3. \end{aligned}$$

Note that $D_{f^{-1}} = [0, \infty)$.

EXERCISE SET 7.8

Write each function as a composition of simpler functions and find the inverse by using the inverses of the component functions.

1. $F(x) = 2x + 11$.
2. $g(x) = 4(x - 2)$.
3. $f = \{(x, y): y = (x + 2)^2, 0 \leq x\}$.
4. $g(x) = x^2 - 4$ on $[0, \infty)$.
5. $g(x) = x^3/3$ on R.
6. $f: x \longrightarrow 2/x^2$ on $[1, 2]$.
7. $H(z) = \sqrt{z} + 5$.
8. $f: x \longrightarrow -\sqrt{x-2}$ on $[2, \infty)$.
9. $H(x) = \dfrac{2}{x-3}$ on $[4, 11]$.
10. $g(x) = \dfrac{5}{\sqrt{x-1}}$ on $]1, \infty)$.
11. $h(x) = x^2 + 2x$ on $[1, \infty)$.
12. $f(x) = (3x + 2)^2$ on $[0, \infty)$.
13. $H(x) = (x + 3)^3 - 2$.
14. $f(x) = 4(3x^2 + 1)^5$ on $[0, 1]$.
15. $h: x \longrightarrow \dfrac{x+2}{x+3}$.

7.13 Restricting Domains to Obtain Inverses

Just as a set of ordered pairs that is not a function can be restricted so that the resulting set of ordered pairs is a function, a function that does not have an inverse can be restricted so that the resulting function is one-to-one.

In Example 7.36 the squaring function was restricted to the non-negative reals producing a function that has an inverse. Let f denote the squaring function, so that $f(x) = x^2$ on R. The graph of f is given in Figure 7.46(a). There are many ways of restricting f to give a one-to-one function

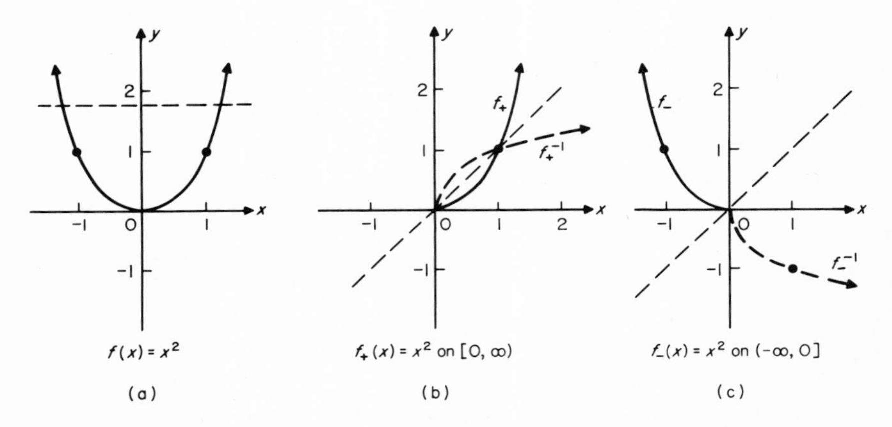

Figure 7.46

on a maximal domain, but the two following restrictions are the most natural:

$$f_+(x) = x^2 \text{ on } [0, \infty),$$

$$f_-(x) = x^2 \text{ on } (-\infty, 0].$$

These are shown together with their inverses in Figures 7.46(b) and (c), respectively. The inverses are defined by

$$f_+^{-1}(x) = \sqrt{x} \text{ on } [0, \infty),$$

$$f_-^{-1}(x) = -\sqrt{x} \text{ on } [0, \infty).$$

It is customary to speak of f_+^{-1} as *the* inverse of the squaring function.

EXAMPLE 7.41 The graph of $g(x) = x^3 - 3x$, given in Figure 7.47(a), does not pass the horizontal line test so the function is not one-to-one. It is seen from the graph that g restricted to $[-1, 1]$ (labeled g_0) is one-to-one as is g restricted to $(-\infty, -1]$ and g restricted to $[1, \infty)$. (Of course there are many other possibilities.) The restriction of g to $[-1, 1]$ and its inverse are graphed in Figure 7.47(b).

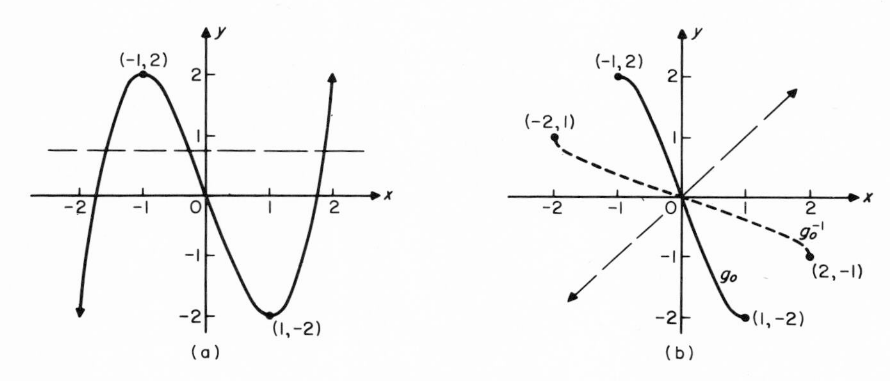

Figure 7.47

The inverse of $g_0(x) = x^3 - 3x$ on $[-1, 1]$ is

$$g_0^{-1} = \{(x, y): x = y^3 - 3y,\ y \in [-1, 1],\ x \in [-2, 2]\}.$$

The rule $x = y^3 - 3y$ which defines g_0^{-1} is not readily solvable for y in terms of x, so the set notation description is used and an explicit statement of the defining rule is avoided.

7.14 Inverse Trigonometric Functions

The trigonometric functions such as sine and cosine do not have inverses unless their domains are restricted. These functions are usually restricted to a maximal uninterrupted domain in the vicinity of the origin in order to obtain a one-to-one function.

The sine function [Figure 7.48(a)] passes the horizontal line test on the maximal interval

$$\left[-\frac{\pi}{2}, \frac{\pi}{2}\right].$$

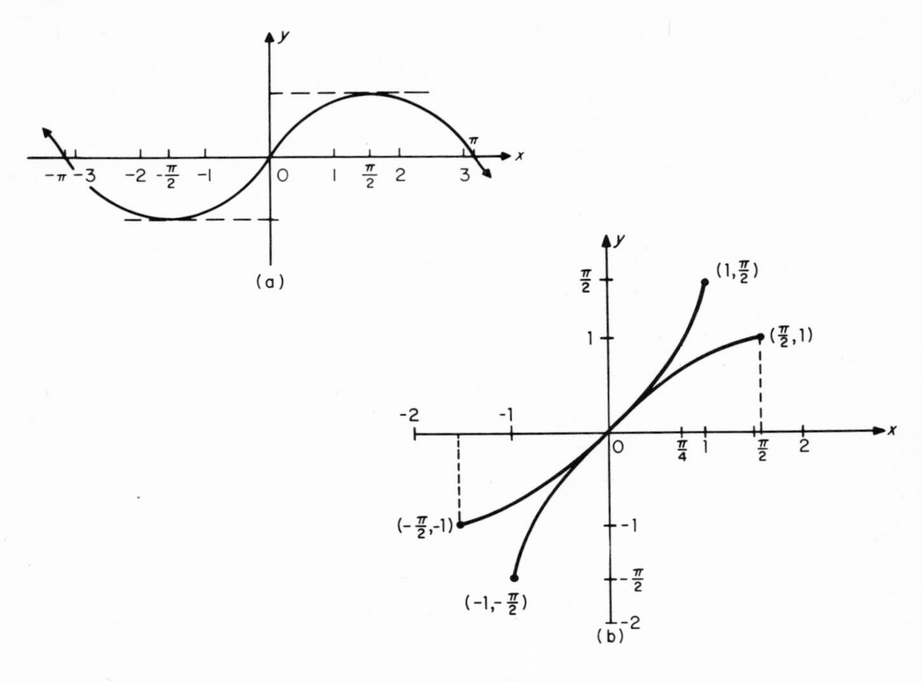

Figure 7.48

The inverse of

$$f(x) = \sin x \text{ on } \left[-\frac{\pi}{2}, \frac{\pi}{2}\right]$$

is then

$$f^{-1} = \left\{(x, y) : x = \sin y,\ y \in \left[-\frac{\pi}{2}, \frac{\pi}{2}\right]\right\}.$$

For each $x \in [-1, 1]$, $f^{-1}(x)$ is the number in $[-\pi/2, \pi/2]$ whose sine is x. As with sine itself, no algebraic rule can be given to define the inverse of the sine function.

It is customary to denote the inverse of sine by "$\sin^{-1}$" or by "arc sin," so

$$\sin^{-1} x = f^{-1}(x) = \text{arc sin } x \text{ on } [-1, 1].$$

In all cases $\sin^{-1} x$ means the value of the inverse sine function at x, and *not* $1/(\sin x)$. [Of course, $(\sin x)^{-1}$ does mean $1/(\sin x)$.]

Since $\sin^{-1}$ is by definition the inverse of sine,

$$[\sin \circ \sin^{-1}](x) = x \text{ for each } x\ [-1, 1]$$

and

$$[\sin^{-1} \circ \sin](x) = x \text{ for each } x \left[-\frac{\pi}{2}, \frac{\pi}{2}\right].$$

From the graph of cosine [Figure 7.49(a)], it is seen that $f(x) = \cos x$ on $[0, \pi]$ is one-to-one on a maximal domain which includes 0. Although there are many other choices for restrictions of cos, $[0, \pi]$ is standard. Since f is one-to-one, f^{-1} exists. The inverse is denoted "$\cos^{-1}$" and

$$\cos(\cos^{-1}(x)) = x \text{ on } [-1, 1].$$

The graphs of cos restricted to $[0, \pi]$ and $\cos^{-1}$ are given in Figure 7.49(b).

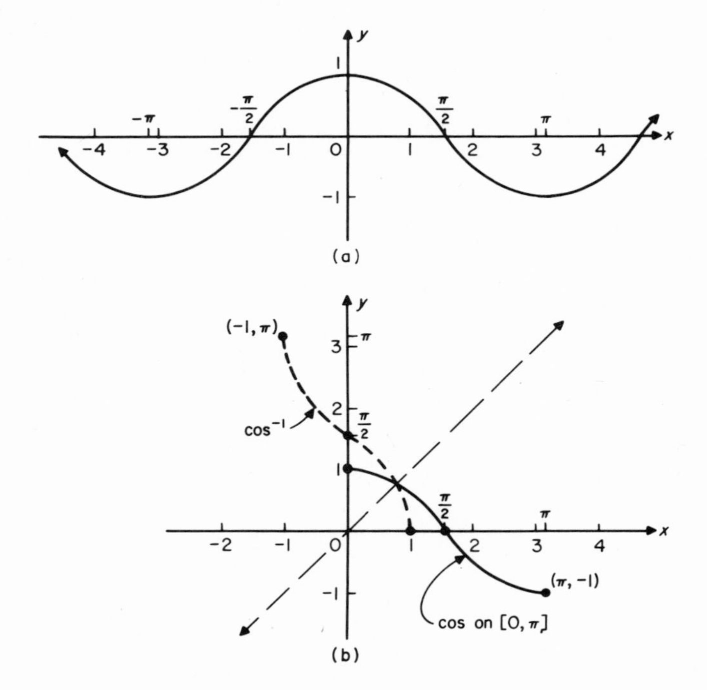

Figure 7.49

The other trigonometric functions may be treated in the same manner as sin and cos. Table 7.3 is a summary of the notation and standard domains and ranges of the inverse trigonometric functions.

The value of any of these functions at a given number can be found by the methods of Chapter Six. Except for special numbers, the trigonometric tables are used to give approximate values.

TABLE 7.3

INVERSE OF TRIGONOMETRIC FUNCTIONS

Function	Inverse	Standard Domain of Inverse	Standard Range of Inverse
sin	$\sin^{-1}$ (arc sin)	$[-1, 1]$	$\left[-\frac{\pi}{2}, \frac{\pi}{2}\right]$
cos	$\cos^{-1}$ (arc cos)	$[-1, 1]$	$[0, \pi]$
tan	$\tan^{-1}$ (arc tan)	$(-\infty, \infty)$	$\left]-\frac{\pi}{2}, \frac{\pi}{2}\right[$
cot	$\cot^{-1}$ (arc cot)	$(-\infty, \infty)$	$]0, \pi[$
sec	$\sec^{-1}$ (arc sec)	$(-\infty, -1] \cup [1, \infty)$	$\left[0, \frac{\pi}{2}\right[\cup \left]\frac{\pi}{2}, \pi\right]$
csc	$\csc^{-1}$ (arc csc)	$(-\infty, -1] \cup [1, \infty)$	$\left[-\frac{\pi}{2}, 0\right[\cup \left]0, \frac{\pi}{2}\right]$

EXAMPLE 7.42 $\sin^{-1} 0.6$ is found from Table 1 to be (approximately) 0.644 since $\sin 0.644 = 0.6$.

EXAMPLE 7.43 $\sin^{-1} 0.5 = \pi/6$ since $\sin \pi/6 = 0.5$ and

$$\pi/6 \in [-\pi/2, \pi/2].$$

EXAMPLE 7.44 From the diagram of Figure 7.50 it is seen that

$$\sin [\cos^{-1} x] = \sqrt{1 - x^2}.$$

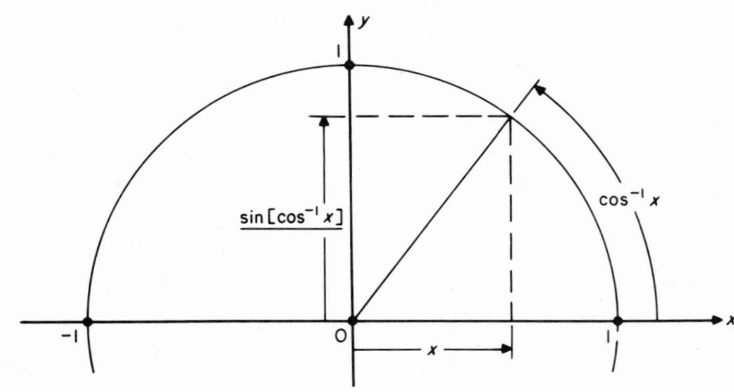

Figure 7.50

(It sometimes helps to read "$\cos^{-1} x$" as "the arc whose cos is x," which is an expansion of "arc cos x.")

EXAMPLE 7.45 Simplify $\tan [2 \sin^{-1} x]$.

$$\tan [2 \sin^{-1} x] = \frac{2 \tan [\sin^{-1} x]}{1 - \tan^2 [\sin^{-1} x]}$$

$$= \frac{2 \cdot \dfrac{x}{\sqrt{1 - x^2}}}{1 - \left[\dfrac{x}{\sqrt{1 - x^2}}\right]^2}$$

$$= \frac{2x\sqrt{1 - x^2}}{1 - 2x^2}.$$

EXAMPLE 7.46 Find the inverse of

$$F(x) = \sin^{-1} (x^2 - 7)$$

by writing F as a composition of simple functions and then applying the inverses of these functions in reverse order. (Assume an appropriate domain.)
Let $f(x) = x^2$, $g(x) = x - 7$, $h(x) = \sin^{-1} x$. Then

$$F(x) = h \circ g \circ f,$$

$$F^{-1}(x) = f^{-1} \circ g^{-1} \circ h^{-1},$$

where $f^{-1}(x) = \sqrt{x}$, $g^{-1}(x) = x + 7$, $h^{-1}(x) = \sin x$, so

$$F^{-1}(x) = f^{-1}(g^{-1}(h^{-1}(x)))$$

$$= f^{-1}(g^{-1} (\sin x))$$

$$= f^{-1} ((\sin x) + 7)$$

$$= \sqrt{7 + \sin x} \text{ (on an appropriate domain).}$$

EXERCISE SET 7.9

Restrict the domain of each function so that the resulting function has an inverse. Graph the original function and indicate the restriction on the domain. Graph the inverse of the restriction.

1. $f(x) = x^2 + 1$.
2. $g(x) = x^2 + 8x$.
3. $H(x) = x^2 - 2$.
4. $h(x) = |x|$.
5. $g(x) = \begin{cases} x \text{ on } (-\infty, 0], \\ 2 - x^2 \text{ on }]0, \infty). \end{cases}$

Find the value.

6. $\sin^{-1} 1$.
7. $\cos^{-1} 0$.
8. $\tan^{-1} 1$.
9. $\sin^{-1} 0.4$.
10. $\cos^{-1} 0.2$.
11. $\text{arc tan } \sqrt{3}$.
12. $\text{arc sin } \frac{1}{2}$.
13. $\text{arc cos } (\sqrt{3}/2)$.
14. $\text{arc sec } 2$.
15. $\text{arc csc } (2\sqrt{3}/3)$.

Graph.

16. $\tan^{-1}$.
17. $\cot^{-1}$.
18. $\sec^{-1}$.
19. $\csc^{-1}$.
20. $f(x) = \sin^{-1} (x/2)$.
21. $g(x) = 3 \cos^{-1} 2x$.
22. $h(x) = \sin^{-1} (2x + 1)$.
23. $H(x) = \text{arc cos } (-x)$.

Find the value.

24. $\sin (\sin^{-1} 0.3)$.
25. $\cos (\sin^{-1} \frac{1}{2})$.
26. $\cos (\sin^{-1} \frac{3}{5})$.
27. $\sin (\cos^{-1} \frac{5}{13})$.
28. $\tan (\tan^{-1} 0.4)$.
29. $\sin^{-1} (\sin (\pi/6))$.
30. $\cos^{-1} (\cos 0.2)$.
31. $\sin^{-1} (\cos (\pi/3))$.
32. $\sin^{-1} (\cos x)$.
33. $\tan^{-1} (\cos 0.3)$.
34. $\cos (\sin^{-1} x)$.
35. $\sin (2 \cos^{-1} x)$.
36. $\cos (\frac{1}{2} \cos^{-1} x)$.
37. $\sin (\frac{1}{2} \sin^{-1} x)$.
38. $\tan (\frac{1}{2} \sin^{-1} x)$.
39. $\cos (2 \sin^{-1} x)$.

Write each function as a composition of simpler functions and find its inverse using the inverses of the components.

40. $G(x) = 2 \sin x$.
41. $H(x) = 8 \sin [2x + 11]$.
42. $f(x) = \frac{1}{2} \cos (x + \pi)$.
43. $g(x) = 7 + 3 \sin (2 + \tan x)$.
44. $F(x) = \sec (\sin (\sin^{-1} (\sec^{-1} (2x + \pi))))$.

Solve for x.

45. $\tan^{-1} x + 2 \tan^{-1} 1 = \dfrac{3\pi}{4}$.

46. $\sin^{-1} x + 2 \cos^{-1} x = \dfrac{\pi}{2}$.

7.15 Exponential Functions

The function f defined by

$$f(x) = 2^x$$

on the set of rational numbers is assumed to have values on the irrational numbers as well so that its graph appears as in Figure 7.51.

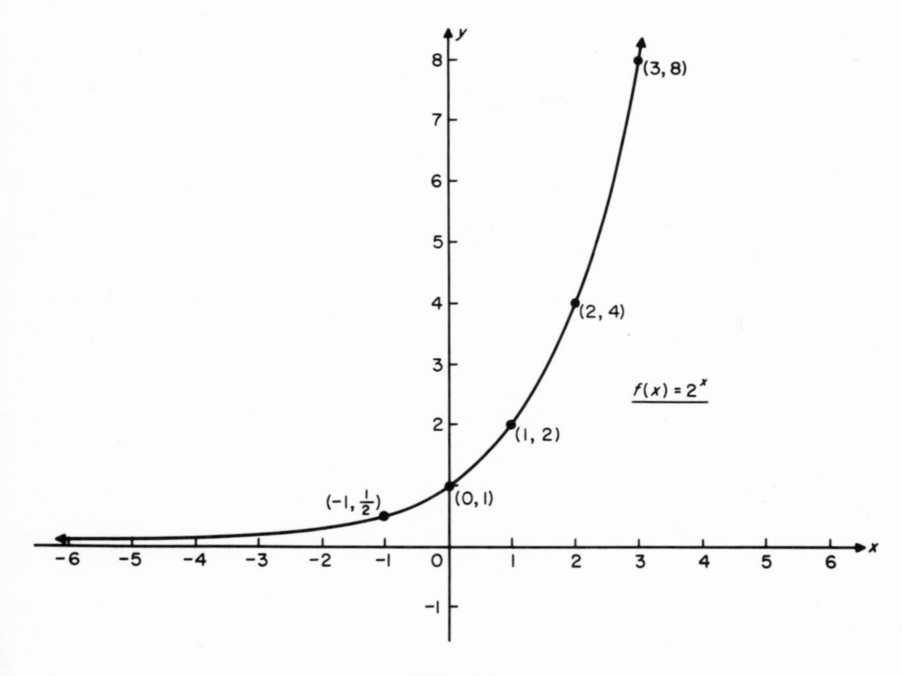

Figure 7.51

The point (3, 8) is on the graph because $2^3 = 8$; so is $(-1, \frac{1}{2})$ since $2^{-1} = \frac{1}{2}$, and so is $(\frac{1}{2}, \sqrt{2})$ since $2^{1/2} = \sqrt{2}$. For each rational number p/q, $(p/q, \sqrt[q]{2^p})$ is on the graph. The point $(\sqrt{3}, 2^{\sqrt{3}})$ is on the graph where $2^{\sqrt{3}}$

denotes the real number second coordinate of the point on the graph with first coordinate $\sqrt{3}$. Similarly, $(\pi, 2^{\pi})$ and $(1 - \sqrt{5}, 2^{(1-\sqrt{5})})$ are on the graph.

This function is called the *exponential function with base* 2 and is often denoted by "$\exp_2$." Thus,

$$\exp_2(x) = 2^x \text{ on } R.$$

In like manner, for any positive real number a, rational or irrational, different from 1, the function

$$\{(x, y) : y = a^x, x \in R\}$$

is called the *exponential function with base a* and is denoted by "$\exp_a$." (Why is 1 excluded as a base of an exponential function?)

The graphs of several exponential functions are given in Figure 7.52.

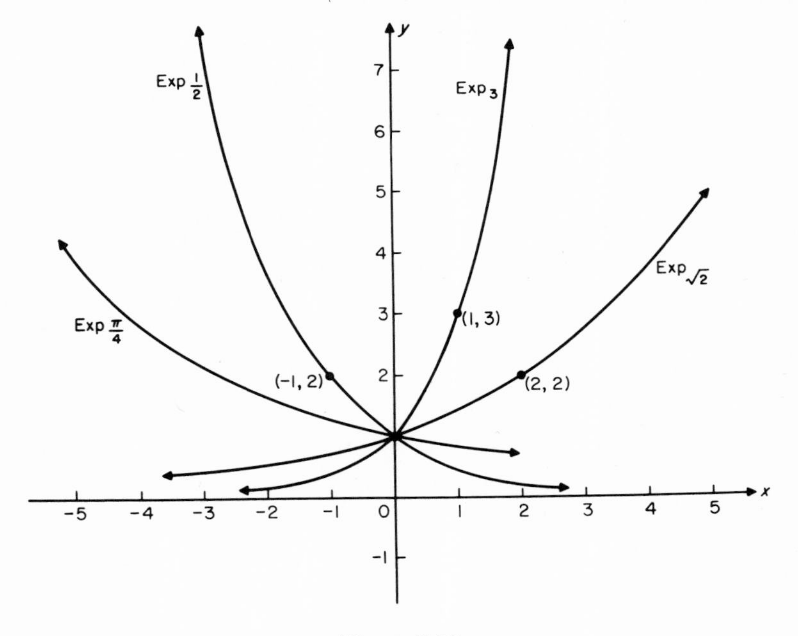

Figure 7.52

The following properties of exponential functions can be seen from the graphs of Figure 7.52.

(1) The domain of each exponential function is R and the range is R^+.

(2) $\exp_a(0) = 1$.

(3) If $0 < a < 1$, then $\exp_a$ is decreasing.†

(4) If $a > 1$, then $\exp_a$ is increasing.†

(5) $\exp_a$ is one-to-one.

Other important properties of exponential functions can be derived from familiar laws of exponents for rational arguments and can be proved to hold for all real number arguments.

(6) $a^x a^y = a^{x+y}$ or $\exp_a x \exp_a y = \exp_a (x + y)$.

(7) $(a^x)^y = a^{xy}$ or $\exp_{(\exp_a x)} (y) = \exp_a xy$.

(8) $a^x b^x = (ab)^x$ or $\exp_a x \exp_b x = \exp_{ab} x$.

EXAMPLE 7.47 Find the value of $\exp_{\sqrt{2}} (3)$.

$$\exp_{\sqrt{2}} (3) = (\sqrt{2})^3 = 2\sqrt{2}.$$

EXAMPLE 7.48 Simplify $\exp_{\sqrt{2}} (3) \exp_{\sqrt{8}} (3) \exp_4 (\pi)$.

$$\begin{aligned}
\exp_{\sqrt{2}} (3) \exp_{\sqrt{8}} (3) \exp_4 (\pi) &= (\sqrt{2})^3(\sqrt{8})^3 \exp_4 (\pi) \\
&= (\sqrt{16})^3 \exp_4 (\pi) \\
&= 4^3 \exp_4 (\pi) \\
&= \exp_4 (3) \exp_4 (\pi) \\
&= \exp_4 (3 + \pi).
\end{aligned}$$

A particularly important exponential function is the one with an irrational base denoted by e. The number e is defined in calculus books and can be given approximately by $e = 2.71828$. Its graph, which appears in Figure 7.53, has the important property that the slope of the tangent line at each point on it is equal numerically to the second coordinate of the point. This is the only function with this property.

The exponential function with base e is commonly referred to as "*the* exponential function," and when no base is mentioned this is the function which is meant. Also, it is denoted without indicating any base

† See Exercises 39–42, Exercise Set 7.2 for discussion of decreasing and increasing functions.

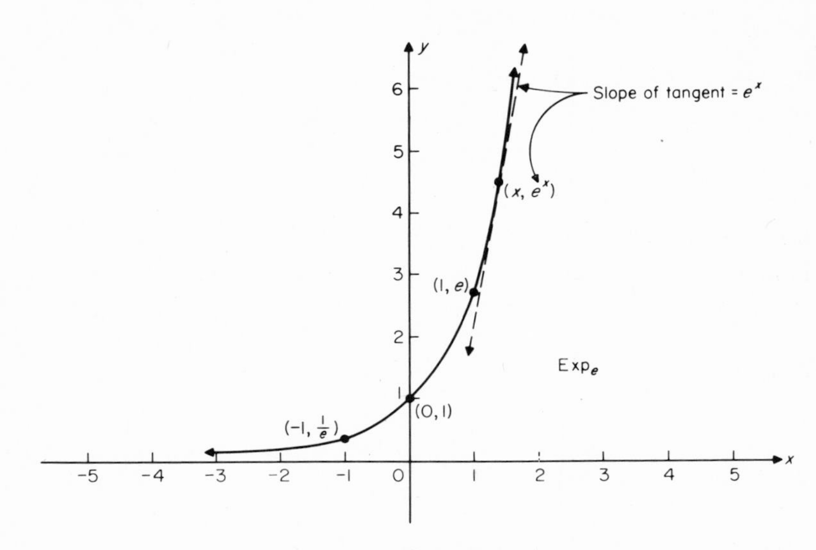

Figure 7.53

by "exp." Approximate values of the function exp are given in Table 3 of the appendix.

EXAMPLE 7.49 Find the value of exp 2.4.
Using Table 3, exp 2.4 = 11.02.

EXAMPLE 7.50 Find the value of exp 3.72.
Using Table 3 and interpolation, exp 3.72 = 41.5.

EXERCISE SET 7.10

Find the value.

1. $\exp_3 2$.
2. $\exp_5 4$.
3. $\exp_{\frac{1}{2}} 3$.
4. $\exp_{\frac{3}{4}} \frac{1}{2}$.
5. $\exp_{\sqrt{3}} 5$.
6. $\exp_\pi 4$.
7. exp 3.
8. $\exp_2 3^2$.
9. exp 5.
10. exp 1.
11. $\exp_4 1$.
12. $\exp_{\frac{1}{2}} 1$.

Sketch the graph.

13. $\exp_5$.
14. $\exp_{\frac{1}{4}}$.
15. 2 $\exp_3$.
16. $(\frac{3}{4})^x$.
17. $(1.2)^x$.
18. e^x.

Find the argument x for each function value.

19. $\exp_2 x = 4$.
20. $\exp_{\frac{1}{2}} x = 1$.
21. $\exp_3 x = 1/\sqrt{3}$.
22. $\exp x = 1.1$.
23. $\exp x = 100$.
24. $\exp x = 20$.

Simplify.

25. $\exp_2 3 \exp_2 2$.
26. $\exp_6 4 \exp_{\frac{1}{2}} 4$.
27. $\exp_{\sqrt{3}} 2 \exp_{2\sqrt{3}} 2$.
28. $\exp_2 \pi \exp_2 (2/\pi) \exp_3 2$.
29. $\exp_{\frac{1}{2}} \sqrt{2} \exp_{\frac{3}{2}} \sqrt{2} \exp_{\frac{3}{4}} \pi$.
30. $\exp_{(\exp_2 4)} (\frac{1}{2})$.

7.16 Logarithmic Functions

Since $\exp_a$ is one-to-one (for any given positive number a different from 1), it has an inverse. This inverse is called the *logarithmic function with base a* and is denoted by "$\log_a$." That is,

$$\exp_a^{-1} = \log_a .$$

Log_e is called the *natural logarithmic function* and is sometimes denoted "ln." Approximate values of $\log_e$ are given in Table 3.

As sets of ordered pairs,

$$\exp_a = \{(x, y) : y = a^x\}$$

and

$$\log_a = \{(x, y) : x = a^y\}.$$

Since $\exp_a$ and $\log_a$ are inverses,

$$(x, y) \in \exp_a \leftrightarrow (y, x) \in \log_a .$$

That is,

$$\exp_a x = y \leftrightarrow \log_a y = x,$$

which is equivalent to

$$a^x = y \leftrightarrow \log_a y = x.$$

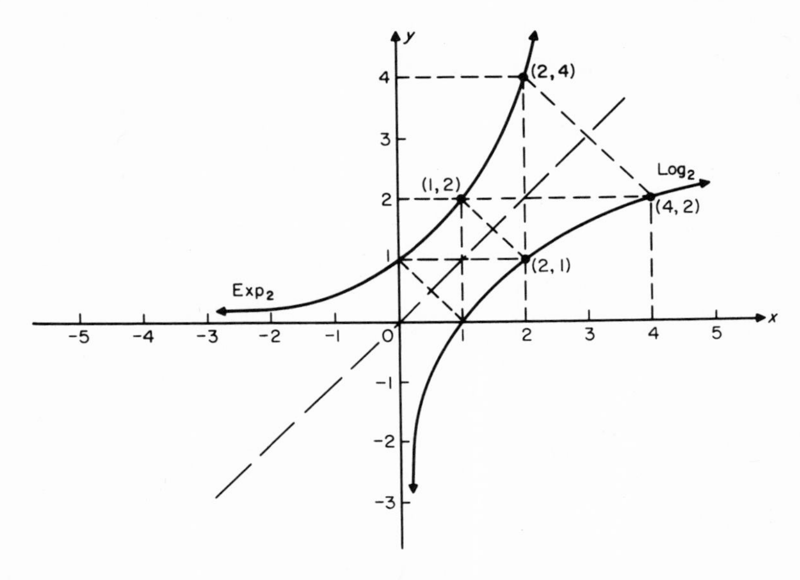

Figure 7.54

The graph of $\log_a$ can be obtained by reflecting the graph of $\exp_a$ in the line of $y = x$. (See Figure 7.54 for the case $a = 2$.)

Since $\exp_a$ and $\log_a$ are one-to-one functions,

$$x = y \leftrightarrow \exp_a x = \exp_a y \text{ for all } x, y$$

and

$$x = y \leftrightarrow \log_a x = \log_a y \text{ for } x, y > 0.$$

EXAMPLE 7.51 Find $\log_2 8$.

$$\log_2 8 = x \leftrightarrow 2^x = 8,$$

but $2^3 = 8$. Hence $x = 3$ and $\log_2 8 = 3$.

EXAMPLE 7.52 Find $\log_e 4$ approximately.

$\log_e 4 = 1.386$, using Table 3.

EXAMPLE 7.53 Find $\log_e e^\pi$.

$$\log_e e^\pi = x \leftrightarrow e^x = e^\pi.$$

Hence $x = \pi$ and $\log_e e^\pi = \pi$. Indeed, since $\log_e$ and $\exp_e$ are inverse functions,

$$\log_e e^x = x \text{ for each } x \in R.$$

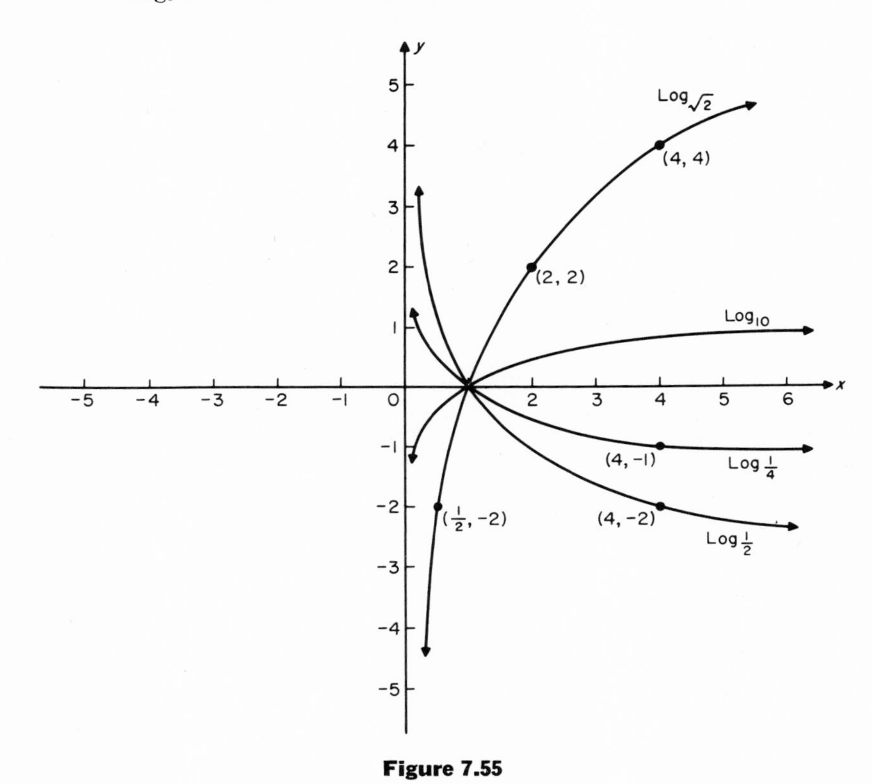

Figure 7.55

The properties of exponential functions have counterparts for logarithmic functions. (See Figure 7.55.)

(1) The domain of $\log_a$ is R^+ and the range is R.

(2) $\log_a 1 = 0$.

(3) If $0 < a < 1$, then $\log_a$ is decreasing.

(4) If $a > 1$, then $\log_a$ is increasing.

(5) $\log_a$ is one-to-one.

Properties of $\log_a$ that follow from corresponding properties of $\exp_a$ are

(6) $\log_a (xy) = \log_a x + \log_a y$.

(7) $\log_a (x^y) = y \log_a x.$

(8) If $\log_a u = \log_b v = x$, then $\log_{ab} (uv) = x$.

Property (6) can be shown as follows:

$$\exp^y [\log_a (xy)] = xy$$

since $\exp_a$ is the inverse of $\log_a$, and, by the property (6) for exponents,

$$\begin{aligned} \exp_a [\log_a x + \log_a y] &= [\exp_a (\log_a x)][\exp_a (\log_a y)] \\ &= xy; \end{aligned}$$

but $\exp_a$ is one-to-one and

$$\exp_a [\log_a (xy)] = \exp_a [\log_a x + \log_a y],$$

so

$$\log_a (xy) = \log_a x + \log_a y.$$

Two other properties of $\log_a$ are

(9) $\log_a \left(\frac{1}{x}\right) = -\log_a x.$

(10) $\log_a \left(\frac{x}{y}\right) = \log_a x - \log_a y.$

These properties of logarithmic functions make them useful for computations; for instance, lengthy long divisions and multiplications can be reduced to subtractions and additions. For such purposes $\log_{10}$ is most often used, and values of this function are given in Table 4. The table is for numbers between 1 and 10, so numbers outside this range should be expressed as the product of a power of 10 and a number in this range. For instance,

$$\begin{aligned} \log_{10} 317 &= \log_{10} [(10^2)(3.17)] \\ &= \log_{10} (10^2) + \log_{10} (3.17) \\ &= 2 + 0.5011 \text{ (from Table 4)} \\ &= 2.5011. \end{aligned}$$

$$\log_{10} 0.04312 = \log_{10} [(10^{-2})(4.312)]$$
$$= \log_{10} (10^{-2}) + \log_{10} (4.312)$$
$$= -2 + \log_{10} (4.312).$$

This is usually written

$$-2 + \log_{10} (4.312) = 8 + \log_{10} (4.312) - 10$$
$$= 8.6347 - 10.$$

EXAMPLE 7.54 Find the value of $\log_{10} 4$.

$\log_{10} 4 = 0.6021$ (Table 4).

EXAMPLE 7.55 Find $\left[\frac{32 \times 17}{27}\right]^3$.

$$\log_{10} \left[\frac{32 \times 17}{27}\right]^3 = 3[\log_{10} 32 + \log_{10} 17 - \log_{10} 27]$$
$$= 3[1.5051 + 1.2304 - 1.4314]$$
$$= 3 \times 1.3041$$
$$= 3.9123.$$

Thus, the logarithm of the answer is 3.9123. The argument of $\log_{10}$ that has 3.9123 as a value is about 8172. Hence

$$\left[\frac{32 \times 17}{27}\right]^3 = 8172, \quad \text{approximately.}$$

EXAMPLE 7.56 Find $\frac{0.3142}{751.4}$

$$\log_{10} 0.3142 = \log_{10} (10^{-1})(3.142)$$
$$= \log_{10} (10^{-1}) + \log_{10} (3.142)$$
$$= -1 + \log_{10} 3.142$$
$$= 9 + 0.4972 - 10$$
$$= 9.4972 - 10.$$

$$
\begin{aligned}
\log_{10} 751.4 &= \log_{10} (10^2)(7.514) \\
&= \log_{10} (10^2) + \log_{10} (7.514) \\
&= 2 + \log_{10} (7.514) \\
&= 2.8759.
\end{aligned}
$$

$$
\begin{aligned}
\log \frac{0.3142}{751.4} &= \log 0.3142 - \log 751.4 \\
&= 9.4972 - 10 - 2.8759 \\
&= 6.6213 - 10 \\
&= -4 + 0.6213 \text{ (reversing the procedure for finding values of } \log_{10}) \\
&= -4 + \log 4.181 \\
&= \log_{10} 10^{-4} + \log 4.181 \\
&= \log_{10} (10^{-4})(4.181) \\
&= \log_{10} (0.0004181).
\end{aligned}
$$

Hence

$$\frac{0.3142}{751.4} = 0.0004181, \quad \text{approximately.}$$

Values of exponential functions of any base can be determined using Table 4, as Example 7.57 shows.

EXAMPLE 7.57 Find the value of $3^{5.2}$.

$$
\begin{aligned}
\log_{10} 3^{5.2} &= 5.2 \log_{10} 3 \\
&= 5.2(0.4771) = 2.4809.
\end{aligned}
$$

Since $\log_{10} 302.6 = 2.4809$ (from Table 4),

$$3^{5.2} = 302.6, \quad \text{approximately.}$$

When logarithmic and exponential functions appear in compositions, such compositions can frequently be simplified using the inverse relationships between these functions.

EXAMPLE 7.58 Simplify $\log_2 [(\exp_2 x)(\exp_2 y)]^2$.

$$\begin{aligned}\log_2 [(\exp_2 x)(\exp_2 y)]^2 &= 2 \log_2 [(\exp_2 x)(\exp_2 y)] \\ &= 2 \log_2 [\exp_2 (x + y)] \\ &= 2(x + y).\end{aligned}$$

EXAMPLE 7.59 Find an expression which explicitly defines the inverse of

$$f(x) = 3e^{2x}.$$

f is the composite of the doubling function, the exponential function, and the tripling function, given by

$$\begin{aligned}\text{double } (x) &= 2x, \\ \exp (x) &= e^x, \\ \text{triple } (x) &= 3x.\end{aligned}$$

By the inverse of a composite rule, f^{-1} is the composite of the inverses of the above functions, in the reverse order. These inverses are

$$\begin{aligned}\text{third } (x) &= \frac{x}{3}, \\ \log_e (x) &= \ln x, \\ \text{half } (x) &= \frac{x}{2}.\end{aligned}$$

So,

$$f^{-1}(x) = \frac{1}{2} \ln \left[\frac{x}{3}\right].$$

Logarithmic and exponential functions of any base a can be expressed in terms of $\log_e$ and $\exp_e$.

Since $a = (e^{\log_e a})$,

$$a^x = (e^{\log_e a})^x = e^{x \log_e a},$$

and since $x = a^{\log_a x}$,

$$\log_e x = \log_e a^{(\log_a x)} = (\log_a x)(\log_e a),$$

or

$$\log_a x = \frac{\log_e x}{\log_e a}.$$

EXAMPLE 7.60 Write 7^x in terms of $\exp_e$.
Since $7 = e^{\log_e 7}$,

$$7^x = (e^{\log_e 7})^x = e^{x \log_e 7}.$$

EXAMPLE 7.61 Write $\log_6 x$ in terms of $\log_e$, and find $\log_6 3$.
Since $x = 6^{\log_6 x}$,

$$\log_e x = \log_e (6^{\log_6 x}) = (\log_6 x)(\log_e 6).$$

Therefore,

$$\log_6 x = \frac{\log_e x}{\log_e 6}.$$

$$\log_6 3 = \frac{\log_e 3}{\log_e 6} = \frac{1.099}{1.792} = 0.613 \quad \text{(approximately)}.$$

EXERCISE SET 7.11

Find the value.

1. $\log_2 8$.
2. $\log_5 5^2$.
3. $\log_2 4^2$.
4. $\log_2 8^2$.
5. $\log_5 5.^3$
6. $\log_e 2.3$.
7. $\ln 6.3$.
8. $\ln 0.62$.
9. $\log_{10} 3.21$.
10. $\log_{10} (\exp_{10} \pi)$.
11. $\log_{10} (12.4)(0.513)$.
12. $\log_{10} 4.32$.

Sketch the graph.

13. $\log_3$.
14. $\log_{10}$.
15. $\log_{1/2}$.
16. $\log_3 \circ \exp_3$.

Solve for x.

17. $\log_2 x = 4.$
18. $3^x = 81.$
19. $2^{3x} = \frac{1}{8}.$
20. $\log_e x = 2.$
21. $\log_x 8 = 2.$
22. $\log_x \frac{1}{27} = -3.$
23. $10^x = 0.0001.$
24. $\log_3 x = -1.$
25. $\log_e x = 6.4.$
26. $\log_e x = 4.2.$

Simplify.

27. $2^{\log_2 7}.$
28. $\exp_3 (\log_3 5).$
29. $\exp_3 (2 \log_3 5).$
30. $\exp_2 (2 \log_2 x + \log_2 y).$
31. $\log_2 [(\exp_2 x)(2 \exp_2 y)].$
32. $\log_3 [(\exp_3 x)(\exp_2 y)]^4.$
33. $\exp_4 [\log_2 x].$
34. $\log_2 [\exp_4 x].$
35. $\exp_3 [2 \log_{\sqrt{3}} x].$

Find the inverse and its domain. Check results by composing the given function with your answer.

36. $f(x) = 2^x$ on $\{1, 2, 3, 4\}.$
37. $h(x) = 3^x - 1.$
38. $g(x) = e^{x^5}.$
39. $f(x) = e^{5x}.$
40. $g(x) = \ln x.$
41. $f(x) = 2 \ln x.$
42. $h(x) = \ln x^2.$
43. $f(x) = e^{x/5}.$

Compute using Table 4.

44. $(27.63)(0.6431).$
45. $\dfrac{(0.09763)(71.53)}{(2.134)}.$
46. $(7.912)^3.$
47. $\sqrt{2.431}.$
48. $5^{4.3}.$
49. $(2.4)^{1.7}.$

Prove from properties (6), (7), and (8) of logarithmic functions.

50. $\log_a \frac{1}{x} = -\log_a x.$

51. $\log_a \left(\frac{x}{y}\right) = \log_a x - \log_a y.$

Prove from properties of exponential functions.

52. $\log_a (x^y) = y \log_a x.$
53. If $\log_a u = \log_b v = x$, then $\log_{ab} (uv) = x.$

Express Exercises 54–57 in terms of $\log_e$ or $\exp_e$.

54. $\log_{10} x.$
55. $\log_7 3.4.$
56. $\log_2 4.$
57. $\log_a 2x.$
58. $\exp_{10} 5.$
59. $2^x.$
60. $\exp_5.$
61. $\exp_{10} (2x + 1).$
62. Prove that $\log_{ab} a + \log_{ab} b = 1.$
63. Let f be a function such that for each positive real number a and b, $f(ab) = f(a) + f(b)$. Prove that $f(1) = 0$.
64. Show that for the function f of Exercise 63, if $f(0)$ is defined then $f(b) = 0$ for each b in D_f.
65. Let g be a function defined on the reals such that

$$g(a + b) = g(a)g(b) \text{ for each } a, b \in R.$$

Prove that if for some $a \in R$, $g(a) \neq 0$, then $g(0) = 1$.

7.17 Algebra of Functions

In the previous sections it was shown how function composition can be used to separate some complicated functions into several simple functions. There are other operations on functions that also allow complicated functions to be analyzed in terms of functions that are easier to handle.

For two functions f and g, h is the *sum* of these functions if for each x,

$$h(x) = f(x) + g(x).$$

The sum is written as $f + g$.

If $f(x) = 2x - 3$ and $g(x) = 4 - 4x$, then the sum is given by

$$h(x) = f(x) + g(x) = (2x - 3) + (4 - 4x),$$

$$h(x) = -2x + 1.$$

In a similar manner, $H(x)$ is the difference of $f(x)$ and $g(x)$ if for each x,

$$H(x) = f(x) - g(x).$$

For the specific functions above, the difference function $f - g$ is given by

$$H(x) = f(x) - g(x) = (2x - 3) - (4 - 4x),$$

$$H(x) = 6x - 7.$$

EXAMPLE 7.62 Let $F: x \longrightarrow 3x^2 - 5$ and $G: x \longrightarrow x^2 + 4$. Find the sum $F + G$, the difference $F - G$, and the difference $G - F$.

$$[F + G]: x \longrightarrow (3x^2 - 5) + (x^2 + 4) = 4x^2 - 1.$$

$$[F - G]: x \longrightarrow (3x^2 - 5) - (x^2 + 4) = 2x^2 - 9.$$

$$[G - F]: x \longrightarrow (x^2 + 4) - (3x^2 - 5) = -2x^2 + 9.$$

So far the functions that have been used as illustrations have all had the same domain. In the event that $D_f \neq D_g$, $f + g$ and $f - g$ are defined on the set of points common to the two domains; thus

$$D_{f+g} = D_{f-g} = D_{g-f} = D_f \cap D_g.$$

EXAMPLE 7.63 Let $f(x) = \sin x$ on $]0, 6]$ and $g(x) = \sqrt{x}$ on $[4, 8]$. Then

$$[f + g](x) = (\sin x) + \sqrt{x} \text{ on } [4, 6]$$

and

$$[f - g](x) = (\sin x) - \sqrt{x} \text{ on } [4, 6].$$

EXAMPLE 7.64 Let $f(x) = 1/x$, $g(x) = \sqrt{x}$. Then

$$D_f = \overline{\{0\}} \quad \text{and} \quad D_g = [0, \infty).$$

$$[f + g](x) = \frac{1}{x} + \sqrt{x} \text{ on } D_f \cap D_g =]0, \infty),$$

$$[g - f](x) = \sqrt{x} - \frac{1}{x} \text{ on }]0, \infty).$$

The product and quotient of a pair of functions is defined in like manner:

$$[f \times g](x) = [f(x)]\cdot[g(x)] \text{ on } D_f \cap D_g,$$

$$\frac{f}{g}(x) = \frac{f(x)}{g(x)} \text{ on } D_f \cap \{z : z \in D_g \text{ and } g(z) \neq 0\}.$$

The extra restriction ($g(x) \neq 0$) on the domain of f/g is necessary to prevent a zero denominator.

Since $3f(x) = f(x) + f(x) + f(x)$, it is natural to define $3f$ to be the function $f + f + f$. In general, for each $r \in R$ and for each function f, rf is the function such that

$$[rf](x) = r[f(x)] \text{ on } D_f.$$

Similarly,

$$[f^k](x) = [f(x)]^k \text{ on } D_f \text{ for all } k \in I^+.$$

EXAMPLE 7.65 Let $f(x) = x - 5$ on R and $g(x) = 3x$ on R. Then:

$$[f + g](x) = f(x) + g(x) = (x - 5) + 3x = 4x - 5.$$

$$[f - g](x) = f(x) - g(x) = (x - 5) - 3x = -2x - 5.$$

$$[f \times g](x) = f(x)\cdot g(x) = (x - 5)\cdot 3x = 3x^2 - 15x.$$

$$\left[\frac{f}{g}\right](x) = \frac{f(x)}{g(x)} = \frac{x-5}{3x} \text{ on nonzero reals.}$$

$$\left[\frac{g}{f}\right](x) = \frac{g(x)}{f(x)} = \frac{3x}{x-5} \text{ on } (-\infty, 5[\ \cup\ ]5, \infty).$$

$$[f \circ g]\,(x) = f[g(x)] = 3x - 5.$$

$$[g \circ f]\,(x) = g[f(x)] = 3(x - 5) = 3x - 15.$$

$$[7f](x) = 7\cdot[f(x)] = 7(x - 5) = 7x - 35.$$

$$[f^2](x) = [f(x)]^2 = (x - 5)^2.$$

$$[f + g^2](x) = f(x) + [g(x)]^2 = (x - 5) + (3x)^2.$$

Many functions can be separated into the sum, difference, product, or quotient of simple functions, as for example the function f where

$$f(x) = \sqrt{x} + \cos x,$$

which is the sum $g + \cos$ where $g(x) = \sqrt{x}$. One advantage of visualizing f as the sum of g and cos is as an aid in graphing. To find the graph of f, quickly graph g and cos (the graphs of which are familiar and easy to plot) and then "add ordinates" to get f. This is illustrated in Figure 7.56.

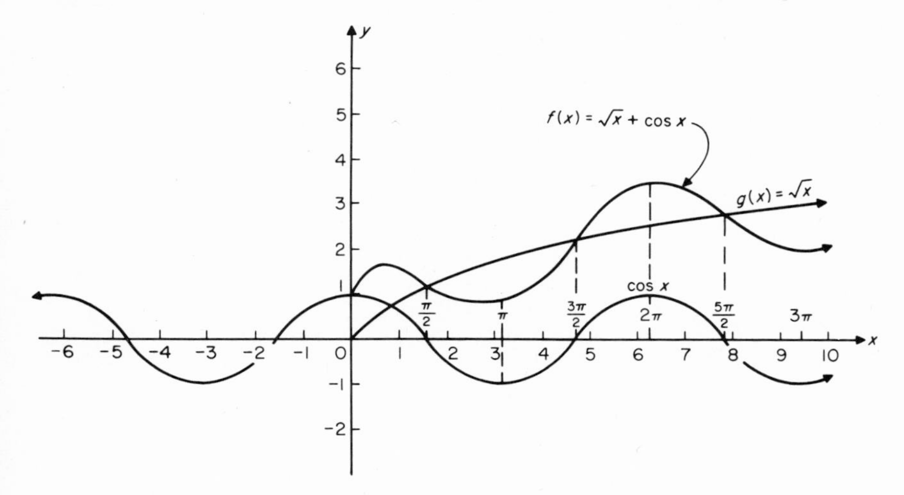

Figure 7.56

EXAMPLE 7.66 Graph $f(x) = |x| \cos x$.
Since $f(x)$ is the product of $|x|$ and $\cos x$, these functions are graphed first. Each ordinate of $f(x)$ is found by multiplying the ordinate of $|x|$ with the ordinate of $\cos x$ for each x. So, for $x = \pi/4$, $|x| = \pi/4$ and $\cos x = \sqrt{2}/2$. Therefore, $f(x) = \pi/4 \cdot \sqrt{2}/2 = \sqrt{2}\pi/8 = 0.55$, approximately. [See Figure 7.57.]

EXERCISE SET 7.12

Find the (a) sum, (b) difference, (c) product, and (d) quotient (when there is one) of each pair of functions and give the domain for each. In Exercises 1–6 graph the given functions, their sum, difference, product, and quotient.

1. $f(x) = x + 3$; $g(x) = x - 7$.
2. $f(x) = x^2$; $G(x) = 3x - x^2$.
3. $F(x) = 1/x$; $f(x) = x$.

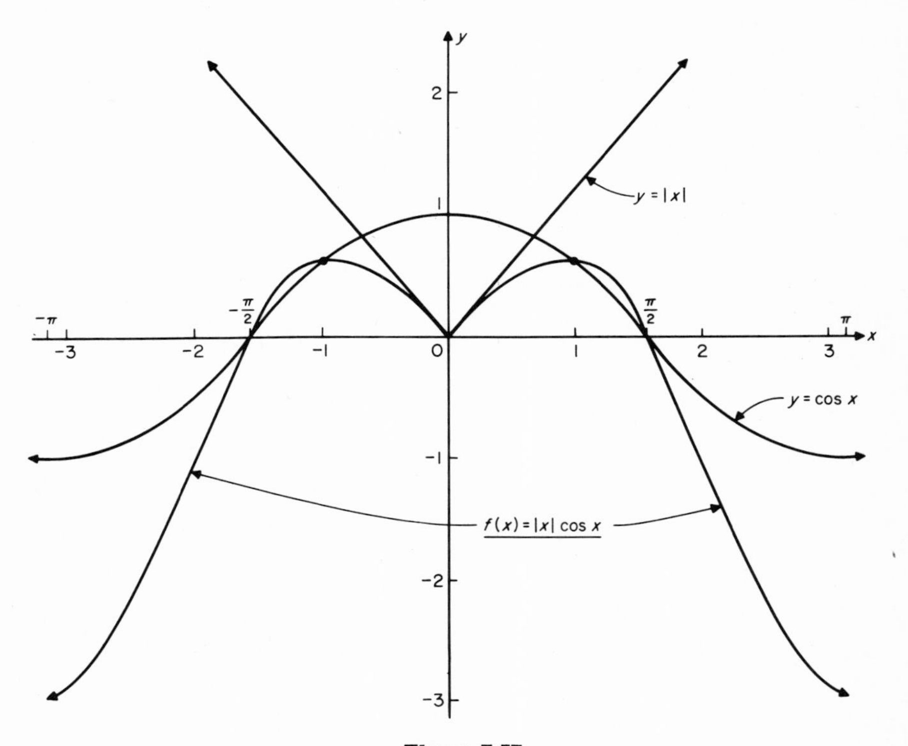

Figure 7.57

4. $a(x) = 2$; $b(x) = 3$.
5. $f: x \longrightarrow \sin x$; $g: x \longrightarrow 2x + 9$.
6. $f(x) = \sin x$; $g(x) = \cos x$.
7. $a(x) = 2^x$; $b(x) = 3^x$.
8. Sine; tangent.
9. $f(x) = (6 - x)$; $g(x) = f(6 + x)$.
10. $f: n \longrightarrow 2n - 1$ on $\{-1, 0, 2, 3, 5\}$; $g(x) = x^2 + 2x - 1$.
11. $F(x) = \dfrac{x + 1}{x - 2}$; $G(x) = \dfrac{3 - x}{x - 2}$.
12. $f(x) = \sqrt{x^2 - 2}$; $G(x) = \sqrt{1 - x}$.
13. $f(x) = e^x$; $g(x) = f(\ln(x))$.
14. $F(x) = e^x$; $g(x) = e^{-x}$.

Graph by writing as the sum or product of simpler functions and graphing those first.

15. $f(x) = 3 \sin x + 2 \cos 2x$.
16. $f(x) = x \sin x$.
17. $f(x) = x + \sin x$.
18. $f(x) = (1/x) \sin x$ on $]0, \infty)$.

In Exercises 19–23 define the functions f, g, h, F, and G by $f(x) = 3x - 1$, $F(x) = 4 + 2 \sin x$, $g(x) = x^2 + 1$, $G(x) = x^2$, $h(x) = \sin x$.

19. Find $G \times F^2$ (that is, $[G \times F^2](x) = ?$).
20. Find $[2f - g] \times h$.
21. Find $F \circ [f \times G]$.
22. Find $([F - 2h] \circ G) + 4f$.
23. Prove that $2[(f \circ g) + h] - F = 6G$.
24. Is the set of all one-to-one functions closed with respect to the addition of functions?
25. Is the set of all one-to-one functions closed with respect to the multiplication of functions?

A function f is said to be an *odd function* if for each $x \in D_f$, $f(-x) = -f(x)$. A function g is an *even function* if for each $x \in D_g$, $g(-x) = g(x)$.

26. Which of the basic trigonometric functions are odd functions?
27. Which of the basic trigonometric functions are even functions?
28. Tell which of these functions are odd and which are even:

$$\sin^2 x, \quad \cos^3 x, \quad \sin x \cos x, \quad x \sin x.$$

29. Show that if f and g are odd functions, then $f + g$ is an odd function.
30. Show that if f and g are even functions, then $f + g$ is an even function.
31. Show that if f and g are odd functions, then $f \times g$ is an even function.
32. Show that the product of even functions is even.
33. What is the symmetry of the graph of an odd function?
34. What is the symmetry of the graph of an even function?

For each positive integer n, let f_n be the function

$$f_n(x) = x^n \text{ on } R.$$

f_n is called the nth *power function.*

35. Which of the power functions are odd functions?
36. Which of the power functions are even functions?

7.18 Expressing Relationships with Functions

Most mathematics problems require for their solution that the behavior of one entity be described in terms of the behavior of a second entity. For example, to find the length of a chord in a circle of radius 5 that is just as long as its distance from the center, first draw a picture to show the entities involved (see Figure 7.58). The length of a chord is a function $C(x)$ of its distance x from the center. If x is zero, then the chord is a diameter and $C(x) = 10$. As x increases to 5, the chord length decreases to zero. Values for x outside $[0, 5]$ are meaningless. The function $C(x)$ is given by

$$C(x) = 2\sqrt{25 - x^2} \text{ on } [0, 5].$$

To find when $C(x) = x$, solve $x = 2\sqrt{25 - x^2}$, $x \in [0, 5]$. The solution is when $x = 2\sqrt{5}$.

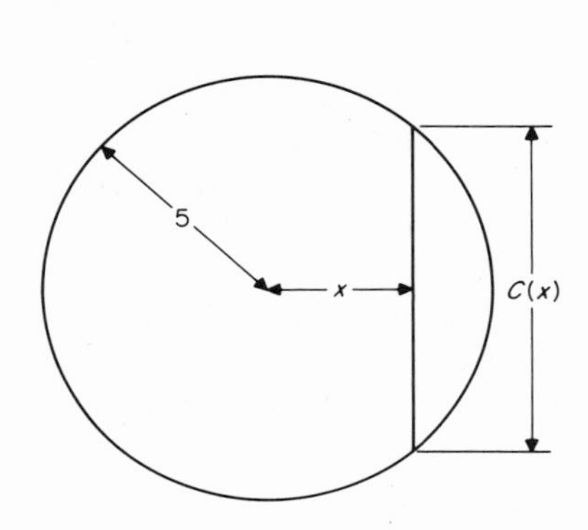

Figure 7.58

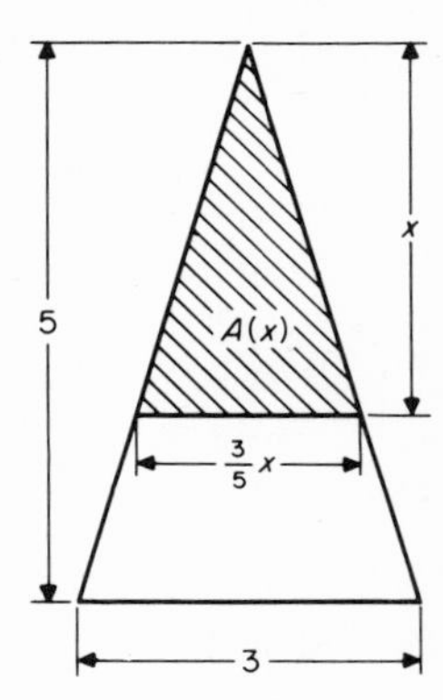

Figure 7.59

As another example, how far from the vertex of a triangle should a line parallel to the base be drawn so that it separates the triangle into two regions of equal area if the base is 3 and the altitude 5? The area $A(x)$ of the shaded region in Figure 7.59 is a function of x, the distance the line is from the vertex. The function A is given by

$$A(x) = \tfrac{3}{10}x^2 \text{ on } [0, 5].$$

Since the area of the entire triangle is $\frac{15}{2}$, we wish to find x when $A(x) = \frac{15}{4}$. That is,

$$\tfrac{3}{10}x^2 = \tfrac{15}{4}, \text{ and } x \in [0, 5].$$

The answer is $(5\sqrt{2}/2)$.

In each of these examples the problem was solved by a routine computation once the correct functional relation between the critical parts of the problem was described. The exercises to follow are concerned with these functional relations which are typically encountered in mathematics and science.

EXERCISE SET 7.13

In Exercises 1–12, answer *yes* or *no*. If the answer is *yes*, define the function.

1. Is the volume of a cube a function of its edge?
2. Is the circumference of a circle a function of its radius?
3. Is the circumference of a circle a function of its area?
4. Is the area of a square a function of its perimeter?
5. Is the area of a rectangle a function of its perimeter?
6. Is the surface area of a cube a function of its volume?
7. Is the surface area of a cube a function of its edge?
8. Is the area of a sphere a function of its radius?
9. Is the radius of a sphere a function of its area?
10. Is the radius of a sphere a function of its volume?
11. Is the area of an equilateral triangle a function of its perimeter?
12. Is the area of a triangle a function of its perimeter?

For each of Exercises 13–34, define a function which determines the measure of the indicated entity for each value of x.

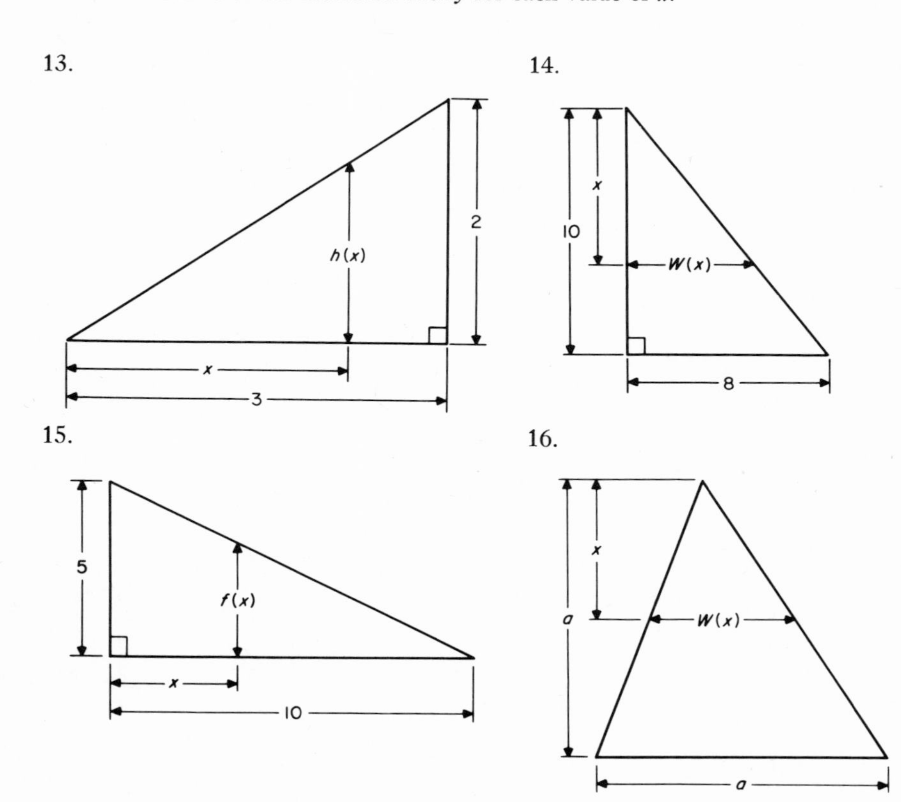

17.

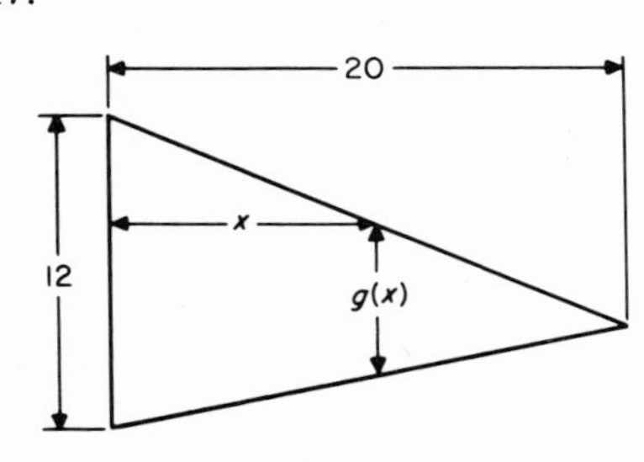

18.

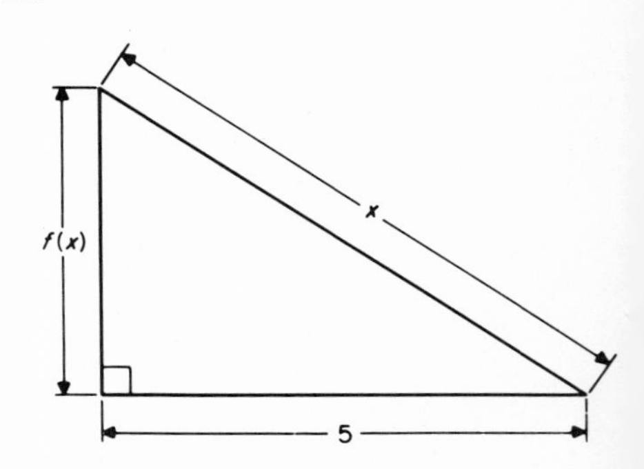

19.

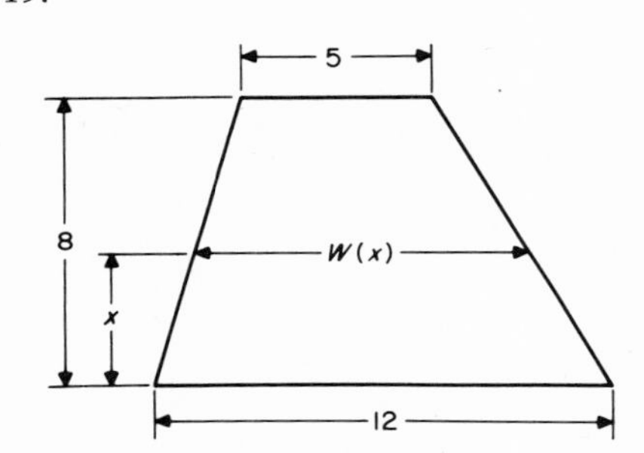

20.

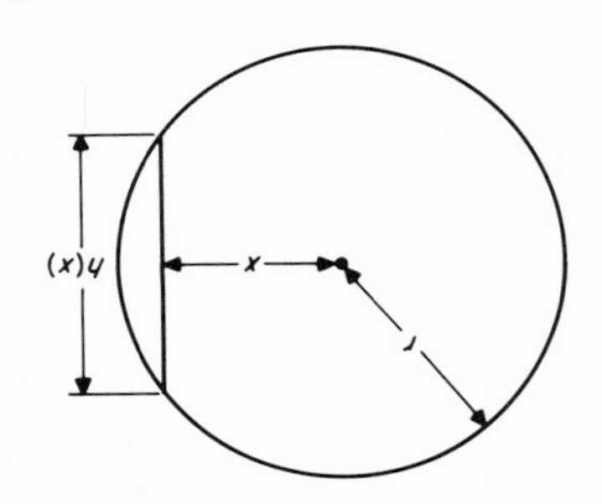

21.

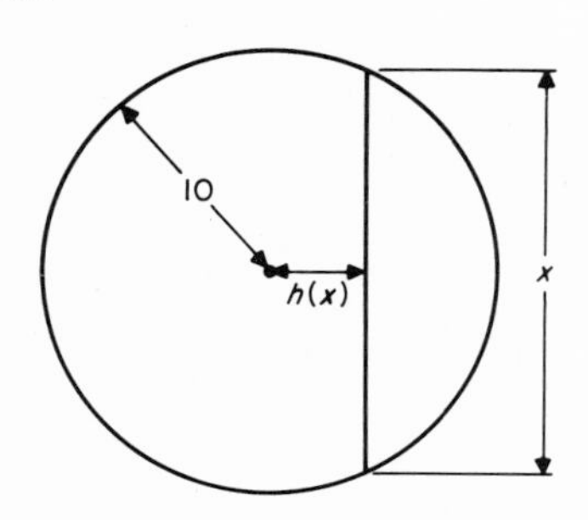

22.

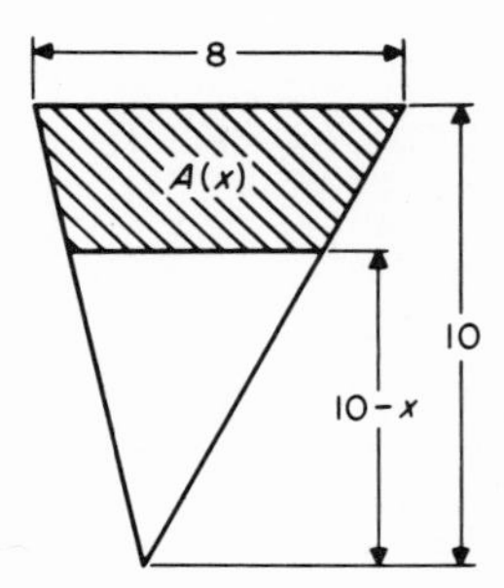

23.

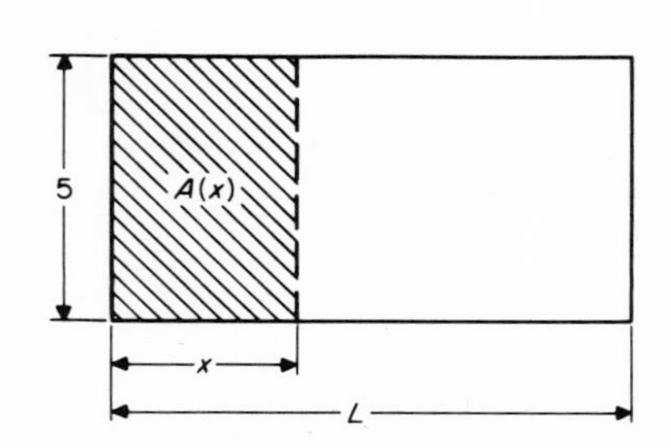

24.

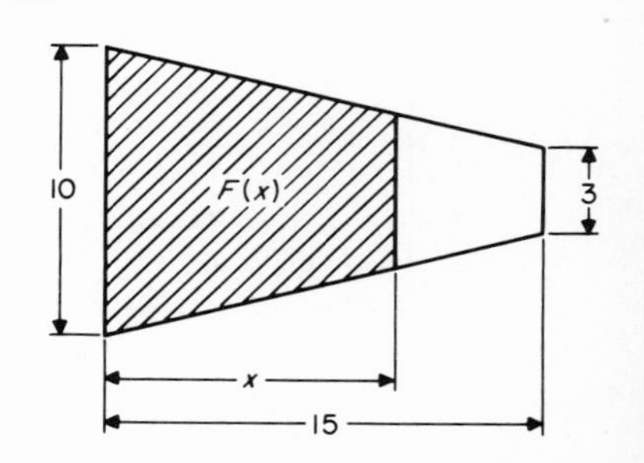

25.

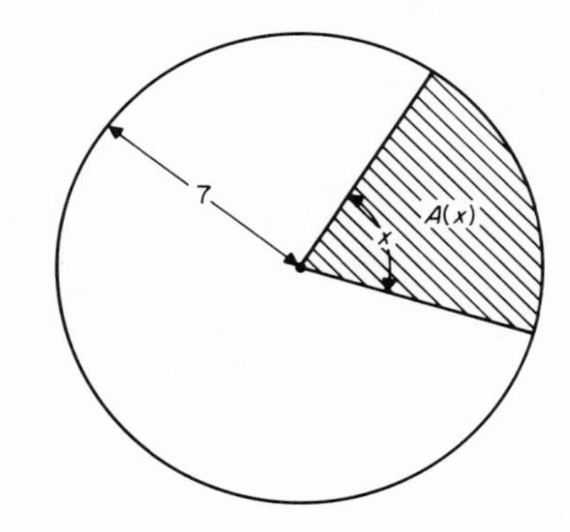

26.

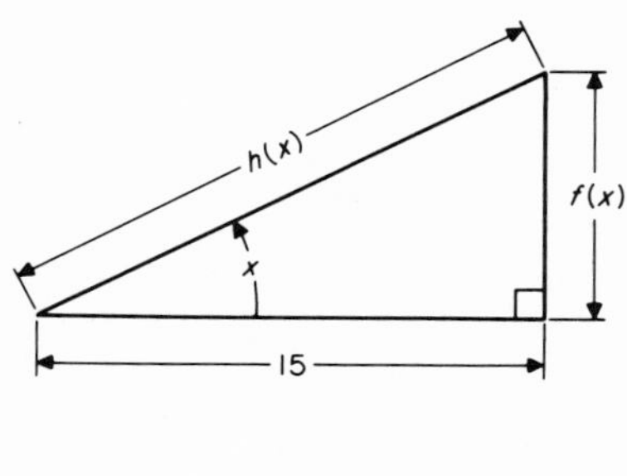

27.

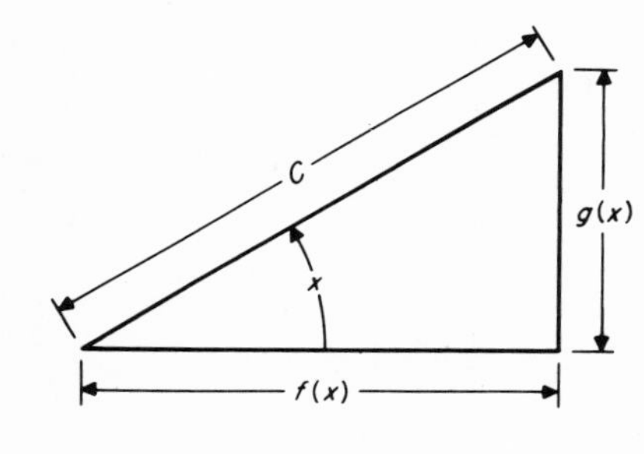

28.

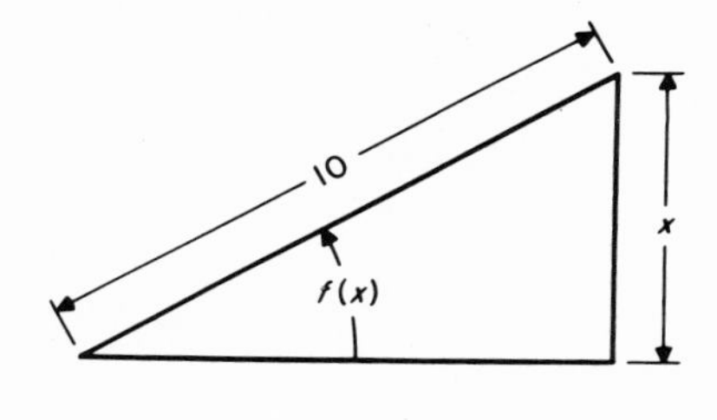

29.

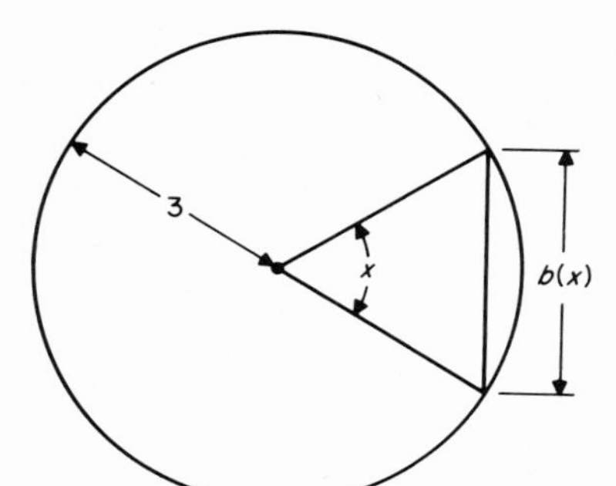

30.

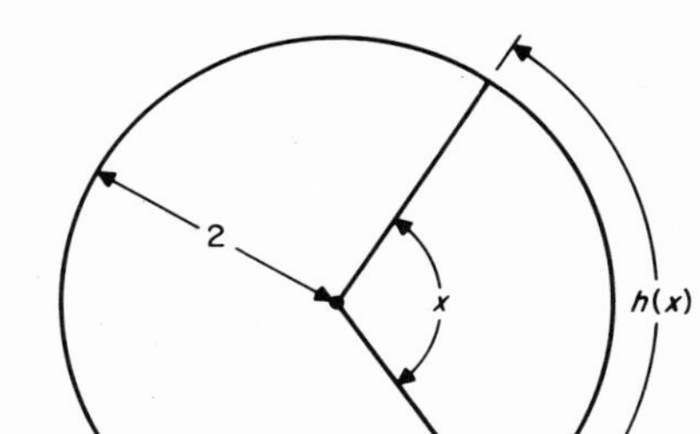

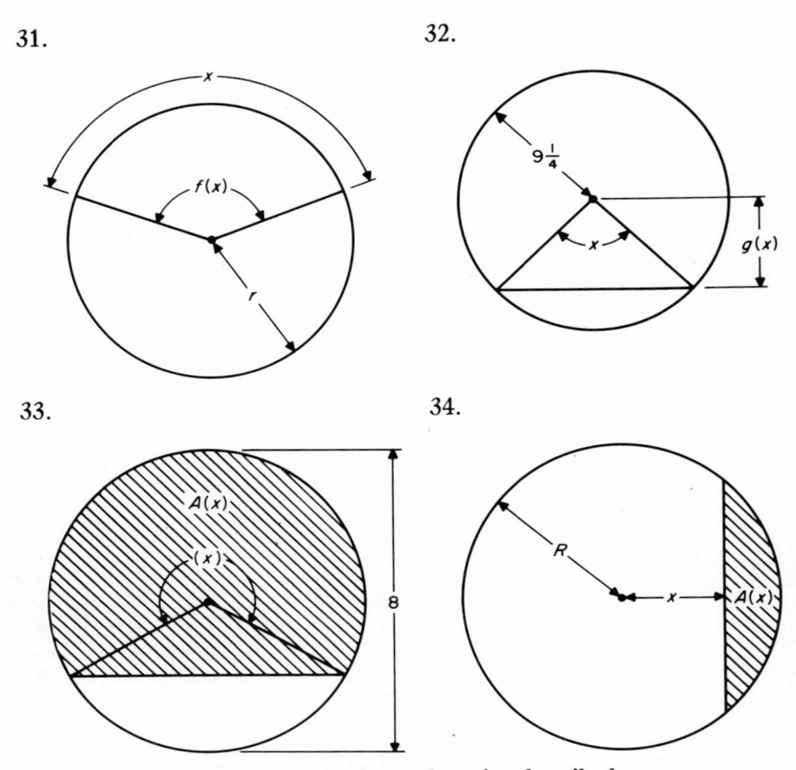

Define a function of x for each entity described.

35. The distance $D(x)$ (as a function of x alone) of the point (x, y) on the curve, $y = x^2 - 2x$ from the origin.
36. The distance $D(x)$ (as a function of x alone) of the point (x, y) on the curve $y = 2x^2 - 5$ from the point $(2, -3)$.
37. The perimeter $P(x)$ of a rectangle of width x which is twice as long as it is wide.
38. The area $A(x)$ of a rectangle of length x and height 5.
39. The area $A(x)$ of a triangle of base 10 and height x.
40. The surface area $S(x)$ of a cube with edge x.
41. The lateral surface area $S(x)$ of a cylinder of height 10 and radius x.
42. The total surface area of a cylinder of height a and radius x.
43. The volume $V(x)$ of a cylinder of height x and radius R.
44. The volume $V(x)$ of a cylinder of height h and radius x.
45. The number of cubic feet of oil in a horizontal cylindrical tank 10 ft long with a 4-ft diameter, if the oil is x ft deep.
46. The number of cubic feet of water in a V-shaped trough, 10 ft long, 3 ft deep, 3 ft across the top if the water is x ft deep.
47. The volume of a spherical balloon at time x if the radius at time x is $2x$ ft.

48. The volume $V(x)$ of water in a cylindrical tank of radius 2 ft at time x if the height is $4x^2/\pi$ ft at time x.
49. The volume of water in a conical tank (point down) of height 6 ft and top diameter 4 ft at time x if the depth of the water at time x is $\frac{1}{2}x$ ft.
50. The height of water in a conical tank (point down) of height 6 ft and top diameter 4 ft at time x if the volume of water in the tank at time x is $4x$ cu ft.

Rules of Inference

CHAPTER EIGHT

8.1 Introduction

Most proofs in mathematics are a series of sentences, each of which follows from previous sentences in the proof or from assumptions previously made. That each step of the argument in a proof follows "logically" from previous steps or assumptions is of prime importance, for if one used *faulty* reasoning in arriving at a conclusion, that conclusion would be of little value. This chapter is concerned with identifying and using the acceptable patterns of reasoning—the rules of logical inference.

8.2 Sentential Variables and Tautologies

The denial of the compound sentence

$x < 3$ and x is even

is the sentence

It is false that ($x < 3$ and x is even).

This denial can be rewritten in the equivalent form

$x \not< 3$ or x is not even

Likewise, the denial of

$x > 4$ and x is a square

is equivalent to

$x \not> 4$ or x is not a square.

For each denial of a conjunction, there is an equivalent sentence which is the disjunction of the denials of the components. This pattern can be indicated in general by the use of *variables* for the components or sentences. Such variables are called *sentential variables*.

Using sentential variables, the general form of the statements about denials of conjunctions is

$\sim (P \,\&\, Q)$ is equivalent to $\sim P \vee \sim Q$.

This is an open sentence (unquantified) which has the initial statements as instances. Other instances are

"The denial of ($\theta = 40°$ and $\phi = 30°$)" is equivalent to "$\theta \neq 40°$ or $\phi \neq 30°$"

and

"It is false that ($2 < 3$ and $3 < 4$)" is equivalent to "$2 \nless 3$ or $3 \nless 4$."

Recalling the type of sentence that is equivalent to the denial of a disjunction, the general pattern is represented by the pattern sentence

$\sim (P \vee Q)$ is equivalent to $\sim P \;\&\; \sim Q$.

An instance of this open sentence is

"It is false that (2 is even or 2 is odd)" is equivalent to "2 is not even and 2 is not odd."

The pattern sentences

$$\sim (P \;\&\; Q) \leftrightarrow \sim P \vee \sim Q$$

and

$$\sim (P \vee Q) \leftrightarrow \sim P \;\&\; \sim Q$$

are such that for *all* sentences P and Q, the resulting instances are true sentences, regardless of the truth values of P and Q themselves. Such pattern sentences are called logical *tautologies*. The pattern sentence (unquantified)

$$P \rightarrow \sim (\sim P)$$

is a tautology, for no matter which sentence is substituted for P, the resulting instance is true. (In other words, $P \rightarrow \sim (\sim P)$ is a tautology since the universal generalization $\forall P, P \rightarrow \sim (\sim P)$ is true.)

The pattern sentence

$$P \vee Q \rightarrow P$$

is not a tautology, however. (That is, $\forall P \, \forall Q, P \lor Q \rightarrow P$ is false.) If a false sentence is chosen for P and a true sentence for Q, the resulting instance of $P \lor Q \rightarrow P$ is a false sentence. If we choose sentences as follows:

True statement: $1 + 1 = 2$,

False statement: $1 + 1 = 3$,

then we can get a false instance of $P \lor Q \rightarrow P$ as:

$$1 + 1 = 3 \lor 1 + 1 = 2 \rightarrow 1 + 1 = 3.$$

Since finding appropriate truth values of the component sentences is the key to finding a false instance of the pattern sentences, displaying these truth values is accepted as adequate proof that a false instance exists. So we prove that $P \lor Q \rightarrow P$ is not a tautology by displaying

P: F

Q: T

EXAMPLE 8.1 Determine whether or not each pattern sentence is a tautology. If the sentence is *not* a tautology, exhibit a truth value set for a false instance.

(a) $P \rightarrow P$. A tautology. Either a true or a false sentence substituted for P results in a true conditional.

(b) $P \lor Q$. Not a tautology.
Truth values for a false instance:

P: F

Q: F

(Can you find another truth value set for a false instance?)

(c) $P \rightarrow P \,\&\, Q$. Not a tautology.
Truth values of a false instance:

P: T

Q: F

(Can you find another set of truth values for a false instance?)

(d) $P \& Q \rightarrow P$. A tautology. The conditional can be false only if P is false; but then the antecedent, $P \& Q$, is false, which means the conditional is true.

EXAMPLE 8.2 Find a pattern sentence which has the given sentence as an instance. Label each pattern sentence as a *tautology* or *not a tautology*.

(a) If x is even, x is odd.

Pattern sentence: $P \rightarrow Q$.

Not a tautology.

(b) If x is less than 4, then x is less than 4 or x is equal to 4.

Pattern sentence: $P \rightarrow P \vee Q$.

A tautology.

Pattern sentences for which each instance is a false sentence are called *contradictions*. As an example,

$$\mathrm{P} \,\&\sim P$$

is a contradiction since it has no true instances. The pattern sentence

$$P \vee Q \rightarrow P \,\&\, Q$$

is neither a tautology nor a contradiction. To show that it is not a tautology, truth values for a false instance are given. To show it is not a contradiction, truth values for a true instance are given.

Truth values for a false instance:

P: T

Q: F

Truth values for a true instance:

P: T

Q: T

If a pattern sentence is a tautology, i.e., all instances are true, then surely it is *not* a contradiction. Equivalently if a pattern sentence is a contradiction, i.e., all instances are false, then it is *not* a tautology.

EXERCISE SET 8.1

Label each pattern sentence as a *tautology*, a *contradiction*, or *neither*. If your answer is "neither," prove that the pattern sentence is *not* a tautology by exhibiting truth values for a false instance, and prove that the pattern sentence is *not* a contradiction by exhibiting truth values for a true instance.

1. $P \vee P \leftrightarrow P$.
2. $P \,\&\, Q \leftrightarrow Q \,\&\, P$.
3. $P \,\&\, Q$.
4. $\sim(\sim P) \leftrightarrow P$.
5. $P \leftrightarrow \sim P$.
6. $P \rightarrow \sim P$.
7. $P \vee \sim P$.
8. $P \,\&\, \sim P$.
9. $\sim(P \rightarrow Q) \leftrightarrow (P \,\&\, \sim Q)$.
10. $\sim(P \rightarrow Q) \leftrightarrow (P \rightarrow \sim Q)$.
11. $\sim(P \rightarrow Q) \leftrightarrow (\sim P \rightarrow \sim Q)$.
12. Q.
13. $P \rightarrow P \vee Q$.
14. $P \vee Q \rightarrow P$.
15. $P \,\&\, Q \rightarrow Q$.
16. $\sim P \rightarrow (P \rightarrow Q)$.

Find a pattern sentence using sentential variables such that the given sentence is an instance of it. State whether or not the pattern sentence is a tautology.

17. $x < 3$ and $x > 4$.
18. The number is even or odd.
19. Ten is a multiple of 2 and a multiple of 5.
20. If x is a multiple of 4, then x is a multiple of 2.
21. If x is a multiple of 4, then x is a multiple of 2 and of 4.
22. If x is a multiple of 4, then x is a multiple of 2 or of 4.
23. It is false that x is even and x is odd.
24. "If x is even, then x is divisible by 2," is equivalent to saying, "If x is not divisible by 2, then x is not even."
25. For x to be a multiple of 3, it is necessary that x not be an odd number.
26. If x is even or odd, and not even, then x is odd.

8.3 Inference Patterns, Validity

From the statement

x is even and x is positive,

one can conclude that

x is even;

from the statement

$x^2 < 12 \quad \text{and} \quad x^2 > 4,$

one can conclude

$x^2 < 12;$

and from the statement

The curve C_1 is a parabola and passes through the origin,

one can conclude that

The curve C_1 is a parabola.

Each of these *inferences* has the same general form and is an instance of the *inference pattern*

From: $P \& Q$,

one can conclude: P.

The statement which is given, or assumed, is called the *premise* or *hypothesis* of the inference, while the statement which allegedly "follows" from the premise is called the *conclusion*. The inference pattern is written more concisely by placing the premise above a bar, with the conclusion below. The bar is read "therefore." The above pattern is shown as

$$\frac{P \& Q}{P}$$

Sometimes an inference pattern is shown by listing the premises and conclusion as

premise: $P \& Q$,

conclusion: P,

or as

given: $P \& Q$,

conclusion: P.

There are many inference patterns, some of which are *logically* correct and some of which are not. Our concern is to determine those inference patterns which are logically correct. For a pattern to be logically correct, or *valid*, it must be the case that for *no* instance of the pattern is it possible to have the premises *true* while the conclusion is *false*. A pattern which does have instances with the premises true and the conclusion false is said to be *invalid*, or *logically incorrect*. Each instance of such a pattern is invalid.

The above pattern

$$\frac{P \& Q}{P}$$

is a valid pattern, but the pattern

$$\frac{P \vee Q}{P}$$

is invalid. To show this pattern to be invalid, it is sufficient to show truth values for the sentences which result in a true premise but a false conclusion. Such truth values are

P: F,

Q: T.

Since the pattern is invalid, each of its instances is also invalid. So,

$$\frac{\text{8 is even or 8 is odd}}{\text{8 is even}}$$

is invalid, even though both the premise and the conclusion happen to be true. Each of the following instances is also invalid.

$$\frac{x \leq 4}{x < 4}$$

$$\frac{\theta \text{ is in Quadrant I or II}}{\theta \text{ is in Quadrant I}}$$

The validity of the inference pattern *cannot* be determined by the truth value of the conclusion alone. Instances of valid patterns may have true or false conclusions as may instances of invalid patterns. This is illustrated below.

Valid Pattern	Instance with False Conclusion	Instance with True Conclusion
$\frac{P \,\&\, Q}{P}$	$\frac{\text{4 is odd and even}}{\text{4 is odd}}$	$\frac{\text{4 is even and odd}}{\text{4 is even}}$
Invalid Pattern		
$\frac{P \vee Q}{P}$	$\frac{3 < 2 \quad \text{or} \quad 2 < 3}{3 < 2}$	$\frac{\text{7 is odd or even}}{\text{7 is odd}}$

Correct or valid reasoning is *not* dependent on the truth values of the sentences used, but on the *validity* or *invalidity* of the inference patterns used. To say that from

$$2 + 2 = 4 \quad \text{or} \quad 2 + 3 = 5$$

one can conclude that

$$2 + 2 = 4$$

may sound correct since all of the sentences which appear are true, and, in particular, the conclusion is true. But the pattern of inference used to obtain the conclusion is *not* acceptable; the reasoning is *incorrect* or *invalid*. If this pattern were accepted, then using this same pattern, which is

$$\frac{P \vee Q}{P},$$

one could reason that since

2 is odd or 2 is even,

it follows that

2 is odd.

This type of conclusion one can do without.

Valid patterns of reasoning frequently used include

$$\text{(i)}\ \frac{P \,\&\, Q}{P}, \qquad \text{(ii)}\ \frac{P \,\&\, Q}{Q}, \qquad \text{(iii)}\ \frac{P, Q}{P \,\&\, Q} \qquad (\textit{rules of}\ \&).$$

These patterns are referred to as the *rules of* &. In the third rule (iii), the premise consists of two separate sentences, P, Q.

The statements of equivalence which are logical tautologies give rise to numerous other valid patterns. Since

$$\sim (P \vee Q) \leftrightarrow \sim P \,\&\, \sim Q,$$

the patterns

$$\frac{\sim (P \vee Q)}{\sim P \,\&\, \sim Q} \quad \text{and} \quad \frac{\sim P \,\&\, \sim Q}{\sim (P \vee Q)}$$

are valid. (Since the premise and conclusion have the *same* truth values for all instances, no instance could have a true premise with a false conclusion.) All such valid patterns derived from equivalences are labeled *substitution* since, in one sense, the conclusion is obtained by substituting an equivalent sentence for the premise.

Other examples of *substitution* are

$$\frac{\sim (P \,\&\, Q)}{\sim P \vee \sim Q}, \qquad \frac{P \rightarrow Q}{\sim P \vee Q}, \qquad \frac{\sim (P \rightarrow Q)}{P \,\&\, \sim Q},$$

$$\frac{P \,\&\, \sim Q}{\sim (P \rightarrow Q)}, \qquad \frac{\sim (\sim P)}{P}, \qquad \frac{P}{\sim (\sim P)},$$

$$\frac{\sim \forall x, P(x)}{\exists x, \sim P(x)}, \qquad \frac{\sim \exists x, P(x)}{\forall x, \sim P(x)}.$$

EXAMPLE 8.3 Give an inference pattern of which the inference is an instance. Is the pattern valid or invalid?

(a) $\dfrac{2 > 3 \text{ and } 7 > 8}{2 > 3}$.

Inference pattern: $\dfrac{P \,\&\, Q}{P}$.

Valid. Rule of &.

(b) $\dfrac{\text{If } \theta < \pi \text{ then } \sin\theta < 0}{\sin\theta < 0}$.

Inference pattern: $\dfrac{P \to Q}{Q}$.

Invalid. Truth values of an instance with a true premise and a false conclusion:

P: F,

Q: F.

(c) $\dfrac{\text{If } x > 4 \text{ then } x > 3.}{\text{If } x \not> 4 \text{ then } x \not> 3.}$

Inference pattern: $\dfrac{P \to Q}{\sim P \to \sim Q}$.

Invalid. Truth values of an instance with a true premise and a false conclusion:

P: F,

Q: T.

EXERCISE SET 8.2

1. *Given*: 10 is even and 10 is greater than 8.
   Conclusion: 10 is greater than 8.
   (a) Is the premise true?
   (b) Is the conclusion true?
   (c) In view of your answers to (a) and (b), can you conclude that the reasoning is valid or invalid?

(d) Using sentential variables, give a pattern of which this inference is an instance.

(e) Is this inference pattern [see part (d)] a valid or invalid pattern?

(f) Give an instance of this pattern with a false premise.

(g) Give an instance of this pattern with a false conclusion.

(h) Give an instance of this pattern with a false premise and with a true conclusion.

(i) Give an instance of this pattern with a true premise and with a false conclusion.

2. 8 is a multiple of 2 or of 4.
   ____
   8 is a multiple of 4.

   (a) Is the premise true?

   (b) Is the conclusion true?

   (c) From your answers to (a) and (b), can you conclude that the reasoning was correct (valid) or incorrect (invalid)?

   (d) Using sentential variables, give a pattern of which this inference is an instance.

   (e) Give instances of this inference pattern (d) with each of the following truth value combinations.

      (i) Premise true, conclusion false.

      (ii) Premise false, conclusion true.

      (iii) Premise false, conclusion false.

   (f) Do any of the instances given in (e) show the reasoning to be valid or invalid?

3. x is a rational number.
   x is nonnegative.
   ____
   x is rational and nonnegative.

   (a) Is the premise true? Is the conclusion true?

   (b) Using sentential variables, give an inference pattern of which this is an instance.

   (c) Is the inference pattern (b) valid or invalid?

   (d) Can a number be found for x such that the premises are true and the conclusion is false?

4. If $x < 4$ then $x < 8$.
   ____
   $x < 4$ or $x \nless 8$.

   (a) Select an x such that the conclusion is false.

   (b) Select an x such that the premise is false.

   (c) Using sentential variables, give a general inference pattern of which this is an instance.

   (d) Is the pattern (c) valid or invalid? Why?

5. 7 is a prime number.
   ____
   $7 > 6$.

   (a) Give the truth values of the premise and conclusion.

(b) From these truth values, can you conclude that the reasoning is valid or invalid?

(c) Give a general inference pattern of which this is an instance.

(d) Give an instance of this pattern (c) with a false premise and a true conclusion.

(e) Does the instance given in (d) show the validity of the pattern.

(f) Give an instance with a true premise and a false conclusion.

(g) Does the instance given in (f) show the validity of the pattern?

Using sentential variables, write an inference pattern for each inference. Be sure that no sentence that is replaced by a single sentential variable contains a connective, and also be sure that different occurrences of the same component sentence are replaced by the same sentential variable. Determine whether the pattern is valid or invalid, naming the pattern if it is one of the valid patterns listed above. If the pattern is invalid, prove that it is invalid.

6. $\dfrac{1 + 1 = 2 \text{ and } 2 + 2 = 4.}{1 + 1 = 2.}$

7. $\dfrac{3 < 8 < 12.}{3 < 8.}$

8. $\dfrac{3 < 7 \text{ and } 7 < 2.}{7 < 2.}$

9. $\dfrac{x^2 \geq 0.}{x^2 > 0.}$

10. $\dfrac{x > 2 \text{ or } x < 3.}{x \not> 2 \text{ and } 7 \not< 3.}$

11. $\dfrac{x \in A \text{ or } x \in B.}{x \in A.}$

12. $\dfrac{f(x) \text{ is one-to-one.}}{f(x) = 2x - 3.}$

13. $\dfrac{\text{If } m \text{ is rational then } m \text{ is a repeating decimal.}}{m \text{ is rational or } m \text{ is not a repeating decimal.}}$

14. $\dfrac{\text{If } \sin \theta < 1 \text{ then } \theta \neq \pi/2.}{\text{It is false that } \sin \theta < 1 \text{ and } \theta = \pi/2.}$

15. $\dfrac{2 < 4.}{2 < 4 < 7.}$

8.4 Patterns of Inference Involving Disjunctions and Conditionals

The patterns

$$\frac{P}{P \vee Q}, \qquad \frac{P}{Q \vee P} \qquad \textit{(rules of } \vee\textit{)}$$

are valid since a true premise guarantees a true conclusion for any instance. (Recall that if the premise and conclusion were reversed, the pattern is invalid!) Other rules involving disjunctions include:

$$\frac{P \vee Q, \sim P}{Q}, \quad \frac{P \vee Q, \sim Q}{P} \quad (\textit{disjunctive syllogism}).$$

Each of these rules is based on the concept that a disjunctive statement is true if and only if "one or the other" of the components is true. For the disjunctive syllogism, whenever P or Q is true, and P is not, then Q must be true.

A valid pattern dealing with conditionals is

$$\frac{P \rightarrow Q, P}{Q} \quad (\textit{modus ponens}).$$

This important pattern has two premises, P and $P \rightarrow Q$. The premise P should never be omitted in using the rule. [See Example 8.4(c).]

A rule combining both conditional and disjunctive sentences is the rule *proof by cases*.

$$\frac{P \vee Q, P \rightarrow R, Q \rightarrow R}{R} \quad (\textit{proof by cases}).$$

For a true premise, $P \vee Q$ must be true. Then either P is true or Q is true. But, by *modus ponens*, R would be true in either case. So it is impossible to have a true premise and a false conclusion.

EXAMPLE 8.4 Find an inference pattern for each inference and determine whether it is invalid or valid. Prove your answer by citing the rule for valid cases or by listing truth values for a true premise and a false conclusion for invalid cases.

(a) $\dfrac{x < 2 \text{ or } x > 2.\ x \nless 2.}{x > 2.}$

Inference pattern: $\dfrac{P \vee Q, \sim P}{Q}.$

Valid. Disjunctive syllogism.

(b) $\dfrac{x < 2 \text{ or } x > 2. \text{ If } x < 2 \text{ then } x \neq 2. \text{ If } x > 2 \text{ then } x \neq 2.}{x \neq 2.}$

Inference pattern: $\dfrac{P \vee Q,\ P \rightarrow R,\ Q \rightarrow R}{R}$.

Valid. Proof by cases.

(c) If $x > 2$ then $x > 1$.
$\overline{}$
$x > 1$.

Inference pattern: $\dfrac{P \rightarrow Q}{Q}$

Invalid. P: F

Q: F

(Notice that "if $x > 2$ then $x > 1$" is true for all x, but "$x > 1$" is surely not true for all x.)

(d) If $x \in A$ then $x \in B$.
$x \in A$.
$\overline{}$
$x \in B$.

Inference pattern: $\begin{array}{l} P \rightarrow Q \\ P \\ \hline Q \end{array}$

Valid. Modus ponens.

(e) If $4 > 2$ then $4 > 3$.
$4 > 3$.
$\overline{}$
$4 > 2$.

Inference pattern: $\begin{array}{l} P \rightarrow Q \\ Q \\ \hline P \end{array}$

Invalid. P: F

Q: T

An important rule of inference is that of a more general *substitution* than previously used. This rule is illustrated by the following inference pattern.

$$\frac{P \rightarrow \sim (R \vee S)}{P \rightarrow \sim R \ \& \sim S}$$

The conclusion is obtained from the premise by substituting

$$\sim R \,\&\, \sim S$$

for

$$\sim (R \vee S).$$

This type of substitution is acceptable since the sentences are equivalent, and this, in turn, will assure that the premise and conclusion and equivalent.

EXERCISE SET 8.3

Decide whether or not the inference is valid. If the inference is valid, give a valid pattern of which it is an instance. If the inference is invalid, list truth values for a true premise and a false conclusion.

1. The triangle T is isosceles and a right triangle.
   T is a right triangle.
2. If $\sin \theta = \frac{1}{2}$ then $\theta = 30°$.
   $\theta = 30°$.
3. $A \subset B$. If $A \cap B = A$ then $A \subset B$.
   $A \cap B = A$.
4. $A \cap B = A$. If $A \cap B = A$ then $A \subset B$.
   $A \subset B$.
5. $x \leq 4$. $x \neq 4$.
   $x < 4$.
6. $x < 4$ or $x > 4$. $x \nless 4$.
   $x < 4$.
7. $x < 3$ or $x < 4$.
   $x < 3$.
8. $x < 3$ or $x > 3$.
   It is false that ($x \nless 3$ and $x \ngtr 3$).
9. $x < 3$ if $x \ngtr 2$.
   $x \ngtr 2$ or $x < 3$.
10. $x < 3$ or $x > 3$. If $x > 3$ then $x \neq 3$.
    If $x < 3$ then $x \neq 3$.
    $x \neq 3$.
11. $x < 3$.
    $x \leq 3$.

12. Triangle T is equilateral or isosceles.
    If T is equilateral then it is isosceles.
    (If T is isosceles, then it is isosceles!)
    ___
    T is isosceles.

13. $x \leq 4$. If $x < 4$ then $x < 5$.
    If $x = 4$ then $x < 5$.
    ___
    $x < 5$.

14. $x > 4$. If $x > 4$ then $x > 3$.
    ___
    $x > 3$.

15. $a < 2$ only if $a < 1$.
    ___
    $a < 2$ only if $a < 1$ or else a is not a real number.

8.5 Proof

The use of inference patterns in writing mathematical proofs is illustrated in this section. Basically, a proof is an argument from given assumptions showing that a certain conclusion follows. Statements from the hypotheses (assumptions), definitions, and statements which are inferred by other statements in the proof may be used in the argument. (Of course only valid inferences are allowed.)

The proofs of this section are of statements about sets. The definitions needed for this study of sets are as follows:

Let A and B be sets. Then

DEFINITION (OF SUBSET) 8.1

$A \subset B$ if and only if (for each x, if $x \in A$ then $x \in B$).

DEFINITION (OF UNION) 8.2

For each x, $x \in A \cup B$ if and only if $x \in A$ or $x \in B$.

DEFINITION (OF INTERSECTION) 8.3

For each x, $x \in A \cap B$ if and only if $x \in A$ and $x \in B$.

DEFINITION (OF COMPLEMENT) 8.4

For each x, $x \in \bar{A}$ if and only if $x \notin A$.

At the outset, *column* proofs will be used to emphasize the inference patterns. Later the less formal *paragraph* proof will be introduced.

EXAMPLE 8.5

Given: $x \in A \cap B$.

Conclusion: $x \in A$.

Proof:

1. $x \in A \cap B$.	1. Given.
2. $x \in A \cap B \leftrightarrow x \in A \,\&\, x \in B$.	2. Definition.
3. $\therefore x \in A \,\&\, x \in B$.	3. Substitution (steps 1, 2).
4. $\therefore x \in A$.	4. Rule of &.

The symbol $\therefore$ (statements 3, 4) is an abbreviation for *therefore,* and is often used whenever a statement is a *logical* consequence of preceding statements. Step 2 records the definition of $A \cap B$. Such definition statements will be placed in some proofs in this section for emphasis, but in the sections to follow the argument will proceed as from step 1 to step 3.

EXAMPLE 8.6

Hypothesis: $x \in A \cup B$. $x \in \bar{A}$.

Prove: $x \in B$.

Proof:

1. $x \in A \cup B$.	1. Given.
2. $x \in A \cup B \leftrightarrow x \in A \vee x \in B$.	2. Definition.
3. $\therefore x \in A \vee x \in B$.	3. Substitution.
4. $x \in \bar{A}$.	4. Given.
5. $x \in \bar{A} \leftrightarrow x \notin A$.	5. Definition.
6. $\therefore x \notin A$.	6. Substitution.
7. $\therefore x \in B$.	7. Disjunctive syllogism (steps 3, 6).

EXAMPLE 8.7

Given: $x \in A$ and $A \subset B$.

Conclusion: $x \in B$.

Proof:

1. $x \in A \mathbin{\&} A \subset B$.	1. Given.
2. $\therefore A \subset B$.	2. Rule of &.
3. $A \subset B \leftrightarrow x \in A \rightarrow x \in B$.	3. Definition.
4. $\therefore x \in A \rightarrow x \in B$.	4. Substitution.
5. $\therefore x \in A$.	5. Rule of & (step 1).
6. $\therefore x \in B$.	6. Modus ponens (steps 4, 5).

In Example 8.8 notice that the denial

$$x \notin A \cap B$$

is written in the logical form

$$\sim (x \in A \cap B).$$

The changes that are made in this statement are more easily seen when the statement is written this way.

EXAMPLE 8.8

Hypothesis: $x \in \overline{A \cap B}$.

Conclusion: $x \in \bar{A} \cup \bar{B}$.

Proof:

1. $x \in \overline{A \cap B}$. — 1. Given.

2. $x \in \overline{A \cap B} \leftrightarrow x \notin A \cap B$. — 2. Definition.

3. $\therefore x \notin A \cap B$. — 3. Substitution.

4. $\therefore \sim (x \in A \cap B)$. — 4. Substitution.
   (Actually, the same statement.)

5. $\therefore \sim (x \in A \mathbin{\&} x \in B)$. — 5. Substitution.
   (The statement of equivalence for the substitution is not listed for this step nor for steps 6, 7 and 8.)

6. $\therefore \sim x \in A \vee \sim x \in B$. — 6. Substitution.

7. $\therefore x \in \bar{A} \vee x \in \bar{B}$. — 7. Definition.

8. $\therefore x \in \bar{A} \cup \bar{B}$. — 8. Definition.

EXERCISE SET 8.4

Supply the reasons for the statements in each proof.

1. *Given*: $x \notin A \cap B$. $x \in A$.

   Prove: $x \notin B$.

   Proof:
   (a) $x \notin A \cap B$ $(\sim (x \in A \cap B))$.
   (b) $x \in A \cap B \leftrightarrow x \in A \;\&\; x \in B$.
   (c) $\therefore \sim (x \in A \;\&\; x \in B)$.
   (d) $\therefore \sim x \in A \vee \sim x \in B$.
   (e) $x \in A$.
   (f) $\therefore \sim (\sim x \in A)$.
   (g) $\therefore \sim (x \in B)$, that is, $(x \notin B)$.

2. *Assume*: $A \subset B$. $B \subset C$. $x \in A$.

   Prove: $x \in C$.

   Proof:
   (a) $A \subset B$.
   (b) $A \subset B \leftrightarrow (x \in A \rightarrow x \in B)$.
   (c) $\therefore x \in A \rightarrow x \in B$.
   (d) $x \in A$.
   (e) $\therefore x \in B$.
   (f) $B \subset C$.
   (g) $\therefore x \in B \rightarrow x \in C$.
   (h) $\therefore x \in C$.

Write a column proof for each of the following. List all statements of equivalence used for substitutions in the proofs of Exercises 3–6.

3. *Given*: $x \in A$.

   Conclusion: $x \in A \cup B$.

4. *Given*: $x \notin A$.

   Conclusion: $x \notin A \cap B$.

5. *Given*: $A \subset B$. $x \notin B$.

   Prove: $x \notin A$.

6. *Given*: $x \notin A \cup B$. $C \subset B$.

   Prove: $x \in \bar{C}$.

7. *Hypothesis*: $x \in A \cup (B \cap C)$. $x \notin B$.

   Conclusion: $x \in A$.

8. *Hypothesis*: $x \in \overline{A \cup B}$.

   Conclusion: $x \in \bar{A} \cap \bar{B}$.

9. *Hypothesis*: $x \in A$.

   Conclusion: $x \in \bar{\bar{A}}$.

10. *Assume*: $x \in \bar{\bar{A}}$.

    Prove: $x \in A$.

11. *Assume*: If $x \in A$ then $x \in A \cap B$. $x \in A$.

    Prove: $x \in B$.

12. *Assume*: $x \in B$. If $x \in A \cup B$, then $x \in A$.

    Prove: $x \in A$.

13. *Assume*: $A \subset C$. $B \subset C$. $x \in A \cup B$.

    Prove: $x \in C$.

14. *Assume*: $x \in A \cap B$.

    Prove: $x \in A \cup B$.

8.6 Proof of Conditionals

Conditional sentences are generally proved by means of the pattern of proof *conditionalizing*. The pattern is illustrated by the example below. (Notice that there are no premises.)

Given:

Conclusion: If $x \in A$, then $x \in A \cup B$.

Proof:

1. *Assume* $x \in A$.	
2. $\therefore$ $x \in A \vee x \in B$.	2. Rule of $\vee$.
3. $\therefore$ $x \in A \cup B$.	3. Definition (and substitution).
4. $\therefore$ If $x \in A$, then $x \in A \cup B$.	4. *Conditionalizing* (steps 1, 2, 3).

Steps 1–3 of the proof show that the sentence

$x \in A \cup B$ (step 3)

follows logically from

$x \in A$ (step 1).

In other words, any element of A is an element of $A \cup B$. But this is exactly what is asserted by

If $x \in A$, then $x \in A \cup B$.

So, step 4 is accepted as a valid inference from steps 1–3.

The first step of the proof,

1. Assume $x \in A$

(where $x \in A$ is the *antecedent* of the conditional to be proved), is a *temporary* assumption, used to derive the consequent:

3. $\therefore x \in A \cup B$.

When this is the case (as it is here), the conditional can be inferred. The student is cautioned *not* to consider any of the statements of steps 1, 2, or 3 as conclusions of the proof. They are in the proof only on the basis of the *temporary* assumption, and not because of any premises, and so forth, of the problem.

The pattern for conditionalizing, written symbolically, is

$$\begin{array}{l} \text{Assume } P^* \\ \cdot \\ \cdot \qquad\qquad (\textit{conditionalizing}). \\ \cdot \\ \underline{Q\qquad\qquad} \\ P \rightarrow Q \end{array}$$

This pattern indicates that if Q follows from P (and possibly other premises), then $P \rightarrow Q$ may be inferred. The asterisk is used to show that P is not considered as a premise of the inference. The only premise of the inference is

Assuming P, Q can be derived logically.

The following example shows how conditionalizing can be used when there are premises.

EXAMPLE 8.9 Write a column proof for

Hypothesis: $x \notin A$.

Conclusion: If $x \in A \cup B$ then $x \in B$.

Proof:

1. Assume $x \in A \cup B$*.	1. $x \in A \cup B$ is the antecedent of the conditional to be derived.
2. $\therefore$ $x \in A$ or $x \in B$.	2. Definition.
3. $x \notin A$.	3. Given.
4. $\therefore$ $x \in B$.	4. Disjunctive syllogism.
5. $\therefore$ if $x \in A \cup B$ then $x \in B$.	5. Conditionalizing (steps 1–4).

EXAMPLE 8.10 Write a column proof for

Conclusion: $A \cap B \subset A$.

Proof:

[Since $A \cap B \subset A \leftrightarrow (x \in A \cap B \rightarrow x \in A)$, the conditional $x \in A \cap B \rightarrow x \in A$ will be proved. Then, by substitution, the conclusion follows.]

1. Assume $x \in A \cap B$.*	1. $x \in A \cap B$ is the antecedent of the conditional to be derived.
2. $x \in A \cap B \leftrightarrow x \in A \ \& \ x \in B$.	2. ______________?
3. $\therefore$ $x \in A \ \& \ x \in B$.	3. ______________?
4. $\therefore$ $x \in A$.	4. ______________?
5. $\therefore$ $x \in A \cap B \rightarrow x \in A$.	5. Conditionalizing (steps 1–4).
6. $(x \in A \cap B \rightarrow x \in A) \leftrightarrow A \cap B \subset A$.	6. ______________?
7. $\therefore$ $A \cap B \subset A$.	7. ______________?

For the exercises listed below, the following definitions will be needed.

DEFINITION (OF EQUALITY) 8.5 *$A = B$ if and only if $A \subset B$ and $B \subset A$.*

DEFINITION (OF EMPTY SET) 8.6 *For each x, $x \notin \emptyset$.*

DEFINITION (OF UNIVERSAL SET) 8.7 *For each x, $x \in U$.*

EXERCISE SET 8.5

List the reasons for each step of the proof.

1. *Conclusion*: $A \subset A \cup A$.

   Proof:

   (a) Let $x \in A$.* (a) ______
   (b) $\therefore x \in A \vee x \in A$. (b) ______
   (c) $(x \in A \vee x \in A) \leftrightarrow x \in A \cup A$. (c) ______
   (d) $\therefore x \in A \cup A$. (d) ______
   (e) $\therefore$ if $x \in A$ then $x \in A \cup A$. (e) ______
   (f) (If $x \in A$ then $x \in A \cup A) \leftrightarrow A \subset A \cup A$. (f) ______
   (g) $\therefore A \subset A \cup A$. (g) ______

2. *Prove*: If $x \in A$ and $A \subset B$, then $x \in B$.

   Proof:

   (a) Assume $x \in A$ and $A \subset B$.* (a) ______
   (b) $\therefore x \in A$. (b) ______
   (c) $A \subset B \leftrightarrow x \in A \rightarrow x \in B$. (c) ______
   (d) $\therefore A \subset B$. (d) ______
   (e) $\therefore x \in A \rightarrow x \in B$. (e) ______
   (f) $\therefore x \in B$. (f) ______
   (g) $\therefore$ if $x \in A$ and $A \subset B$, then $x \in B$. (g) ______

Write a column proof for each of the following, or disprove.

3. *Given*: $x \in B$.

   Prove: If $x \in A$ then $x \in A \cap B$.

4. *Hypothesis*: $A \subset B$.

   Conclusion: If $x \in A \cap C$ then $x \in B \cap C$.

5. *Hypothesis*: $A \cup B = A$.

   Conclusion: If $x \in B$ then $x \in A$.

6. *Conclusion*: $A \cap B = A$.

7. *Hypothesis*: $A \subset B$. $B \subset C$.

   Conclusion: $A \subset C$.

8. *Given*: $A \subset B$.

   Conclusion: $\bar{A} \subset \bar{B}$.

9. *Given*: $A \subset B$.

   Prove: $\bar{B} \subset \bar{A}$.

10. *Prove*: If $A \subset B$ then $\bar{B} \subset \bar{A}$.

11. *Given*: $A \cap B = A$.

    Prove: $A \subset B$.

12. *Given*: $A \subset B$.

    Prove: $A \subset A \cap B$.

8.7 The Paragraph Proof

Column proofs have been used to show precisely the important logical steps from the beginning to the conclusion of an argument. It is customary in mathematics to use the more informal *paragraph proof*. A *paragraph proof* reads as any paragraph, but includes the principal assertions, in order, which lead to the conclusion.

The examples to follow illustrate paragraph proofs and compare them with column proofs. In writing a paragraph proof, the student should be certain that the reasoning is logically correct from step to step, and, of course, that the paragraph is written in acceptable English.

EXAMPLE 8.11 Write column and paragraph proofs of the following:

Conclusion: $A \cap (B \cup A) \subset A$.

Column Proof

1. Assume $x \in A \cap (B \cup A)$.*
   1. ______________
2. $\therefore x \in A \; \& \; x \in B \cup A$.
   2. ______________
3. $\therefore x \in A$. 3. ______________
4. $\therefore x \in A \cap (B \cup A) \rightarrow x \in A$.
   4. ______________
5. $\therefore A \cap (B \cup A) \subset A$.
   5. ______________

Paragraph Proof

Let $x \in A \cap (B \cup A)$. Then $x \in A$ and $x \in B \cup A$. This means that $x \in A$. Therefore, if $x \in A \cap (B \cup A)$, then $x \in A$. By the definition of subset, $A \cap (B \cup A) \subset A$.

EXAMPLE 8.12 Write a paragraph proof of the following:

Conclusion: If $A \subset A \cap B$ then $A \subset B$.

Proof:
Assume that $A \subset A \cap B$. Therefore, if $x \in A$, then $x \in A \cap B$. (To prove that $A \subset B$, it will be proven that "if $x \in A$, then $x \in B$.") Suppose

$x \in A$. Then by *modus ponens*, $x \in A \cap B$. From the definition of $A \cap B$, $x \in A$ and $x \in B$. Then $x \in B$. This means that if $x \in A$ then $x \in B$ (conditionalizing). Equivalently, $A \subset B$. The conclusion now follows (conditionalizing from "assume $A \subset A \cap B$").

EXAMPLE 8.13 Write paragraph and column proofs of the following:

Conclusion: $A \cup (B \cap C) \subset [(A \cup B) \cap (A \cup C)]$.

Paragraph Proof:

Let $x \in A \cup (B \cap C)$. Then, from the definition of union, $x \in A$ or $x \in B \cap C$. (Proof by cases is now to be applied.)

Case 1. Suppose that $x \in A$. Then $x \in A$ or $x \in B$; that is, $x \in A \cup B$. Similarly, $x \in A \cup C$. It follows that $x \in A \cup B$ and $x \in A \cup C$, which means $x \in [(A \cup B) \cap (A \cup C)]$. If $x \in A$ then $x \in [(A \cup B) \cap (A \cup C)]$ (conditionalizing).

Case 2. Suppose that $x \in B \cap C$. Then $x \in B$ and $x \in C$. Since $x \in B$, $x \in A$ or $x \in B$; hence $x \in A \cup B$. Since $x \in C$, $x \in A$ or $x \in C$; hence $x \in A \cup C$. Finally, $x \in A \cup B$ and $x \in A \cup C$, which means $x \in [(A \cup B) \cap (A \cup C)]$.
If $x \in B \cap C$ then $x \in [(A \cup B) \cap (A \cup C)]$.

By proof by cases, $x \in [(A \cup B) \cap (A \cup C)]$. Therefore,

$$\text{if } x \in A \cup (B \cap C) \text{ then } x \in [(A \cup B) \cap (A \cup C)].$$

From the definition of subset,

$$A \cup (B \cap C) \subset [(A \cup B) \cap (A \cup C)].$$

Column Proof:

1. Assume $x \in A \cup (B \cap C)$.*	1. __________
2. $x \in A \cup (B \cap C)$ $\leftrightarrow x \in A \lor x \in (B \cap C)$.	2. __________
3. $(x \in A) \lor (x \in B \cap C)$.	3. __________
4. Assume $x \in A$.*	4. __________
5. $x \in A \lor x \in B$.	5. __________
6. $x \in A \cup B$.	6. __________
7. $x \in A \lor x \in C$.	7. __________

Step	Reason
8. $x \in A \cup C$.	8. ____________
9. $x \in A \cup B \;\&\; x \in A \cup C$.	9. ____________
10. $x \in (A \cup B) \cap (A \cup C)$.	10. ____________
11. If $x \in A$ then $x \in [(A \cup B) \cap (A \cup C)]$.	11. Conditionalizing (steps 4–10).
12. Assume $x \in B \cap C$.*	12. ____________
13. $x \in B \cap C \leftrightarrow x \in B \;\&\; x \in C$.	13. ____________
14. $x \in B \;\&\; x \in C$.	14. ____________
15. $x \in B$.	15. ____________
16. $x \in A \vee x \in B$.	16. ____________
17. $x \in A \cup B$.	17. ____________
18. $x \in C$.	18. ____________
19. $x \in A \vee x \in C$.	19. ____________
20. $x \in A \cup C$.	20. ____________
21. $x \in A \cup B \;\&\; x \in A \cup C$.	21. ____________
22. $x \in (A \cup B) \cap (A \cup C)$.	22. ____________
23. If $x \in B \cap C$ then $x \in [(A \cup B) \cap (A \cup C)]$.	23. Conditionalizing (steps 12–22).
24. $x \in [(A \cup B) \cap (A \cup C)]$.	24. Proof by cases.
25. $x \in A \cup (B \cap C) \rightarrow x \in [(A \cup B) \cap (A \cup C)]$.	25. Conditionalizing (steps 1–24).
26. $A \cup (B \cap C) \subset [(A \cup B) \cap (A \cup C)]$.	26. Definition of subset, substitution.

EXERCISE SET 8.6

Write column and paragraph proofs for each of the following.

1. If $A \cap B = A$ then $A \subset B$.
2. *Given*: $x \notin A$ or $x \in B$.
   Prove: $A \subset B$.
3. $A \subset \bar{\bar{A}}$.
4. $\bar{\bar{A}} \subset A$.

5. $A = \bar{\bar{A}}$.
6. $\emptyset \subset A$. (*Hint*: Prove that if $x \notin A$ then $x \notin \emptyset$.)
7. $A \subset U$.

Write paragraph proofs for each of the following.

8. *Given*: $x \in A \rightarrow x \in B$.
   Prove: $A \cup B \subset B$.
9. $A \cup \emptyset \subset A$.
10. $A \cup \emptyset = A$.
11. $A \cap U = A$.
12. $\overline{A \cap B} = \bar{A} \cup \bar{B}$.
13. $\overline{A \cup B} = \bar{A} \cap \bar{B}$.
14. *Given*: $A \cap B = \emptyset$. $x \in A$.
    Prove: $x \notin B$.
15. $(A \cap B) \cup A = A$.
16. $(A \cup B) \cap A = A$.
17. $A \cap (B \cup C) = (A \cap B) \cup (A \cap C)$.
18. $A \cup (B \cap C) = (A \cup B) \cap (A \cup C)$.

8.8 Indirect Proof

A basic notion of logic is that a sentence and its denial cannot both be accepted in a proof. If one concludes that $x > 3$ in a proof which already has the sentence $x \not> 3$ in it, something is amiss. Then the statement

$$x > 3 \;\&\; x \not> 3$$

could be inferred, and this sentence is an instance of the contradiction

$$P \;\&\; \sim P.$$

If the premises had no contradictory statements to begin with, the proof itself must be faulty. This consideration leads to a useful strategy of proof called *indirect proof*, or *proof by contradiction*.

The method of indirect proof is used in the following way. To prove that P is a conclusion of given sentences, one assumes its denial, $\sim P$. The procedure is, then, to attempt to obtain a contradiction in the proof using only valid inferences. Since the assumption of $\sim P$ forces the acceptance of a contradictory statement obtained through valid reasoning, this assumption must be incorrect. That is, $\sim (\sim P)$, or, equivalently, P, must follow.

In using indirect proof, since denials are assumed, care must be taken to recognize the quantification of the statements. If the conclusion desired is

$$x \in A,$$

the conclusion universally quantified would appear as

$$\forall x, x \in A.$$

Its denial is equivalent to

$$\exists x, x \notin A.$$

EXAMPLE 8.14 Prove using the method of indirect proof.

Conclusion: If $x \in A$ then $x \in A \cup B$.

Proof: (indirect):

1. Assume that there is an x_0 such that $\sim$ (If $x_0 \in A$, then $x_0 \in A \cup B$).
2. $\therefore x_0 \in A \,\&\! \sim (x_0 \in A \cup B)$. — 2. Substitution.
3. $\therefore \sim x_0 \in A \cup B$. — 3. ____________
4. $\therefore \sim (x_0 \in A \vee x_0 \in B)$. — 4. ____________
5. $\therefore \sim (x_0 \in A) \,\&\! \sim (x_0 \in B)$. — 5. ____________
6. $\therefore \sim (x_0 \in A)$. — 6. Rule of &.
7. $\therefore x_0 \in A$. — 7. Rule of & (step 2).
8. $\therefore x_0 \in A \,\&\! \sim (x_0 \in A)$. — 8. Rule of &.

   This is a contradiction. So, it is not the case that for some x, $\sim$ (if $x \in A$ then $x \in A \cup B$).

9. $\therefore$ if $x \in A$, then $x \in A \cup B$. — 9. Rule of indirect proof.

The paragraph proof lends itself to the method of proof by contradiction as the next example illustrates.

EXAMPLE 8.15 Prove, using the method of proof by contradiction.

Hypothesis: $x \notin A \rightarrow x \notin B$.

Conclusion: $x \in B \rightarrow x \in A$.

Proof:
Suppose that the conclusion is false; that is, for some x_0, $x_0 \in B$ and $x_0 \notin A$. From the hypothesis, $x_0 \notin A \rightarrow x_0 \notin B$. It follows (from *modus ponens*) that $x_0 \notin B$. But $x_0 \in B$ (rule of & from $x_0 \in B$ and $x_0 \notin A$), so $x_0 \in B$ and $x_0 \notin B$. This is a contradiction. Therefore, by the method of indirect proof, the conclusion follows.

At times the method of indirect proof is used within a proof. In the example to follow, steps 2–6 are an indirect proof for step 7. After the assumption of $x \in A$, the desired sentence is $x \in A \cup B$. So the denial of this statement is assumed, with the intent of finding a contradiction.

EXAMPLE 8.16 Write a column proof for:

Conclusion: $A \subset A \cup B$.

Proof:

1. Assume $x \in A$.*	
2. Assume $x \notin A \cup B$.	
3. $\therefore \sim (x \in A \vee x \in B)$.	3. Definition, substitution.
4. $\therefore \sim (x \in A) \ \& \sim (x \in B)$.	4. Substitution.
5. $\therefore \sim (x \in A)$.	5. Rule of &.
6. $\therefore \sim (x \in A) \ \& \ x \in A$. This is a contradiction.	6. Rule of &.
7. $\therefore x \in A \cup B$.	7. Indirect proof (steps 2–6).
8. $\therefore$ If $x \in A$ then $x \in A \cup B$.	8. Conditionalizing (steps 1–7).
9. $\therefore A \subset A \cup B$.	9. Definition, substitution.

EXERCISE SET 8.7

Write a column proof using the method of indirect proof, or disprove.

1. *Given*: $x \in A$. $A \subset B$.

   Prove: $x \in B$.

2. *Prove*: $A \cap B \subset A$.

3. *Given*: $A \cup B \subset A$.

   Prove: If $x \in B$ then $x \in A$.

4. *Given*: $A \cup B \subset A$.

   Prove: $B \subset A$.

5. *Given*: $x \in A \cap (B \cup A)$.

   Prove: $x \in A$.

Write a paragraph proof of each of the following using the method of indirect proof, or disprove.

6. *Given*: $x \in A$.

   Prove: $x \in A \cup (B \cap A)$.

7. *Given*: $x \in \bar{A}$. $B \subset A$.

   Prove: $x \in \bar{B}$.

8. *Prove*: If $x \in A \cup \emptyset$ then $x \in A$.

9. *Prove*: $A \cup \emptyset \subset A$.

10. *Given*: $A \subset B$.

    Prove: $A \cap B = A$.

8.9 Order Properties of the Real Numbers

For a mathematical development of the properties of order of the real numbers using the methods of inference and proof previously developed, a minimum of basic assumptions, called *axioms*, are accepted. From these, together with definitions, other properties are derived.

Throughout the following discussion it will be assumed that one is free to make use of algebraic properties of the real numbers related to the operations of addition, multiplication, and so forth. At the same time, one is not allowed to use (in a proof) any "known" order properties of real numbers such as those discussed in Chapter Four. Only those properties derived in this section (or assumed) are to be accepted.

Some proofs in this section use another valid inference pattern of *substitution*. For any given sentence dependent on a variable a, say $P(a)$, the condition that $a = b$ allows the conclusion $P(b)$. Briefly, this pattern is

$$\frac{P(a),\ a = b}{P(b)} \qquad (\textit{substitution}).$$

So if a statement $x^2 = 0$ appears in a proof, and $x = y$, then $y^2 = 0$ can be placed in the proof.

The theorems in this section are numbered in the order that they are to be proved. In the proof of a given theorem, any theorems listed previously, and only those, may be used. Many of the theorems are not proved in the text but are left as exercises for the reader. Paragraph proofs are generally given, but the inferences involved are frequently mentioned.

The axioms used for the relation "$<$" (less than) are listed below. Definitions are given throughout the section as needed. (The relation "$>$" is not used until later.)

Let $<$ be a relation defined on the real numbers such that

AXIOM 1. *If $x < y$, then $x + z < y + z$.*
(addition transformation)

AXIOM 2. *If $x < y$ and $0 < z$, then $xz < yz$.*
(multiplication transformation)

AXIOM 3. *If $x < y$ and $y < z$, then $x < z$.*
(transitivity)

AXIOM 4. *For each x, exactly one of the following holds:*

(i) $x < 0$, (ii) $0 < x$, (iii) $x = 0$.
(trichotomy)

[NOTE: It is understood that these sentences are universally quantified.]

THEOREM 1. *If $x < y$ and $z < w$, then $x + z < y + w$.*

Proof:
Suppose that $x < y$ and $z < w$. Then $x + z < y + z$ (Axiom 1, rule of &). Likewise, $z + y < w + y$, which means $y + z < y + w$ (substitution). By transitivity (Axiom 3), $x + z < y + w$.

THEOREM 2. *$0 < x$ if and only if $-x < 0$.*

Proof: Exercise 1, Exercise Set 8.8.

THEOREM 3. *$-x < -y$ if and only if $y < x$.*

Proof:
Suppose that $-x < -y$. Then by adding $x + y$ to both sides (Axiom 1),

$$-x + (x + y) < -y + (x + y).$$

This means $y < x$ (substitution, employing rules of algebra). So, if $-x < -y$, then $y < x$ (conditionalizing). (Exercise 2, Exercise Set 8.8, asks for a proof of the converse.)

THEOREM 4. *If* $z < 0$ *and* $x < y$, *then* $yz < xz$.

Proof: Exercise 3, Exercise Set 8.8.

THEOREM 5. *If* $0 < z$ *then* $0 < \frac{1}{z}$.

Proof: Exercise 4, Exercise Set 8.8.

THEOREM 6. *If* $0 < x$ *and* $0 < y$ *then* $0 < x + y$.

Proof:
Suppose $0 < x$ and $0 < y$. Adding y to both sides of the first inequality gives $0 + y < x + y$, or $y < x + y$. Then $0 < x + y$ by transitivity, and the theorem follows.

THEOREM 7. *If* $0 < x$ *and* $0 < y$ *then* $0 < x \cdot y$.

Proof: Exercise 5, Exercise Set 8.8.

THEOREM 8. *If* $x < 0$ *and* $y < 0$ *then* $0 < xy$.

Proof:
Suppose $x < 0$ and $y < 0$. Multiplying both sides of $x < 0$ by y, $0 \cdot y < x \cdot y$, or $0 < xy$ (Theorem 4).

THEOREM 9. *If* $x \neq 0$ *then* $0 < x^2$.

Proof:
Assume $x \neq 0$. Then $x < 0$ or $0 < x$. (Why?) If $x < 0$ then $0 < x^2$ (Theorem 8). If $0 < x$ then $0 < x^2$ (Theorem 7). Therefore, by proof by cases, $0 < x^2$.

THEOREM 10. $0 < 1$.

Proof:
Since $1 \neq 0$, $0 < 1^2$; but $1^2 = 1$. Therefore $0 < 1$.

THEOREM 11. *If* $0 < x$ *and* $y < 0$, *then* $xy < 0$.

Proof: Exercise 6, Exercise Set 8.8.

DEFINITION 8.8. *$x < y < z$ if and only if $x < y$ and $y < z$.*

DEFINITION 8.9. *$x \leq y$ if and only if $x < y$ or $x = y$.*

THEOREM 12. *If $0 < x < y$, then $0 < \frac{1}{y} < \frac{1}{x}$.*

Proof:
Suppose that $0 < x < y$. Then, $0 < x$ and $x < y$ (Definition 8.8). Therefore, $0 < y$ (Axiom 3). Then $0 < xy$ by Theorem 7. From $0 < xy$, $0 < 1/xy$ by Theorem 5. Since $x < y$, by multiplying both sides by $1/xy$,

$$\frac{x}{xy} < \frac{y}{xy}.$$

That is, $1/y < 1/x$. But $0 < y$ means $0 < 1/y$ (Theorem 5). This means

$$0 < \frac{1}{y} < \frac{1}{x},$$

and the theorem follows (rule of &, conditionalizing).

THEOREM 13. *If $x < y < 0$, then $\frac{1}{y} < \frac{1}{x} < 0$.*

Proof: Exercise 7, Exercise Set 8.8.

EXERCISE SET 8.8

1. Prove Theorem 2.
2. Prove the converse of Theorem 3 (if $y < x$ then $-x < -y$).
3. Prove Theorem 4. (*Hint*: Use a method analogous to the proof of Theorem 1.)
4. Prove Theorem 5.
5. Prove Theorem 7.
6. Prove Theorem 11.
7. Prove Theorem 13.
8. Another version of the trichotomy axiom (Axiom 4) is "For each x, y, exactly one of the following holds:

   (i) $x < y$, (ii) $y < x$, (iii) $x = y$."

   Write a proof for this statement.
9. Prove that if $x < 0$ then $1/x < 0$.

8.10 More Order Theorems

Continuing from the previous section and assuming all the axioms, definitions, and theorems from that section, the order topics of *greater than*, *positive*, *negative*, and *absolute value* follow.

DEFINITION 8.10. *A number x is positive if and only if $0 < x$.*

DEFINITION 8.11. *A number x is negative if and only if $-x$ is positive.*

Proofs for most of the theorems follow almost directly from Theorems 1–13.

THEOREM 14. *The product of two positive numbers is a positive number.*

Proof:
Let x and y be positive numbers. Then $0 < x$, $0 < y$. By Theorem 7, $0 < xy$. This means xy is a positive number.

THEOREM 15. *The sum of two positive numbers is a positive number.*

Proof: Exercise 1, Exercise Set 8.9.

THEOREM 16. *The sum of two negative numbers is a negative number.*

Proof: Exercise 2, Exercise Set 8.9.

THEOREM 17. *A number x is negative if and only if $x < 0$.*

Proof:
Suppose x is negative. Then $-x$ is positive. This means $0 < -x$. By Theorem 2, $-(-x) < 0$, or by substitution, $x < 0$. The conditional "if x is negative then $x < 0$" follows.
Suppose that $x < 0$. Then, $0 < -x$ (Theorem 3). This means $-x$ is positive; hence, x is negative. The conditional "if $x < 0$ then x is negative" follows.
From the two conditionals, the statement of equivalence of the theorem follows.

THEOREM 18. *The product of two negative numbers is positive.*

Proof: Exercise 3, Exercise Set 8.9.

THEOREM 19. *The product of a positive and a negative number is a negative number.*

Proof: Exercise 4, Exercise Set 8.9.

THEOREM 20. *For each number x, one and only one of the following is true: (i) x is positive, (ii) x is negative, (iii) $x = 0$.*

Proof: Exercise 5, Exercise Set 8.9.

The concept of "greater than" ($>$) has not been introduced up to this time. The following definition relates $>$ to the relation $<$. Most of the theorems that would follow are the previous theorems rewritten using $>$ rather than $<$. Only a few such theorems are given.

DEFINITION 8.12. *For each x, $x > 0$ if and only if $0 < x$.*

DEFINITION 8.13. *For each x, $x \geq 0$ if and only if $x > 0$ or $x = 0$.*

DEFINITION 8.14. *$x > y > z$ if and only if $x > y$ and $y > z$.*

THEOREM 21. *A number x is positive if and only if $x > 0$.*

Proof: Use Definitions 8.10 and 8.12 and substitution.

THEOREM 22. *For each number x, exactly one of the following holds: (i) $0 > x$, (ii) $x > 0$, (iii) $x = 0$.*

Proof: Definition 8.12, Axiom 4.

THEOREM 23. *If $x > y > 0$, then $x^2 > y^2 > 0$.*

Proof: Exercise 6, Exercise Set 8.9.

THEOREM 24. *For each number x, $x^2 \geq 0$.*

Proof: Exercise 7, Exercise Set 8.9.

DEFINITION 8.15. *For each real number x,*

$$|x| = \begin{cases} x, \text{ if } x \geq 0, \\ -x, \text{ if } x < 0. \end{cases}$$

($|x|$ is read "the absolute value of x.")

The alternative for the absolute value of x being x or $-x$ leads to many *proofs by cases*. This is illustrated in the proof of Theorem 25.

THEOREM 25. $|x| < y$ *only if* $x < y$.

Proof:
Suppose that $|x| < y$. But $x \geq 0$ or $x < 0$.

Case 1. Suppose $x \geq 0$. Then $|x| = x$ and $x < y$ by substitution. Then $x \geq 0$ implies $x < y$.

Case 2. Suppose $x < 0$. Then $-x > 0$, so $x < -x$. Since $|x| = -x$, $x < |x| < y$. It follows that $x < y$. So, $x < 0$ implies $x < y$.

By proof by cases, $x < y$. The theorem follows.

THEOREM 26. *If* $|x| < y$ *then* $-y < x < y$.

Proof: Exercise 8, Exercise Set 8.9.

THEOREM 27. $|x^2| = |x|^2$.

Proof:
By Theorem 24, $x^2 \geq 0$. Then $|x^2| = x^2$; but $|x|^2 = (x)^2$ or $|x|^2 = (-x)^2$. In either case, $|x|^2 = x^2$ since $(-x)^2 = x^2$. Therefore, $|x^2| = |x|^2$.

THEOREM 28. *For each* x, $x \leq |x|$.

Proof: Exercise 9, Exercise Set 8.9.

THEOREM 29. *If* $|x| < |y|$ *then* $x^2 < y^2$.

Proof: Exercise 10, Exercise Set 8.9.

THEOREM 30. *If* $x^2 < y^2$ *then* $|x| < |y|$.

Proof: Exercise 11, Exercise Set 8.9.

EXERCISE SET 8.9

Prove.

1. Theorem 15.
2. Theorem 16.
3. Theorem 18.
4. Theorem 19.
5. Theorem 20.

6. Theorem 23.
7. Theorem 24.
8. Theorem 26.
9. Theorem 28.
10. Theorem 29.
11. Theorem 30.

Prove or disprove each of the following.

12. If $x < y$ then $x < \frac{x + y}{2} < y$.
13. If $a < xy < b$ and $0 < y$, then $\frac{a}{y} < x < \frac{b}{y}$.
14. If $x \leq y$ and $y \leq x$, then $x = y$.
15. $|x + y| \leq |x| + |y|$.
16. $|x| = |-x|$.
17. $|(|x|)| = |x|$.
18. $|x - y| \leq |x| - |y|$.
19. $|x - y| \leq |x| + |y|$.
20. $|x| - |y| \leq |x - y|$.

Mathematical Induction and the Binomial Theorem

CHAPTER NINE

9.1 Introduction

Many important theorems of mathematics are generalizations about the counting numbers (or some subset of them). For example, the sum of the first n counting numbers is half the product of the nth counting number by the $(n + 1)$th counting number.

One may convince himself that this is a theorem by examining a few instances such as

$$1 = \tfrac{1}{2}(1)(1 + 1) \qquad \text{for } n \text{ equal to } 1,$$

$$1 + 2 = \tfrac{1}{2}(2)(2 + 1) \qquad \text{for } n \text{ equal to } 2,$$

$$1 + 2 + 3 = \tfrac{1}{2}(3)(3 + 1) \qquad \text{for } n \text{ equal to } 3,$$

and so on. However, no matter how many instances one might prove, there would remain many more to be proved. For this reason, the above theorem cannot be proved simply by examining instances.

Before exploring the possibilities of proving theorems such as the above, it will be helpful to introduce some notation.

9.2 Sigma Notation

For $n = 12$ the theorem of the previous section generates the instance

$$1 + 2 + 3 + 4 + 5 + 6 + 7 + 8 + 9 + 10 + 11 + 12 = \tfrac{1}{2}(12)(13).$$

Because the left member of this equation is cumbersome to write, it is customary to adopt an abbreviation for it that can also be extended to any continued sum that exhibits a convenient pattern.

One way to abbreviate the sum of the first 12 counting numbers is to write the sum for the first two or three terms, followed by three dots, followed by an expression that will generate the kth term when evaluated at k, followed by three dots, followed by the last term of the sum. With this abbreviation, the instance of the above theorem for $n = 12$ is

$$1 + 2 + 3 + 4 \ldots + k + \ldots + 12 = \tfrac{1}{2}(12)(13).$$

The convenience of this notation is especially appreciated when the summation consists of a large number of terms. The instance of the above theorem for $n = 1000$ is

$$1 + 2 + 3 + \ldots + k + \ldots + 1000 = \tfrac{1}{2}(1000)(1001).$$

In this notation the sum of the first 15 odd numbers is

$$1 + 3 + \ldots + (2k - 1) + \ldots + 29.$$

When one substitutes 1 for k in $2k - 1$, the result is the first term, 1; substituting 2 for k results in the second term, 3; and the fifteenth term, 29, is obtained by substituting 15 for k in $2k - 1$.

The use of an expression to generate the kth term of a summation can be utilized in other ways. For example, instead of saying

the sum of the first 17 odd counting numbers,

one can say

the sum of the numbers $2k - 1$ for all counting numbers k from 1 to 17.

Although the second method is longer than the first in this case, its advantage is that it allows a greater variety of summations. Thus one can speak of

the sum of the numbers $6m + 5$ for all counting numbers m from 5 to 37.

It is customary to use the symbol $\sum$ (the Greek capital letter sigma) in place of the phrase "the sum of the numbers" so that the above examples become

$\sum (2n - 1)$, for all counting numbers n from 1 to 17

and

$\sum (6m + 5)$, for all counting numbers m from 5 to 37.

Further economy can be obtained by shortening phrases such as

for all counting numbers n from 1 to 17.

Since the pertinent information in each such phrase is the pair of numbers which bound n (in this case 1 and 17), these numbers are exhibited with the summation symbol, $\sum$. In this complete *sigma notation* the above examples are

$$\sum_{n=1}^{17} (2n - 1) \quad \text{and} \quad \sum_{m=5}^{37} (6m + 5).$$

A summation in which all the terms of the summation are written out is said to be written in *expanded form.* The summation that has the following sigma notation form,

$$\sum_{k=3}^{6} (k^2 + 3k),$$

becomes in expanded form

$$18 + 28 + 40 + 54.$$

Sometimes the last (or first) term of a summation is not specified by a particular number. For example,

$$\sum_{n=1}^{2k} (n^3 + 1)$$

has the specific number 2 for first term. But since the upper limit of the summation is $2k$, the last term is $[(2k)^3 + 1]$. Expanded, this becomes

$$2 + 9 + 28 + \ldots + (n^3 + 1) + \ldots + [(2k)^3 + 1].$$

The importance of listing the general term in the expanded form of a summation in which the middle terms are not listed but are indicated as being absent by writing three dots can be seen in the following example. What is the third term of

$$1 + 2 + \ldots + 10?$$

What is the nth term? If the summation is

$$1 + 2 + \ldots + n + \ldots + 10,$$

then the third term is 3, but if the summation is

$$1 + 2 + \ldots + (n^3 - 13n^2 + 33n - 20) + \ldots + 10,$$

then the third term is -11. In both summations the first term is 1, the second term is 2, and the tenth term is 10.

Part of the job of discovering theorems about sums is being able to guess the general term of the sum. In view of the above example, one needs to realize that there are many expressions that will generate the terms of the sum that are given Fortunately, the most apparent expression is usually correct. If you were asked to find the general term of

$$2 + 7 + 12 + 17 + 22 + 27 + \dots + 102,$$

you would probably list $5n - 3$ since it is by far the most apparent expression that will generate all the terms of the sum that are listed. However, you should realize that there are other such expressions, some of which generate different terms between 27 and 102.

One can use the general or nth term to determine how many terms there are in the summation. For the summation

$$2 + 7 + \dots + (5n - 3) + \dots + 102,$$

the last term is 102, so there must be a number k such that

$$5k - 3 = 102.$$

Since 21 is the unique solution to this equation, 102 must be the 21st term of the summation.

The sigma notation can be used for an indicated summation such as

$$1 + 3 + 5 + \dots + 2n - 1 + \dots,$$

which has no end number. The notation is

$$\sum_{n=1}^{\infty} 2n - 1,$$

where the symbol ∞ is used to show that the indicated summation continues on for each counting number.

EXERCISE SET 9.1

Write in expanded form.

1. $\sum_{n=1}^{6} (n + 2)$.
2. $\sum_{k=1}^{5} (2k + 3)$.
3. $\sum_{m=1}^{8} (m^2 - 1)$.
4. $\sum_{n=4}^{10} (n)(n + 1)(n - 1)$.

Write in modified expanded form. (That is, list the first two or three terms as a sum followed by three dots and an expression for the general term, followed by three dots and the last term.)

5. $\sum_{n=1}^{13} (n + 2)$.

6. $\sum_{m=1}^{8} (m^2 - 1)$.

7. $\sum_{n=1}^{k} (n + 1)$.

8. $\sum_{n=1}^{k+1} (n + 1)$.

9. $\sum_{n=4}^{k+1} (2n - 1)$.

10. $\sum_{i=1}^{k} i(i + 1)(i - 1)$.

11. $\sum_{n=k}^{k+1} (2n + 1)$.

12. $\sum_{n=1}^{8} \frac{n}{n + 1}$.

13. $\sum_{n=5}^{k+1} \frac{n}{n + 1}$.

14. $\sum_{n=2}^{k} \frac{n!}{(n - 2)!}$.

15. $\sum_{n=2}^{k+1} \frac{n!}{(n - 1)!}$.

16. $\sum_{n=1}^{m-1} \cos \frac{n}{2}$.

17. The sum of the first 8 squares of counting numbers.

Rewrite each of the following in sigma notation.

18. $1 + 2 + 3 + 4 + 5 + 6 + 7 + 8$.

19. $1 + 3 + 5 + \ldots + (2n - 1) + \ldots + 17$.

20. $2 + 5 + \ldots + (3k - 1) + \ldots + 29$.

21. $2 + 5 + \ldots + (k^2 + 1) + \ldots + 50$.

22. $1 + 8 + 27 + 64 + 125 + 216$.

23. $1 - 1 + 1 + \ldots + (-1)^{n+1} + \ldots + (-1)^m$.

24. $1 - 2 + 3 - 4 + \ldots + (-1)^{n-1}n + \ldots + 27$.

25. $\sin \frac{\pi}{2} + \sin \frac{\pi}{1} + \ldots + \sin \frac{n\pi}{2}$.

26. $\cos \frac{\pi}{4} + \cos \frac{\pi}{2} + \ldots + \cos \frac{k\pi}{4}$.

27. $\cot \frac{\pi}{6} + 2 \cot^2 \frac{\pi}{6} + \ldots + n \cot^n \frac{\pi}{6} + \ldots + 22 \cot^{22} \frac{\pi}{6}$.

28. The sum of the squares of the first k counting numbers.

29. The sum of the first k natural number multiples of 4.

30. The sum of the cubes of the 10 positive integers from 4 to 13.

31. $1 \cdot 2 + 2 \cdot 3 + 3 \cdot 4 + \dots + n(n+1) + \dots + 156.$

32. $\dfrac{2 \cdot 4}{3} + \dfrac{3 \cdot 5}{4} + \dfrac{4 \cdot 6}{5} + \dots + \dfrac{(k+1)(k+3)}{(k+2)}.$

33. $k^2 + (k+1)^2 + (k+2)^2.$

34. $3k + 2 + 3k + 5 + 3k + 8 + 3k + 11.$

35. $k^2 - 6k + 9 + k^2 - 4k + 4 + k^2 - 2k + 1.$

Find an expression for the nth general term in each summation. Rewrite the summation in sigma notation. (It is understood that there is no unique selection for the nth term.)

36. $2 + 4 + 6 + 8 + 10 + \dots + 100.$

37. $4 + 5 + 6 + 7 + 8 + \dots + 57.$

38. $7 + 9 + 11 + 13 + 15 + \dots + 205.$

39. $3 + 7 + 11 + 15 + 19 + 23 + \dots.$

40. $2 + 5 + 10 + 17 + 26 + 37 + 50.$

41. $\cos \dfrac{\pi}{2} + \cos \pi + \cos \dfrac{3\pi}{2} + \cos 2\pi + \dots.$

42. $\sin \dfrac{\pi}{6} - 2 \sin \dfrac{\pi}{6} + 3 \sin \dfrac{\pi}{6} - 4 \sin \dfrac{\pi}{6} + 5 \sin \dfrac{\pi}{6}.$

43. $1 + 2 + 6 + 24 + 120 + 720 + 5040 + 40{,}320.$

44. $1 + \frac{1}{2} + \frac{1}{3} + \frac{1}{4} + \frac{1}{5} + \frac{1}{6} + \dots + \frac{1}{27}.$

45. $1 - \frac{1}{2} + \frac{1}{4} - \frac{1}{8} + \frac{1}{16} - \frac{1}{32} + \dots.$

46. $2 - 2 + 2 - 2 + 2 - 2 + \dots.$

47. $3 + 3 + 3 + 3 + 3 + 3 + 3 + \dots.$

48. $0 - \frac{1}{2} + \frac{2}{3} - \frac{3}{4} + \frac{4}{5} - \frac{5}{6} + \frac{6}{7} - \frac{7}{8} + \dots.$

49. $3 + 8 + 15 + 24 + 35 + 48 + 63.$

Find the limits of summation so that the summation written in sigma notation is the same as the given summation written in expanded form.

50. $2 + 4 + 6 + 8 + 10 = \sum_{i=?}^{?} 2(i-3).$

51. $(k-5)^2 + (k-4)^2 + (k-3)^2 + (k-2)^2 + (k-1)^2 = \sum_{n=?}^{?} n^2.$

52. $(k-5)^2 + (k-4)^2 + (k-3)^2 + (k-2)^2 + (k-1)^2$

$$= \sum_{r=?}^{?} (r-2)^2.$$

9.3 The P(n) Notation

The substitution of 1 for n in the open sentence

$n^2 + n$ is an even number

generates the sentence

$1^2 + 1$ is an even number.

Similarly, the instance for $n = 2$ is

$2^2 + 2$ is an even number

and for $n = k + 1$ is

$(k + 1)^2 + (k + 1)$ is an even number.

This pairing of the counting numbers with the instances of the sentence, "$n^2 + n$ is an even number," is a function which will be denoted by P. Thus $P(1)$ is the sentence "$1^2 + 1$ is an even number," $P(2)$ is the sentence "$2^2 + 2$ is an even number," and $P(k + 1)$ is the sentence "$(k + 1)^2 + (k + 1)$ is an even number." As is usual with function notation, the symbol $P(k)$ is read "P of k"; it is also read "the proposition at k."

For example, suppose a function P is defined by

$P(m)$ is the sentence "$2 + 4 + \ldots + 2m = m^2 + m$."

Then, using a colon (:) for "is the sentence",

$$P(1): 2 = 1^2 + 1,$$

$$P(2): 2 + 4 = 2^2 + 2,$$

$$P(10): 2 + 4 + 6 + \ldots + 2m + \ldots + 20 = 10^2 + 10,$$

and

$$P(k): 2 + 4 + 6 + \ldots + 2k = k^2 + k.$$

Given

$$P(n): \mathrm{n} + 3 > n,$$

then the sentence

If $P(n)$ then $P(n + 1)$

becomes

If $n + 3 > n$ then $(n + 1) + 3 > (n + 1)$.

EXERCISE SET 9.2

1. Given $P(n)$: $2 + 4 + 6 + \ldots + 2n = n(n + 1)$. Find:

(a) $P(1)$. (e) $P(k)$.
(b) $P(2)$. (f) $P(k + 1)$.
(c) $P(3)$. (g) $P(k - 1)$.
(d) $P(8)$. (h) If $P(k)$ then $P(k + 1)$.

2. Given $P(k)$: The number $k(k + 1)$ is an even number. Find:

(a) $P(1)$. (e) $P(m)$.
(b) $P(2)$. (f) $P(m - 1)$.
(c) $P(3)$. (g) $P(m + 1)$.
(d) $P(10)$. (h) $P(m)$ and $P(m - 1)$.

3. Given $P(n)$: $2^{2n} - 1$ is a multiple of 3. Find the values of P for each of the given arguments (values for n).

(a) 1. (e) k.
(b) 2. (f) $2k$.
(c) 3. (g) $3k + 5$.
(d) 99. (h) 2^k.

4. If $P(m)$ is "$m + 1 > m$," find:

(a) $P(1)$. (f) $P(n)$.
(b) $P(2)$. (g) $P(n + 1)$.
(c) $P(3)$. (h) $P(k + 2)$.
(d) $P(10)$. (i) If $P(1)$ then $P(2)$.
(e) $P(k)$. (j) If $P(k)$ then $P(k + 1)$.

5. Let $P(n)$: $\sum_{k=1}^{n} k^2 = 2^{n+1}$. Find:

(a) $P(1)$. (c) $P(3)$.
(b) $P(2)$. (d) $P(4)$.

(e) $P(5)$.
(f) $P(k+1)$.
(g) $P(k-1)$.
(h) $P(k)$.
(i) If $P(3)$ then $P(4)$.
(j) If $P(k)$ then $P(k+1)$.

6. If $P(m)$ is "$x + y$ is a factor of $x^{2m} - y^{2m}$," find the value of P at the argument listed:

(a) 1.
(b) 2.
(c) k.
(d) $k + 1$.
(e) $k + 2$.
(f) $2(p - 1)$.

7. Find the value of P at the argument listed where

$$P(n): \frac{1}{1\cdot 2} + \frac{1}{2\cdot 3} + \ldots + \frac{1}{n(n+1)} = \frac{1}{n+1}.$$

(a) $n = 1$.
(b) $n = 2$.
(c) $n = 100$.
(d) $n = m - 1$.
(e) $n = m$.
(f) $n = m + 1$.

8. If $P(n)$ is "$n^2 + n + 41$ is a prime number," find:

(a) $P(1)$.
(b) $P(2)$.
(c) $P(10)$.
(d) $P(k - 1)$.
(e) $P(n)$ where $n = k$.
(f) $P(n)$ where $n = k + 1$.
(g) If $P(1)$ then $P(2)$.
(h) If $P(k)$ then $P(k + 1)$.

9.4 The Axiom of Mathematical Induction

Let S be a set of numbers. Suppose $1 \in S$. Furthermore, suppose that for each counting number k, if $k \in S$ then $(k + 1) \in S$. Is $2 \in S$? Here is a proof that $2 \in S$:

$\forall k$, if $k \in S$ then $(k + 1) \in S$.

$\therefore$ if $1 \in S$ then $(1 + 1) \in S$.

But $1 \in S$.

$\therefore$ $(1 + 1) \in S$.

Equivalently, $2 \in S$.

Is $3 \in S$? Is $4 \in S$? Is $100 \in S$? Can you prove your answer? Is there any natural number that is *not* in S?

Any set of numbers that contains the number 1 and for each counting number in the set also contains the *next* counting number must itself contain all the counting numbers. A more formal statement of this property of the counting numbers is:

THE AXIOM OF MATHEMATICAL INDUCTION: *For each subset S of the set I^+ of counting numbers, if*

(i) $1 \in S$ *and*

(ii) if $k \in S$ *then* $(k + 1) \in S$,

then $S = I^+$; *that is, S is the set of all counting numbers.*

It is now possible to prove the theorem of the introduction section of this chapter:

The sum of the first n counting numbers is half the product of the nth counting number by the $(n + 1)$th counting number.

This theorem can be restated as:

$$\forall n \in I^+, \sum_{i=1}^{n} i = \tfrac{1}{2}(n)(n+1).$$

It will be shown that the solution set of

$$\sum_{i=1}^{n} i = \tfrac{1}{2}(n)(n+1)$$

is the set I^+ of all counting numbers. By the axiom of mathematical induction, if it can be shown that 1 is in the solution set and also that whenever k is in the solution set, then $(k + 1)$ is also in the solution set, the solution set will be I^+. [In $P(n)$ notation, it is to be shown that $P(1)$ is true, and also that $P(k) \rightarrow P(k + 1)$ is true for each counting number k.]

$P(1)$ is the sentence

$$1 = \tfrac{1}{2}(1)(1+1),$$

which is true. To prove

$$P(k) \rightarrow P(k+1),$$

using the standard method of proof of a conditional, assume the antecedent $P(k)$. That is, assume

$$1 + 2 + 3 + \ldots + k = \tfrac{1}{2}(k)(k + 1).$$

The goal is to show that $P(k + 1)$ follows from this assumption.

By adding $(k + 1)$ to each side of the equation $P(k)$ one obtains

$$1 + 2 + \ldots + k + (k + 1) = \tfrac{1}{2}(k)(k + 1) + (k + 1).$$

The left-hand side of this equation is exactly the left-hand side of $P(k + 1)$. The following algebraic manipulation shows that the right-hand side is equivalent to the right-hand side of $P(k + 1)$:

$$\begin{aligned} \tfrac{1}{2}(k)(k + 1) + (k + 1) &= [\tfrac{1}{2}k + 1](k + 1) \\ &= \tfrac{1}{2}[k + 2](k + 1) \\ &= \tfrac{1}{2}(k + 1)[(k + 1) + 1]. \end{aligned}$$

So,

$$1 + 2 + \ldots + (k + 1) = \tfrac{1}{2}(k + 1)[(k + 1) + 1],$$

which is $P(k + 1)$. Therefore, if $P(k)$, then $P(k + 1)$.

Since 1 *is in the solution set of* $P(n)$, and *if* k *is in the solution set of* $P(n)$ *then* $(k + 1)$ *is in the solution set of* $P(n)$, by the axiom of mathematical induction the solution set of $P(n)$ is the set of all counting numbers. That is,

$$\forall n \in I^+, 1 + 2 + 3 + \ldots + n = \tfrac{1}{2}(n)(n + 1).$$

EXAMPLE 9.1 Let $P(n)\colon (n + 2)! > (n + 2)$.†

(a) $P(1)$—that is, $(1 + 2)! > (1 + 2)$—is true since $(1 + 2)! = 6$ and $1 + 2 = 3$, and $6 > 3$.

---

† For each counting number n, $n!$ (read "n factorial") is defined by

$$1! = 1,$$
$$(n + 1)! = (n + 1)n!.$$

This definition is usually extended to include $0!$, which is defined to be 1.

(b) $P(2)$ is true—that is, $(2 + 2)! > (2 + 2)$ since $(2 + 2)! = 24$ and $(2 + 2) = 4$, and $24 > 4$.

(c) Suppose $P(20)$ is true. Does it follow that $P(21)$ must also be true? Assume $(20 + 2)! > 20 + 2$. That is, $22! > 22$. Then $23 \cdot (22!) > 23 \cdot 22$. That is, $23! > 23 \cdot 22$. But $23 \cdot 22 > 23$ (why?). Therefore $23! > 23$. That is $(21 + 2)! > (21 + 2)$. But this is $P(21)$. This shows that if $P(20)$ then $P(21)$.

(d) $P(n)$ is true for each $n \in I^+$.

(i) $P(1)$ is true from part (a).

(ii) If $P(k)$ then $P(k + 1)$ since, assuming $P(k)$, i.e.,

$$(k + 2)! > k + 2,$$

then by multiplying both sides by $k + 3$ this becomes

$$(k + 2)!(k + 3) > (k + 2)(k + 3)$$

or

$$(k + 3)! > (k + 3)(k + 2).$$

Now $(k + 2) \geq 1$ if $k \in I^+$. Therefore,

$$(k + 3)(k + 2) \geq k + 3.$$

Thus

$$(k + 3)! > (k + 3)(k + 2) \geq k + 3,$$

$$(k + 3)! > k + 3.$$

But this is $P(k + 1)$. Thus if $P(k)$ then $P(k + 1)$.

By the axiom of mathematical induction, $P(n)$ is true for each $n \in I^+$.

EXAMPLE 9.2 Let $P(n): 2 + 4 + 6 + \cdots + 2n = n^2 + n + 1$.

(a) Show that $P(10)$ implies $P(11)$.
Assume $P(10)$ is true; that is,

$$2 + 4 + 6 \cdots + 20 = 10^2 + 10 + 1.$$

Adding 22 to both sides,

$$2 + 4 + 6 + \cdots + 20 + 22 = 10^2 + 10 + 1 + 22,$$

$$2 + 4 + 6 + \cdots + 20 + 22 = 133,$$

$$2 + 4 + 6 + \cdots + 20 + 22 = 11^2 + 11 + 1.$$

But this is $P(11)$.

$$\therefore\ P(10) \rightarrow P(11).$$

(b) Prove $P(k) \rightarrow P(k + 1)$ for each k.
Assume $P(k)$. That is

$$2 + 4 + 6 + \cdots + 2k = k^2 + k + 1.$$

Add $2(k + 1)$ to both sides.

$$2 + 4 + 6 + \cdots + 2k + 2(k + 1) = k^2 + k + 1 + 2(k + 1).$$

Then

$$2 + 4 + 6 + \cdots + 2k + 2(k + 1) = k^2 + 3k + 3,$$

$$2 + 4 + 6 + \cdots + 2k + 2(k + 1) = (k + 1)^2 + (k + 1) + 1.$$

But this is $P(k + 1)$.

$$\therefore\ P(k) \rightarrow P(k + 1).$$

(c) Is $P(n)$ true for each n?
In spite of part (b) above, one cannot conclude that $P(n)$ is true for each n since $P(1)$ is false. Check this! Is there any counting number n for which $P(n)$ holds?

Example 9.2 shows that the first part of an inductive proof, establishing $P(1)$, is essential.

EXAMPLE 9.3 Prove by mathematical induction, or disprove.

For each counting number n, $n + 1 > n$.

(a) $P(1): 1 + 1 > 1$. $P(1)$ is seen to be true.

(b) Assume $P(k)$, that is, $k + 1 > k$. By adding 1 to each side, $k + 2 > k + 1$ is obtained. But this is $P(k + 1)$.

$$\therefore P(k) \to P(k + 1).$$

By the axiom of mathematical induction, $P(n)$ is true for each $n \in I^+$.

EXAMPLE 9.4 Prove by mathematical induction, or disprove.

$$\text{For each } n \in I^+, \sum_{i=1}^{n} i^2 = n^3.$$

(a) $P(1)$ is $1^2 = 1^3$. (This is true!)

(b) Suppose $P(k)$; that is,

$$\sum_{i=1}^{k} i^2 = k^3$$

or

$$1^2 + 2^2 + 3^2 + \cdots + k^2 = k^3.$$

Add $(k + 1)^2$ to both sides:

$$1^2 + 2^2 + 3^2 + \cdots + k^2 + (k + 1)^2 = k^3 + (k + 1)^2$$

or

$$1^2 + 2^2 + 3^2 + \cdots + k^2 + (k + 1)^2 = k^3 + k^2 + 2k + 1.$$

Now $P(k + 1)$ is

$$1^2 + 2^2 + 3^2 + \cdots + (k + 1)^2 = (k + 1)^3.$$

Since $k^3 + k^2 + 2k + 1 \neq (k + 1)^3$ for some k, the induction step appears to fail. This suggests that one should be able to find a counterexample to $P(n)$.

$$P(2) \text{ is } 1^2 + 2^2 = 2^3,$$

which is false $(5 \neq 8)$. Therefore, 2 is a *counterexample*.

EXERCISE SET 9.3

1. $P(n)$: $n^2 + n$ is an even integer.
   (a) Write the statements $P(1)$, $P(k)$, and $P(k + 1)$.

(b) Is $P(1)$ true?

(c) Is $P(2)$ true?

(d) Is $P(100)$ true?

(e) Is $P(k) \rightarrow P(k+1)$ true for each $k \in I^+$?

(f) Is $P(n)$ true for each n?

2. $P(n)\colon 3 + 6 + 9 + 12 + \ldots + 3n = \dfrac{3n^2 + 3n}{2}$.

(a) Write $P(1)$.

(b) Is $P(1)$ true?

(c) Is $P(2)$ true?

(d) Suppose (without checking) that $P(20)$ is true. Using this supposition, prove that $P(21)$ follows from it.

(e) Prove $P(100) \rightarrow P(101)$.

(f) Assume $P(k)$. Prove $P(k+1)$ from this.

(g) Prove that $P(m+2)$ follows from $P(m)$.

(h) Is $P(n)$ true for each $n \in I^+$?

(i) Have you shown by parts (a)–(g) that $P(n)$ is true for each $n \in I^+$?

3. $S(n)\colon 2^n > n^2$.

(a) Is $S(1)$ true?

(b) Is $S(2)$ true?

(c) Is $S(3)$ true?

(d) Write out $S(20)$.

(e) Prove that if $S(20)$, then $S(21)$.

(f) Prove that if $S(20)$, then $S(22)$.

(g) Show that $S(99) \rightarrow S(100)$.

(h) Show that $S(k) \rightarrow S(k+1)$.

(i) Is $S(n)$ true for each $n \in I^+$? Justify your answer.

(j) Is $S(n)$ true for each $n \in I^+$, $n > 2$. Justify your answer.

4. Let $P(n)$ be $n < 100$.

(a) Is $P(1)$ true? $P(2)$? $P(3)$? $P(17)$?

(b) Is $P(n)$ true for each n? Justify your answer.

(c) In view of your answer to (b), could $P(k) \rightarrow P(k+1)$ be true? Why or why not?

Prove by mathematical induction that the sentence (Exercises 5–55) is true for each counting number, or disprove.

5. $1 + 2 + \ldots + n = \frac{1}{2}(n)(n+1)$.

6. $1^2 + 2^2 + \ldots + n^2 = \frac{1}{6}(n)(n+1)(2n+1)$.

7. $\sum_{i=1}^{n} 4i = 2n^2 + 2n.$

8. $1! + 2! + 3! + \dots + n! = \dfrac{n(n^2 - 2n + 3)}{2}.$

9. $n \geq 1.$

10. $n < n + 1.$

11. The sum of the first n odd counting numbers is n^2.

12. $n^2 + n$ is a multiple of 2.

13. $\dfrac{n^3 - n}{3}$ is a counting number, if $n \geq 2$.

14. $\sum_{0}^{k} n(n + 1) = (\frac{1}{3})k(k + 1)(k + 2).$

15. $3n > n + 1.$

16. $n^2 < 2^n$, if $n \geq 4$.

17. $1 + 2 + 3 + \dots + n = n(n + 1).$

18. $(1 + n)^2 > 1 + n^2.$

19. $x^n - y^n$ contains the factor $x - y$.

20. $k^3 < 3^k.$

21. $\sum_{0}^{n} k^2 = 2^{n+1}.$

22. $\dfrac{1}{1\cdot 2} + \dfrac{1}{2\cdot 3} + \dfrac{1}{3\cdot 4} + \dots + \dfrac{1}{n(n + 1)} = \dfrac{1}{n + 1}.$

23. The sum of the first n powers of 2 is $2^{n+1} - 1$.

24. $1 - 2^2 + 3^2 - 4^2 + \dots + (-1)^{n-1}n^2 = (-1)^{n-1}\left[\dfrac{n(n + 1)}{2}\right].$

25. $1 + 2 + 4 + \dots + 2^n = 2^{n+1} - 1.$

26. $2 + 6 + 18 + \dots + 2\cdot 3^n = (3^{n+1} - 1).$

27. $\sum_{i=1}^{n} i^3 = \left[\dfrac{n + 1}{2}\, n\right]^2.$

28. $1(1!) + 2(2!) + 3(3!) + \dots + n(n!) = (n + 1)! - 1.$

29. $\dfrac{2\cdot 4\cdot \dots \cdot 2n}{1\cdot 3\cdot \dots \cdot (2n - 1)} < 2\sqrt{n}.$

30. $2^{2n} - 1$ is a multiple of 3.

31. $\sum_{i=1}^{k} \dfrac{1}{i(i + 2)} = \dfrac{k(3k + 5)}{4(k + 1)(k + 2)}.$

32. The sum of three successive cubes is divisible by 9.

33. $n! < \left(\dfrac{n + 1}{2}\right) n$ for $n \geq 2$.

34. $a + ar + ar^2 + \ldots + ar^n = \dfrac{a(r^{n+1} - 1)}{r - 1}$.

35. $n < n^2 + 1$.

36. If $x > 1$, then $x^n > 1$.

37. If $x < 1$, then $x^n < 1$.

38. If $x < 0$, then $x^{2n-1} < 0$ and $x^{2n} > 0$.

39. $\dfrac{4^n - 1}{3} \in I^+$ if $n > 1$.

40. $\dfrac{5^n - 1}{4} \in I^+$ if $n \geq 1$.

41. $\dfrac{n^4 + 2n^3 + n^2}{4}$ is a whole number.

42. $(-1)^{2n} = 1$.

For Exercises 43–45, define positive integral powers of a real number a by

$$a^1 = a$$
$$a^{n+1} = a \cdot a^n$$

43. $(ab)^n = a^n b^n$.

44. $a^m a^n = a^{m+n}$.

45. $(a^m)^n = a^{mn}$.

46. $\cos n\pi = (-1)^n$.

47. $\sin n(\pi/2) = (-1)^{n-1}$.

48. $\tan n(\pi/4) = (-1)^{n+1}$.

49. n distinct planes all on the same line separate space into $2n$ regions.

50. n distinct points separate a line into $n + 1$ sections.

51. n distinct lines all on the same point separate the plane into $2n$ regions.

52. n distinct lines of which no two are parallel and no three are on the same point separate the plane into $(n^2 + n + 2)/2$ regions.

53. n distinct planes on a point, no three of which are on the same line, separate space into 2^n regions.

54. $(a + b)^n = \displaystyle\sum_{j=0}^{n} \frac{n!}{(n - j)!j!} a^{n-j} b^j$.

55. A set of u elements has 2^u subsets.

56. Consider $P(n)$: $n^2 + n + 41$ is a prime number. Show that $P(n)$ is true for

$$n \in \{1, 2, 3, 4, 5, 6, 7, 8, 9, 10\}.$$

Is $P(n)$ true for each n?

57. Letting $\prod$ represent "product" as $\sum$ represents "sum," for example,

$$\prod_{i=1}^{4} (i + 2) = (1 + 2)(2 + 2)(3 + 2)(4 + 2),$$

prove that for each n,

$$\prod_{i=1}^{2n+1} (x + n + 1 - i) = x \prod_{i=1}^{n} (x^2 - i^2),$$

for each real number x.

58. Prove: $(1 - a) \sum_{i=1}^{n-1} a^i = 1 - a^n$, for each n.

9.5 The Binomial Theorem

From the definition of a positive integral exponent

$$(a + b)^1 = a + b$$

and by simple expansion,

$$(a + b)^2 = a^2 + 2ab + b^2,$$

$$(a + b)^3 = a^3 + 3a^2b + 3ab^2 + b^3,$$

$$(a + b)^4 = a^4 + 4a^3b + 6a^2b^2 + 4ab^3 + b^4,$$

and,

$$(a + b)^5 = a^5 + 5a^4b + 10^3b^2 + 10a^2b^3 + 5ab^4 + b^5.$$

Similarly, one can find the sixth, seventh, and higher-power expansions of $(a + b)$. You have probably already noticed from the pattern of the examples above that you are able to predict some of the terms of the higher-power expansions. The formula for the expansion of $(a + b)^n$ is called the *binomial formula* and can be stated as

$$(a + b)^n = \sum_{j=0}^{n} \frac{n!\dagger}{(n - j)!j!} a^{n-j}b^j.$$

The statement that this formula holds for each counting number n is the *binomial theorem*. The following is a proof by mathematical induction of

† Recall that $0! = 1$, by definition.

this theorem:

(i) $P(1)$: $(a+b)^1 = \sum_{j=0}^{1} \frac{1!}{(1-j)!j!} a^{1-j}b^j$

$$= \frac{1!}{(1-0)!0!} a^{1-0}b^0 + \frac{1!}{(1-1)!1!} a^{1-1}b^1$$

$$= a + b.$$

(ii) $P(k) \to P(k+1)$:

Assume $P(k)$; i.e., $(a+b)^k = \sum_{j=0}^{k} \frac{k!}{(k-j)!j!} a^{k-j}b^j$.

Then $(a+b)^k(a+b) = \sum_{j=0}^{k} \frac{k!}{(k-j)!j!} a^{k-j}b^j(a+b)$.

That is,

$$(a+b)^{k+1} = \sum_{j=0}^{k} \frac{k!}{(k-j)!j!} a^{k+1-j}b^j + \sum_{j=0}^{k} \frac{k!}{(k-j)!j!} a^{k-j}b^{j+1}$$

$$= \frac{k!}{k!0!} a^{k+1-0}b^0 + \sum_{j=1}^{k} \frac{k!}{(k-j)!j!} a^{(k+1)-j}b^j$$

$$+ \sum_{j=1}^{k+1} \frac{k!}{(k+1-j)!(j-1)!} a^{k+1-j}b^j$$

$$= a^{k+1} + \sum_{j=1}^{k} \frac{k!}{(k-j)!j!} a^{k+1-j}b^j$$

$$+ \sum_{j=1}^{k} \frac{k!}{(k+1-j)!(j-1)!} a^{k+1-j}b^j + b^{k+1}$$

$$= a^{k+1} + \sum_{j=1}^{k} \frac{1}{(k-j)!j!}$$

$$+ \frac{1}{(k+1-j)!(j-1)!} k!a^{k+1-j}b^j + b^{k+1}$$

$$= a^{k+1} + \sum_{j=1}^{k} \frac{k+1-j+j}{(k+1-j)!j!} k!a^{k+1-j}b^j + b^{k+1}$$

$$= \frac{(k+1)!}{(k+1-0)!0!} a^{k+1-0}b^0$$

$$+ \sum_{j=1}^{k} \frac{(k+1)!}{[(k+1)-j]!j!} a^{(k+1)-j}b^j$$

$$+ \frac{(k+1)!}{[(k+1)-(k+1)]!(k+1)!} a^{(k+1)-(k+1)}b^{(k+1)}$$

$$= \sum_{j=0}^{k+1} \frac{(k+1)!}{[(k+1)-j]!j!} a^{(k+1)-j}b^j.$$

But

$$(a+b)^{k+1} = \sum_{j=0}^{k+1} \frac{(k+1)!}{[(k+1)-j]!j!} a^{(k+1)-j}b^j$$

is $P(k+1)$. Therefore, by the axiom of mathematical induction, $P(n)$ is true for each n.

EXAMPLE 9.5 Find the first 4 terms in the expansion of $(x + 2y)^{10}$.

$$(x+2y)^{10} = x^{10} + \frac{10!}{(10-1)!1!} x^{10-1}(2y)^1 + \frac{10!}{(10-2)!2!} x^{10-2}(2y)^2$$

$$+ \frac{10!}{(10-3)!3!} x^{10-3}(2y)^3 + \cdots$$

$$= x^{10} + 10x^9(2y) + 45x^8(2y)^2 + 120x^7(2y)^3 + \cdots$$

$$= x^{10} + 20x^9y + 180x^8y^2 + 960x^7y^3 + \cdots.$$

EXAMPLE 9.6 The expansion of $(2x - \frac{1}{2})^5$ is

$$32x^5 - 40x^4 + 20x^3 - 5x^2 + \tfrac{5}{8}x - \tfrac{1}{32}.$$

EXAMPLE 9.7 Find the 8th term of $(3x - 1)^{12}$.
The 8th term is

$$\frac{12!}{5!7!} (3x)^5(-1)^7 = -11\cdot 9\cdot 8\cdot 3^5x^5.$$

EXERCISE SET 9.4

Expand Exercises 1–4 by the binomial formula and show that they agree with the expansions given in the text.

1. $(a + b)^4$.
2. $(a + b)^3$.
3. $(a + b)^2$.
4. $(a + b)^5$.
5. Does the binomial formula hold for $(a + b)^0$?

Find the first four terms in the expansion of each of the following.

6. $(x + 3y)^3$.
7. $(x + 7)^9$.
8. $(1 + 5x)^{12}$.
9. $(1 + 0.03)^{100}$.
10. $(3x - 1)^7$.
11. $(x^2 - y^5)^8$.
12. $(1 + 0.0001)^{1000}$.
13. $(1 - 0.008)^{10}$.

Find the term asked for in the indicated expansion.

14. The 7th term of $(2x - 1)^7$.
15. The 5th term of $(x + 2y)^{17}$.
16. The term that involves x^5 in $(x - 3)^8$.
17. The 4th term of $(x + 7)^{16}$.
18. The 8th term of $(x - 3y)^{12}$.
19. The term involving y^4 of $(x^2 + y^2)^4$.
20. The last term of $(a + bc)^7$.

Appendix

TABLE 1

TRIGONOMETRIC FUNCTIONS FOR ROTATIONS IN RADIANS

x	Sin x	Cos x	Tan x	x	Sin x	Cos x	Tan x
.00	.0000	1.0000	.0000	.41	.3986	.9171	.4346
.01	.0100	1.0000	.0100	.42	.4078	.9131	.4466
.02	.0200	.9998	.0200	.43	.4169	.9090	.4586
.03	.0300	.9996	.0300	.44	.4259	.9048	.4708
.04	.0400	.9992	.0400	.45	.4350	.9004	.4831
.05	.0500	.9988	.0500	.46	.4439	.8961	.4954
.06	.0600	.9982	.0601	.47	.4529	.8916	.5080
.07	.0699	.9976	.0701	.48	.4618	.8870	.5206
.08	.0799	.9968	.0802	.49	.4706	.8823	.5334
.09	.0899	.9960	.0902	.50	.4794	.8776	.5463
.10	.0998	.9950	.1003	.51	.4882	.8727	.5594
.11	.1098	.9940	.1104	.52	.4969	.8678	.5726
.12	.1197	.9928	.1206	.53	.5055	.8628	.5859
.13	.1296	.9916	.1307	.54	.5141	.8577	.5994
.14	.1395	.9902	.1409	.55	.5227	.8525	.6131
.15	.1494	.9888	.1511	.56	.5312	.8473	.6269
.16	.1593	.9872	.1614	.57	.5396	.8419	.6410
.17	.1692	.9856	.1717	.58	.5480	.8365	.6552
.18	.1790	.9838	.1820	.59	.5564	.8309	.6696
.19	.1889	.9820	.1923	.60	.5646	.8253	.6841
.20	.1987	.9801	.2027	.61	.5729	.8196	.6989
.21	.2085	.9780	.2131	.62	.5810	.8139	.7139
.22	.2182	.9759	.2236	.63	.5891	.8080	.7291
.23	.2280	.9737	.2341	.64	.5972	.8021	.7445
.24	.2377	.9713	.2447	.65	.6052	.7961	.7602
.25	.2474	.9689	.2553	.66	.6131	.7900	.7761
.26	.2571	.9664	.2660	.67	.6210	.7838	.7923
.27	.2667	.9638	.2768	.68	.6288	.7776	.8087
.28	.2764	.9611	.2876	.69	.6365	.7712	.8253
.29	.2860	.9582	.2984	.70	.6442	.7648	.8423
.30	.2955	.9553	.3093	.71	.6518	.7584	.8595
.31	.3051	.9523	.3203	.72	.6594	.7518	.8771
.32	.3146	.9492	.3314	.73	.6669	.7452	.8949
.33	.3240	.9460	.3425	.74	.6743	.7385	.9131
.34	.3335	.9428	.3537	.75	.6816	.7317	.9316
.35	.3429	.9394	.3650	.76	.6889	.7248	.9505
.36	.3523	.9359	.3764	.77	.6961	.7179	.9697
.37	.3616	.9323	.3879	.78	.7033	.7109	.9893
.38	.3709	.9287	.3994	.79	.7104	.7038	1.009
.39	.3802	.9249	.4111	.80	.7174	.6967	1.030
.40	.3894	.9211	.4228				
x	Sin x	Cos x	Tan x	x	Sin x	Cos x	Tan x

TABLE 1—(CONTINUED)

x	Sin x	Cos x	Tan x	x	Sin x	Cos x	Tan x
.81	.7243	.6895	1.050	1.21	.9356	.3530	2.650
.82	.7311	.6822	1.072	1.22	.9391	.3436	2.733
.83	.7379	.6749	1.093	1.23	.9425	.3342	2.820
.84	.7446	.6675	1.116	1.24	.9458	.3248	2.912
.85	.7513	.6600	1.138	1.25	.9490	.3153	3.010
.86	.7578	.6524	1.162	1.26	.9521	.3058	3.113
.87	.7643	.6448	1.185	1.27	.9551	.2963	3.224
.88	.7707	.6372	1.210	1.28	.9580	.2867	3.341
.89	.7771	.6294	1.235	1.29	.9608	.2771	3.467
.90	.7833	.6216	1.260	1.30	.9636	.2675	3.602
.91	.7895	.6137	1.286	1.31	.9662	.2579	3.747
.92	.7956	.6058	1.313	1.32	.9687	.2482	3.903
.93	.8016	.5978	1.341	1.33	.9711	.2385	4.072
.94	.8076	.5898	1.369	1.34	.9735	.2288	4.256
.95	.8134	.5817	1.398	1.35	.9757	.2190	4.455
.96	.8192	.5735	1.428	1.36	.9779	.2092	4.673
.97	.8249	.5653	1.459	1.37	.9799	.1994	4.913
.98	.8305	.5570	1.491	1.38	.9819	.1896	5.177
.99	.8360	.5487	1.524	1.39	.9837	.1798	5.471
1.00	.8415	.5403	1.557	1.40	.9854	.1700	5.798
1.01	.8468	.5319	1.592	1.41	.9871	.1601	6.165
1.02	.8521	.5234	1.628	1.42	.9887	.1502	6.581
1.03	.8573	.5148	1.665	1.43	.9901	.1403	7.055
1.04	.8624	.5062	1.704	1.44	.9915	.1304	7.602
1.05	.8674	.4976	1.743	1.45	.9927	.1205	8.238
1.06	.8724	.4889	1.784	1.46	.9939	.1106	8.989
1.07	.8772	.4801	1.827	1.47	.9949	.1006	9.887
1.08	.8820	.4713	1.871	1.48	.9959	.0907	10.98
1.09	.8866	.4625	1.917	1.49	.9967	.0807	12.35
1.10	.8912	.4536	1.965	1.50	.9975	.0707	14.10
1.11	.8957	.4447	2.014	1.51	.9982	.0608	16.43
1.12	.9001	.4357	2.066	1.52	.9987	.0508	19.67
1.13	.9044	.4267	2.120	1.53	.9992	.0408	24.50
1.14	.9086	.4176	2.176	1.54	.9995	.0308	32.46
1.15	.9128	.4085	2.234	1.55	.9998	.0208	48.08
1.16	.9168	.3993	2.296	1.56	.9999	.0108	92.62
1.17	.9208	.3902	2.360	1.57	1.000	.0008	1256
1.18	.9246	.3809	2.427	1.58	1.000	−.0092	−108.7
1.19	.9284	.3717	2.498	1.59	.9998	−.0192	−52.07
1.20	.9320	.3624	2.572	1.60	.9996	−.0292	−34.23

TABLE 2

TRIGONOMETRIC FUNCTIONS FOR ROTATIONS IN DEGREES

x	Sin x	Cos x	Tan x	Cot x	
0	.0000	1.0000	.0000	......	90
1	.0175	.9998	.0175	57.290	89
2	.0349	.9994	.0349	28.636	88
3	.0523	.9986	.0524	19.081	87
4	.0698	.9976	.0699	14.301	86
5	.0872	.9962	.0875	11.430	85
6	.1045	.9945	.1051	9.514	84
7	.1219	.9925	.1228	8.144	83
8	.1392	.9903	.1405	7.115	82
9	.1564	.9877	.1584	6.314	81
10	.1736	.9848	.1763	5.671	80
11	.1908	.9816	.1944	5.145	79
12	.2079	.9781	.2126	4.705	78
13	.2250	.9744	.2309	4.332	77
14	.2419	.9703	.2493	4.011	76
15	.2588	.9659	.2679	3.732	75
16	.2756	.9613	.2867	3.487	74
17	.2924	.9563	.3057	3.271	73
18	.3090	.9511	.3249	3.078	72
19	.3256	.9455	.3443	2.904	71
20	.3420	.9397	.3640	2.748	70
21	.3584	.9336	.3839	2.605	69
22	.3746	.9272	.4040	2.475	68
23	.3907	.9205	.4245	2.356	67
24	.4067	.9135	.4452	2.246	66
25	.4226	.9063	.4663	2.145	65
26	.4384	.8988	.4877	2.050	64
27	.4540	.8910	.5095	1.963	63
28	.4695	.8829	.5317	1.881	62
29	.4848	.8746	.5543	1.804	61
30	.5000	.8660	.5774	1.732	60
31	.5150	.8572	.6009	1.664	59
32	.5299	.8480	.6249	1.600	58
33	.5446	.8387	.6494	1.540	57
34	.5592	.8290	.6745	1.483	56
35	.5736	.8192	.7002	1.428	55
36	.5878	.8090	.7265	1.376	54
37	.6018	.7986	.7536	1.327	53
38	.6157	.7880	.7813	1.280	52
39	.6293	.7771	.8098	1.235	51
40	.6428	.7660	.8391	1.192	50
41	.6561	.7547	.8693	1.150	49
42	.6691	.7431	.9004	1.111	48
43	.6820	.7314	.9325	1.072	47
44	.6947	.7193	.9657	1.036	46
45	.7071	.7071	1.0000	1.000	45
	Cos x	Sin x	Cot x	Tan x	x

TABLE 3

VALUES OF LN(x), EXP (x), $[e^x]$, AND EXP $(-x)$, $[e^{-x}]$

x	Ln(x)	Exp (x)	Exp $(-x)$
0.0	....	1.000	1.000
0.1	−2.303	1.105	0.905
0.2	−1.610	1.221	0.819
0.3	−1.204	1.350	0.741
0.4	−0.916	1.492	0.670
0.5	−0.693	1.649	0.607
0.6	−0.511	1.822	0.549
0.7	−0.357	2.014	0.497
0.8	−0.223	2.226	0.449
0.9	−0.105	2.460	0.407
1.0	0.000	2.718	0.368
1.1	0.095	3.004	0.333
1.2	0.182	3.320	0.301
1.3	0.262	3.669	0.273
1.4	0.336	4.055	0.247
1.5	0.405	4.482	0.223
1.6	0.470	4.953	0.202
1.7	0.531	5.474	0.183
1.8	0.588	6.050	0.165
1.9	0.642	6.686	0.150
2.0	0.693	7.389	0.135
2.1	0.742	8.166	0.122
2.2	0.788	9.025	0.111
2.3	0.833	9.974	0.100
2.4	0.875	11.02	0.091
2.5	0.916	12.18	0.082
2.6	0.956	13.46	0.074
2.7	0.993	14.88	0.067
2.8	1.030	16.44	0.061
2.9	1.065	18.17	0.055
3.0	1.099	20.09	0.050
3.2	1.163	24.53	0.041
3.4	1.224	29.96	0.033
3.6	1.281	36.60	0.027
3.8	1.335	44.70	0.022
4.0	1.386	54.60	0.018
5.0	1.609	148.4	0.007
6.0	1.792	403.4	0.002
8.0	2.079	2981.0	0.000
10.0	2.303	22026.	0.000

TABLE 4

TABLE OF COMMON LOGARITHMS

N	0	1	2	3	4	5	6	7	8	9
10	0000	0043	0086	0128	0170	0212	0253	0294	0334	0374
11	0414	0453	0492	0531	0569	0607	0645	0682	0719	0755
12	0792	0828	0864	0899	0934	0969	1004	1038	1072	1106
13	1139	1173	1206	1239	1271	1303	1335	1367	1399	1430
14	1461	1492	1523	1553	1584	1614	1644	1673	1703	1732
15	1761	1790	1818	1847	1875	1903	1931	1959	1987	2014
16	2041	2068	2095	2122	2148	2175	2201	2227	2253	2279
17	2304	2330	2355	2380	2405	2430	2455	2480	2504	2529
18	2553	2577	2601	2625	2648	2672	2695	2718	2742	2765
19	2788	2810	2833	2856	2878	2900	2923	2945	2967	2989
20	3010	3032	3054	3075	3096	3118	3139	3160	3181	3201
21	3222	3243	3263	3284	3304	3324	3345	3365	3385	3404
22	3424	3444	3464	3483	3502	3522	3541	3560	3579	3598
23	3617	3636	3655	3674	3692	3711	3729	3747	3766	3784
24	3802	3820	3838	3856	3874	3892	3909	3927	3945	3962
25	3979	3997	4014	4031	4048	4065	4082	4099	4116	4133
26	4150	4166	4183	4200	4216	4232	4249	4265	4281	4298
27	4314	4330	4346	4362	4378	4393	4409	4425	4440	4456
28	4472	4487	4502	4518	4533	4548	4564	4579	4594	4609
29	4624	4639	4654	4669	4683	4698	4713	4728	4742	4757
30	4771	4786	4800	4814	4829	4843	4857	4871	4886	4900
31	4914	4928	4942	4955	4969	4983	4997	5011	5024	5038
32	5051	5065	5079	5092	5105	5119	5132	5145	5159	5172
33	5185	5198	5211	5224	5237	5250	5263	5276	5289	5302
34	5315	5328	5340	5353	5366	5378	5391	5403	5416	5428
35	5441	5453	5465	5478	5490	5502	5514	5527	5539	5551
36	5563	5575	5587	5599	5611	5623	5635	5647	5658	5670
37	5682	5694	5705	5717	5729	5740	5752	5763	5775	5786
38	5798	5809	5821	5832	5843	5855	5866	5877	5888	5899
39	5911	5922	5933	5944	5955	5966	5977	5988	5999	6010
40	6021	6031	6042	6053	6064	6075	6085	6096	6107	6117
41	6128	6138	6149	6160	6170	6180	6191	6201	6212	6222
42	6232	6243	6253	6263	6274	6284	6294	6304	6314	6325
43	6335	6345	6355	6365	6375	6385	6395	6405	6415	6425
44	6435	6444	6454	6464	6474	6484	6493	6503	6513	6522

TABLE 4—(CONTINUED)

N	0	1	2	3	4	5	6	7	8	9
45	6532	6542	6551	6561	6571	6580	6590	6599	6609	6618
46	6628	6637	6646	6656	6665	6675	6684	6693	6702	6712
47	6721	6730	6739	6749	6758	6767	6776	6785	6794	6803
48	6812	6821	6830	6839	6848	6857	6866	6875	6884	6893
49	6902	6911	6920	6928	6937	6946	6955	6964	6972	6981
50	6990	6998	7007	7016	7024	7033	7042	7050	7059	7067
51	7076	7084	7093	7101	7110	7118	7126	7135	7143	7152
52	7160	7168	7177	7185	7193	7202	7210	7218	7226	7235
53	7243	7251	7259	7267	7275	7284	7292	7300	7308	7316
54	7324	7332	7340	7348	7356	7364	7372	7380	7388	7396
55	7404	7412	7419	7427	7435	7443	7451	7459	7466	7474
56	7482	7490	7497	7505	7513	7520	7528	7536	7543	7551
57	7559	7566	7574	7582	7589	7597	7604	7612	7619	7627
58	7634	7642	7649	7657	7664	7672	7679	7686	7694	7701
59	7709	7716	7723	7731	7738	7745	7752	7760	7767	7774
60	7782	7789	7796	7803	7810	7818	7825	7832	7839	7846
61	7853	7860	7868	7875	7882	7889	7896	7903	7910	7917
62	7924	7931	7938	7945	7952	7959	7966	7973	7980	7987
63	7993	8000	8007	8014	8021	8028	8035	8041	8048	8055
64	8062	8069	8075	8082	8089	8096	8102	8109	8116	8122
65	8129	8136	8142	8149	8156	8162	8169	8176	8182	8189
66	8195	8202	8209	8215	8222	8228	8235	8241	8248	8254
67	8261	8267	8274	8280	8287	8293	8299	8306	8312	8319
68	8325	8331	8338	8344	8351	8357	8363	8370	8376	8382
69	8388	8395	8401	8407	8414	8420	8426	8432	8439	8445
70	8451	8457	8463	8470	8476	8482	8488	8494	8500	8506
71	8513	8519	8525	8531	8537	8543	8549	8555	8561	8567
72	8573	8579	8585	8591	8597	8603	8609	8615	8621	8627
73	8633	8639	8645	8651	8657	8663	8669	8675	8681	8686
74	8692	8698	8704	8710	8716	8722	8727	8733	8739	8745
75	8751	8756	8762	8768	8774	8779	8785	8791	8797	8802
76	8808	8814	8820	8825	8831	8837	8842	8848	8854	8859
77	8865	8871	8876	8882	8887	8893	8899	8904	8910	8915
78	8921	8927	8932	8938	8943	8949	8954	8960	8965	8971
79	8976	8982	8987	8993	8998	9004	9009	9015	9020	9025
80	9031	9036	9042	9047	9053	9058	9063	9069	9074	9079
81	9085	9090	9096	9101	9106	9112	9117	9122	9128	9133
82	9138	9143	9149	9154	9159	9165	9170	9175	9180	9186
83	9191	9196	9201	9206	9212	9217	9222	9227	9232	9238
84	9243	9248	9253	9258	9263	9269	9274	9279	9284	9289

TABLE 4—(CONTINUED)

N	0	1	2	3	4	5	6	7	8	9
85	9294	9299	9304	9309	9315	9320	9325	9330	9335	9340
86	9345	9350	9355	9360	9365	9370	9375	9380	9385	9390
87	9395	9400	9405	9410	9415	9420	9425	9430	9435	9440
88	9445	9450	9455	9460	9465	9469	9474	9479	9484	9489
89	9494	9499	9504	9509	9513	9518	9523	9528	9533	9538
90	9542	9547	9552	9557	9562	9566	9571	9576	9581	9586
91	9590	9595	9600	9605	9609	9614	9619	9624	9628	9633
92	9638	9643	9647	9652	9657	9661	9666	9671	9675	9680
93	9685	9689	9694	9699	9703	9708	9713	9717	9722	9727
94	9731	9736	9741	9745	9750	9754	9759	9763	9768	9773
95	9777	9782	9786	9791	9795	9800	9805	9809	9814	9818
96	9823	9827	9832	9836	9841	9845	9850	9854	9859	9863
97	9868	9872	9877	9881	9886	9890	9894	9899	9903	9908
98	9912	9917	9921	9926	9930	9934	9939	9943	9948	9952
99	9956	9961	9965	9969	9974	9978	9983	9987	9991	9996

Answers to odd-numbered Exercises

APPENDIX

Chapter one

EXERCISE SET 1.1, PAGE 7

1. x, unquantified. 3. x, existential. 5. x, existential. 7. x, existential. b, unquantified. 9. x, existential. y, existential. 11. x, universal. y, universal. a, unquantified. 13. Existential generalization. 15. Universal generalization. 17. Existential generalization. 19. Existential generalization. 21. x is quantified universally. That is, for each x, it is not so that x is both positive and negative.

EXERCISE SET 1.2, PAGE 10

1. $\forall x, x < 3$. 3. $\exists x$, x is a perfect square. 5. $\exists x, x^2 = 2$. 7. $\exists x, x > x^2$. 9. $\exists x \exists y, xy = 0$ and $y \neq 0$. 11. $\forall x$, x is positive or negative. 13. $\exists x$, x is positive, and $\exists y$, y is negative. 15. $\forall x$, x^2 is positive. 17. $\forall x$ (x is a natural number), $x = 0$ or x is positive. 19. $\forall_A$ (A is an angle), A is acute or obtuse. 21. $\forall_L$ (L is a line), $L \parallel L_1$ or $L \nparallel L_1$. 23. $\exists_R$ (R is a rectangle), R is not a square.

EXERCISE SET 1.3, PAGE 14

For instances of proof and counterexamples there are often many choices. In these answers, the words "and others" are used to indicate this.

1. False, counterexample: 4, and others. 3. True, instances of proof: $(\sqrt{2})^2 = 2$, $(-\sqrt{2})^2 = 2$. 5. Open sentence in y. 7. True. 9. False, counterexample: 0. 11. True. Since $x > 3$, and $3 > 2$, then $x > 2$. 13. True, instance of proof: $3(4) - 2 = 10$. 15. False. From $y = y + 1$, it would follow that $0 = 1$. Hence $y \neq y + 1$, for each y. 17. False. x must be $\frac{5}{2}$ to satisfy $2x - 5 = 0$, but x must be $\frac{2}{5}$ to satisfy $5x - 2 = 0$. 19. False. Counterexample: $x = \pi$, and others. 21. Open sentence. 23. Open sentence. 25. True, (commutative property of addition). 27. False. Let $y = 4 - x$. Then $x + y = x + (4 - x) = 4$. 29. True. Let $y = 0$. 31. True. Let $y = x$ in each case. 33. False. Counterexample: $2 = 3$. (This is a trivial use of the quantifier since no variable appears. However, it is correct to say that for each value of x, $2 = 3$ is false. Similar usage occurs frequently in mathematics.) 35. False. Counterexample: $2 + 3 = 1$, and others. 37. True, instance of proof: $2 + 2 = 4$, and others. 39. True, let $y = x$. 41. True, instance of proof: $0(0 + 1) = 0^2$. 43. False. For $x = 0$, $x \cdot y = 0$ for each y. Therefore, $x \cdot y \neq 1$ for each y. 45. False. Counterexample: $t = 0$. 47. True. Definition of an even number. 49. $x(x + 1) = x^2 + x$, and others. 51. Only if the sentence is understood to be universally quantified.

EXERCISE SET 1.4, PAGE 19

1. $\exists x$, (x is rational) & (x is a perfect square). 3. $(2 < 3)$ & $(3 < 4)$. 5. $\forall x$ (x is a counting number), $(x^2 > 0)$ & $(-x^2 < 0)$. 7. $\exists x$, $[(x > 3) \vee (x = 3)]$ & $(x < 5)$. 9. $\forall x$, [(The absolute value of x is positive) $\vee$ (the absolute value of x is 0)] & [$\sim$ (the absolute value of x is negative)]. Alternate answer: $\forall x$, $[(|x| > 0) \vee (|x| = 0)]$ & $[\sim (|x| < 0)]$. 11. $\exists x \exists y$, $[\sim (x < y)]$ & $[\sim (y < x)]$.

13. $\exists a \forall b$, $(b > a) \vee (\sim [b \text{ is positive}])$. 15. $(2 < 3) \vee (2 = 3)$. 17. $\sim (2 < 3)$. 19. $\exists x$ (x is an integer), [$\sim$ (x has a square root)]. 21. $\exists x$, ($\sim$ [x is negative]) & ($\sim$ [x is positive]). 23. No. With one grouping arrangement x may be -4 but not in the other. 25. True sentences: 1, 3, 5, 6, 7, 9, 11, 12, 13, 15. False sentences: 2, 10. Open sentences: 4, 8, 14.

EXERCISE SET 1.5, PAGE 21

1. $\forall x$, $(x > 3) \rightarrow (x > 2)$. 3. $(x < 0) \rightarrow$ (x is negative). 5. [$(x > 2)$ and (x is even)] $\rightarrow (x > 3)$. 7. [(x is even) & $(x > 3)$] $\rightarrow (x > 2)$. 9. $[(x > 0) \rightarrow (-x < 0)]$ & $[(x < 0) \rightarrow (-x > 0)]$. 11. [($x$ is an integer) & (x has an integral square root)] $\rightarrow$ (x is a perfect square). 13. (A is the sum of two right angles) $\rightarrow$ (A is a straight angle). 15. $[(A = \pi/4) \vee (A = 5\pi/4)] \rightarrow (\sin A = \cos A)$.

EXERCISE SET 1.6, PAGE 24

1. False. Counterexample: 0. 3. True. Instance of proof: $\sqrt{2} \not> 0$ or $\sqrt{2} = 0$ or $\sqrt{2} > 0$. 5. False. Counterexample: $x = \pi$, and others. 7. True. Instance of proof: -2 is an even integer and is less than 0, and others. 9. True. 11. True. Instance of proof: $\sin 45° = \cos 45°$ and $\tan 45° = 1$. 13. True. Instance of proof: $(-1)^2 + 3(-1) + 2 = 0$ and $(-1)^2 - 4(-1) - 5 = 0$. 15. True. Instance of proof: let $A = \pi/4$. 17. $\exists x$, (x is positive) $\vee$ [(x is negative) & (x^2 is positive)]. True. Instance of proof: (Let x be any nonzero number.) 19. $\forall x$, (x has a square root) $\vee$ (x is negative). True. Each non-negative number has a square root. 21. $\exists_T$ (T is a triangle), (T is isosceles) & (T is equilateral) & (T is a right triangle). False. If T were a right triangle, one angle would be 90°. Since it is equilateral, this would mean each angle would be 90°. 23. (a) Yes ("$2 < 3$ and 2 is even" is an instance of proof.) (b) No. (c) No, the original sentence is not a universal generalization, and therefore can have no counterexamples. (d) No. (e) $(6 < 3)$ is false; therefore the instance "$6 < 3$ and 6 is even" is false. (f) "1 is even" is false, hence the sentence is false. (g) Yes, it asserts this, and more! (h) All even numbers less than 3. 25. (a) $\forall x$, $(x < 3)$ & (x is even). (b) Yes. (c) No. (d) No. (e) No, "$2 < 3$ and 2 is even" is a true instance. (f) No.

EXERCISE SET 1.7, PAGE 27

1. True. Let x be any negative number. 3. False. Counterexample: $x = 2$. 5. True. Property of zero. 7. False. Counterexample: 2. 9. True. Property of zero. 11. False. Counterexample: $x = 1$, $y = 0$, and others. 13. True. Let $y = 1$. 15. True. 17. True. $1/a$ represents a positive number divided by a negative number, hence is negative. 19. True. Trigonometric fact. 21. (a) $\forall x$, (x is even) $\rightarrow$ ($2x$ is even). (b) Yes. (c) Yes. (d) No. (e) No. $2(\frac{1}{2})$ is not even; 2π is not even. (f) No. (g) No. (h) Yes. (i) No. Since 3 is not even, the sentence makes no assertion about $2 \cdot 3$. (j) No. (k) Yes. Each instance with a false antecedent is true. (l) There are none. 23. (a) $\forall x, x^2 > 0 \rightarrow x > 0$. (b) No. (c) Yes. (d) No, since 0^2 is not greater than 0, no assertion is made about 0. (e) Yes. (f) No, counterexample: $x = -1$, and others.

EXERCISE SET 1.8, PAGE 32

1. If $x + 2 < 5$, then $x < 3$. True, true (converse). 3. If $x^2 < 4$, then $x < 2$. False, true (converse). 5. If $-x > 3$, $x < 3$ or $x = 3$. False, true (converse). 7. If $(x - 2)x \neq 0$, then $x > 2$. True, false (converse). 9. If $L \parallel N$, then $L \parallel M$ and $M \parallel N$. False, (True if a line is considered to be parallel to itself), false (converse). 11. If $xz = yz$, then $x = y$. True, false (converse). 13. If nx is an integer for some n, x is not an integer. False, false (converse). 15. $\forall x$, $(x < 0) \leftrightarrow (-x > 0)$. True. 17. $\forall x$, ($2x$ is even) $\leftrightarrow$ (x is even). False: $x = 5$, and others. 19. $\forall x$, $(x > 0) \leftrightarrow (x^2 > 0)$. False. $x = -1$, and others. 21. $\forall_T$ (T is a triangle), (T is equilateral) $\leftrightarrow$ (T is equiangular). True. 23. $\forall x$, $(2x = 5) \leftrightarrow (x = \frac{5}{2})$. True. 25. $\forall_C$ (C is a conditional), (C is true) $\leftrightarrow$ (the consequent of C is true). False. Counterexample: Let C be the conditional "$x > 3 \rightarrow x > 2$", or others. 27. If $x \ngtr 4$, then $x \ngtr 3$. Both false. 29. If $xy \neq 0$, then $x \neq 0$. Both true. 31. $q \rightarrow p$. 33. $\sim q \rightarrow \sim(p \;\&\; r)$. 35. It is either true or false. 37. It is true.

EXERCISE SET 1.9, PAGE 35

1. $\forall x$, $(x < 5) \rightarrow (x < 4)$. False. 3. $\forall x$, $(x < 5) \rightarrow (x < 4)$. False. 5. $\forall x$, (x is divisible by 6) $\rightarrow$ (x is divisible by 2). True. 7. $\forall x$, (x is divisible by 6) $\leftrightarrow$ (x is divisible by 2). False. 9. $\forall x \forall y$, $(x = 0) \rightarrow (xy = 0)$. True. 11. $\forall x \forall y$, $(x = 0) \rightarrow (xy = 0)$. True. 13. $\forall_T$ (T is a triangle), (T is isosceles) $\rightarrow$ [(T is equiangular) $\vee$ (T is equilateral)]. False. 15. $\forall_T$ (T is a triangle), (T is equiangular) $\leftrightarrow$ (T is equilateral). True. 17. $\forall x$, $(x + 2 > 2) \rightarrow (x > 0)$. True. 19. $\forall_T$ (T is a triangle), (the two acute angles of T are complementary) $\rightarrow$ (T is a right triangle). True. 21. If $x > 0$, then $x^2 > 0$. $x > 0$ only if $x^2 > 0$. For $x^2 > 0$, it is sufficient that $x > 0$. For $x > 0$, it is necessary that $x^2 > 0$. 23. If $x + a = b$, then $x = b - a$. $x + a = b$ only if $x = b - a$. $x + a = b$ is sufficient for $x = b - a$. For $x + a = b$, it is necessary that $x = b - a$.

EXERCISE SET 1.10, PAGE 40

1. Some number is not less than 3. True. 3. For some x, $x + x \neq 2x$. False. 5. Some triangle does not have three sides. False. 7. For some x, $x \neq 2$ and $x = 2$. False. 9. Some integer is not even and is not odd. False. 11. Each parallelogram is not a square or is not a rectangle. False. 13. For each x, x is not divisible by 6 or x is divisible by 3. (The connective in the original sentence is "but" which is a variation for &.) True. 15. Each number is not less than and not equal to 0 or it does not have a positive square. False. 17. Some number is not divisible by 2 or is not divisible by 3, and is divisible by 6. False. 19. $\exists x \forall y$, $y \ngtr x$ or $y \nless 0$; and $x \ngtr 0$ and $x \neq 0$. Alternate answer: $\exists x \forall y$, $y \leq x$ or $y \geq 0$, and $x \geq 0$ and $x \neq 0$. False. 21. Some x is not greater than 0, and for each y, y is not larger than x or not less than 0. True. 23. $\sim p \;\&\; \sim q$. 25. $\sim p \vee \sim q$. 27. $(\sim p \;\&\; \sim q) \vee (\sim r)$.

EXERCISE SET 1.11, PAGE 44

1. Some x is less than 5 and not less than 4. True. 3. Some x is divisible by 7 and not divisible by 14. True. 5. For some x, $x(x - 2) = 0$ and $x \neq 0$. True.

7. Some number is even or odd, and 1 added to the number is not odd and is not even. False. 9. Some pentagon is regular, and its angles are not all 180° or some side is not 1 cm. in length. True. 11. Some integer is not negative and is not positive. True. 13. Some pair of lines are on the same plane and do not have a point in common and are not parallel. False. 15. $\exists x \exists y, xy = 0$ and $x \neq 0$. True. 17. $\exists x$, $x = 2$ and $x^2 \neq 4$. False. 19. $\exists x, |x| = x$ and $x \leq 0$. True. 21. $\exists x$, x is even and $x - 1$ is not odd, or $x - 1$ is odd and x is not even. False. 23. Some parallelogram is a square, and is not a rectangle or does not have equal diagonals; or, the parallelogram is not a square and is a rectangle and has equal diagonals. True. 25. Each triangle has a pair of equal sides and does not have a pair of equal angles. False. 27. $p \,\&\, (\sim q \,\&\, \sim r)$. 29. $[(p \,\&\, q) \,\&\, \sim r] \vee [(\sim p \vee \sim q) \,\&\, r]$.

Chapter two

EXERCISE SET 2.1, PAGE 49

1. $\{x: x < 2\}$. 3. $\{x: x < 2 \,\&\, x > 0\}$. 5. $\{x: x > 0\}$. Alternate answer: $\{x: x$ is positive$\}$. 7. $\{x: x \geq 0\}$. 9. $\{x: 2 \leq x \leq 4\}$. 11. $\{x: x^2 + 2x + 1 = 0\}$. 13. $\{x: x^2 - 3x + 2 \neq 0\}$. 15. $\{A: \sin A = \cos A\}$. 17. $\{(x, y): y = 0\}$. 19. The set of all numbers x such that x is greater than 3 and less than 5. The set of all numbers greater than 3 and less than 5. 21. The set of all angles A such that $\tan A = 1$. The set of all angles whose tangent is 1. 23. The set of all x such that if x is greater than 3, then x is greater than 4. The set of all numbers less than or equal to 3 or greater than 4. 25. True. 27. True. 29. True. 31. True. 33. True. 35. True. 37. True. 39. False.

EXERCISE SET 2.2, PAGE 54

1. True. 3. True. 5. True. 7. True. 9. False. 11. False. 13. True. 15. True. 17. True. 19. False.

21. $]2,4[$

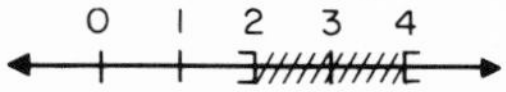

0 1 2 3 4

23. $]0,1]$

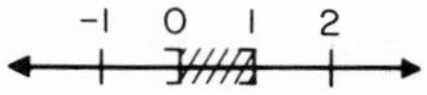

-1 0 1 2

25. $[1,\infty)$

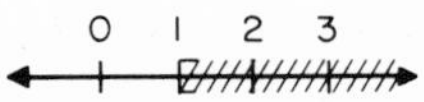

0 1 2 3

27. $(-\infty,4[$

2 3 4 5

29. $]2,4[$

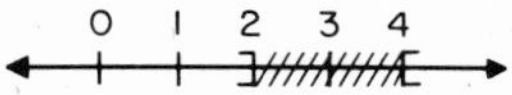

0 1 2 3 4

31. $(-\infty,0[$

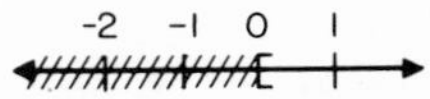

-2 -1 0 1

33. $]-3,0]$

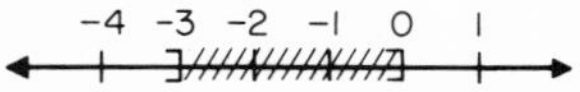

-4 -3 -2 -1 0 1

35. $\{x: -1 < x < 3\}$.
37. $\{x: -3 < x \leq 4\}$.

39. $\{x: x \in R\}$.
41. $\{x: x > 3 \text{ and } x < 3\}$.
43. $\{3, 4, 5, 6, \cdots\}$.
45. $\{0, -3, -6, -9, -12, \cdots\}$.

EXERCISE SET 2.3, PAGE 57

(To disprove the false statements, there are often many other choices of numbers which give a false instance.)

1. True. 3. False; $-\sqrt{3} \in [-\sqrt{3}, \sqrt{3}]$ and $-\sqrt{3} \notin]-\sqrt{3}, \sqrt{3}]$. 5. False; $5 \in \{1, 2, 3, \cdots\}$ and $5 \notin \{1, 2, 3, 4\}$. 7. True. 9. False; Suppose $x \in \{x: x > 2\}$; then $x > 2$. Therefore, $x > 2$ or $x < 0$. This means $x \in \{x: x > 2 \text{ or } x < 0\}$. $\therefore \{x: x > 2\} \subset \{x: x > 2 \text{ or } x < 0\}$. 11. False; Suppose $x \in \{x: 0 < x < 1\}$. Then $0 < x < 1$. Therefore, $0 \leq x \leq 1$. Therefore, $x \in [0, 1]$. This means that $\{x: 0 < x < 1\} \subset [0, 1]$. 13. True. 15. False; $5 \in \{x: x > 0\}$ and $5 \notin \{y: y > 0 \text{ and } y < 5\}$. 17. True. 19. True. 21. $\{x: x < 4\} \subset \{x: x < 3\}$. Alternate: $(-\infty, 4[\subset (-\infty, 3[$. False. 23. $\{x: x > 0\} \subset \{x: x \geq 0\}$. Alternate: $]0, \infty) \subset [0, \infty)$. True. 25. $x \in \{y: y \text{ is prime}\} \rightarrow (\{x\} \subset \{y: y \text{ is prime}\})$. True. 27. $z \in I \rightarrow z \in R^+ \vee z \in I^-$. Alternate: $\{z: z \text{ is an integer}\} \subset \{x: x > 0\}$ or $\{z: z \text{ is an integer}\} \subset \{x: x \text{ is a negative integer}\}$. False. 29. $\{1, 2, 4, 8\}$, $\{1, 2, 4\}$, $\{1, 2, 8\}$, $\{1, 4, 8\}$, $\{2, 4, 8\}$, $\{1, 2\}$, $\{1, 4\}$, $\{1, 8\}$, $\{2, 4\}$, $\{2, 8\}$, $\{4, 8\}$, $\{1\}$, $\{2\}$, $\{4\}$, $\{8\}$, $\emptyset$, 31. $\{0, 1, 2\}$, $\{0, 1\}$, $\{0, 2\}$, $\{1, 2\}$, $\{0\}$, $\{1\}$, $\{2\}$, $\emptyset$. 33. *Hint*: There are 32 distinct subsets. 35. $A \subset B$. 37. $B \subset A$. 39. $A \subset B$. 41. $B \subset A$. 43. $A \subset B$. 45. $A \subset B$, $B \subset A$. 47. $B \subset A$.

EXERCISE SET 2.4, PAGE 62

1. $[-1, 1]$

3. $[7, +\infty)$

5. $[1, \pi[$

7. $]0, \pi[$

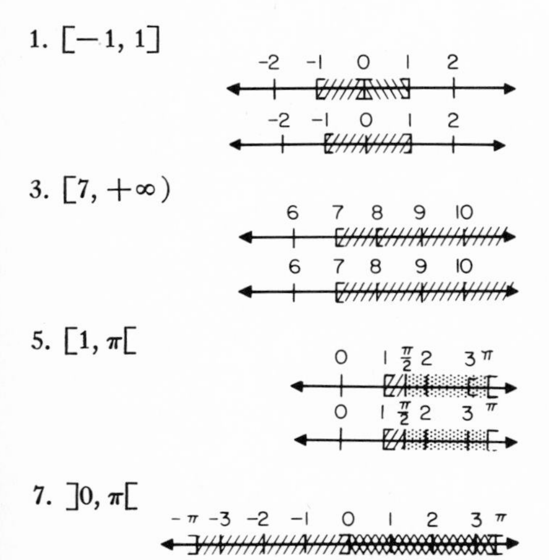

9. $\{3\}$ (Graph not provided.)
11. $]1, \sqrt{2}[$ (Graph not provided.)
13. $(-\infty, \pi[$
15. $(-\infty, \infty)$
17. $[2, 5]$
19. $]0, \pi[$
21. $[0, \frac{1}{2}] \cup]2, 3[$.
23. $(-\infty, -3[\cup]4, \infty)$.
25. $]-\sqrt{2}, 3[$.
27. $\{1, 3, 4\}$.
29. $\{x: x \text{ is an integer}, x > 10, x \text{ is prime}\}$.
31. $\{2, 3, 4\}$.
33. False; Counterexample: $A = R$, $B = \emptyset$, and others.
35. False; Counterexample: $A = [0, 1]$, $B = \emptyset$, and others.
37. True.
39. True.

EXERCISE SET 2.5, PAGE 65

1. $(-\infty, 0[$. 3. $(-\infty, 0[\cup]\pi, +\infty)$. 5. $(-\infty, 7]$. 7. $]3, +\infty)$. 9. $(-\infty, -1[$. 11. $\emptyset$. 13. $(-\infty, 1[\cup]3, +\infty)$. 15. $(-\infty, 2[\cup]2, +\infty)$. 17. $(-\infty, 1[\cup]3, +\infty)$. 19. $(-\infty, 0[\cup]1, +\infty)$. 21. $(-\infty, 0[\cup]1, +\infty)$. 23. $(-\infty, \infty)$. 25. $\emptyset$. 27. $(-\infty, 0]$. 29. $[0, 1]$. 31. $\overline{[2, 3]}$. 33. $\overline{[3, 3]}$. 35. $\overline{(-\infty, 0]}$. 37. $\overline{]\frac{1}{2}, 1[}$. 39. Not possible; one may consider $\overline{\overline{[0, 1]}}$, but this is the complement of the complement of an interval. 41. $\overline{]3, 5]}$. 43. $\overline{[0, 0]}$.

Chapter three

EXERCISE SET 3.1, PAGE 71

1. The set with only zero. (Answers will vary a great deal on Exercises 1–13.) 3. The set of nonpositive reals. 5. The set of all reals except 0. 7. I, the set of integers. 9. I, the set of integers. 11. I, the set of integers. 13. The set of non-negative integers. 15. Assume x is an odd integer. Then $4x = 2(2x)$, or $4x/2 = 2x$ which is an integer. Hence $4x$ is even. 17. Assume x and y are even integers. Then $x/2 = k$ and $y/2 = m$ for some integers k and m.

$$\therefore\ x = 2k \quad \text{and} \quad y = 2m; \qquad xy = 2k(2m) = 2(2km).$$

Then $xy/2 = 2km$, where $2km$ is an integer. Hence xy is even.

EXERCISE SET 3.2, PAGE 73

1. Let x^2 be an odd integer, x an integer. Suppose x is an even integer (and not odd). Then $x = 2k$ for some integer k, and $x^2 = 4k^2 = 2(2k^2)$.
   Thus x^2 is an even integer. But this contradicts the statement that x^2 is odd. This means that the assumption that x is an even integer is wrong. Since x is an integer, and it is not even, x must be an odd integer.
3. Let A be an integer such that 3 divides A^2. Suppose 3 does not divide A. Then $A = 3k + 1$ (Case 1) or $A = 3k + 2$ (Case 2) for some integer k. (The remainder of division by 3 can be $+1$ or $+2$).

Case 1.

$A^2 = 9k^2 + 6k + 1$
$A^2 = 3(3k^2 + 2k) + 1$
Now $3(3k^2 + 2k)$ is divisible by 3.
But A^2 as $3(3k^2 + 2k) + 1$ is not divisible by 3.
This is a contradiction.

Case 2.

$A^2 = 9k^2 + 12k + 4$
$= 9k^2 + 12k + 3 + 1$
$= 3(3k^2 + 4k + 1) + 1$
Now $3(3k^2 + 4k + 1)$ is divisible by 3.
Hence A^2 as $3(3k^2 + 4k + 1) + 1$ is not divisible by 3.
This is a contradiction.

Since a contradiction appears in either case, the supposition that 3 does not divide A must be wrong. Therefore, 3 must divide A.

5. *Hint:* Assume 5 is rational; then there exist integers p and q such that $5 = p/q$ and p/q is reduced to lowest terms. $5 = p^2/q^2$, $5q^2 = p^2$. Thus p^2 is divisible by 5, etc. (You will need the theorem: If 5 divides A^2, and A is an integer, then 5 divides A.) 7. Assume 4 is rational. Then $4 = p/q$ where p/q is in lowest terms, $4 = p^2/q^2$, $4q^2 = p^2$. Hence p^2 is even and p is even. Thus for some integer s, $p = 2s$, $p^2 = 4s^2$, $4q^2 = 4s^2$, $q^2 = s^2$, and from this we do not know q^2 is even.

Likewise, $4q^2 = p^2$ says p^2 is divisible by 4. However, p may not be divisible by 4. (36 is divisible by 4, but 6 is not!)

EXERCISE SET 3.3, PAGE 77

1. $\dfrac{1414}{1000} = \dfrac{707}{500}$. 3. $\dfrac{24861}{125}$. 5. $\dfrac{1141}{999}$. 7. $\dfrac{3322}{999900}$. 9. $\dfrac{3889551}{9000000}$. 11. $\dfrac{172058}{9900}$.

13. $0.\overline{428571}$. 15. $2.\overline{428571}$. 17. $0.01\overline{0}$, alternate: $0.00\overline{9}$. 19. $71.5\overline{0}$, alternate: $71.4\overline{9}$. 21. $0.1\overline{36}$. 23. Let two repeating decimals be x and y. Since these can be expressed as fractions of integers, let $x = a/b$ and $y = c/d$. Then

$$x + y = \frac{a}{b} + \frac{c}{d} = \frac{ad + bc}{bd},$$

which is a fraction of integers. As a fraction of integers, it can be represented as a repeating decimal. 25. $\frac{866}{111}$, or $7.\overline{801}$.

EXERCISE SET 3.4, PAGE 78

1. $\forall x > 0, \forall y > 0, (x + y) > 0$. Alternate: $\forall x \in R^+, \forall y \in R^+, (x + y) \in R^+$. True. 3. $\forall a \in N, \forall b \in N, a/b \in N$; False. Counterexample: Let $a = 3$, $b = 2$, and others. 5. $\forall m \in I, \forall n \in I, (m - n) \in I$. True. 7. $\forall n \in I^+, \forall m \in I^-$, $n + m \in I^+$. False. Counterexample: $n = 5$, $m = -8$; and others. 9. $\forall a \in Q$, $\forall b \in Q, a/b \in Q$. False. Counterexample:

$$a = \frac{3}{1}, \qquad b = \frac{0}{1},$$

and others. 15. $\forall n \in I, \forall m \in I, n + m = m + n$. True. 17. $\forall x \forall y \forall z$, $x + y + z = z + y + x$. True. 19. $\exists y \forall x, x + y = y$. False. 21. $\forall x \exists y, xy = 0$. True. 23. $\forall x \exists y, x + y = 0$. True. 25. $\forall p \in Q, \exists q \in Q, p + q = 0$. True. 27. $\forall m \in I, \exists n \in I, m + n = 0$. True. 29. $\exists n \in N, \forall m \in I, nm = m$. True. 31. $\forall x \forall y \forall z, x + (yz) = (x + y)(x + z)$. False. Counterexample: $x = y = z = 1$, and others. 33. $\forall x \forall y \forall z, (x + y) \div z = (x \div z) + (y \div z)$. False. Counterexample: $x = y = z = 0$, and others with $z = 0$.

EXERCISE SET 3.5, PAGE 81

1. Closed. 3. Closed. 5. Closed. 7. Closed. 9. Not closed, $3 + 1$ is not odd. 11. Closed. 13. Closed. 15. Not closed, $3 \div 2$ is not an integer. 17. Not closed, $(4 - 5)$ is not a counting number. 19. Not closed, $3 \div 2$ is not a natural number. 21. Closed. 23. Not closed, $3 \div 0$ is not a rational number. 25. Closed. 27. Not closed, $8 \div 4 \notin \{0, 4, 8, \cdots\}$. 29. Closed. 31. Closed.

33. Answers will vary. For example: $x * y = |x - y|$, Yes, Yes. Another example: $x * y = 3$, No, No. 35.

$$a + b = \frac{m}{n} + \frac{p}{q} = \frac{mq + np}{nq}.$$

For closure, since $n \neq 0$, $q \neq 0$, then $nq \neq 0$. Also, $mq + np \in I$, and $nq \in I$ (why?). Thus $a + b \in Q$.

$$a \times b = \frac{m}{n} \times \frac{p}{q} = \frac{mp}{nq}.$$

(Show closure.) Answers for subtraction and division not given.

EXERCISE SET 3.6, PAGE 85

1. Commutative, addition. 3. Commutative, multiplication. 5. Commutative, addition. 7. Associative, addition. 9. Commutative, addition, or associative, addition. 11. Commutative, addition.

13. $(7 + 4) + 2 = 2 + (7 + 4)$ Commutative, addition.
$= 2 + (4 + 7)$ Commutative, addition.

(Variations will occur in proofs of exercises to follow.)

15. $a + b + c = (a + b) + c$ Definition.
$= c + (a + b)$ Commutative, addition.
$= (c + a) + b$ Associative, addition.
$= (a + c) + b$ Commutative, addition.
$= a + c + b$ Definition.

17. $3 \times (8 \times 7) = (8 \times 7) \times 3$ Commutative, multiplication.
$= (7 \times 8) \times 3$ Commutative, multiplication.

19. $a \times b \times c = (a \times b) \times c$ Definition.
$= a \times (b \times c)$ Associative, multiplication.
$= a \times (c \times b)$ Commutative, multiplication.
$= (a \times c) \times b$ Associative, multiplication.
$= a \times c \times b$ Definition.

21. $(a \times b) \times (c \times d) = [(a \times b) \times c] \times d$ Associative, multiplication.
$= [a \times (b \times c)] \times d$ Associative, multiplication.
$= [a \times (c \times b)] \times d$ Commutative, multiplication.
$= [(a \times c) \times b] \times d$ Associative, multiplication.
$= (a \times c) \times (b \times d)$ Associative, multiplication.

23. $(x + x) + x = x + (x + x)$ Associative or commutative, addition.

25.
$$\begin{aligned} abcde &= [\{(ab)c\}d]e && \text{Definition.} \\ &= [(ab)(cd)]e && \text{Associative, multiplication.} \\ &= (ab)[(cd)e] && \text{Associative, multiplication.} \end{aligned}$$

27. Both valid. 29. Neither valid. False instance: $(3 - 2) = (2 - 3)$, $(4 - 3) - 2 = 4 - (3 - 2)$, and others. 31. Neither valid. False instance: $3 \div 2 = 2 \div 3$, $3 \div (6 \div 2) = (3 \div 6) \div 2$, and others. 33. Commutative principle valid. Associative principle is not valid.

$$\begin{aligned} (1 * 2) * 3 &= 2[(1 * 2) + 3] & \qquad 1 * (2 * 3) &= 2[1 + (2 * 3)] \\ &= 2[2(1 + 2) + 3] & &= 2[1 + 2(2 + 3)] \\ &= 18 & &= 22. \end{aligned}$$

35. Neither valid. Counterexamples: $x = 1$, $y = 2$, and others. $x = 1$, $y = 2$, $z = 3$, and others. 37. Both valid. 39. Both valid. 41. (Commutative property only.) Let $a = m/n$, $l = p/q$, for integers m, n, p, q.

$$\begin{aligned} a + b &= \frac{m}{n} + \frac{p}{q} && \text{Substitution} \\ &= \frac{mq + np}{nq} && \text{Definition} \\ &= \frac{np + mq}{nq} && \text{Commutative, addition} \\ &= \frac{pn + qm}{qn} && \text{Commutative, multiplication} \\ &= \frac{p}{q} + \frac{m}{n} && \text{Definition} \\ &= b + a && \text{Substitution.} \end{aligned}$$

EXERCISE SET 3.7, PAGE 90

1. Addition: a, b, c, e, h. Multiplication: a, b, c, e, f, g, h. 3. (a) No, no inverse for 2. (b) No, no inverse for 2. (c) No, no inverse for 0. (d) No, no inverse for 0. (e) Yes. (f) Yes. (g) Yes. (h) Yes. (i) Yes. (j) Yes. 5. Identity is $+2$, since $a * 2 = a + 2 - 2 = a$, and $2 * a = 2 + a - 2 = a$, for each a. Inverses exist. The inverse of a is $-a + 4$. 7. No, 0 is not the identity for subtraction. 9. Hint: show $(-m)/n + m/n = 0$ and $m/(-n) + m/n = 0$.

EXERCISE SET 3.8, PAGE 92

1. (Left) distributive. 3. Associative, addition. 5. (Left) distributive.

7. $(5 \times 31) + 6 + (2 \times 31) = [(5 \times 31) + 6] + (2 \times 31)$ Definition.
$= [6 + (5 \times 31)] + (2 \times 31)$ Commutative, addition.
$= 6 + [(5 \times 31) + (2 \times 31)]$ Associative, addition.
$= 6 + [(5 + 2) \times 31]$ (Right) distributive.
$= 6 + (5 + 2) \times 31.$

9. $25 \times 9 = (20 + 5) \times 9$ Fact of arithmetic.
$= (20 \times 9) + (5 \times 9)$ (Right) distributive.
$= 20 \times 9 + 5 \times 9.$

11. (a) No. (b) Yes. (c) No. (d) No. (e) Yes. (f) No. (g) No. (h) No. (i) No. (j) No. (k) No. 13. Counterexample: $x = 3$, $y = 2$, $z = 5$. (d) $\forall x \forall y \forall z \neq 0\ (x + y) \div z = (x \div z) + (y \div z)$. (f) $\forall x \forall y \forall z \neq 0\ (x - y) \div z = (x \div z) - (y \div z)$.

Chapter four

EXERCISE SET 4.1, PAGE 98

1. $(-\infty, 2[$.

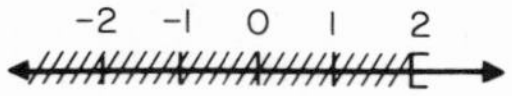

3. $]-2, 3[$.

5. $(-\infty, 2[\cup]3, \infty)$.

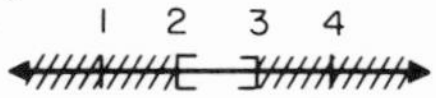

7. $]3, \infty)$.

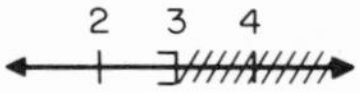

9. $(-\infty, 2[$.

11. $(-\infty, \frac{7}{3}]$.

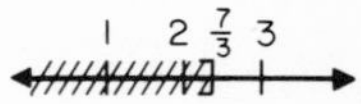

13. $(-0, 1[$.

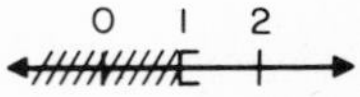

(Graphs will not be provided for the remainder of the exercises.)

15. $(-\infty, 0[\cup]\frac{3}{2}, \infty)$. 17. $]-2, 1[$. 19. $]-\frac{3}{2}, \frac{13}{2}[$. 21. $(-\infty, -1[$. 23. $(-\infty, +\infty)$. 25. $]\frac{5}{2}, +\infty)$. (Why isn't the answer $[\frac{5}{2}, +\infty)$?). 27. $(-\infty, -4[\cup]4, +\infty)$. 29. $]-8, 4[$. 31. $(-\infty, -8[\cup]4, \infty)$. 33. $[-4, 4]$. 35. $(-\infty, -2] \cup [-\frac{2}{3}, +\infty)$. 37. $]1, 2[\cup]6, 7[$. 39. $\{3, -3\}$.

EXERCISE SET 4.2, PAGE 105

1. $(-\infty, -3]$.

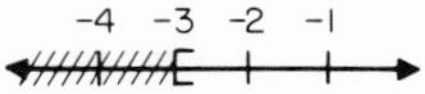

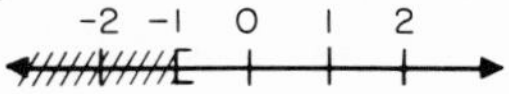

3. $(-\infty, 5[$.

5. $(-\infty, -1[$.

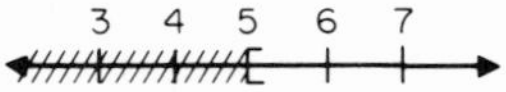

7. $\{-1, 2\}$.

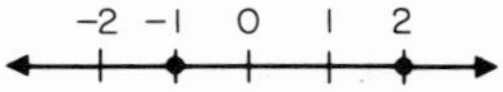

(Graphs not provided for the remainder of the answers.)

9. $]-\frac{3}{2}, 2[$. 11. $]-5, +5[$. 13. $\emptyset$. 15. $(-\infty, \infty)$. (*Hint:* $x^2 - x + 2$ is never 0.) 17. $(-\infty, -2] \cup [1, 3]$. 19. $]-3, 1[$. 21. $(-\infty, +\infty)$. 23. $(-\infty, 0[\cup]0, 1[$ or $(-\infty, 1[\cap R_0$. 25. $[-2, -\frac{3}{2}]$. 27. $x < b - 2a$.

29. $\dfrac{-b - \sqrt{b^2 - 4ac}}{2a} \leq x \leq \dfrac{-b + \sqrt{b^2 - 4ac}}{2a}$ for $a > 0$.

31. Suppose $a < b$, $b < c$. Then $(b - a) \in R^+$ and $c - b \in R^+$. By closure of R^+ under addition, $(b - a) + (c - b) \in R^+$. $\therefore (c - a) \in R^+$. $\therefore a < c$.

EXERCISE SET 4.3, PAGE 109

(Not all graphs are provided.)

1. $(-\infty, \frac{1}{3}[$.

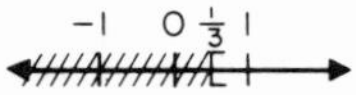

3. $]\frac{11}{3}, +\infty)$.

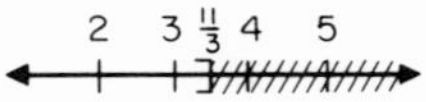

5. $[\frac{13}{4}, +\infty)$. 7. $]19, +\infty)$. 9. $]-4, -1[$. 11. $]-4, -1[$. 13. $]-4, 0[$. 15. $(-\infty, 0[$. 17. $(-\infty, 3[$. 19. $(-\infty, -\frac{3}{2}[\cup]0, +\infty)$. 21. $(-\infty, -2[\cup]0, 2[$.

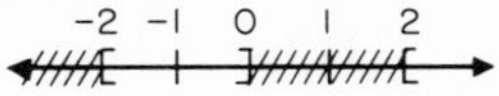

23. $\left(-\infty, \dfrac{a + 2b}{b - a}\right[$.

25. $\left]\dfrac{3b^2 - 2a^2}{a^2 + b^2}, \infty\right)$.

27. Suppose $a < b < 0$.
Then $0 < -b < -a$.
$\therefore 0 < (-b)^2 < (-a)^2$,
(by Exercise 26)
$\therefore 0 < b^2 < a^2$.

EXERCISE SET 4.4, PAGE 114

1. $|x| < 4$, $]-4, 4[$. 3. $|x| = 4$, $\{-4, 4\}$. 5. $|x - 2| < 5$, $]-3, 7[$. 7. $|2x - 5| \geq 3$, $(-\infty, 1] \cup [4, +\infty)$. 9. $|2x - 7| > 0$, $(-\infty, \frac{7}{2}[\cup]\frac{7}{2}, +\infty)$, or $\overline{\{\frac{7}{2}\}}$.

11. $]1, 5[$.

13. $[-2, 5]$.

15. $(-\infty, -\sqrt{3}[\cup]\sqrt{3}, \infty)$ or $\overline{[-3, 3]}$.

17. $(-\infty, -\frac{5}{4}] \cup [\frac{11}{4}, +\infty)$.

19. $(-\infty, 2[$.

21. $]-3, -2[\cup]1, 2[$.

23. $(-\infty, -3[\cup]-3, -2]$

25. $\{-\pi\}$.

27. $a - b < x < b + a$.
Solution Set: $]a - b, a + b[$.

29. $h - |a| < x < h + |a|$.
Solution Set: $]h - |a|, h + |a|[$.

Chapter five

EXERCISE SET 5.2, PAGE 124

1. (0, 3), (1, 1), (2, −1), (3, −3), and others.
3. (0, 5), (1, 2), (2, +1), (10, 10), and others.
5. (5, 1), (10, 2), (15, 3), $(1, \frac{1}{5})$, and others.
7. (1, 1), (0, 0), (2, 4), (3, 9), and others.
9. (1, 1), (1, −1), (2, 2), (0, 0), and others.
11. (0, 0), $(\frac{1}{2}, 0)$, (1, 0), $(\sqrt{2}/2, 0)$, and others.
13. (1, −3), (0, −2), (0, −4), (4, 0), (−2, 0), and others.
15. (0, 0), (1, 1), (−1, 1), (−3, 3), and others.

Note: Geometric descriptions will vary, especially in the choice of points on which a curve lies.

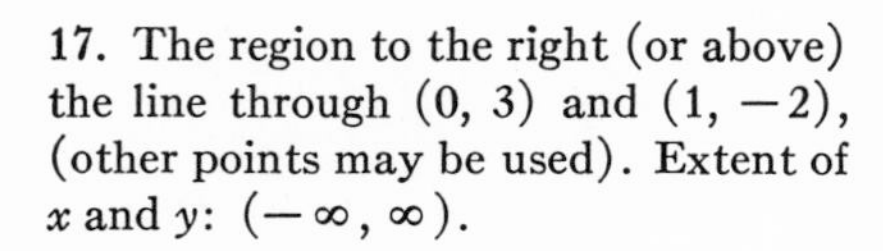

17. The region to the right (or above) the line through (0, 3) and (1, −2), (other points may be used). Extent of x and y: $(-\infty, \infty)$.

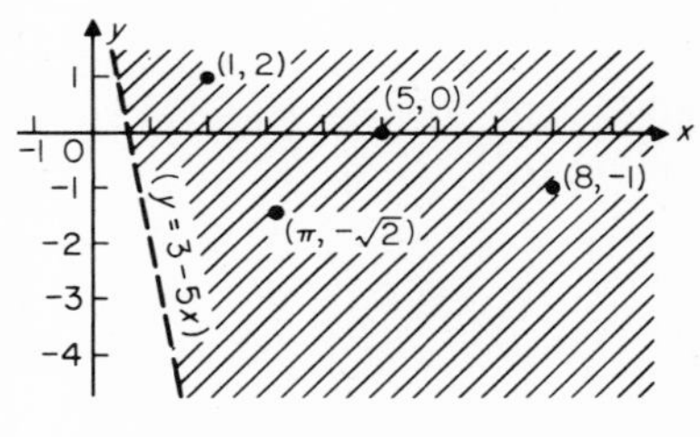

Ex. 17

19. The line through (3, 0) and (1, 1), (other points may be used. See Ex. 21). Extent of x and y: $(-\infty, \infty)$.

21. The region to the left of (or below) the line through (3, 0) and (1, 1) including the line. Extent of x and y: $(-\infty, \infty)$.

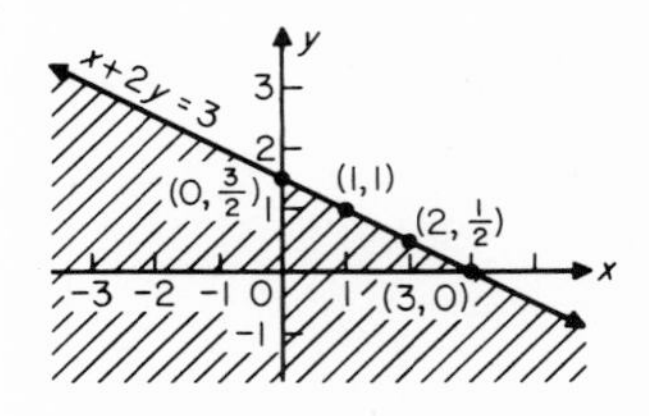

Ex. 21

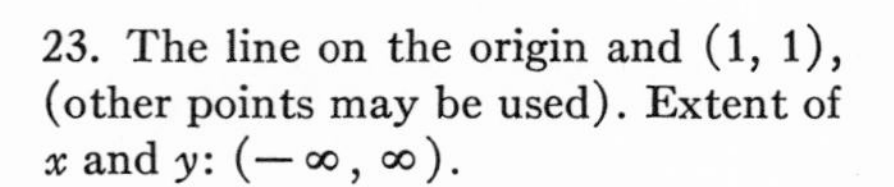

23. The line on the origin and (1, 1), (other points may be used). Extent of x and y: $(-\infty, \infty)$.

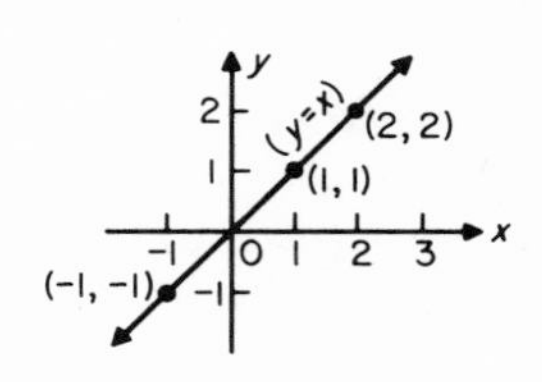

Ex. 23

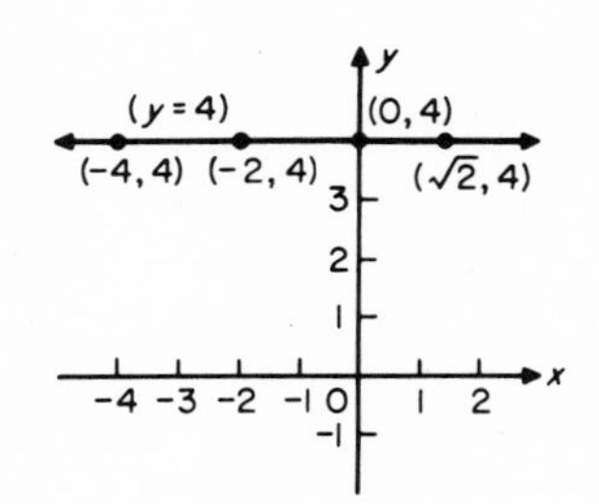

Ex. 25

25. The horizontal line on (0, 4), (other points may be used). Extent of x: $(-\infty, \infty)$. Extent of y: $\{4\}$.

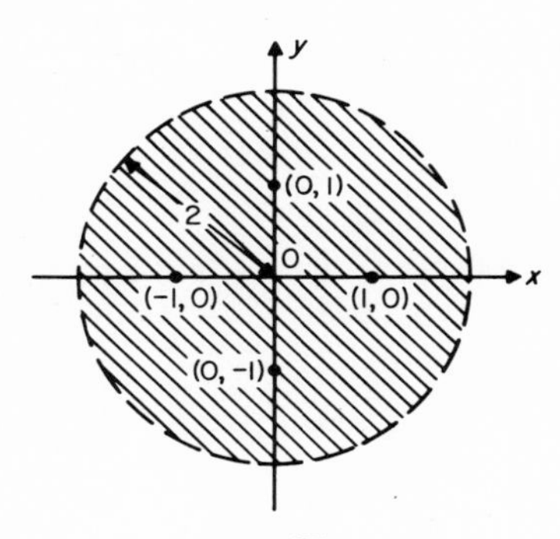

Ex. 27

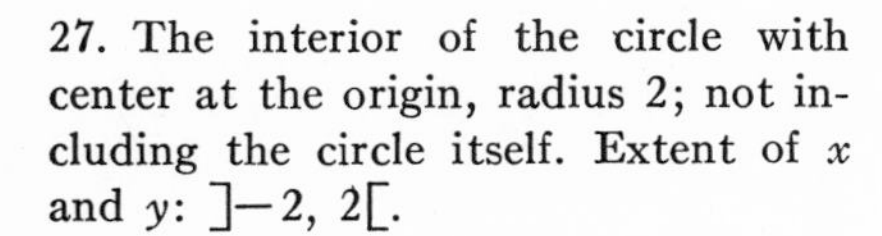

27. The interior of the circle with center at the origin, radius 2; not including the circle itself. Extent of x and y: $]-2, 2[$.

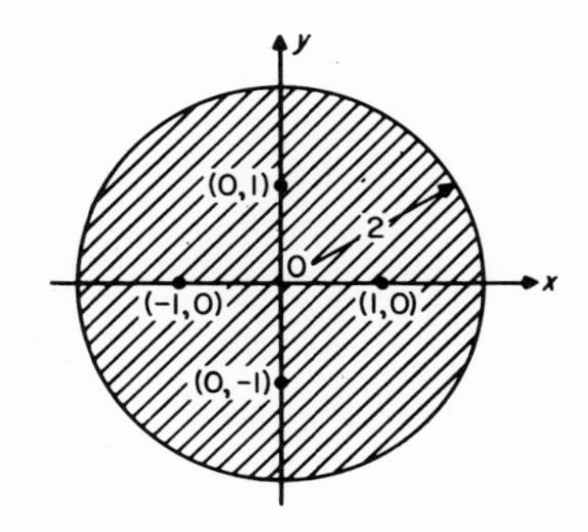

Ex. 29

29. The interior of the circle and the circle itself, with center at the origin, radius 2. Extent of x and y: $[-2, 2]$.

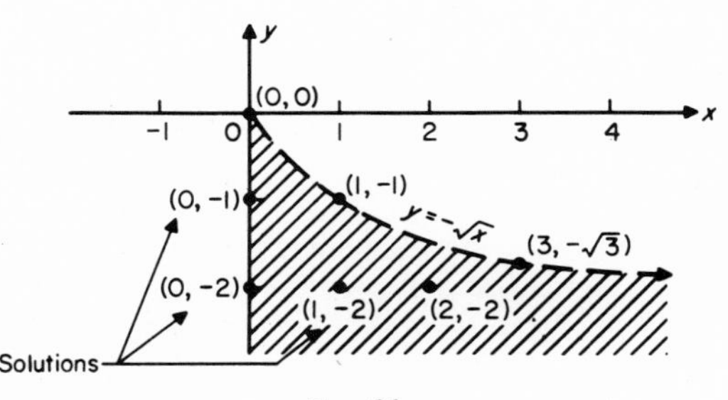

Ex. 31

31. The region under the (parabolic) curve beginning at the origin and passing through $(1, -1)$, $(2, -\sqrt{2})$, $(3, -\sqrt{3})$, etc., (not including the curve. Extent of x: $[0, \infty)$. Extent of y: $(-\infty, 0]$. Notice the difficulty in precisely defining this less general curve.

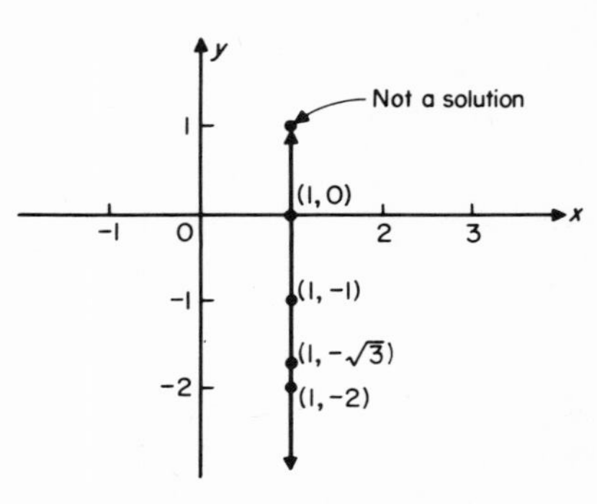

Ex. 33

33. The vertical half line from (1, 1) downward, not including (1, 1). Extent of x: $\{1\}$. Extent of y: $(-\infty, 1[$.

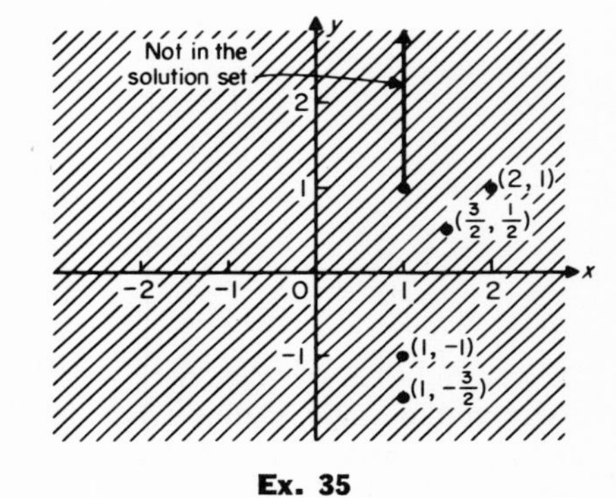

Ex. 35

35. The entire plane save for the vertical ray from (1, 1) upward. (Recall when a conditional is true!) Extent of x and y: $(-\infty, \infty)$.

37. Two perpendicular lines on the origin; one on (1, 1), the other on $(1, -1)$, (other points may be used). Extent of x and y: $(-\infty, \infty)$.

39. The region above the (parabolic) curve on $(-4, 0)$, $(-3, -4)$, $(-2, -6)$, $(-1, -6)$, $(0, -4)$, $(1, 0)$, etc., not including the curve. Extent of x and y: $(-\infty, \infty)$.

Ex. 39

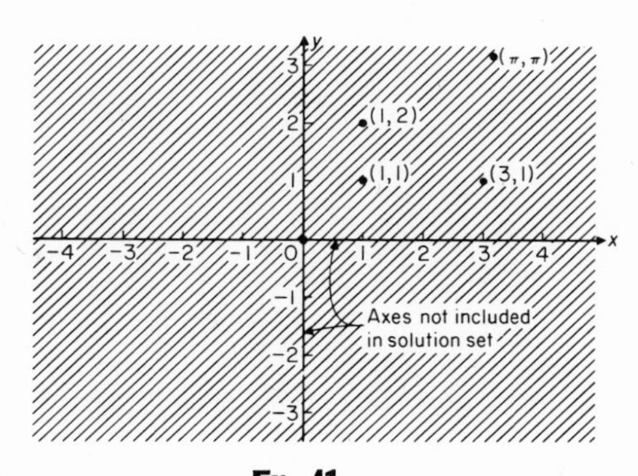

Ex. 41

41. The entire plane save for the union of the x- and y-axes. Extent of x and y: $(-\infty, 0[\cup]0, \infty)$.

EXERCISE SET 5.3, PAGE 129

1. Symmetric to the y-axis.
3. None.
5. Symmetric to the y-axis.
7. None.
9. Symmetric to the origin.
11. None.
13. Symmetric to each point on itself. Extent in x and y: $(-\infty, \infty)$.
15. Symmetric to each point on itself and to the origin. Extent of x and y: $(-\infty, 0[\cup]0, \infty)$. Why isn't $(0, 0)$ a solution?

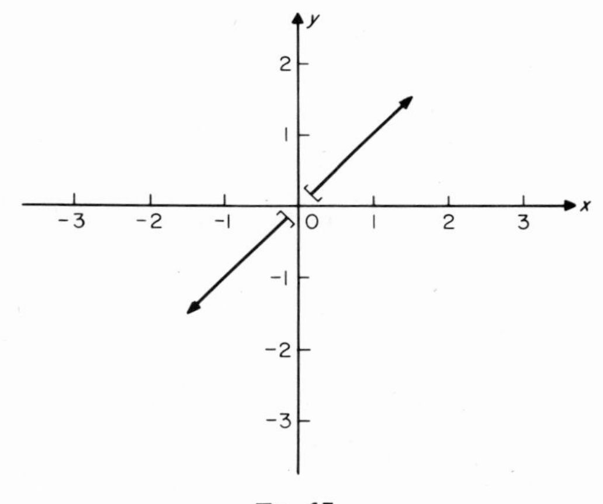

Ex. 15

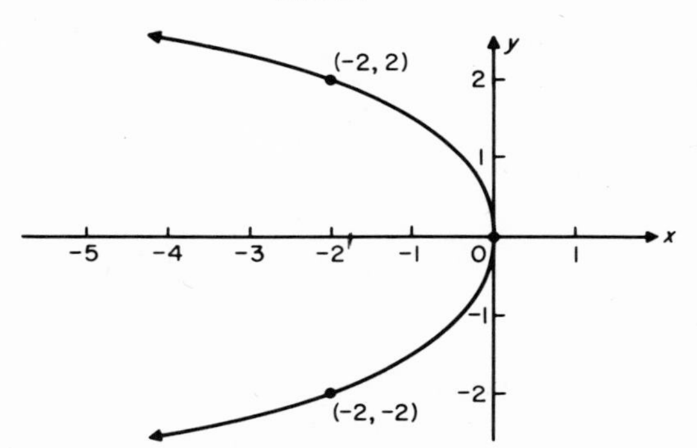

17. Symmetric to the x-axis. Extent of x: $(-\infty, 0]$; of y: $(-\infty, \infty)$.

Ex. 17

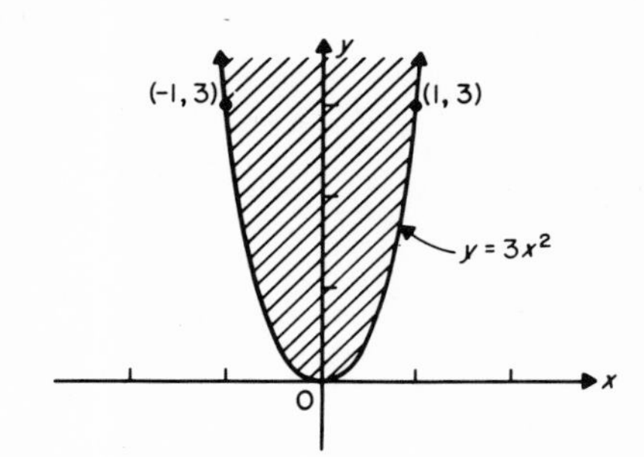

19. Symmetric to the y-axis. Extent of x: $(-\infty, \infty)$, extent of y: $]0, \infty)$.

Ex. 19

21. Symmetric to the x-axis, and to each point on itself. Extent of x: $\{5\}$. Extent of y: $(-\infty, \infty)$.

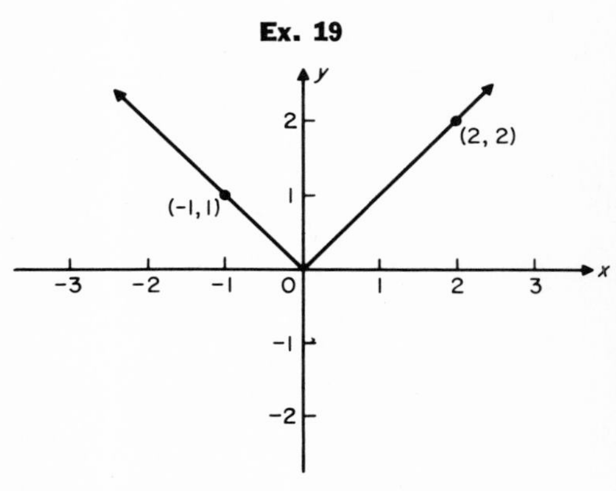

23. Symmetric to the y-axis. Extent of x: $(-\infty, \infty)$. Extent of y: $[0, \infty)$.

Ex. 23

25. Symmetric to the x- and y-axes, and to the origin. Extent of x and y: $(-\infty, \infty)$.

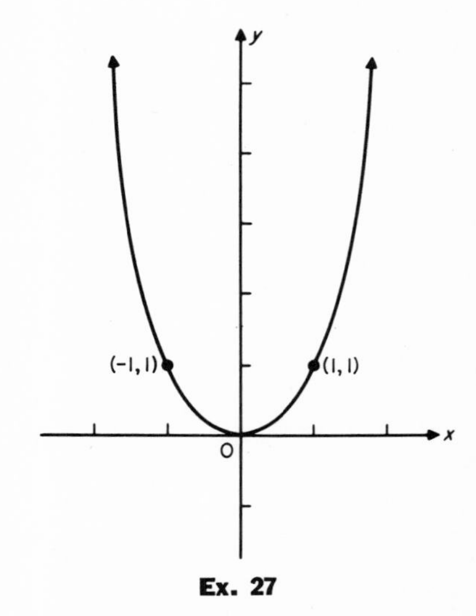

27. Symmetric to the y-axis. Extent of x: $(-\infty, \infty)$. Extent of y: $[0, \infty)$.

Ex. 27

29. Extent of x and y: $(-\infty, \infty)$.

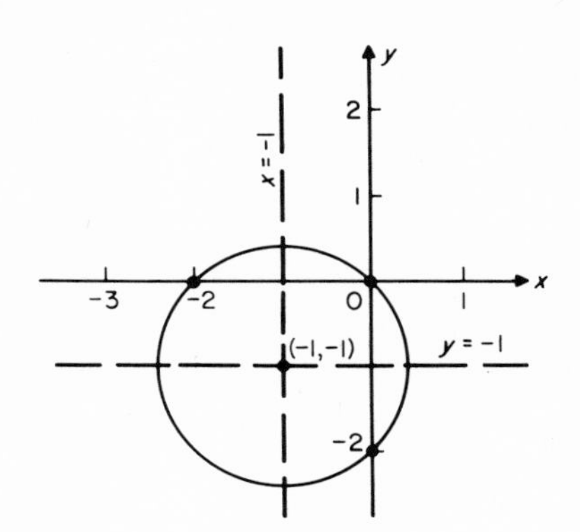

Ex. 33

33. $(x + 1)^2 + (y + 1)^2 = 2$. Horizontal line of symmetry on $(0, -1)$, vertical line of symmetry on $(-1, 0)$.

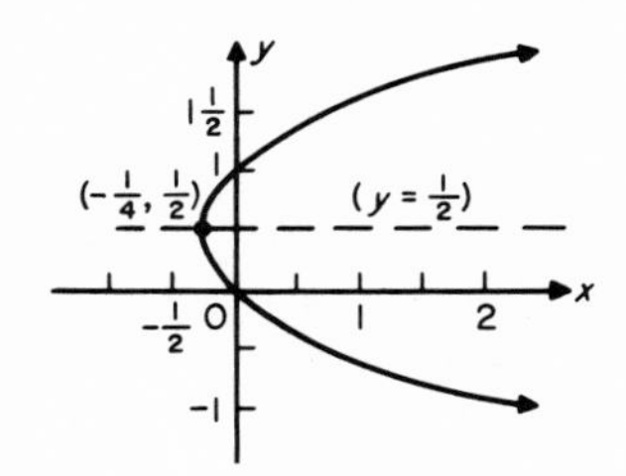

Ex. 35

35. $x + \frac{1}{4} = (y - \frac{1}{2})^2$. Horizontal line of symmetry on $(0, \frac{1}{2})$.

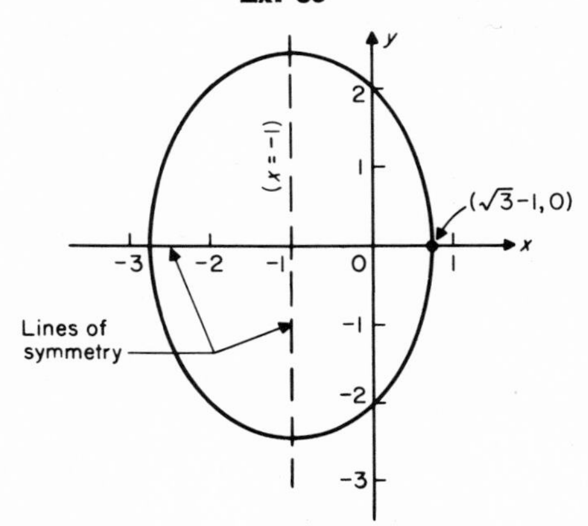

Ex. 37

37. $2(x + 1)^2 + y^2 = 6$. Vertical line of symmetry on $(-1, 0)$, horizontal line of symmetry is the x-axis.

EXERCISE SET 5.4, PAGE 132

1. 12.
3. $\sqrt{10}$.
5. 5.
7. 25.
9. $\sqrt{a^2 + b^2}$.
11. 2.
13. $\sqrt{(x - 3)^2 + (y - 4)^2}$
15. $|a - b|$.
17. $|a - b|\sqrt{2}$.
19. $\sqrt{81 + b^2}$.

21. 2.

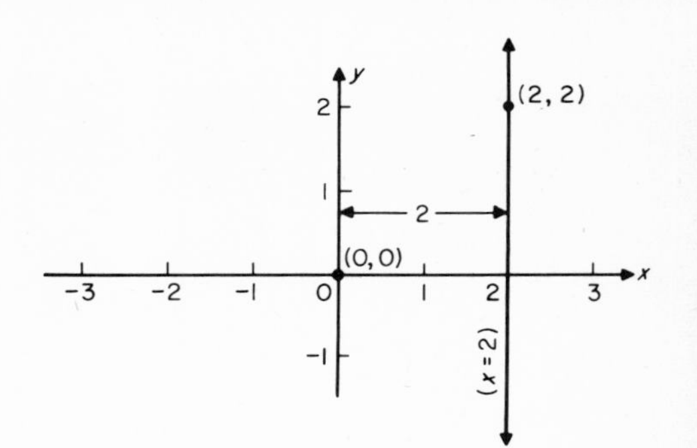

Ex. 21

23. 1.

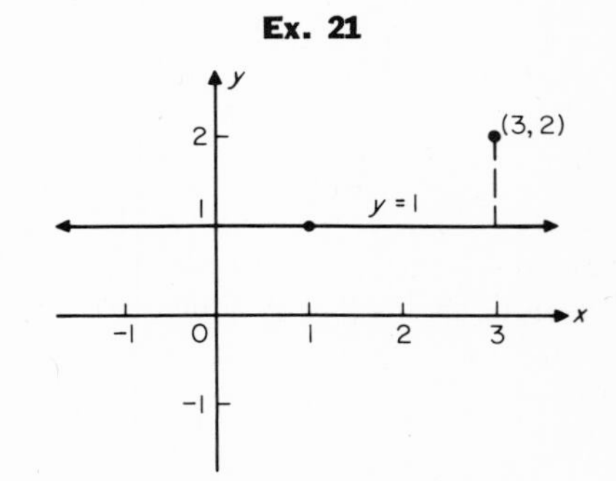

Ex. 23

25. 5.

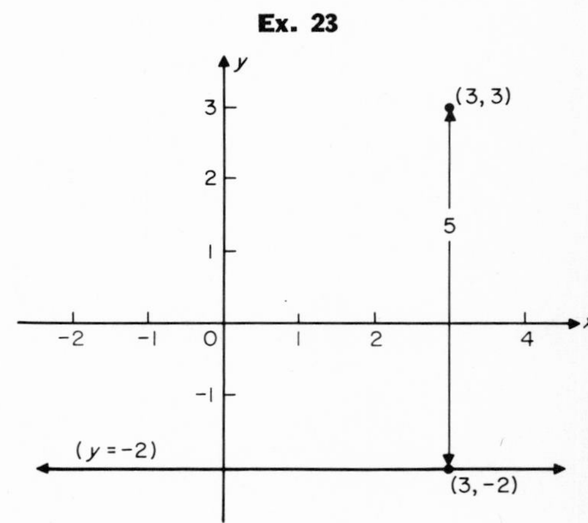

Ex. 25

27. 2.

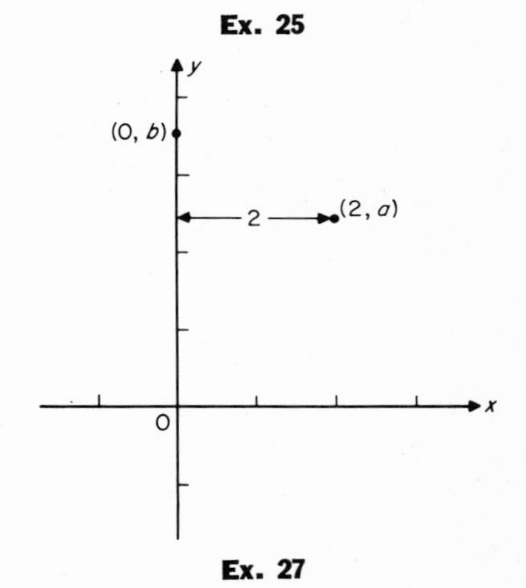

Ex. 27

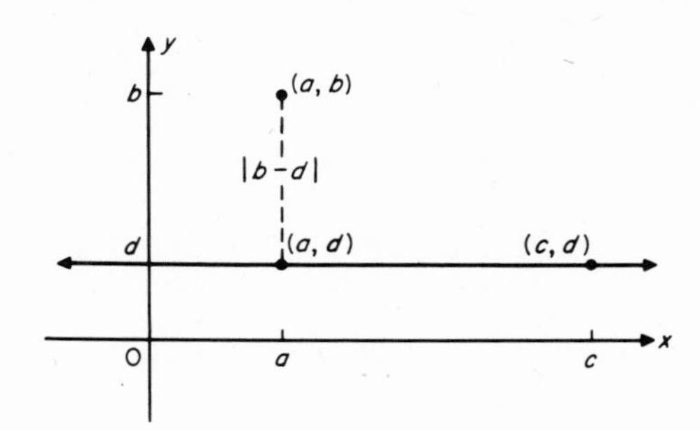

Ex. 29

29. $|b - d|$.

33. $(4, \frac{5}{2})$.
35. $2x + 3y + 5 = 0$.

EXERCISE SET 5.5, PAGE 138

Note that many graphs are not given!

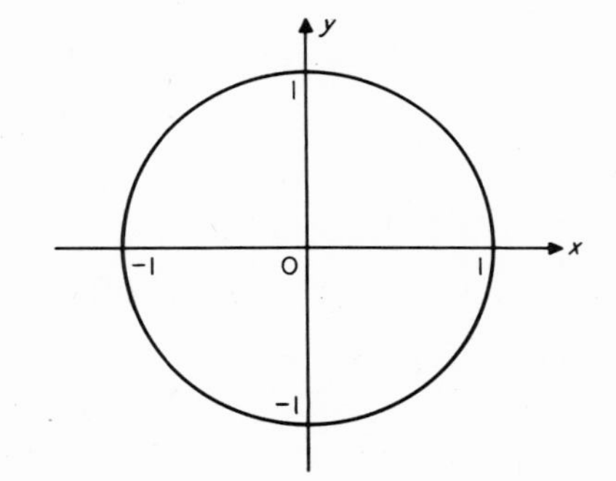

Ex. 1

1. $x^2 + y^2 = 1$.

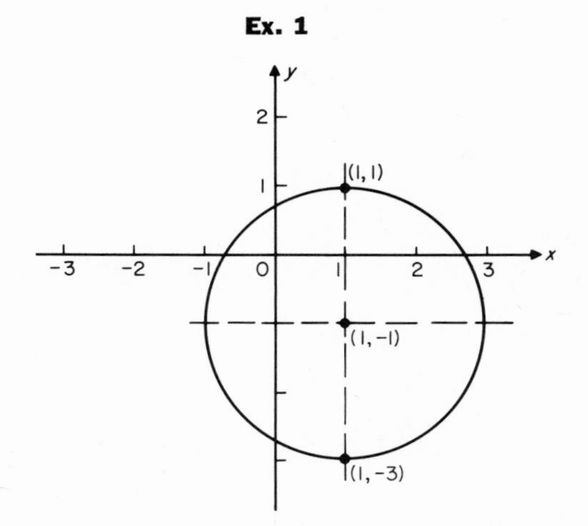

Ex. 3

3. $(x - 1)^2 + (y + 1)^2 = 4$, or $x^2 + y^2 - 2x + 2y + 2 = 0$.

5. $(x - 2)^2 + (y - 4)^2 > 9$, or $x^2 + y^2 - 4x - 8y + 11 > 0$.

7. $x = 1$ or $x = 5$.

Ex. 7

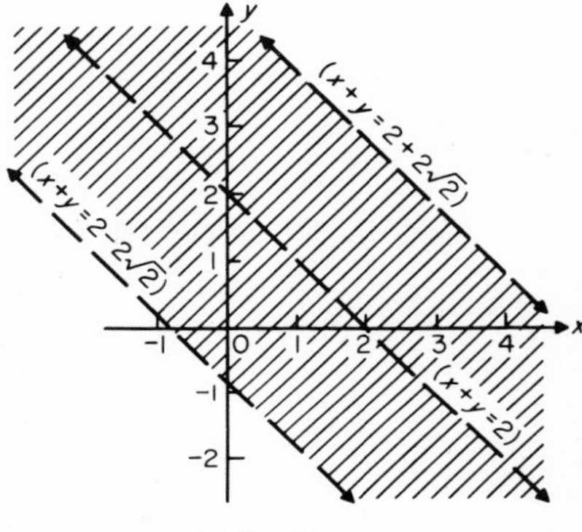

Ex. 9

9. $2 - 2\sqrt{2} < x + y < 2 + 2\sqrt{2}$.

11. $2x + 4y - 5 = 0$.

Ex. 13

13. $x + y < 2$.

15. (x, y)

$$= \left(\frac{16\sqrt{2} + 37}{6}, \frac{4\sqrt{2} + 37}{6}\right), \text{ or}$$

(x, y)

$$= \left(\frac{-16\sqrt{2} + 37}{6}, \frac{-4\sqrt{2} + 37}{6}\right).$$

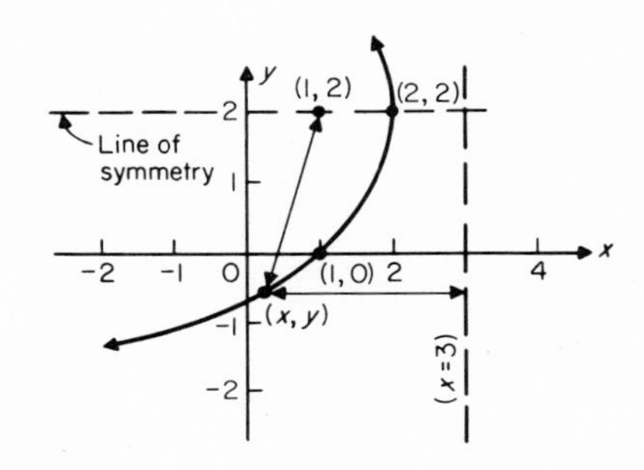

Ex. 17

17. $(y - 2)^2 + 4(x - 2) = 0$, or
$y^2 - 4y + 4x - 4 = 0$.

19. $9 < x^2 + (y - 2)^2 < 16$, or
$5 < x^2 + y^2 - 4y < 12$.

21. $y^2 - 2x + 1 = 0$.

23. $(x, y) = (2\sqrt{2}, \sqrt{2})$
or $(x, y) = (\sqrt{2}, 2\sqrt{2})$
or $(x, y) = (-\sqrt{2}, -2\sqrt{2})$
or $(x, y) = (-2\sqrt{2}, -\sqrt{2})$.

25. $y = 1$ and $-1 \leq x \leq 3$.

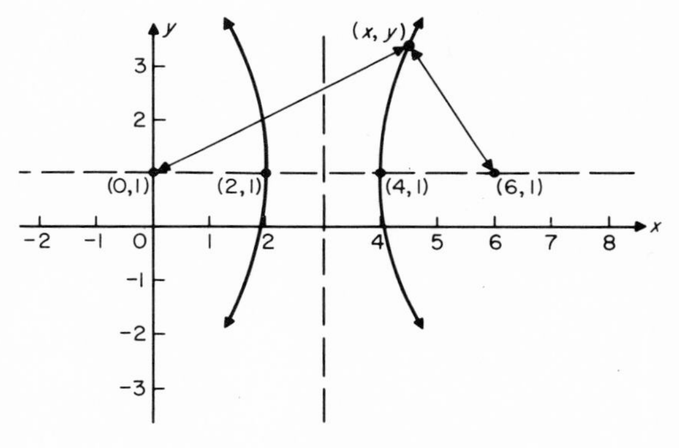

Ex. 27

27. $(x - 3)^2 - \dfrac{(y - 1)^2}{8} = 1$, or

$8x^2 - y^2 - 48x + 2y + 63 = 0$.

29. $(x - \frac{16}{3})^2 + (y - 2)^2 = (\frac{8}{3})^2$, or
$3x^2 + 3y^2 - 32x - 12y + 76 = 0$.

EXERCISE SET 5.6, PAGE 143

Note that graphs for Exercises 7–15 are not provided.

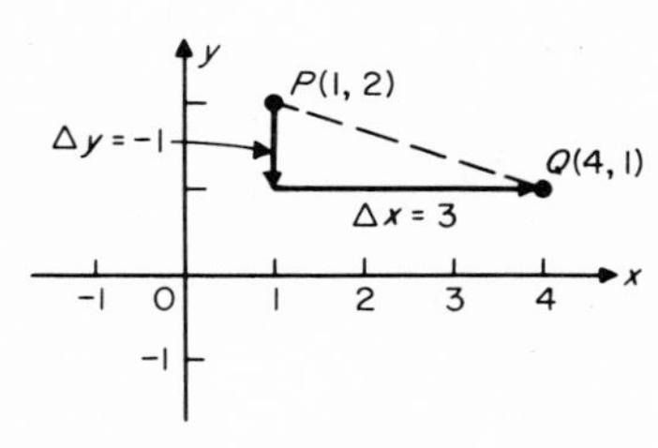

Ex. 1

1. $\Delta y = -1, \Delta x = 3, \dfrac{\Delta y}{\Delta x} = -\dfrac{1}{3}$.

3. $\Delta y = 2, \Delta x = -6, \dfrac{\Delta y}{\Delta x} = -\dfrac{1}{3}$.

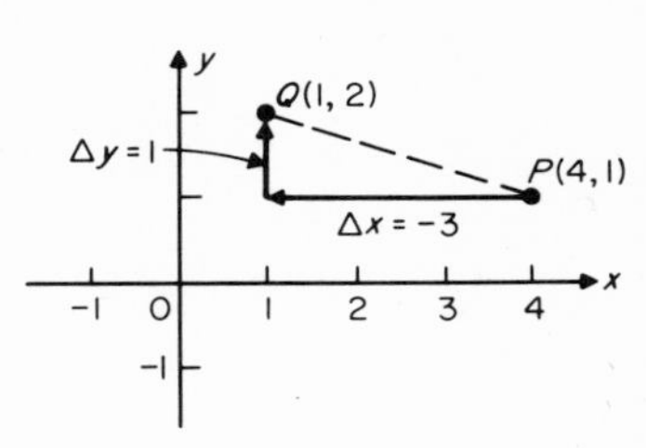

Ex. 3

5. $\Delta y = -4, \Delta x = -5, \dfrac{\Delta y}{\Delta x} = \dfrac{4}{5}$.

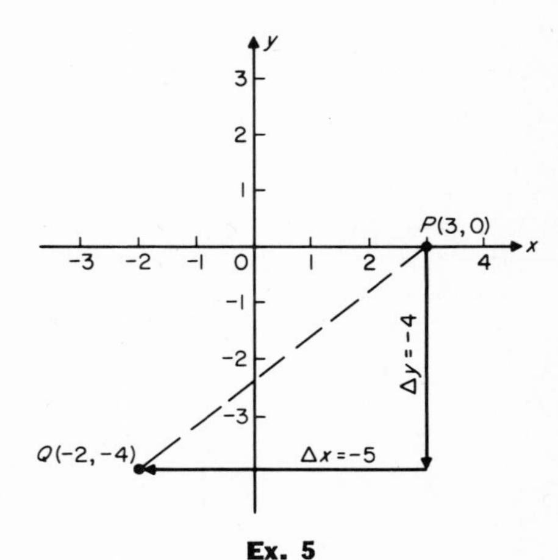

Ex. 5

7. $\Delta y = 12, \Delta x = 15, \dfrac{\Delta y}{\Delta x} = \dfrac{4}{5}$.

9. $\Delta y = y_2 - y_1, \Delta x = x_2 - x_1,$

$\dfrac{\Delta y}{\Delta x} = \dfrac{y_2 - y_1}{x_2 - x_1}$.

11. $\Delta y = y_1 - y, \Delta x = x_1 - x$

$\dfrac{\Delta y}{\Delta x} = \dfrac{y_1 - y}{x_1 - x}$.

13. $\Delta y = x, \Delta x = x, \dfrac{\Delta y}{\Delta x} = 1$

(assuming $x \neq 0$).

15. $\Delta y = 2, \Delta x = 0,$

$\dfrac{\Delta y}{\Delta x}$ is undefined.

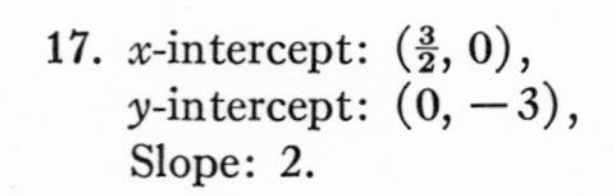

17. x-intercept: $(\frac{3}{2}, 0)$,
y-intercept: $(0, -3)$,
Slope: 2.

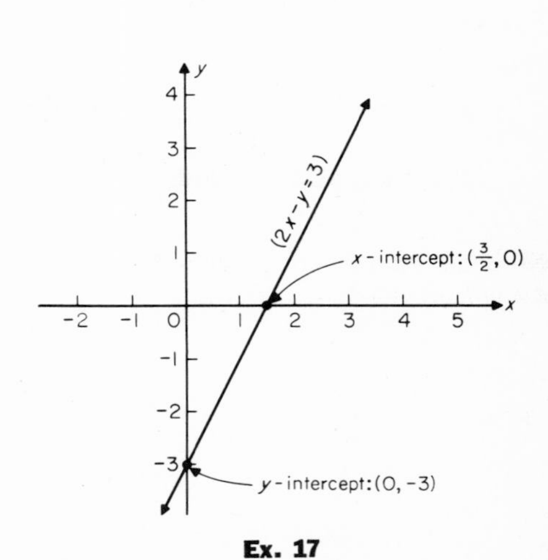

Ex. 17

19. x-intercept: $(\frac{7}{3}\ 0)$,
y-intercept: $(0, \frac{7}{5})$,
Slope: $-\frac{3}{5}$.

21. x-intercept: none,
y-intercept: $(0, 4)$,
Slope: 0.

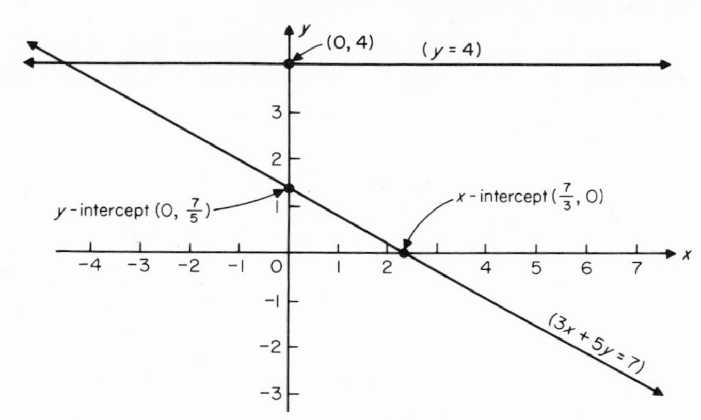

Exs. 19 and 21

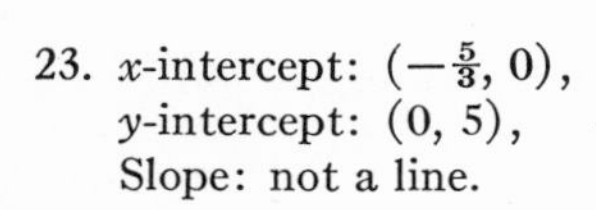

23. x-intercept: $(-\frac{5}{3}, 0)$,
y-intercept: $(0, 5)$,
Slope: not a line.

25. x-intercept: none,
y-intercept: none,
Slope: not a line.

27. x-intercept: $(-8, 0)$,
y-intercept: $(0, \frac{8}{5})$,
Slope: not a line.

29. x-intercept: $(1, 0)$,
y-intercept: $(0, -\frac{1}{3})$,
Slope: $\frac{1}{3}$.

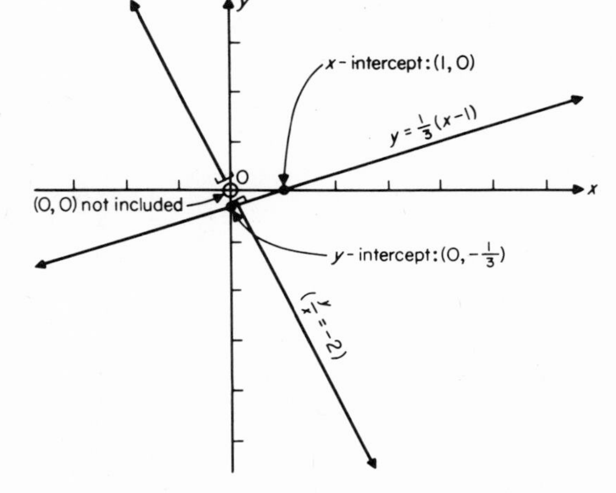

Exs. 25 and 29

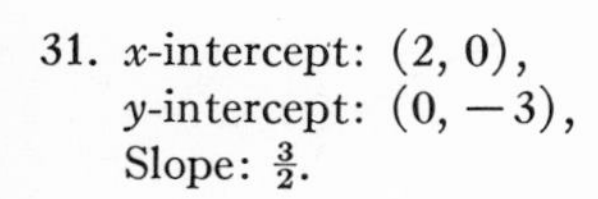

31. x-intercept: $(2, 0)$,
y-intercept: $(0, -3)$,
Slope: $\frac{3}{2}$.

33. x-intercept: $(0, 0)$,
y-intercept: $(0, 0)$,
Slope: $-\frac{2}{3}$.

35. Set of x-intercepts:
$\{(x, 0) : x \geq 0\}$.
Set of y-intercepts:
$\{(0, y) : y \geq 0\}$.
Slope: not a line.

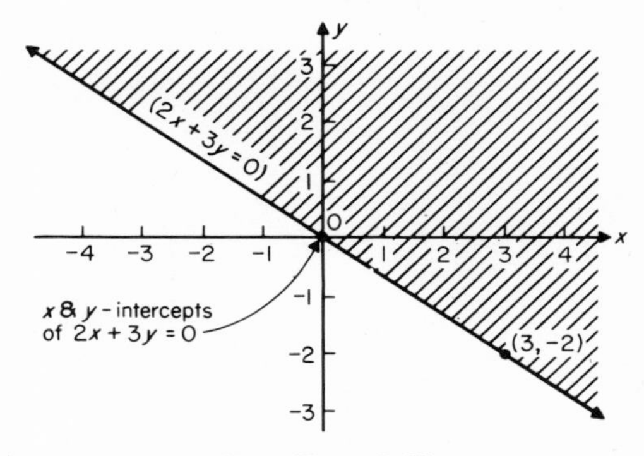

Exs. 33 and 35

37. x-intercepts: $(\frac{3}{2}, 0)$, $(-\frac{3}{2}, 0)$.
y-intercepts: $(0, 3)$, $(0, -3)$.
Slope: not a line. (Actually, a pair of lines, each with slope 2.)

39. Let (x_0, y_0), (x, y) be distinct points on the line $ax + by + c = 0$. Then

$$\text{slope of the line} = \frac{\Delta y}{\Delta x}[(x, y) \text{ to } (x_0, y_0)] = \frac{y_0 - y}{x_0 - x}.$$

But $y = \frac{-a}{b}x + \frac{-c}{b}$, $b \neq 0$, so

$$\frac{\Delta y}{\Delta x} = \frac{\left(\frac{-a}{b}x_0 + \frac{-c}{b}\right) - \left(\frac{-a}{b}x + \frac{-c}{b}\right)}{x_0 - x}$$

$$= \frac{\frac{-a}{b}(x_0 - x)}{x_0 - x} = \frac{-a}{b}.$$

To show $(0, -c/b)$ is the y-intercept, let $x = 0$. Then $by + c = 0$ and $y = -c/b$. 41. *Hint:* Place lines on coordinate plane and consider the angles formed by them and the x-axis. 43. $3x - 2y - 5 = 0$. 45. $4x - 3y + 11 = 0$.

EXERCISE SET 5.7, PAGE 147

1. $2x + y - 6 = 0$.
3. $5x - y + 11 = 0$.
5. $3x - 2y - 6 = 0$.
7. $3x - 2y + 6 = 0$.
9. $x - 2 = 0$.
11. $2x + y + 3 = 0$.
13. $2x + y = 0$.
15. $x - 3 = 0$.
17. $5x + 2y = 0$.
19. $x + 2 = 0$.
21. $7x + 3y + 5 = 0$.
23. $x + y - 2\sqrt{2} = 0$.
25. $y - 1 = 0$.
27. $x + y = 0$, $x - y = 0$.
29. All lines of the form $y - m(x - 2) = 0$, where m is a real number, and the line $x = 2$.

EXERCISE SET 5.8, PAGE 151

1. $x^2 + y^2 = 4$. 3. $(x - 1)^2 + (y - 2)^2 = 3$, or $x^2 + y^2 - 2x - 4y + 2 = 0$. 5. $x^2 + (y + 9)^2 = 81$, or $x^2 + y^2 + 18y = 0$. 7. $(x - a)^2 + (y - b)^2 = c^2$, or $x^2 + y^2 - 2ax - 2bx + a^2 + b^2 - c^2 = 0$.

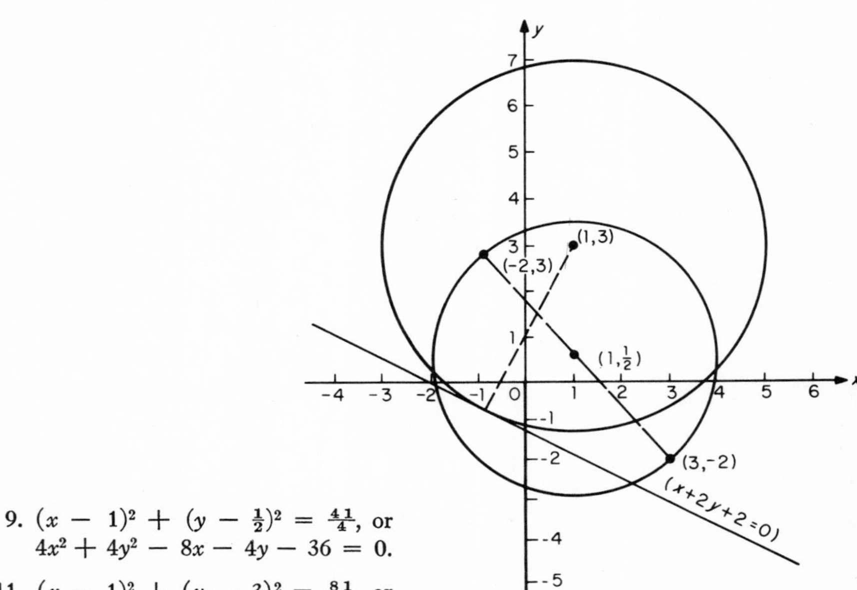

9. $(x - 1)^2 + (y - \frac{1}{2})^2 = \frac{41}{4}$, or $4x^2 + 4y^2 - 8x - 4y - 36 = 0$.

11. $(x - 1)^2 + (y - 3)^2 = \frac{81}{5}$, or $5x^2 + 5y^2 - 10x - 30y - 31 = 0$.

Exs. 9 and 11

13. $x^2 + y^2 - 4x - 20y - 2 = 0$, or $(x - 2)^2 + (y - 10)^2 = 106$.
15. $x^2 + y^2 - 4x - 6y - 156 = 0$, or $(x - 2)^2 + (y - 3)^2 = 13^2$.

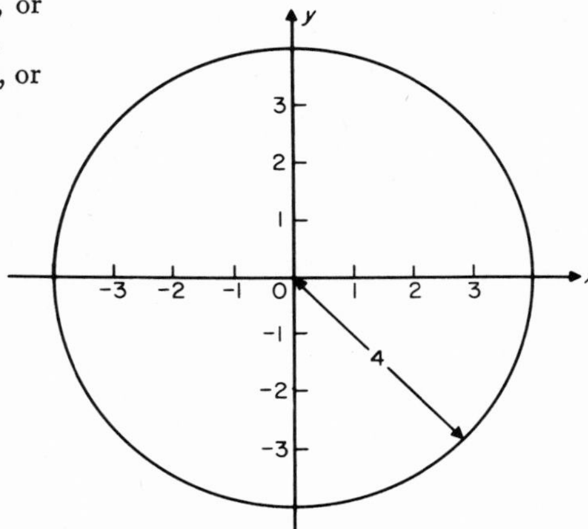

17. Center: $(0, 0)$. Radius: 4.

Ex. 17

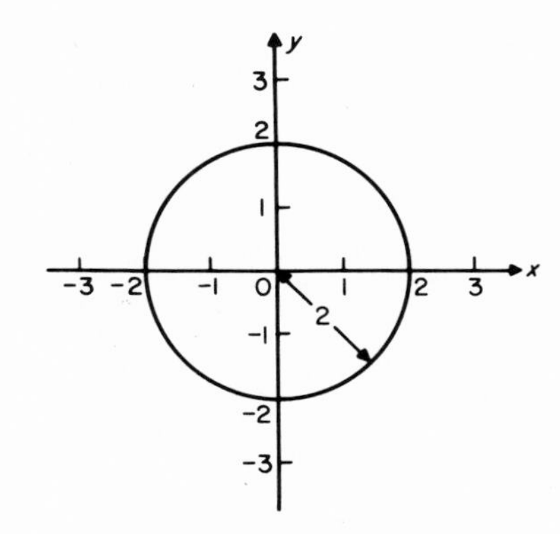

19. Center: $(0, 0)$. Radius: 2.

Ex. 19

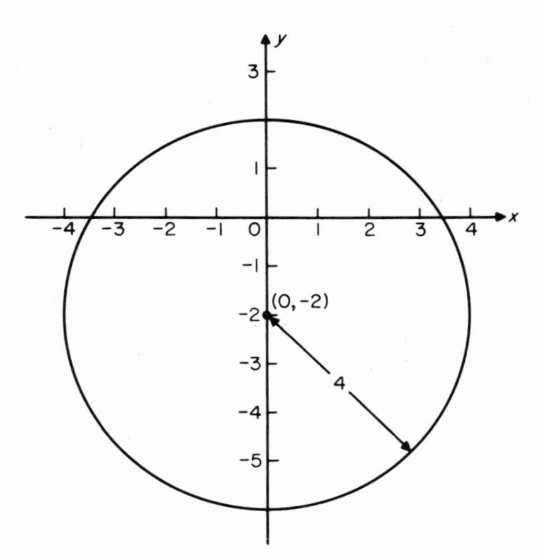

21. Center: $(0, -2)$. Radius: 4.

Ex. 21

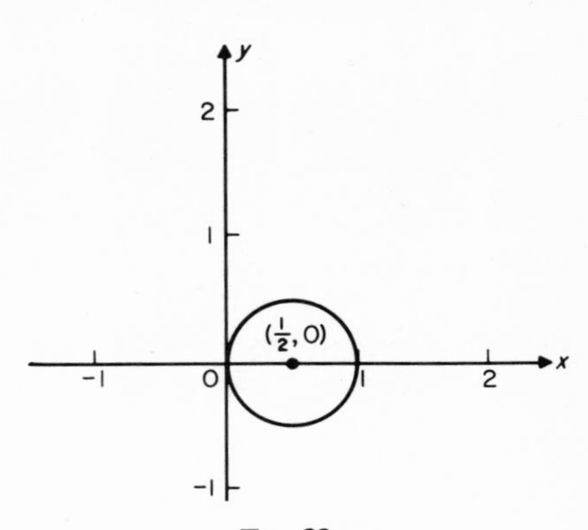

23. Center: $(\frac{1}{2}, 0)$. Radius: $\frac{1}{2}$.

Ex. 23

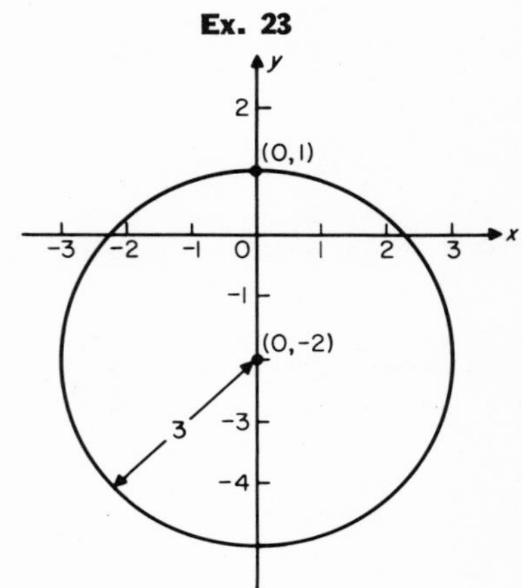

25. Center: $(0, -2)$. Radius: 3.

Ex. 25

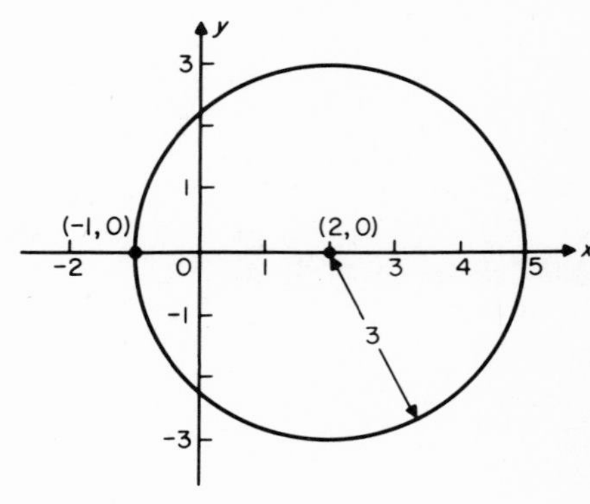

27. Center: $(2, 0)$. Radius: 3.

Ex. 27

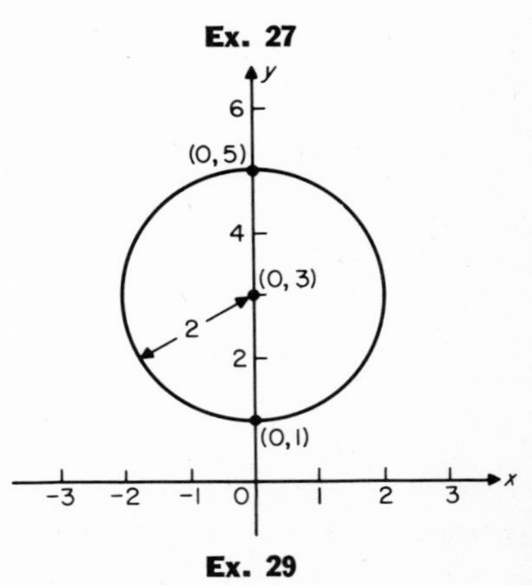

29. Center: $(0, 3)$. Radius: 2.

Ex. 29

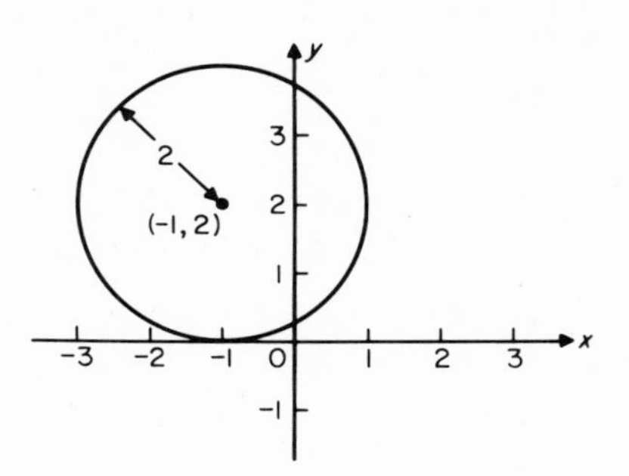

31. Center: $(-1, 2)$. Radius: 2.

Ex. 31

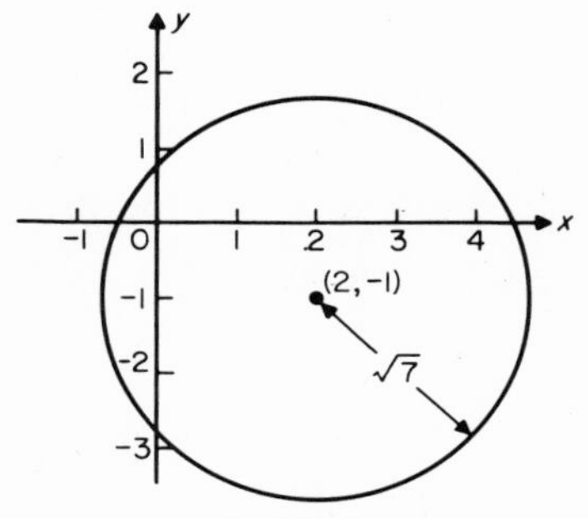

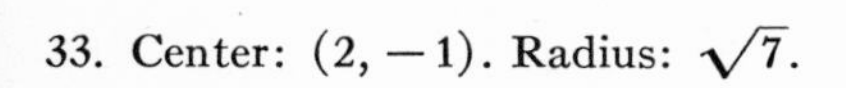

33. Center: $(2, -1)$. Radius: $\sqrt{7}$.

Ex. 33

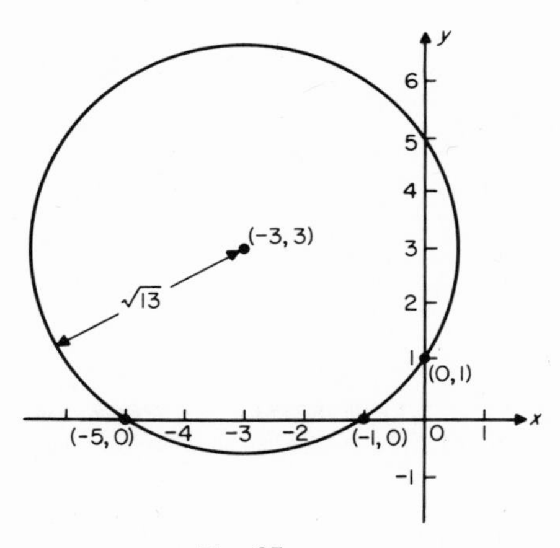

35. Center: $(-3, 3)$. Radius: $\sqrt{13}$.

Ex. 35

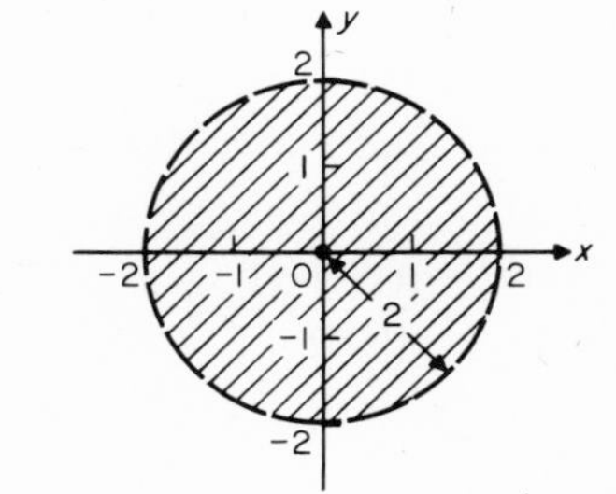

37. Center: $(-4, -\frac{5}{2})$.
    Radius: $\sqrt{181}/2$.
39. Center: $(5, -1)$. Radius: 6.

41. Interior of the circle, center at the origin, radius 2.

Ex. 41

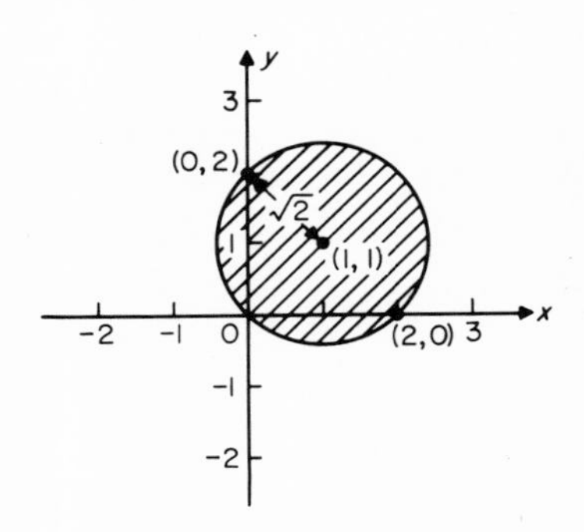

Ex. 43

43. Interior of the circle, center $(1, 1)$, radius $\sqrt{2}$, including the circle itself.

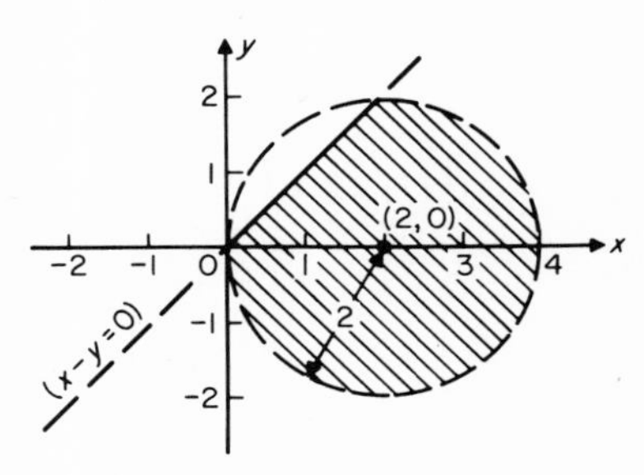

Ex. 47

45. The entire plane save for $(2, -3)$.

47. Solution set is graphed below.

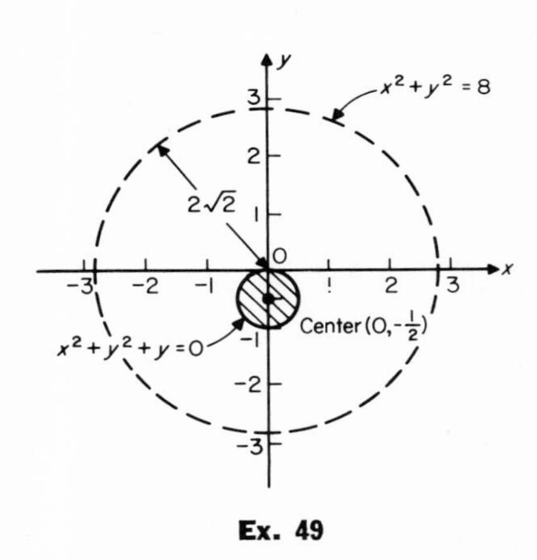

Ex. 49

EXERCISE SET 5.9, PAGE 155

1. $\dfrac{x^2}{5} + \dfrac{y^2}{9} = 1$, or $9x^2 + 5y^2 - 45 = 0$.

3. $\dfrac{(x-1)^2}{9} + \dfrac{(y-2)^2}{5} = 1$, or $5x^2 + 9y^2 - 10x - 36y - 4 = 0$.

5. $x^2 + \dfrac{y^2}{4} = 1$, or $4x^2 + y^2 - 4 = 0$.

7. $\dfrac{(x-1)^2}{5} + \dfrac{(y-1)^2}{9} < 1$, or $9x^2 + 5y^2 - 18x - 10y - 31 < 0$.

9.

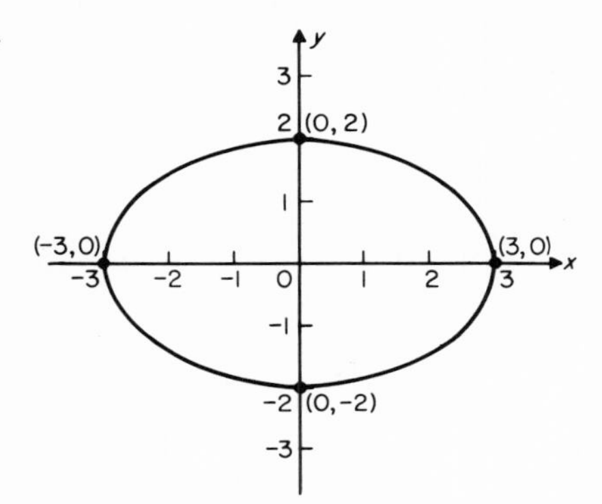

Ex. 9

11.

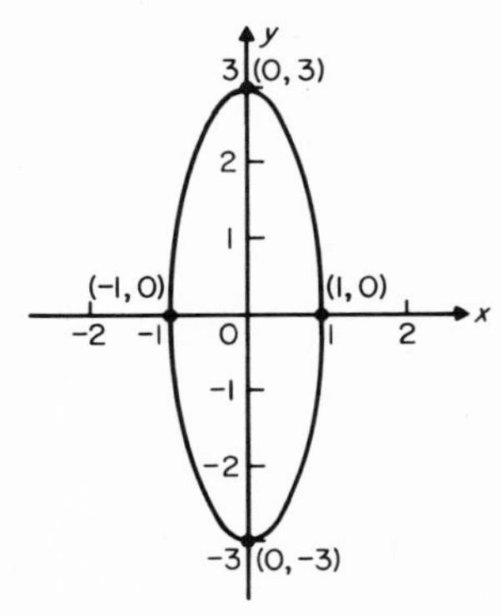

Ex. 11

13.

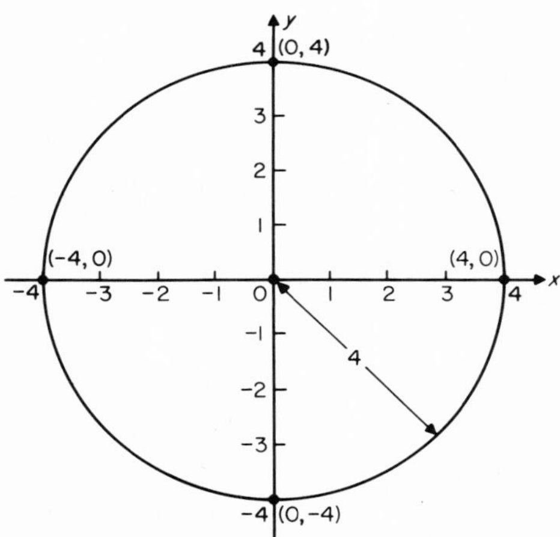

Ex. 13

15.

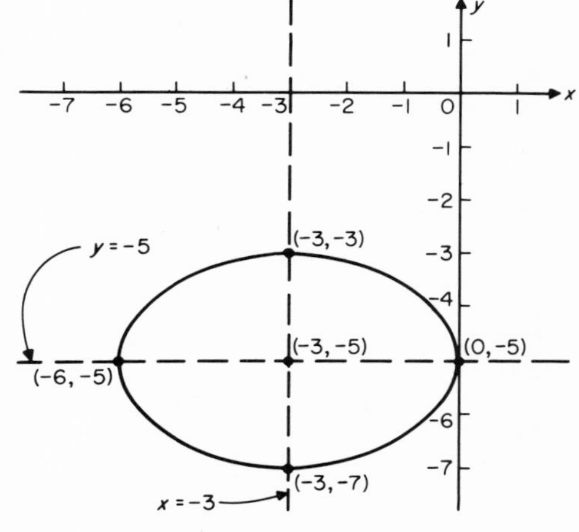

Ex. 15

17.

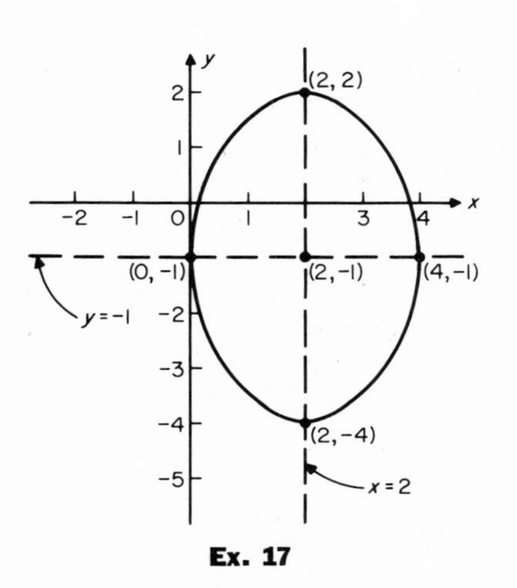

Ex. 17

19.

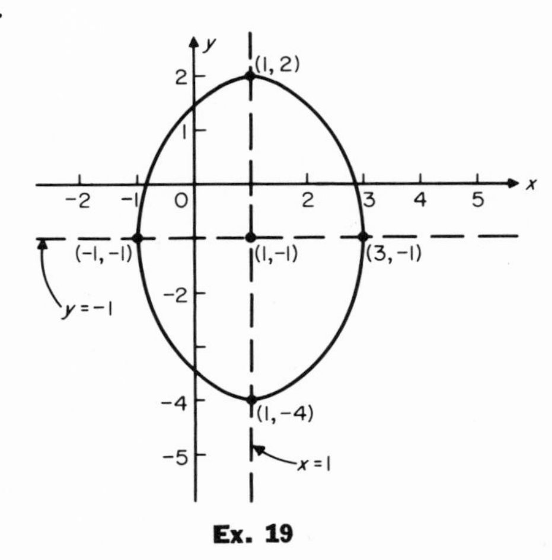

Ex. 19

21.

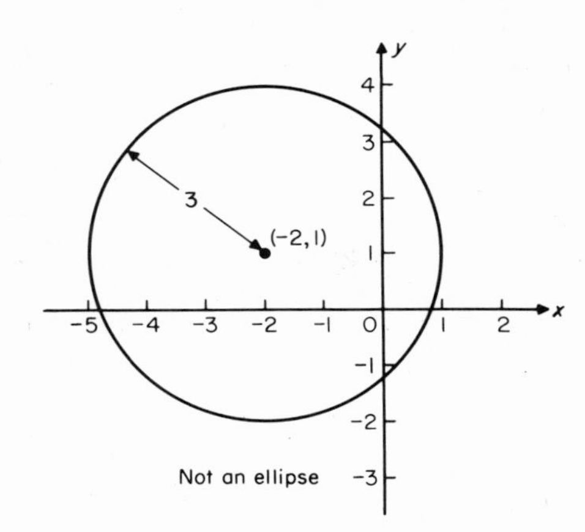

Ex. 21

23.

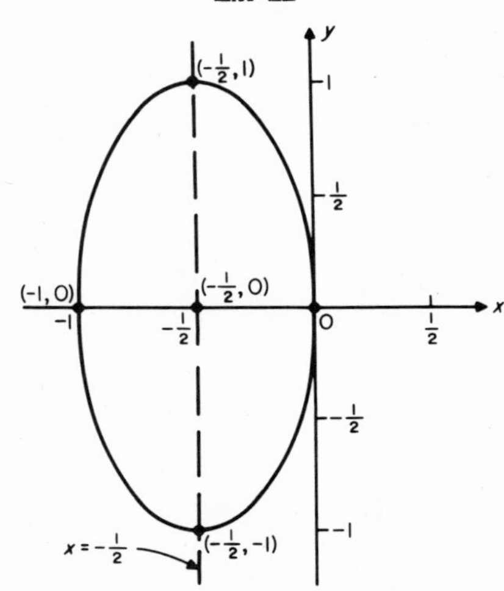

Ex. 23

25.

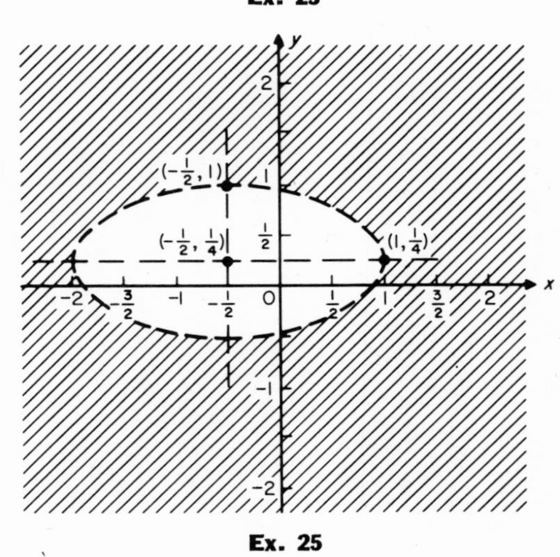

Ex. 25

EXERCISE SET 5.10, PAGE 158

1–4.

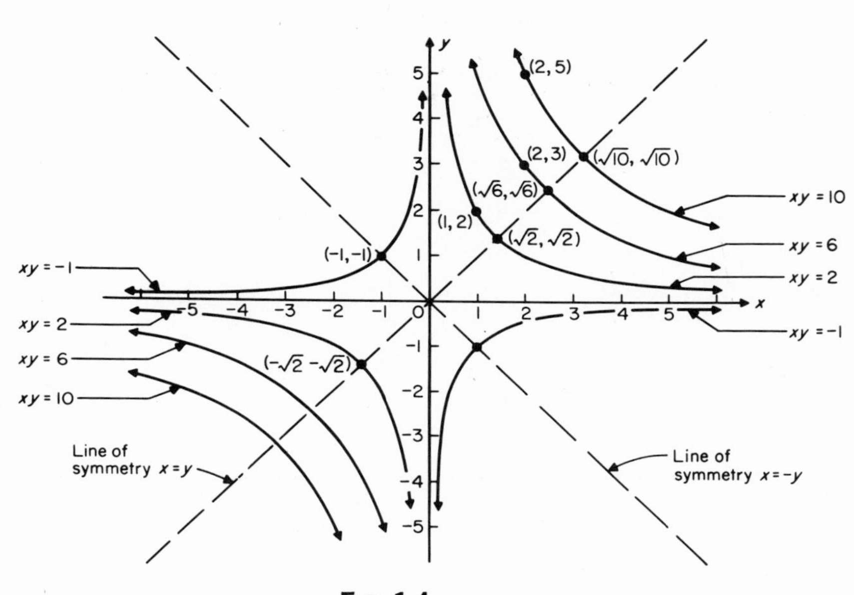

Exs. 1–4

5.

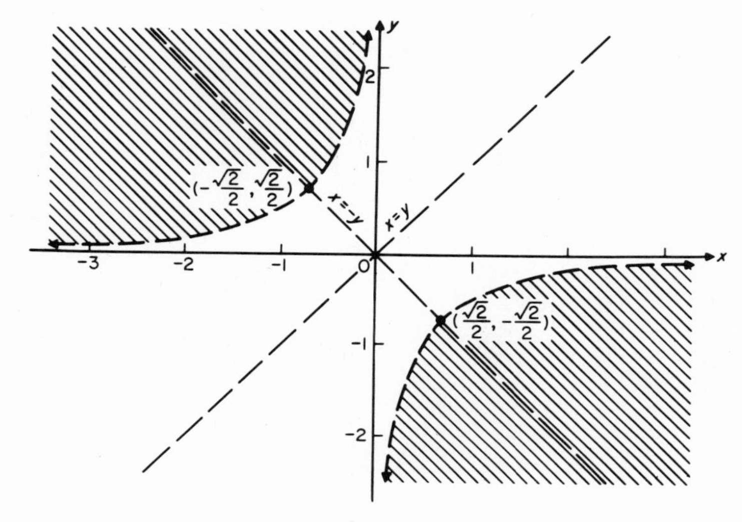

Ex. 5

7. $k = 0$. 9. $x = 3$ and $y = 0$ (the x-axis).

11.

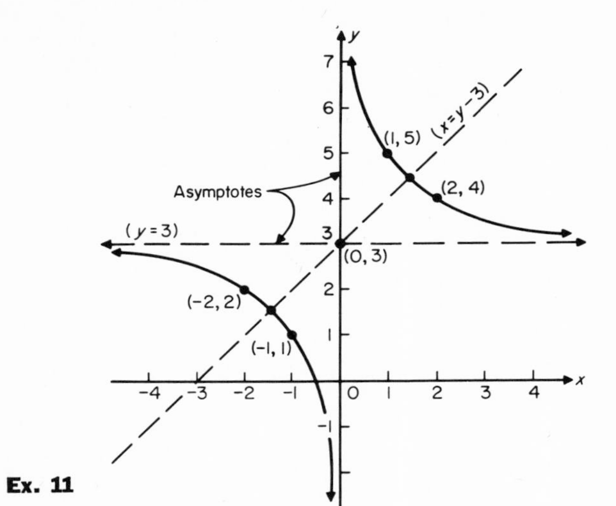

Ex. 11

13.

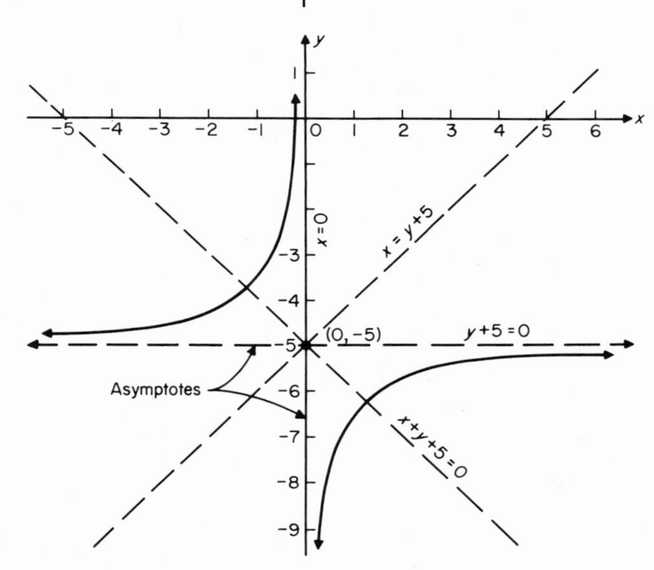

Ex. 13

17.

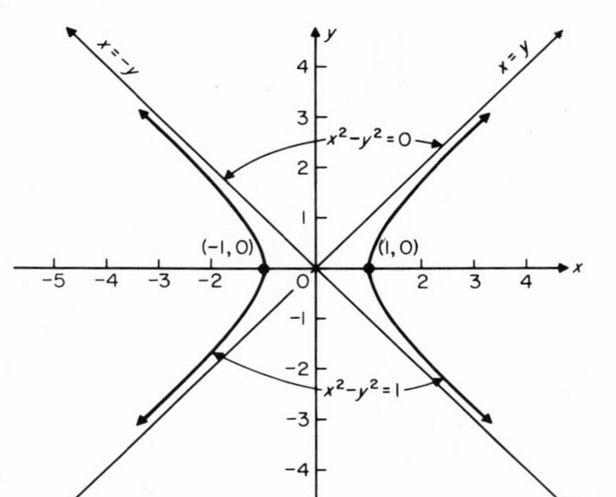

Ex. 17

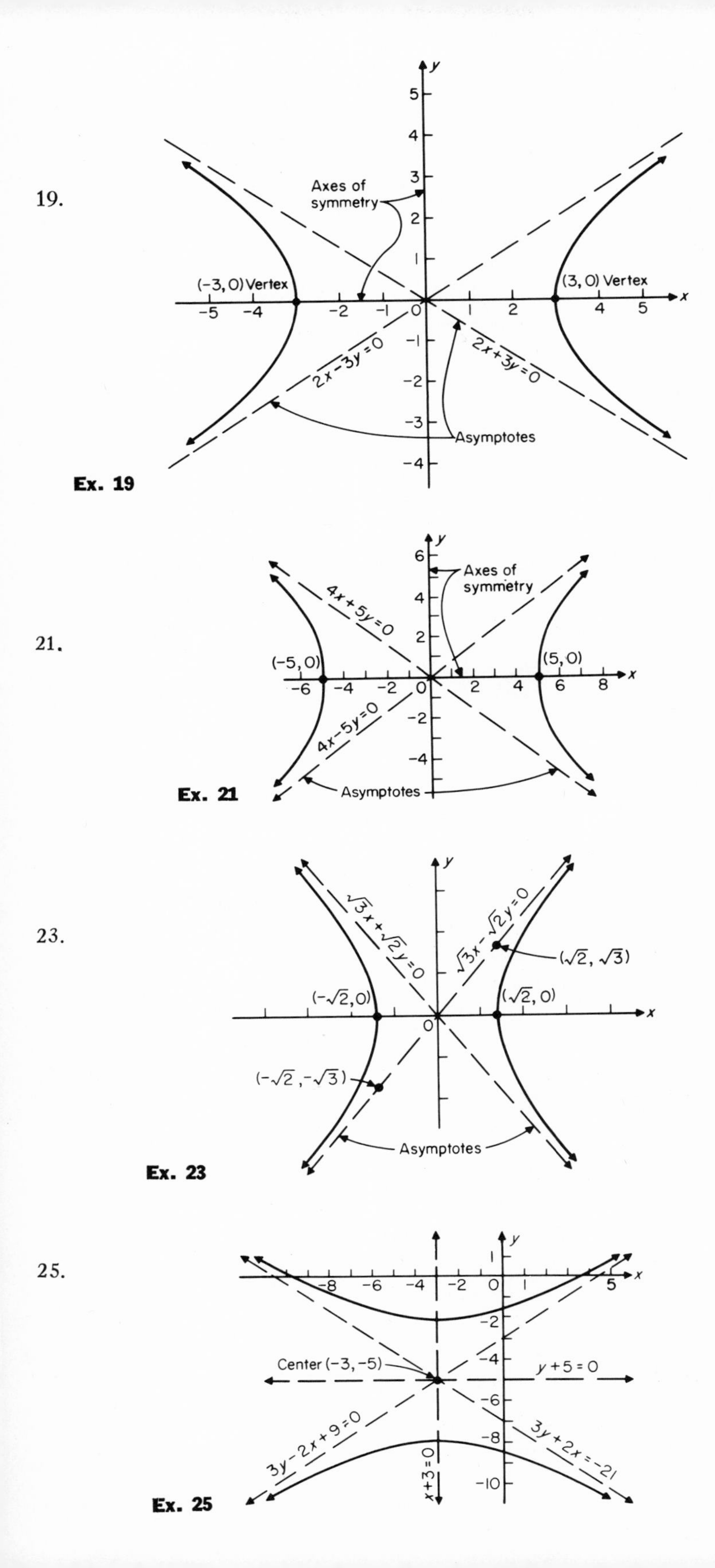
19.
Axes of symmetry
(-3, 0) Vertex
(3, 0) Vertex
2x-3y=0
2x+3y=0
Asymptotes
Ex. 19
21.
Axes of symmetry
4x+5y=0
(-5, 0)
(5, 0)
4x-5y=0
Asymptotes
Ex. 21
23.
√3x+√2y=0
√3x-√2y=0
(√2, √3)
(-√2, 0)
(√2, 0)
(-√2, -√3)
Asymptotes
Ex. 23
25.
Center (-3, -5)
y+5=0
3y-2x+9=0
3y+2x=-21
x+3=0
Ex. 25

27.

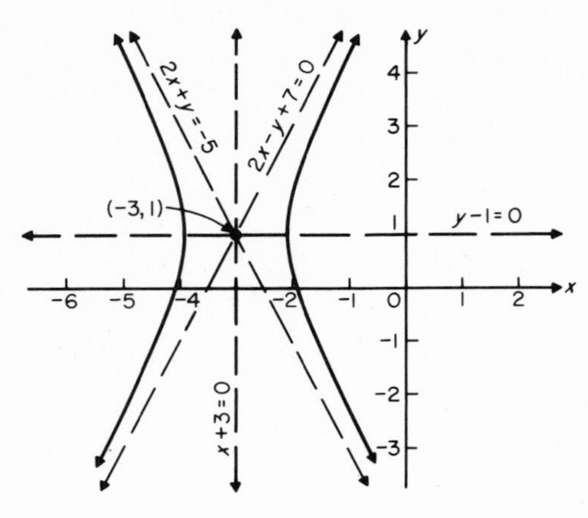

Ex. 27

29.

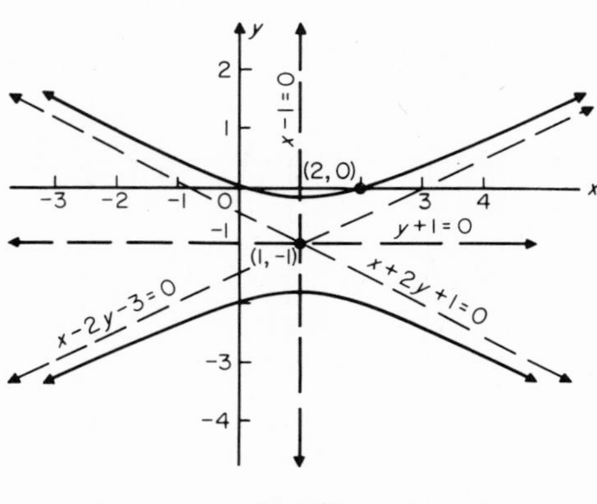

Ex. 29

Graphs not provided for Exercises 31, 33.

EXERCISE SET 5.11, PAGE 161

1–3.

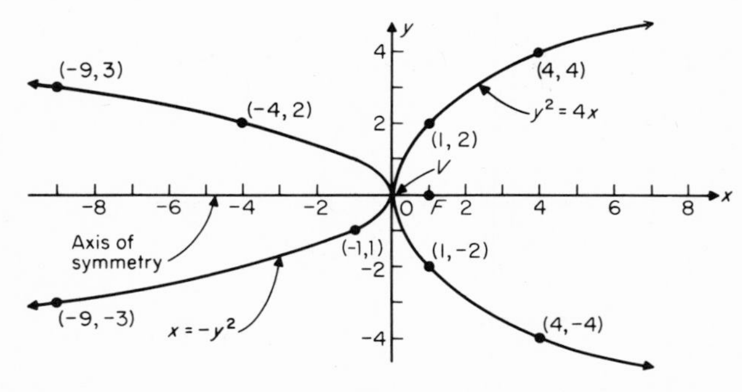

Exs. 1–3

5.

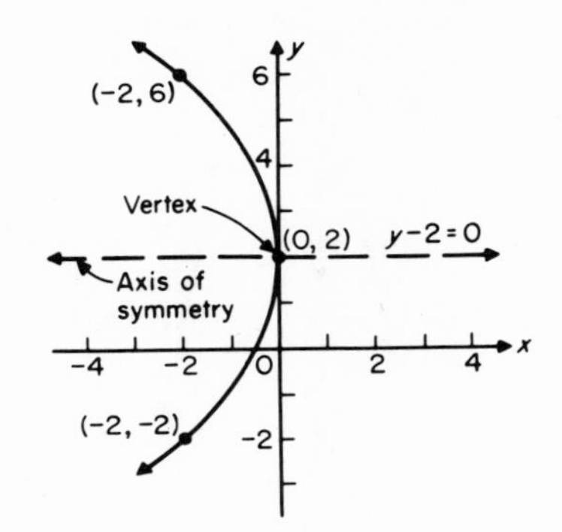

Ex. 5

7.

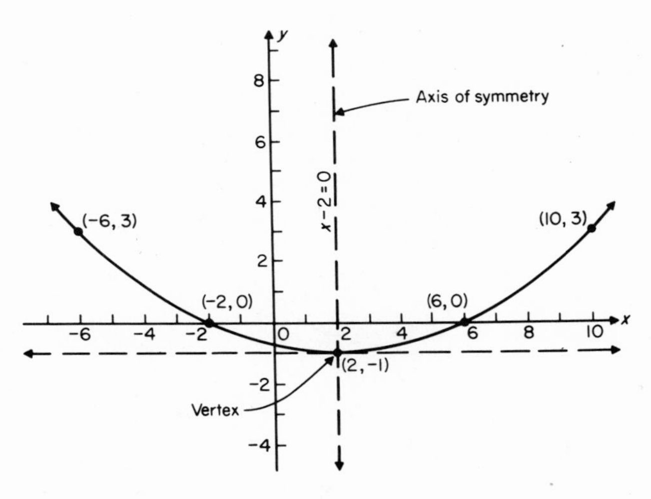

Ex. 7

9.

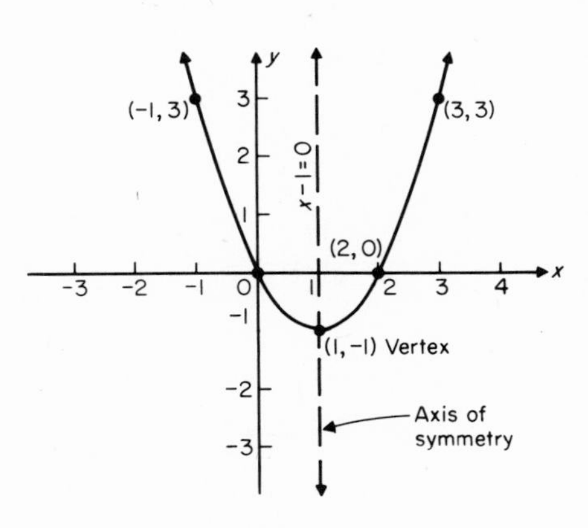

Ex. 9

11.

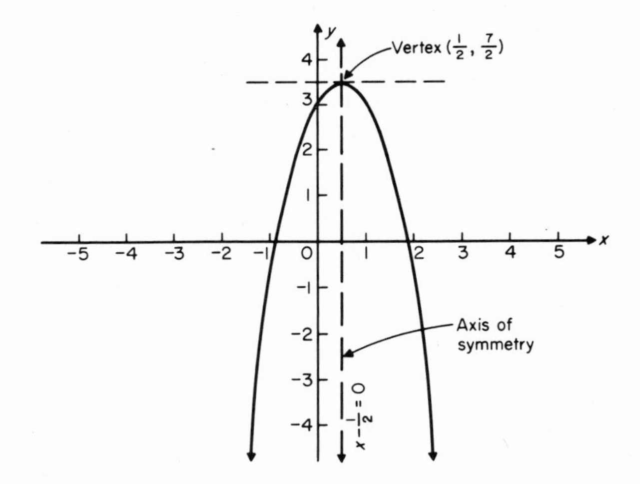

Ex. 11

13.

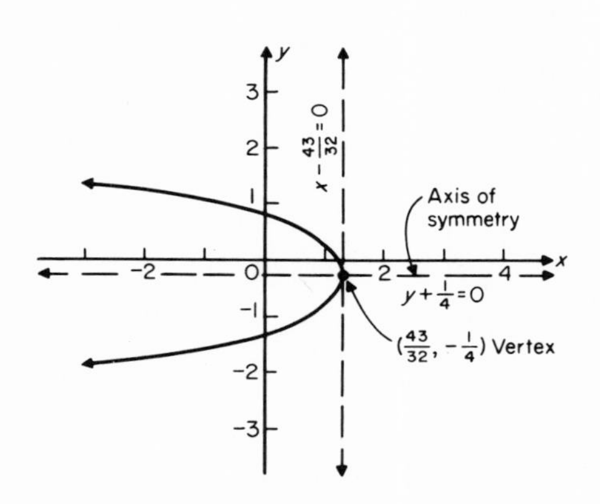

Ex. 13

15. Not a parabola.

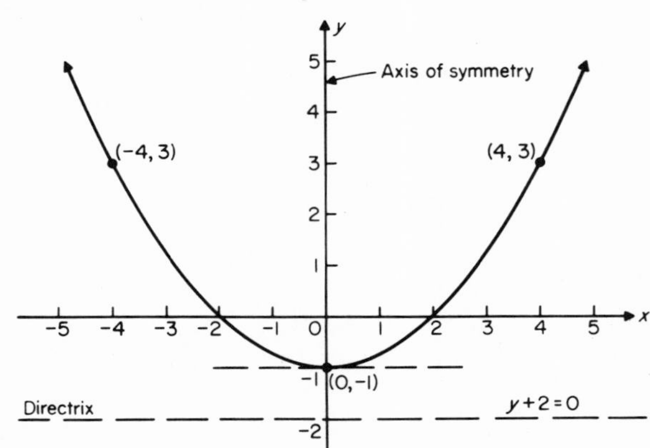

17. $x^2 = 4(y + 1)$,
or $x^2 - 4y - 4 = 0$.

Ex. 17

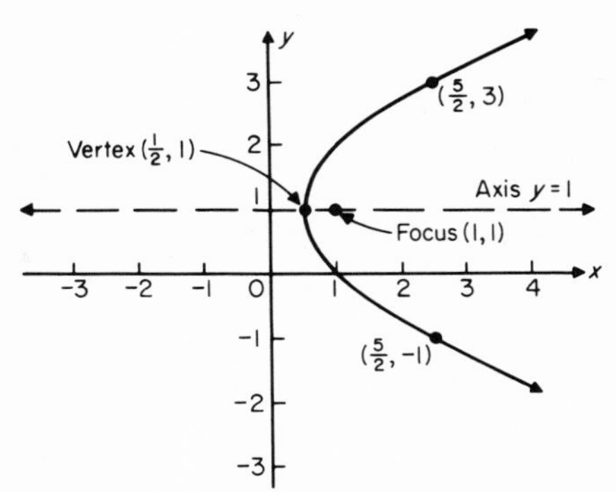

19. $(y - 1)^2 = 2(x - \frac{1}{2})$, or
$y^2 - 2x - 2y + 2 = 0$.

Ex. 19

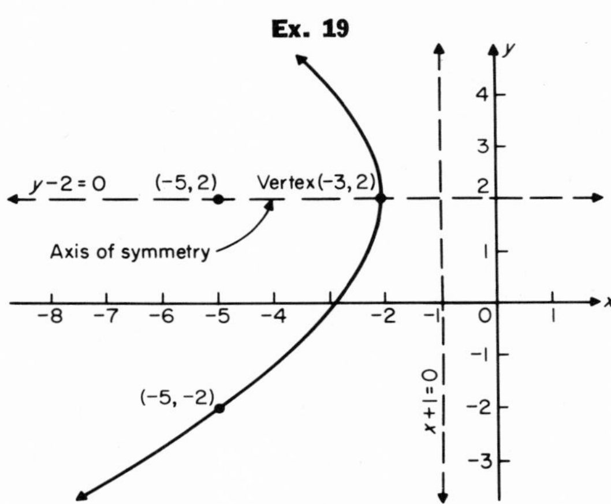

21. $(y - 2)^2 = -8(x + 3)$, or
$y^2 + 8x - 4y + 28 = 0$.

Ex. 21

EXERCISE SET 5.12, PAGE 163

1.

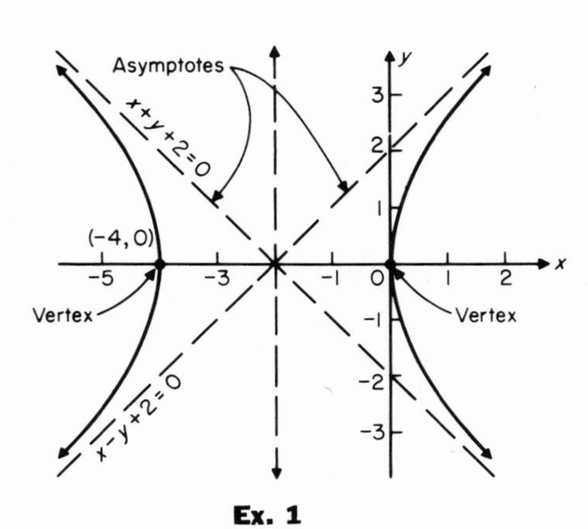

Ex. 1

3.

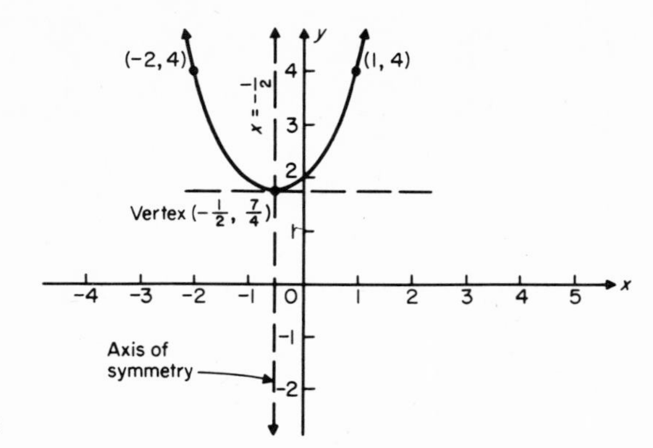

Ex. 3

5.

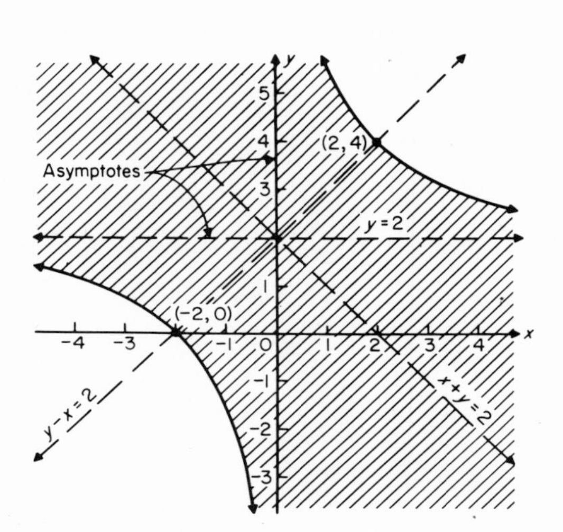

Ex. 5

7.

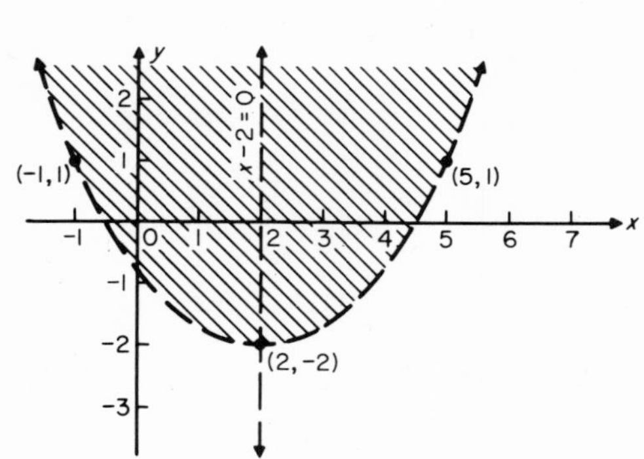

Ex. 7

9.

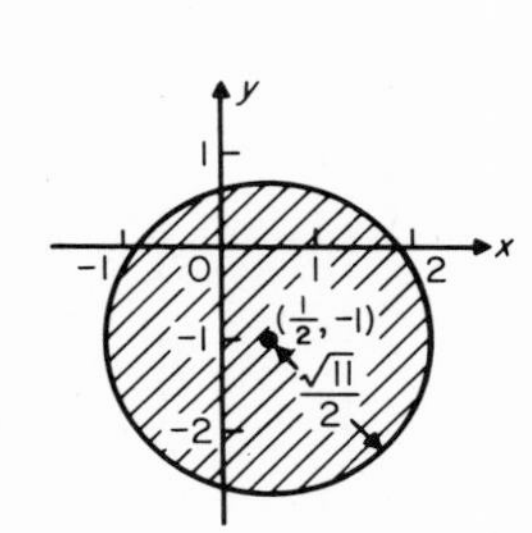

Ex. 9

11.

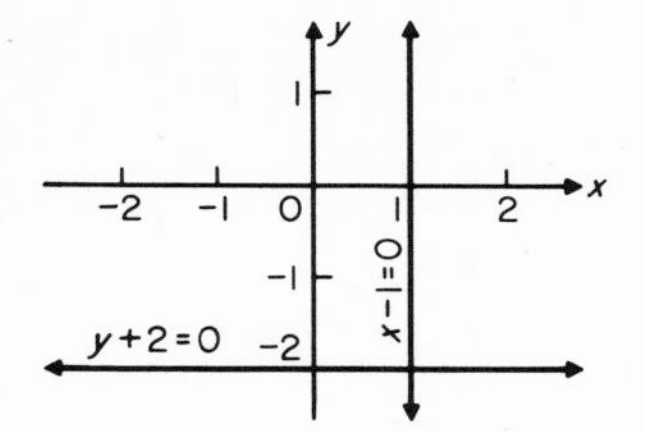

13. Only the point $(0, 0)$.

15.

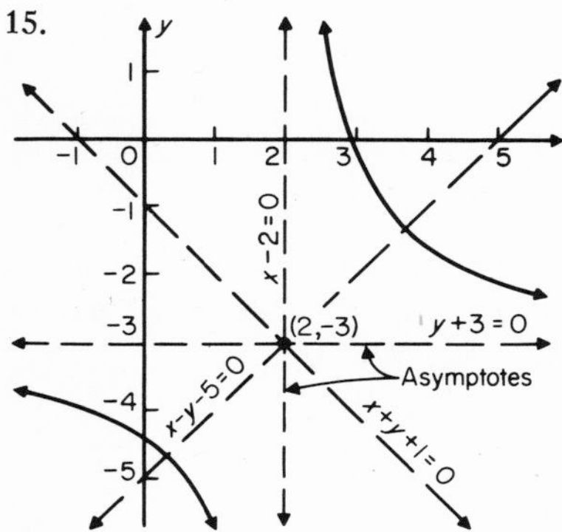

17.

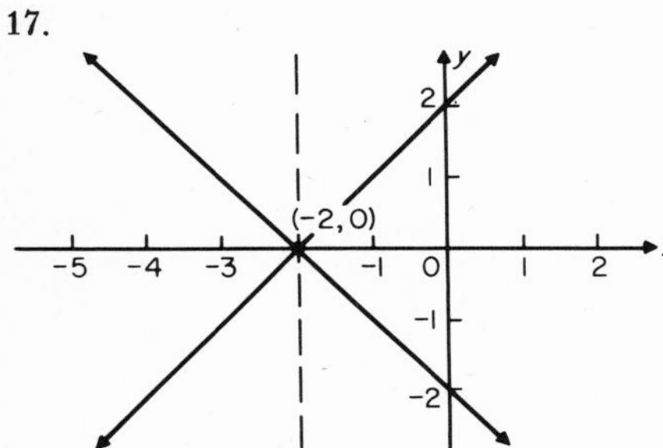

19.

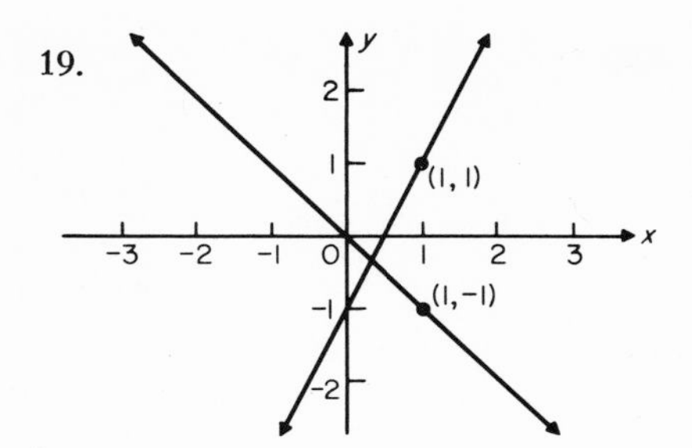

21. Line through $(0, 1)$, $(-1, 0)$.

23.

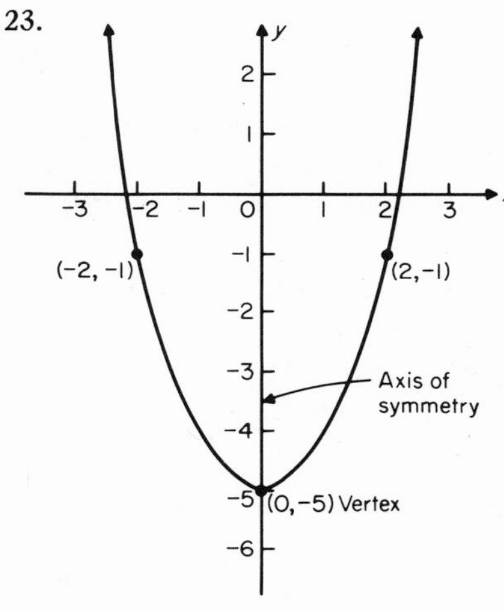

25. $x^2 + y^2 - 6x - 8y - 24 = 0$.

27. $9x^2 - 4y^2 - 9 = 0$.

29. $9x^2 - 16y^2 - 54x - 32y + 173 = 0$.

Chapter six

EXERCISE SET 6.1, PAGE 167

1.–9.

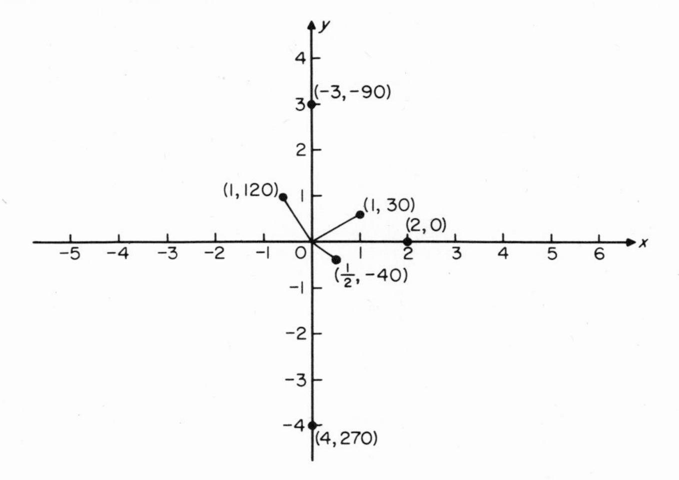

Exs. 1–9

11.–15.

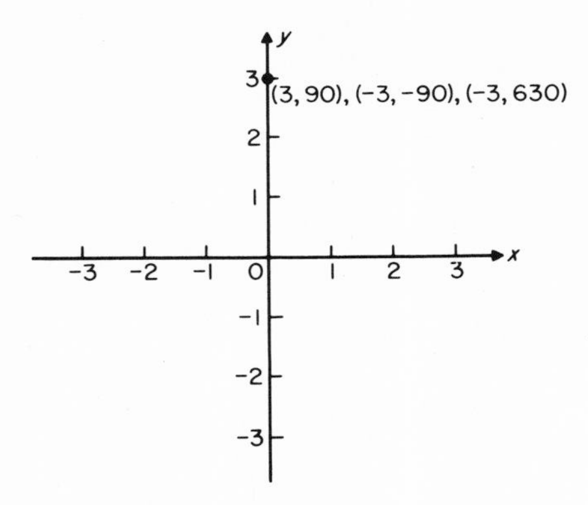

Exs. 11–15

17. (3, 270). 19. (3, 240). 21. (4, 170). 23. (3, 80). 25. (π, 340). 27. (2, $30 + 360n$), (-2, $210 + 360n$), $n \in I$. 29. (-3, $100 + 360n$), (3, $280 + 360n$), $n \in I$. 31. $r = 0$. 33. $\theta \in \{360p \mid p \in I\}$.

EXERCISE SET 6.2, PAGE 172

1. 720, 4π. 3. 21.6, 0.12π. 5. -1224, -6.8π. 7. 7, $7\pi/180$. 9. $-\frac{3}{4}$, $-3\pi/2$. 11. $-\frac{73}{36}$, $-73\pi/18$. 13. $13/36\pi$, $\frac{13}{18}$. 15. 1, 360. 17. $\frac{1}{6}$, 120. 19. $-\frac{23}{6}$, -1380. 21. $-1/4\pi$, $-90/\pi$.

23.–29.

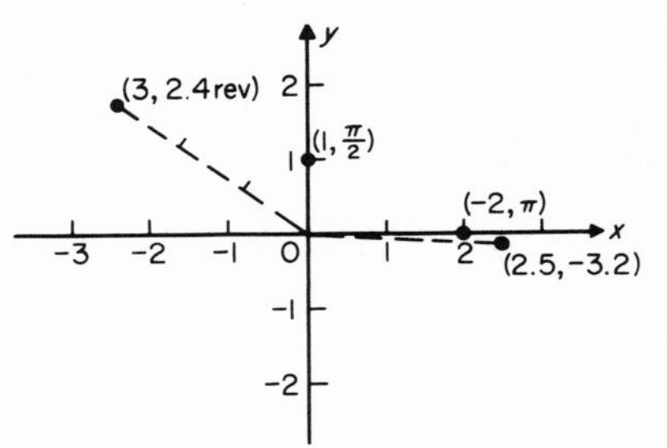

Exs. 23–29

31. (3, π), (3, 3π), (-3, π), and others. 33. (2, $\frac{3}{2} + 2\pi$), (-2, $\frac{3}{2} + \pi$), (2, $\frac{3}{2} + 4\pi$), and others. 35. (3, 0), (3, 1), (3, -1), and others. 37. (1, 0), and others. 39. (4, π), and others. 41. (2.5, $\frac{5}{6}$). 43. π. 45. $3\pi/4$. 47. 6. 49. 60π.

51. 53.

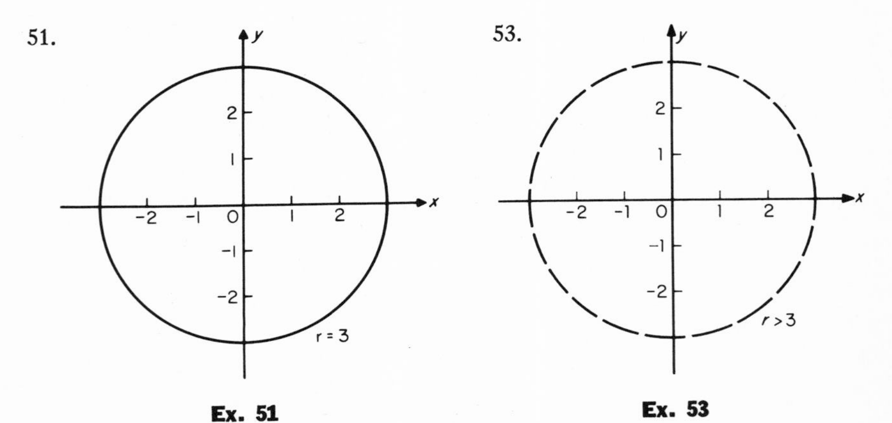

Ex. 51 **Ex. 53**

55.

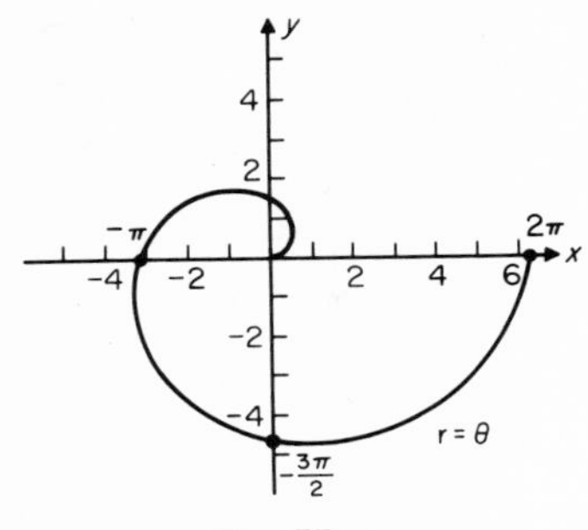

Ex. 55

EXERCISE SET 6.3, PAGE 180

1. 1. 3. 1. 5. $\sqrt{2}/2$. 7. $-\sqrt{3}/2$. 9. $-\sqrt{3}/2$. 11. $-\sqrt{2}/2$. 13. $-\sqrt{3}/2$. 15. $\sqrt{3}/2$. 17. $\frac{1}{2}$. 19. -1. 21. $0°$, $180°$; 0, π. 23. $90°$; $\pi/2$. 25. $30°$, $150°$; $\pi/6$, $5\pi/6$. 27. $45°$, $135°$; $\pi/4$, $3\pi/4$. 29. .3051. 31. 0.9996. 33. 0.2482. 35. 0.2419. 37. 0.9272. 39. $(\sqrt{2}/2, \sqrt{2}/2)$. 41. (0.7986, 0.6018). 43. (0, 1). 45. $(\sqrt{2}/2, \sqrt{2}/2)$. 47. (2, 0). 49. $(5\sqrt{2}/2, 5\sqrt{2}/2)$. 51. (1, .39), and others. 53. (1, .67), and others. 55. $(1, \pi - 1.46)$, and others. 57. I. 59. x-axis. 61. y-axis.

EXERCISE SET 6.4, PAGE 183

1. 0.3140. 3. 0.4587. 5. 0.0419. 7. 0.9394. 9. 0.9454. 11. 0.515. 13. 1.466. 15. 83.0. 17. 33.5.

EXERCISE SET 6.5, PAGE 189

1. $\text{Sin}\ (\pi - \theta) = \sin - (\theta - \pi) = -\sin\ (\theta - \pi) = \sin \theta$.
$\cos\ (\pi - \theta) = \cos - (\theta - \pi) = \cos\ (\theta - \pi) = -\cos \theta$.
3. $\text{Sin}\ -\pi/6 = -\sin \pi/6 = -\frac{1}{2}$. 5. $-\sqrt{3}/2$. 7. $\sqrt{2}/2$. 9. $\frac{1}{2}$. 11. $-\sqrt{2}/2$. 13. $-\sqrt{2}/2$. 15. 0.1395. 17. -0.0799. 19. -0.4889. 21. 0.8480. 23. 0.2250. 25. $\pi/3$, $2\pi/3$. 27. $5\pi/4$, $7\pi/4$. 29. $\pi/2$. 31. 0, π, 2π. 33. 0.927, $\pi - 0.927$. 35. 1.438, $2\pi - 1.438$. 37. $5\pi/4 + 2n\pi$, $7\pi/4 + 2n\pi$, $n \in I$. 39. $n\pi$, $n \in I$. 41. $\pm 1.18 + 2n\pi$, $n \in I$. 43. $(-\sqrt{3}/2, -\frac{1}{2})$. 45. $(-\frac{1}{2}, -\sqrt{3}/2)$. 47. (0.1392, 0.9903). 49. (.40, -0.92). 51. (0, 5).

EXERCISE SET 6.6, PAGE 194

1. (1, 0), (1, 2π). 3. (1, $\pi/3$). 5. (1, .927). 7. (2, $2\pi/3$). 9. $(\sqrt{13}, 2\pi - .983)$. 11. (0,0). 13. $(\frac{1}{2}, \sqrt{3}/2)$. 15. $(-\sqrt{3}/2, -\frac{1}{2})$. 17. $(0, -1)$. 19. (0,2). 21. $(3\sqrt{2}/2, 3\sqrt{2}/2)$. 23. $(31\sqrt{3}/20, \frac{31}{20})$. 25. $(\frac{1}{2}, \sqrt{3}/2)$. 27. $(-1, -\sqrt{3})$. 29. (1.98, -0.279). 31. $B = 60°$, $a = \frac{1}{2}$, $b = \sqrt{3}/2$. 33. $B = 45°$, $b = 2$, $c = 2\sqrt{2}$. 35. $B = 53°$, $a = 1.93$, $b = 2.56$. 37. $A = 30°$, $B = 60°$, $b = 2\sqrt{3}$. 39. $A = 18.4°$, $B = 71.6°$, $c = \sqrt{10}$. 41. Not possible.

EXERCISE SET 6.7, PAGE 198

1. 1. 3. $\sqrt{3}/3$. 5. $-\sqrt{3}$. 7. $-\sqrt{3}/3$. 9. $\sqrt{2}$. 11. $-\sqrt{2}$. 13. -1. 15. $-2\sqrt{3}/3$. 17. 2.820. 19. -2.301. 21. 2.833. 23. $\pi/4$, $5\pi/4$. 25. $2\pi/3$, $5\pi/3$. 27. $5\pi/6$, $11\pi/6$. 29. $5\pi/4$, $7\pi/4$. 31. 0.495, 3.636. 33. 0.303, 3.445.

EXERCISE SET 6.8, PAGE 203

1. Symmetric to vertical lines $x = n\pi$, $n \in I$, and to points $\left(\frac{\pi}{2} + \pi, 0\right)$, $n \in I$.

   Graph not provided. Period: 2π, amplitude: 2. For graph, see Figure 6.7, page 170.

3. Symmetric to lines $x = 2n\pi$, $n \in I$, and to points $(\pi + 2n\pi, 0)$, $n \in I$. Period: 4π, amplitude: 1.

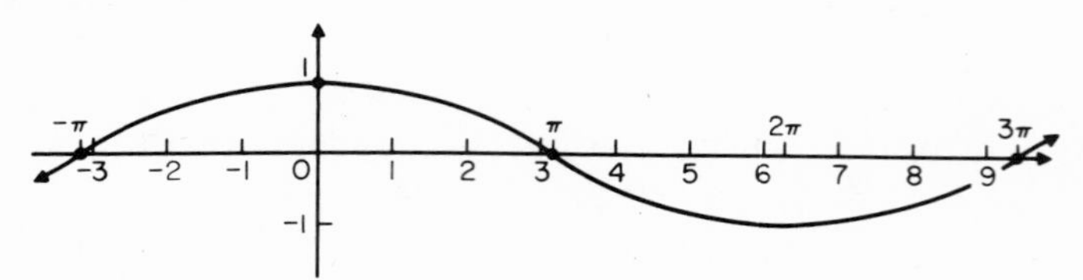

Ex. 3

5. Symmetric to lines $x = (\pi/4) + n\pi$, $n \in I$, and to points $\left(\frac{3\pi}{4} + n\pi, 0\right)$, $n \in I$.

   Period: 2π, amplitude: 1.

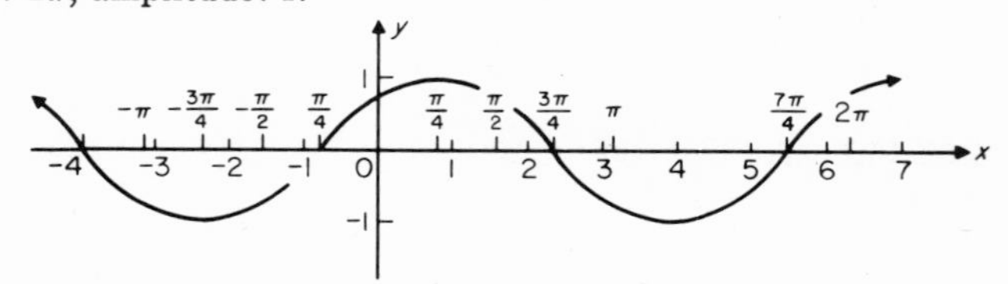

Ex. 5

7. Symmetric to lines $x = 1 + (\pi/4) + (n\pi/2)$, $n \in I$, and to points $\left(1 + \frac{3\pi}{4} + \frac{n\pi}{2}, 0\right)$, $n \in I$. Period: π, amplitude: 1.

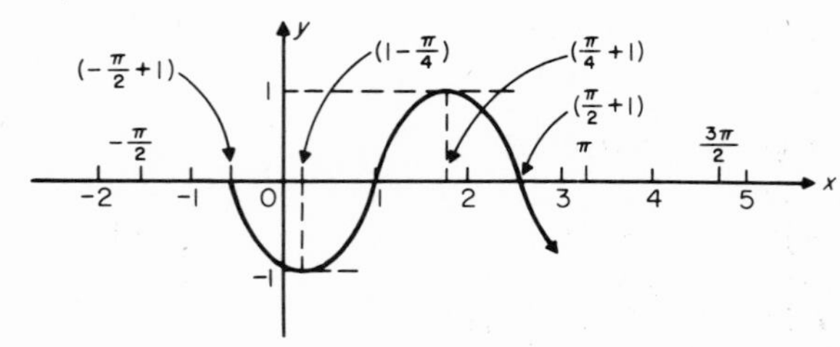

Ex. 7

9.

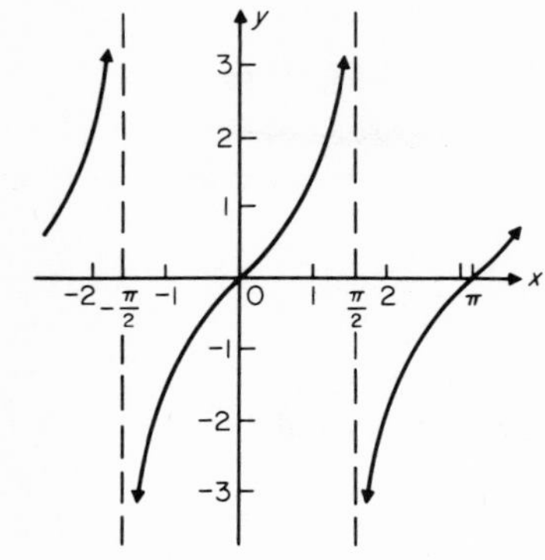

Ex. 9

13.

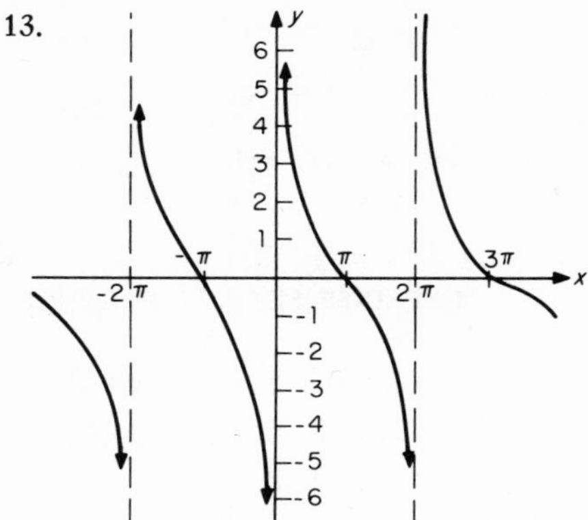

Ex. 13

11.

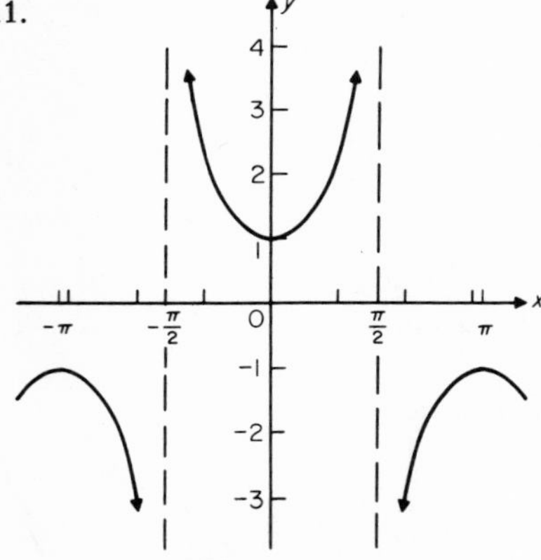

Ex. 11

EXERCISE SET 6.9, PAGE 207

1. $\cos x = \sqrt{1 - \sin^2 x} = \frac{4}{5}$. $\qquad \tan x = \dfrac{\sin x}{\cos x} = \dfrac{3}{4}$.

$\cot x = \dfrac{1}{\tan x} = \dfrac{4}{3}$. $\qquad \sec x = \dfrac{1}{\cos x} = \dfrac{5}{4}$.

$\csc x = \dfrac{1}{\sin x} = \dfrac{5}{3}$.

3. $\sin x = \sqrt{15}/4$, $\cos x = \frac{1}{4}$, $\tan x = \sqrt{15}$.

5. $\sin x = \sqrt{1 - \cos^2 x}$, quadrants I, II.
   $\sin x = -\sqrt{1 - \cos^2 x}$, quadrants III, IV.

7. $1 + \dfrac{\sqrt{1 - \sin^2 x}}{\sin x}$, $0 < x < \pi/2$, $3\pi/2 < x < 2\pi$. (Answer incomplete).

9. $\dfrac{\text{Sin } x + \sqrt{1 - \sin^2 x}}{\text{Sin } x - \sqrt{1 - \sin^2 x}}$,

11. $-2\sqrt{2}/3$. 13. $-1/\sqrt{3}$. 15. $5\sqrt{6}/12$. 17. -42. (Answers will vary).

EXERCISE SET 6.10, PAGE 212

1. $\text{Sin } (\theta - \pi/2) = \sin \theta \cos \pi/2 - \cos \theta \sin \pi/2 = -\cos \theta$.

3. $\text{Cos } (\theta - \pi/2) = \cos \theta \cos \pi/2 + \sin \theta \sin \pi/2 = \sin \theta$.

5. $\text{Sin } (\theta - \pi/6) = \sin \theta \cos \pi/6 - \cos \theta \sin \pi/6 = \sqrt{3}/2 \sin \theta - \dfrac{\cos \theta}{2}$.

7. $\dfrac{\text{Tan } \theta - 1}{\text{Tan } \theta + 1}$.

9. $$\text{Tan } (x - y) = \tan (x + (-y)) = \frac{\tan x + \tan (-y)}{1 - \tan x \tan (-y)} = \frac{\tan x - \tan y}{1 + \tan x \tan y}.$$

11. $\dfrac{1 + \tan x \tan y}{\tan x - \tan y}$. 13. $\text{Cos}^2 x - \sin^2 x - 2 \cos x \sin x$, and others.

15. $\dfrac{\sqrt{6} + \sqrt{2}}{4}$. 17. $\dfrac{\sqrt{2} - \sqrt{6}}{4}$. 19. $\dfrac{\sqrt{6} - \sqrt{2}}{4}$. 21. $\dfrac{\sqrt{3} - 1}{\sqrt{3} + 1}$.

23. $\dfrac{2\sqrt{2}}{3}$. 25. $\dfrac{1 + 8\sqrt{3}}{15}$. 27. $-\dfrac{25\sqrt{2} + 9\sqrt{6}}{8}$. 29. $\dfrac{4\sqrt{6}}{25}$. 31. $\dfrac{4\sqrt{2}}{7}$.

33–39. Answers will vary. 41. $\{\pi/6, \pi/2, 5\pi/6, 7\pi/6, 3\pi/2, 11\pi/6\}$.

43. $\{0, 2\pi/3, \pi, 4\pi/3, 2\pi\}$.

EXERCISE SET 6.11, PAGE 217

1. $\text{Sin } \dfrac{\pi}{12} = \sin \dfrac{1}{2}\left(\dfrac{\pi}{6}\right) = \sqrt{\dfrac{1 - \cos \pi/6}{2}} = \tfrac{1}{2}\sqrt{2 - \sqrt{3}}$.

3. $\dfrac{1}{2 - \sqrt{3}}$. 5. $-\dfrac{\sqrt{2 - \sqrt{3}}}{2}$. 7. $2 + \sqrt{3}$. 9. $\dfrac{1}{2 + \sqrt{3}}$. 11. $\dfrac{\sqrt{2 + \sqrt{3}}}{2}$.

13. $\dfrac{\sqrt{2}}{2 + \sqrt{2}}$. 15. $\dfrac{2}{\sqrt{2 - \sqrt{3}}}$. 17. Solving $\cos 2x = 1 - 2 \sin^2 x$ for $\sin x$,

$$|\sin x| = \frac{\sqrt{1 - \cos 2x}}{2}. \qquad \text{Letting } x = \frac{\theta}{2},$$

this becomes

$$\left|\sin \frac{\theta}{2}\right| = \frac{\sqrt{1 - \cos \theta}}{2}.$$

Sin $x/2 > 0$ if $0 \leq x \leq 2\pi$ (or more generally, $4n\pi \leq x \leq (4n + 2)\pi$).
19. Suppose $\theta/2$ is the measure of a rotation ending in quadrant III. Then

$$(2n + 1)\pi < \theta/2 < (2n + \tfrac{3}{2})\pi, \; n \in I,$$

or

$$(4n + 2)\pi < \theta < (4n + 3)\pi.$$

Since $(4n + 2)\pi = 2\pi(2n + 1)$, it is a rotation ending on the positive x-axis, and since $(4n + 3)\pi = 2\pi(2n + 1) + \pi$, it is a rotation ending on the negative x-axis. Therefore θ is a rotation ending in quadrant I or II.

21. $\dfrac{1 - 3 \cos x}{2}$. 23. $2 \cos x$. 25. $\cos x + \sin x$. 27. $\dfrac{\sec x \csc x}{2}$.

29. $\pm\sqrt{\dfrac{2}{1 + \cos x}}$. 31–37. Answers will vary.

EXERCISE SET 6.12, PAGE 222

3. $C = 106°$, $b = 11.3$, $c = 14.8$. 5. Not possible. 7. Not possible.
9. $A = 73°$, $C = 47°$, $b = 9.96$. 11. $A = 44.4°$, $B = 74.5°$, $C = 61.1°$.
13. *Hint:* Consult library references if necessary.

Chapter seven

EXERCISE SET 7.1, PAGE 230

1. (2, 1), (2, 0), $(2, -\pi)$, and others with first coordinate 2.

3. Suppose (x, y_1) and (x, y_2) are in the set. Then $y_1 = x + 3$, and $y_2 = x + 3$. Therefore $y_1 = y_2$, that is, for each x, there is only one point (x, y) in the set.

5. Suppose (x, y_1) and (x, y_2) are in the set. But $y_1 = |x|$ and $y_2 = |x|$. Thus $y_1 = y_2$, which means that for each x, there is only one point (x, y) in the set.

7. Not a function.

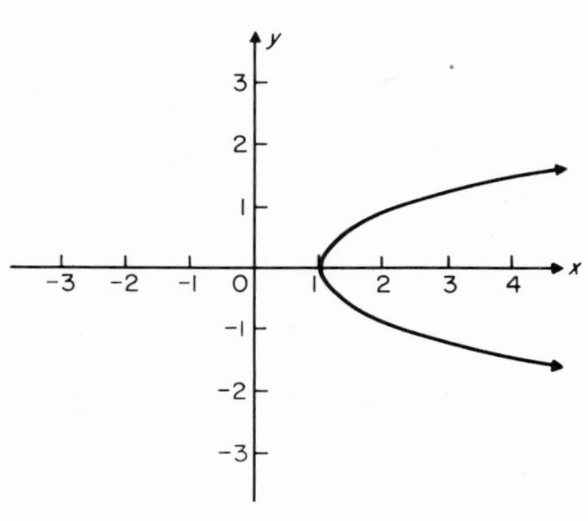

Ex. 7

9. Domain: $(-\infty, \infty)$.
Range: $(-\infty, \infty)$.

11. Not a function.

13. Domain: R^+.
Range: R^+.

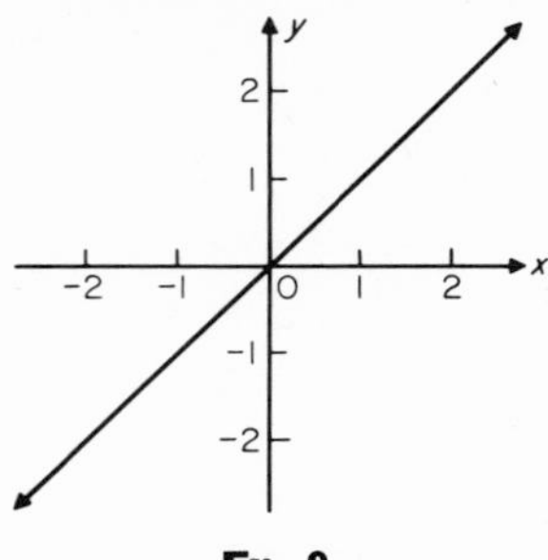

Ex. 9

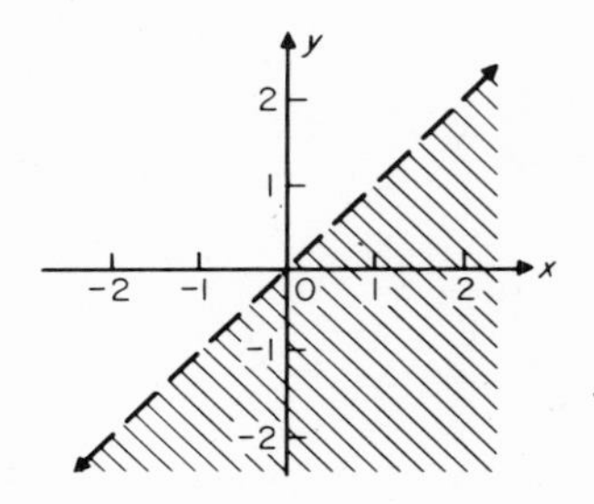

Ex. 11

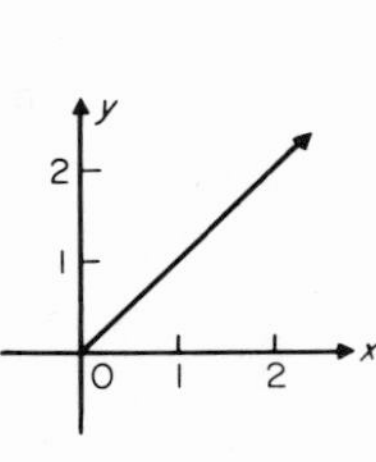

Ex. 13

15. Domain: $[-\sqrt{2}, \sqrt{2}]$. Range: $(-\infty, 0]$.

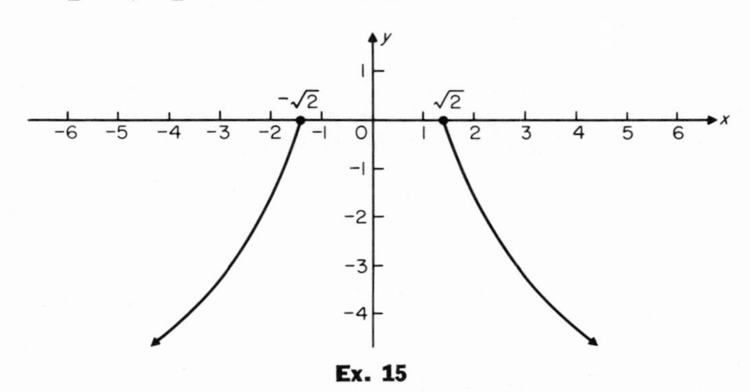

Ex. 15

17. (8) 1, -1. (9) 2. (12) none. (13) 2. (14) 5. (15) none. 19. No special conclusion. 21. No.

EXERCISE SET 7.2, PAGE 234

1. $f(x) = x - 4$. 3. 8, 6, 12, $y + 4$. 5. $g(0) = 1, g(1) = 2, g(2) = 4, g(3) = 0$. 7. 2, 1, none, 3. 9. $f(x) = 2x + 3$. 11. 2, $-\frac{3}{2}$, $a/2$, $(h - 7)/2$. 13. 3, 15, $h^2 + 6h + 8$, $4a^2 + 4a$, $\sin^2 t + 2 \sin t$. 15. $g = \{(x, y): y = x^2 + 2x\}$. 17. 0, 2, -1, 0, 0. 19. $D_f = R$, $R_f = [-1, 1]$. 21. "double the sin." 23. $g(x) = x$; 1, -7, 3, $(a + b)$. 25. $F(x) = \sqrt{4 - x^2}$; 0, 0, not defined. 27. $S(x) = \cos x$; 1, 0, -1, -1. 29. $-\frac{3}{2}$, 0, $a/2$. 31. 0; 1, -1; none; 0 for $b = (4n + 1)\pi/2$, $\exists n \in I$, none otherwise. 33. 6, $x - 1$, $x^2 - 1$. 35. $f(w) = \sin \sqrt{w}$, $w \geq 0$. 37. $(11 \pm \sqrt{129})/2$. 39. Let $x_1 < x_2$. Then $3x_1 < 3x_2$, and so $3x_1 + 2 < 3x_2 + 2$. That is, $f(x_1) < f(x_2)$. 41. Suppose $0 \leq a < b$. Then $a^2 < b^2$, or $h(a) < h(b)$. This means that h is increasing on $[0, \infty)$. Suppose $b < a \leq 0$. Then $0 < -a < -b$, and therefore $a^2 < b^2$. That is, $h(b) > h(a)$, which means h is decreasing on $(-\infty, 0]$. 43. $2\pi, \pi, 4\pi$. 45. $2\pi, 2\pi/5, 14\pi$. 47. $g(x) = g[(x + r) - r] = g(x + r)$.

EXERCISE SET 7.3, PAGE 241

1. $[5, \infty)$. 3. $[-\sqrt{2}, \sqrt{2}]$. 5. $\{-1, 1\}$. 7. $\{n\pi/2: n \in I, n \text{ is odd}\}$. 9. $[-2, 2]$. 11. $[-\frac{21}{4}, \infty)$. 13. $(-\infty, 7]$. 15. $[0, 2[$. 17. $]-4, 14[$. 19. $[0, 4]$. 21. $[0, \infty)$, and others. 23. $[0, \infty)$, and others. 25. $[0, \pi]$, and others. 27. $V(h) = h^3$, $]0, \sqrt{6\pi}/6]$, $]0, (\pi/36)\sqrt{6\pi}]$. 29. $d(t) = 2760\pi t$, $[0, \infty)$, $[0, \infty)$.

EXERCISE SET 7.4, PAGE 247

7. g: $-1 \to 2$
   $1 \to 3$
   $2 \to 2$
   $4 \to -2$.

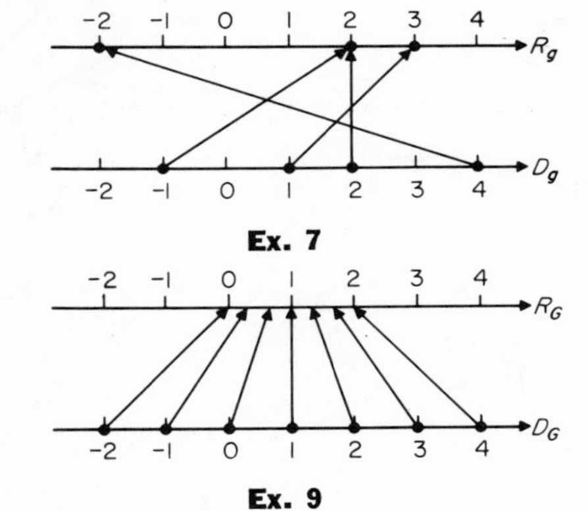

Ex. 7

Ex. 9

9. G: $n \to (n+2)/3$, on $\{-2, -1, 0, 1, 2, 3, 4\}$.

11. H: $n \to 2n$, on I^-. Sketch not provided.

13. f: $x \to x^2$, on $[0, \infty)$. Sketch not provided.

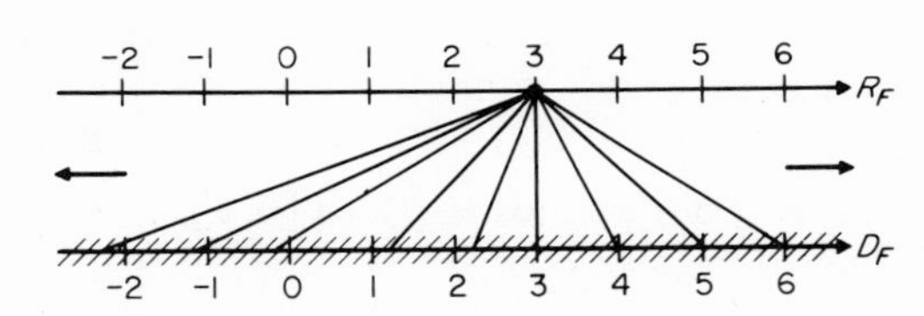

Ex. 15

15. F: $x \to 3$, on R.

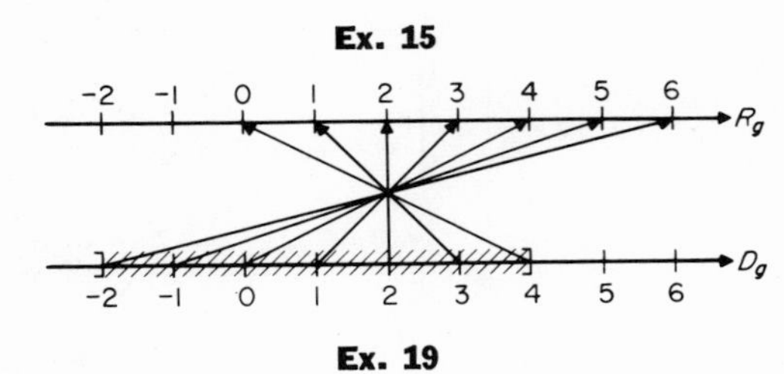

Ex. 19

17. f: $x \to x^2$ on $[-2, 2]$.

19. g: $x \to |x - 4|$, on $]-2, 4]$.

21. f: $\begin{cases} x \to x, & \text{on } (-\infty, 0[\\ x \to x^2, & \text{on } [0, \infty) \end{cases}$ sketch not provided.

23. F: $\begin{cases} x \to 1, & \text{on } [1, 2[\\ x \to 2, & \text{on } [2, 3[\\ x \to 3, & \text{on } [3, 4[\\ x \to 4, & \text{on } [4, 5[\end{cases}$ sketch not provided.

25. The arrows of the sketch fan out symmetrically about the arrow which maps x into x.

EXERCISE SET 7.5, PAGE 254

1. $f \circ g: x \longrightarrow 5 - 3x$. $D_{f \circ g} = R = R_{f \circ g}$.

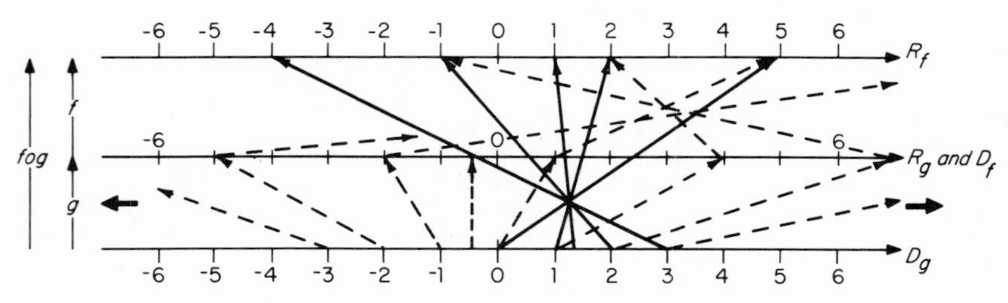

Ex. 1

3. $g \circ f: x \longrightarrow 10x - 3$. $D_{g \circ f} = R$, $R_{g \circ f} = R$.

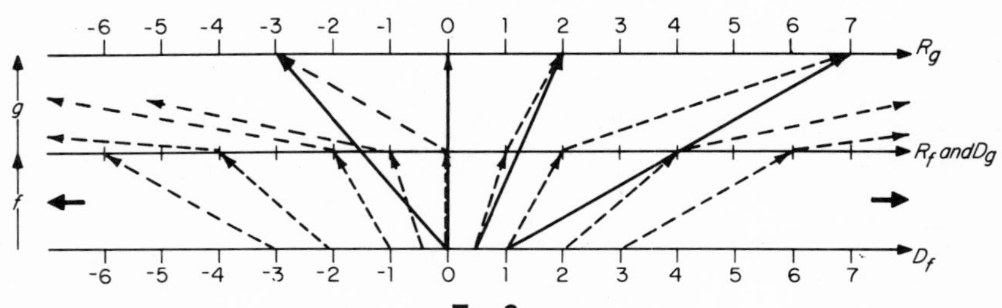

Ex. 3

5. $g \circ f: x \longrightarrow (2x - 3)^2$ on $[0, 1]$. $D_{g \circ f} = [0, 1]$, $R_{g \circ f} = [1, 9]$.

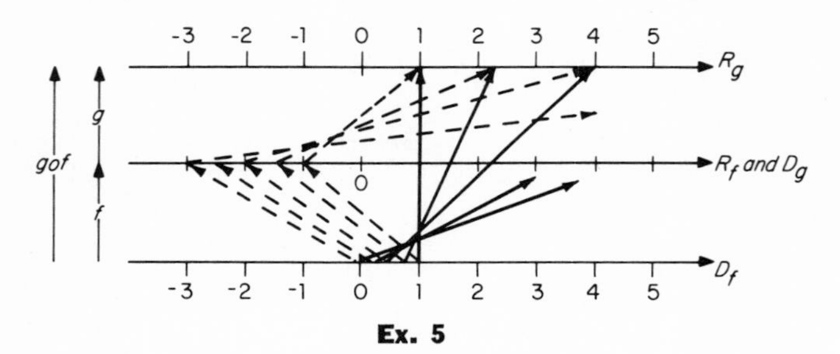

Ex. 5

7. $g \circ f: x \longrightarrow 2x$ on $[0, 4]$. $D_{g \circ f} = [0, 4]$, $R_{g \circ f} = [0, 8]$.

9. $g \circ f: x \longrightarrow 6$. $D_{g \circ f} = R$, $R_{g \circ f} = \{6\}$.

11. $f \circ F: \begin{cases} 1 \longrightarrow 2 \\ 2 \longrightarrow 1 \\ 3 \longrightarrow 2 \end{cases}$ $D_{f \circ F} = \{1, 2, 3\}$, $R_{f \circ F} = \{1, 2, 3\}$.

13. $g \circ h$: $6 \longrightarrow 3$
$7 \longrightarrow 6$
$D_{g \circ h} = \{6, 7\}$
$R_{g \circ h} = \{3, 6\}$.

15. $D_f \cap R_h = \emptyset$, hence the composition mapping is empty.

17. $j \circ h: x \longrightarrow |x|$
$D_{j \circ h} = R$
$R_{j \circ h} = [0, \infty)$.

19. The adding four and then squaring function. Domain: R, Range: $[0, \infty)$.
21. $\{(x, y): y = \sin 2x, x \in [0, \pi/2]\}$. Domain: $[0, \pi/2]$. Range: $[0, 1]$.
23. $h \circ k: x \to \sin(x + \pi/2)$, on $\{-4, -3, -2, -1, 0, 1\}$.
$D_{h\circ k} = \{-4, -3, -2, -1, 0, 1\}$.
$R_{h\circ k} = \{\sin(x + \pi/2): x = -4, -3, -2, -1, 0, 1\}$.
Approximations for these values could be obtained from Table 1, Appendix.
25. $f[g(x)] = \sin(\cos x)$. $D_{f\circ g} = \{x: x \in [2n\pi - \pi/2, 2n\pi + \pi/2]$, for some $n \in I\}$. $R_{f\circ g} = [0, \sin 1]$.
27. $h[g(x)] = \tan^2 x + 1 = \sec^2 x$, on$]-\pi/2, \pi/2[$. $D_{h\circ g} =]-\pi/2, \pi/2[$. $R_{h\circ g} = [1, \infty)$. 29. $[f \circ f \circ f](x) = x + 6$. 31. $\underbrace{[g\circ g\circ \cdots \circ g]}_{n}(x) = x$.

33. $[f \circ g](x) = -x$ on $[0, 1]$. $[g \circ f](x) = -x$ on $[-1, 0]$. 35. $[f \circ g](x) = x^2$ on $[1, 2]$. $[g \circ f](x) = x^2$ on $[1, 3]$. 37. $f \circ g = g \circ f = x$ on R. 39. -12. 41. $f \circ h \circ g(x) = 5x$. 43. Yes. 45. $\{0, \frac{1}{3}\}$.

EXERCISE SET 7.6, PAGE 259

Answers may vary.

1. $g(x) = x + 3$, $h(x) = 2x$.
3. $g(x) = x - 3$, $h(x) = 7x$.
5. $g(x) = 2x$, $h(z) = \sin z$.
7. $g(x) = \sin x$, $h(x) = 2x$.
9. $g(x) = \tan x$, $h(x) = x - \pi$.
11. $f(x) = \sqrt{x}$, $g(x) = \sin x$.
13. $f(x) = \sin x$, $g(x) = \cos x$.
15. $f(x) = x + 5$, $g(x) = x - 5$, and others.
17. $f(x) = x - \frac{1}{4}$, $g(x) = (x - \frac{1}{2})^2$, and others,
19. $f(x) = \sqrt{x}$, $g(x) = x + 2$, $h(x) = x^2$.
21. $f(x) = \sin x$, $g(x) = x + \pi/2$, $h(x) = x^2$.
23. $f(x) = x^2$, $g(x) = 1 - x$, $h(x) = \sin x$.
25. $f(x) = \sin x$, $g(x) = \sqrt{x}$, $h(x) = x + 7$.
27. $h(x) = x + \frac{3}{2}$.
29. $h(x) = 1$.
31. $h(x) = \sin 2x$ on $[0, \pi/2]$.
33. $h(x) = x + \frac{7}{2}$.

35.

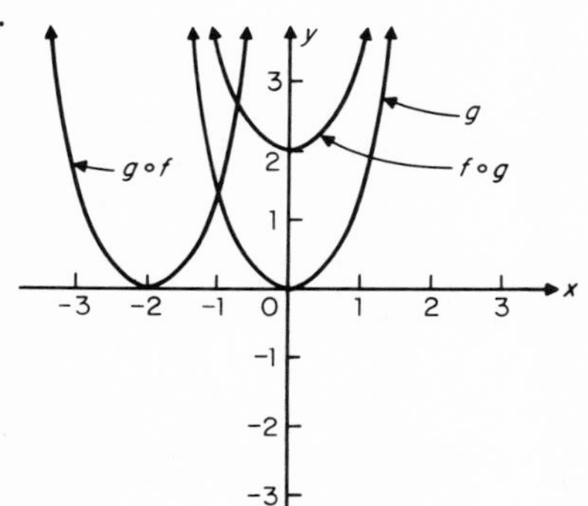

Ex. 35

37.

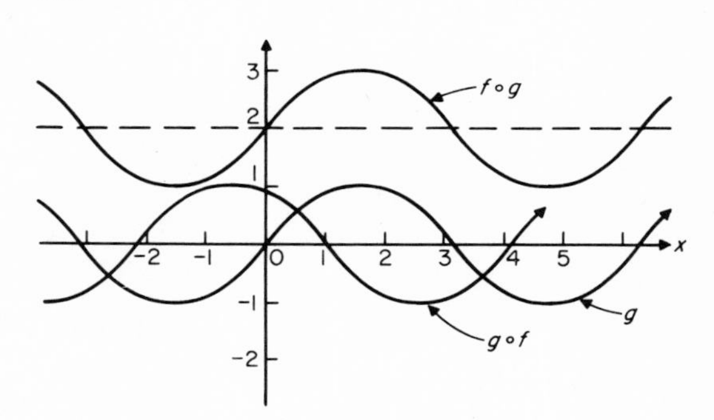

Ex. 37

39. The graph of $f \circ g$ is the graph of g translated 2 upwards. For $f(x) = x + h$, the graph of $f \circ g$ is the graph of g translated $|h|$, upwards for $h \geq 0$ and downwards for $h < 0$.
43. Each portion of the graph of $g \circ f$ is the graph of g "compressed" to "half" its length in the direction of the x-axis, the graph of $f \circ g$ is the graph of g "stretched" to twice its size in the direction of the y-axis. For $f(x) = kx$, the compression or stretching is by a factor of $|k|$. If $k < 0$ the direction is reversed.

41.

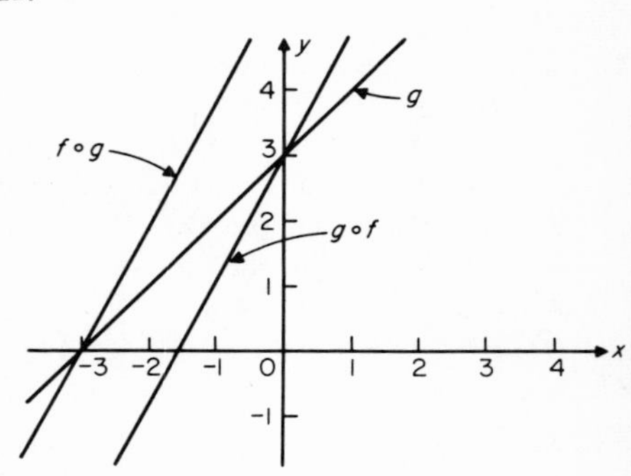

Ex. 41

45. $F = f \circ g \circ h \circ G \circ H$ where $f(x) = 2x$, $g(x) = \cos x$, $h(x) = x + 5$, $G(x) = 3x$, $H(x) = x^2$. 47. $H = f \circ g \circ h \circ R \circ G \circ g \circ K$ where $f(x) = 1 - x$, $g(x) = x^2$, $h(x) = \tan x$, $R(x) = \sqrt{x}$, $G(x) = x - \frac{1}{4}$, $K(x) = x + \frac{1}{2}$.

EXERCISE SET 7.7, PAGE 271

1. Yes. 3. The ordered pairs of f^{-1} are merely those of f reversed.
5. No, their domains differ.
7. $f[g(x)] = f(x - 7) = (x - 7) + 7 = x$;
$g[f(x)] = g(x + 7) = (x + 7) - 7 = x$.
9. $f[g(x)] = f[(x - 4)/2] = 2[(x - 4)/2] + 4 = x$;
$g[f(x)] = g(2x + 4) = [(2x + 4) - 4]/2 = x$.
11. (7) Suppose $(a, c) \in f$, $(b, c) \in f$. Then $c = a + 7$, $c = b + 7$. $\therefore a + 7 = b + 7$, and so $a = b$. (9) Suppose $(a, c) \in f$, $(b, c) \in f$. $c = 2a + 4$, $c = 2b + 4$. $\therefore 2a + 4 = 2b + 4$ and $\therefore a = b$.

13. $g^{-1} = \{(x, y) : y = 2x + 6\}$
$g[g^{-1}(x)] = g(2x + 6)$
$= \frac{1}{2}(2x + 6) - 3 = x$
$g^{-1}[g(x)] = g^{-1}(\frac{1}{2}x - 3)$
$= 2(\frac{1}{2}x - 3) + 6 = x$.

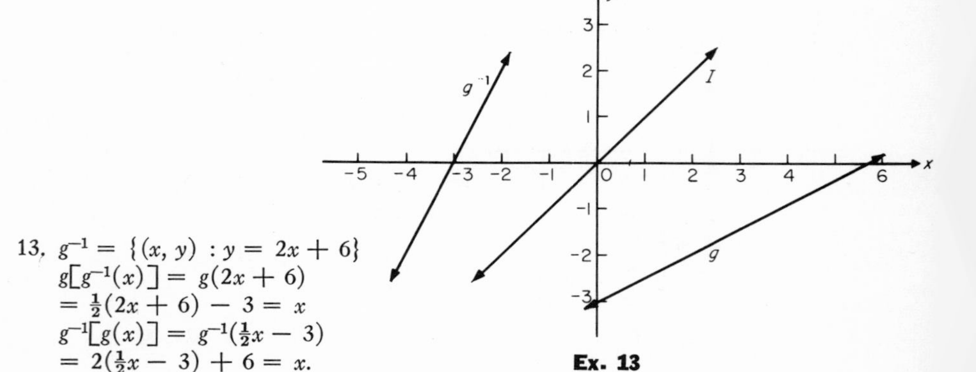

Ex. 13

15. $f^{-1} = \{(x, y): 3y + 2x = 5\} = \left\{(x, y): y = \dfrac{5 - 2x}{3}\right\}$

$$f[f^{-1}(x)] = f\left(\frac{5 - 2x}{3}\right) = \frac{5 - 3\left(\dfrac{5 - 2x}{3}\right)}{2} = x$$

$$f^{-1}[f(x)] = f^{-1}\left(\frac{5 - 3x}{2}\right) = \frac{5 - 2\left(\dfrac{5 - 3x}{2}\right)}{3} = x.$$

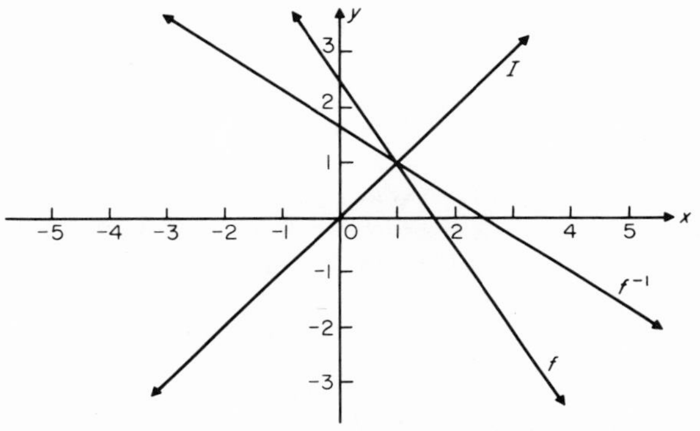

Ex. 15

17. $h^{-1} = \{(x, y): y = -x\}$.
(Incomplete).
19. $G^{-1} = \{(x, y): y = 1/x, x > 0\}$.
(Incomplete).
21. The line of symmetry of $f \cup f^{-1}$ is "the line $y = x$."
29. $h^{-1}(x) = 2x - 4$ on $[3, 5]$.
31. 1, -1; and others.
33. 1, -4; and others.
35. $\{(x, y): xy = 4\}$.
37. 0, π; and others.
39. $-\pi/4$, $\pi/4$; and others.
41. 0, π; and others.
43. $\{(x, y):$
$x = \sin y, -\pi/2 \leq y \leq \pi/2\}$.
45. $\{(-3, -1), (0, 0), (6, 2), (9, 3)\}$.
47. For a function f, and its inverse f^{-1}, $D_f = R_{f^{-1}}$, and $R_f = D_{f^{-1}}$.

49. The set contains two pairs which have the same first element but distinct second elements. 51. Its graph is symmetric to the line $y = x$.
53. Read the table in reverse, i.e., the range values of f are the domain elements of f^{-1}, and the range values of f^{-1} are the domain elements of f.
55. Let f, g be one-to-one functions, and let $h = f \circ g$. If $a, b \in D_h$, $a \neq b$, then $g(a) \neq g(b)$ since g is one-to-one. Likewise, $f[g(a)] \neq f[g(b)]$ since f is one-to-one. Then $h(a) = f[g(a)] \neq f[g(b)] = h(b)$. So h is one-to-one.
57. *Hint:* Find $(f \circ g)^{-1}$, and evaluate at 27. $(z = 0)$.

EXERCISE SET 7.8, PAGE 277

1. $F(x) = [g \circ f](x)$
   where $g(x) = x + 11$
   $f(x) = 2x.$

   $$F^{-1}(x) = f^{-1}[g^{-1}(x)] = f^{-1}(x - 11) = \frac{x - 11}{2}.$$

3. $f = F \circ H,$
   where $F = \{(x, y) : y = x^2\}$
   $H = \{(x, y) : y = x + 2, 0 \leq x\}.$
   $f^{-1}(x) = H^{-1}[F^{-1}(x)] = H^{-1}(\sqrt{x}) = \sqrt{x} - 2$, on $[4, \infty)$.
5. $g(x) = f[h(x)]$
   where $f(x) = x/3$, $h(x) = x^3$.
   $g^{-1}(x) = h^{-1}[f^{-1}(x)] = h^{-1}(3x) = \sqrt[3]{3x}.$
7. $H(x) = f[g(x)]$
   where $f(x) = x + 5$, $g(x) = \sqrt{x}$.
   $H^{-1}(x) = g^{-1}[f^{-1}(x)] = g^{-1}(x - 5) = (x - 5)^2$, on $[5, \infty)$.
9. $H(x) = f(g(x))$ where $f(x) = 2/x$,
   $g(x) = x - 3.$
   $H^{-1}(x) = g^{-1}[f^{-1}(x)] = g^{-1}(2/x) = (2/x) + 3$ on $[\frac{1}{4}, 2]$.
11. $h(x) = f\{g[F(x)]\}$
    where $f(x) = x - 1$, $g(x) = x^2$, $F(x) = x + 1$.
    $h^{-1}(x) = F^{-1}\{g^{-1}[f^{-1}(x)]\} = F^{-1}(g^{-1}(x + 1)) = F^{-1}(\sqrt{x + 1})$
    $= \sqrt{x + 1} - 1$ on $[3, \infty)$.
13. $H(x) = f\{g[F(x)]\}$
    where $f(x) = x - 2$, $g(x) = x^3$, $F(x) = x + 3$.
    $H^{-1}(x) = F^{-1}\{g^{-1}[f^{-1}(x)]\} = F^{-1}[g^{-1}(x + 2)]$
    $= F^{-1}(\sqrt[3]{x + 2}) = \sqrt[3]{x + 2} - 3.$
15. $h = g \circ f \circ F \circ H$
    where $H(x) = x + 3$, $F(x) = 1/x$, $f(x) = -x$, $g(x) = x + 1$.

    $$h^{-1} = H^{-1}\{F^{-1}[f^{-1}(g^{-1}(x))]\} = \frac{3x - 2}{1 - x}$$

EXERCISE SET 7.9, PAGE 283

1. Domain: $[0, \infty)$, and others.

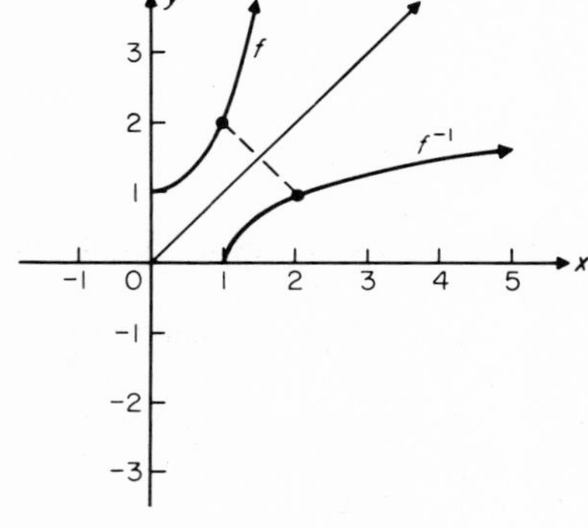

Ex. 1

3. Domain: $[0, \infty)$, and others.

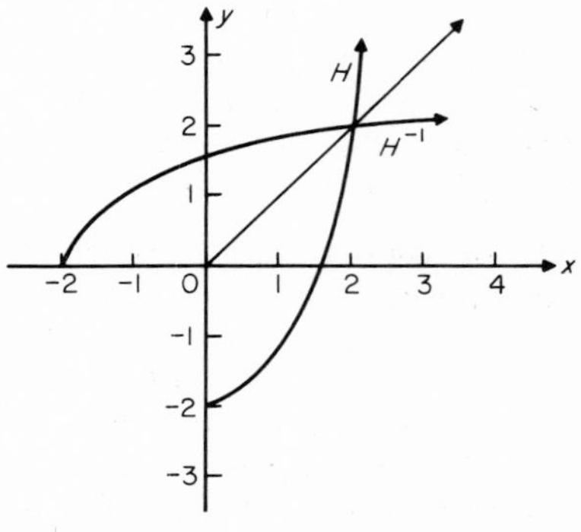

Ex. 3

5. Domain: $(-\infty, \sqrt{2}[\cap \overline{\{0\}},]0, \infty)$, and others.

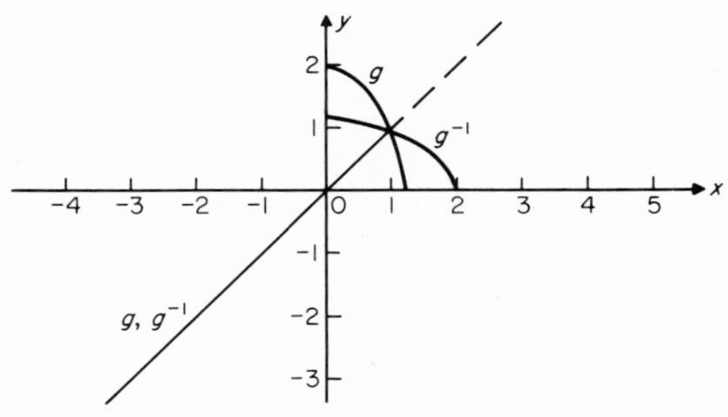

Ex. 5

7. $\pi/2$. 9. .412 (Approximately). 11. $\pi/3$. 13. $\pi/6$. 15. $\pi/3$.

17.

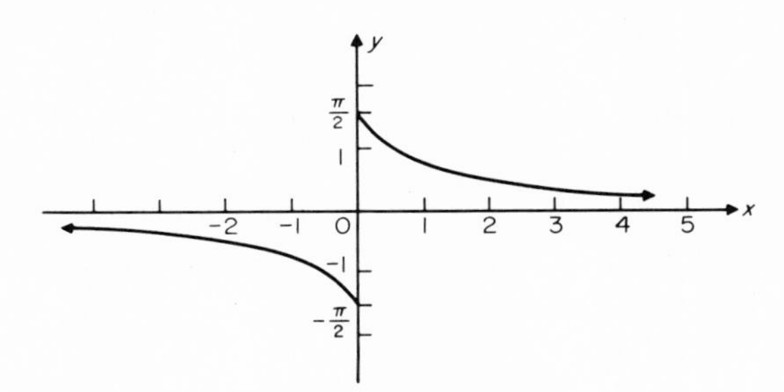

Ex. 17

19.

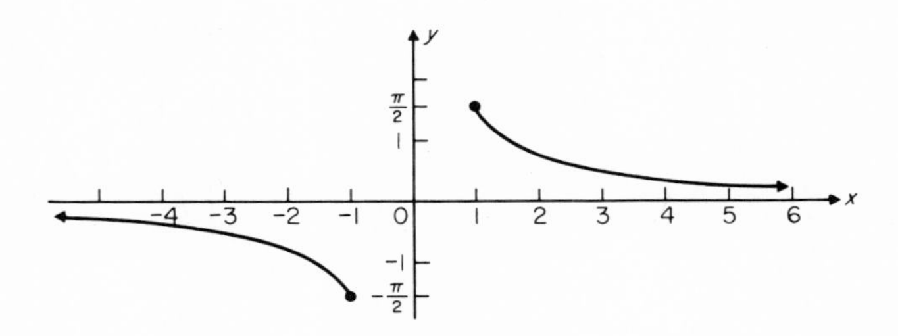

Ex. 19

21.

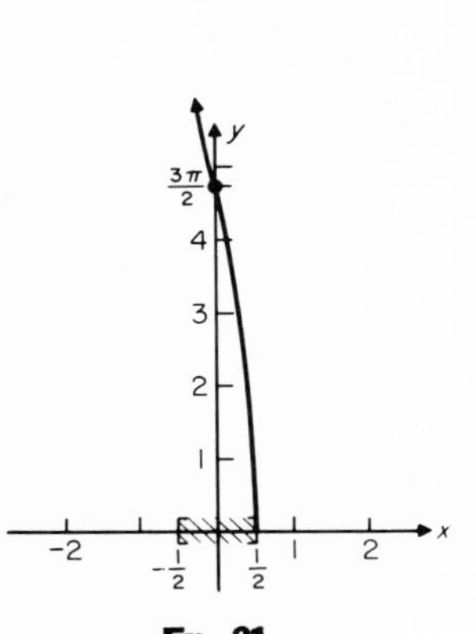

Ex. 21

23.

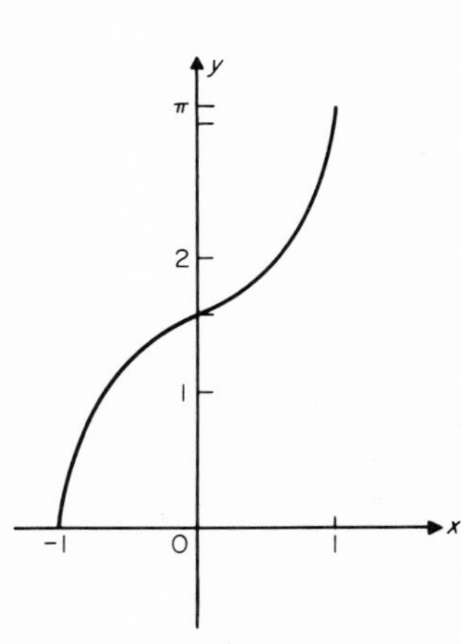

Ex. 23

25. $\sqrt{3}/2$. 27. $\frac{12}{13}$. 29. $\pi/6$. 31. $\pi/6$. 33. $\sqrt{91}/3$. 35. $2x\sqrt{1-x^2}$.

37. $(\pm)\dfrac{\sqrt{1-\sqrt{1-x^2}}}{2}$. 39. $1-2x^2$.

41. $H(x) = f(g(F(G(x))))$ where $f(x) = 8x$, $g(x) = \sin x$, $F(x) = x + 11$, $G(x) = 2x$. $H^{-1}(x) = \frac{1}{2}[\sin^{-1}(x/8) - 11]$.

43. $g^{-1}(x) = \tan^{-1}\left[\sin^{-1}\left[\dfrac{(x-7)}{3}\right] - 2\right]$. 45. 1.

EXERCISE SET 7.10, PAGE 288

1. 9. 3. $\frac{1}{8}$. 5. $9\sqrt{3}$. 7. $e^3 \approx 20.09$. 9. $e^5 \approx 148.4$. 11. 4.

13.

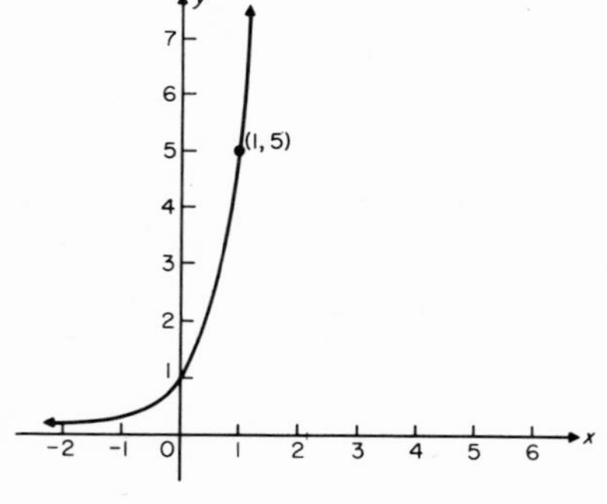

Ex. 13

15.

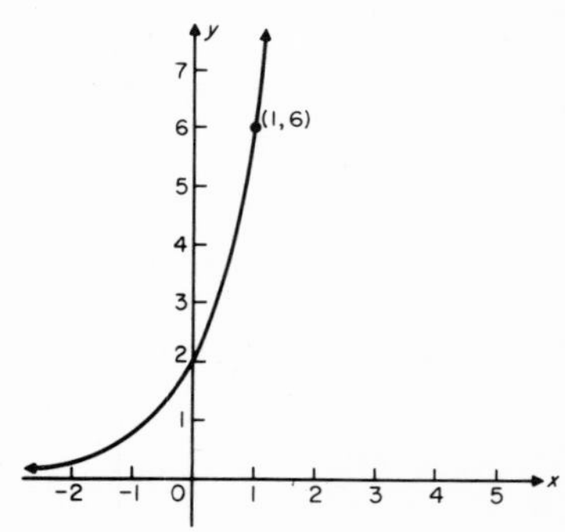

Ex. 15

17.

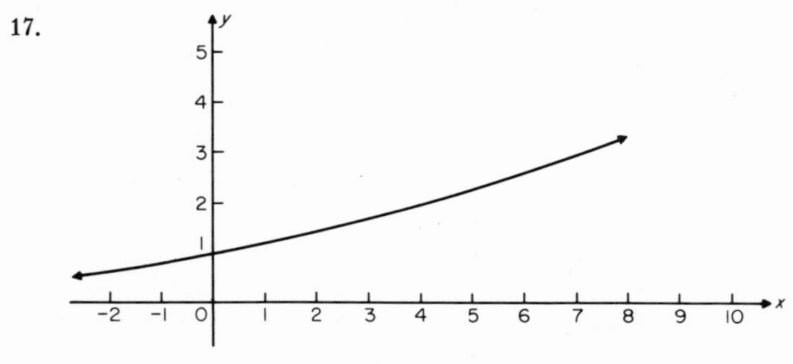

Ex. 17

19. 2. 21. $-\frac{1}{2}$. 23. 4.6 (approx.). 25. $\text{Exp}_2\, 5$, 32. 27. $\text{Exp}_6\, 2$, 36.
29. $\text{Exp}_{3/4}\,(\sqrt{2} + \pi)$.

EXERCISE SET 7.11, PAGE 296

1. 3. 3. 4. 5. 3. 7. 1.84. 9. .5065. 11. 1.0934 + 9.7101–10; or 0.8035.

13.

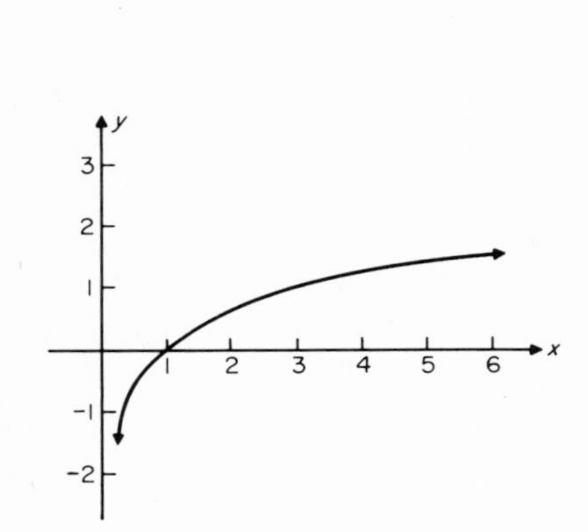

Ex. 13

15.

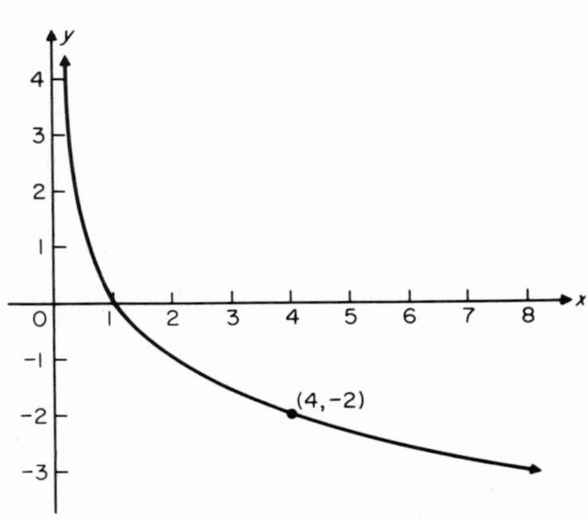

Ex. 15

17. 2.
19. -1.
21. $2\sqrt{2}$.
23. -4.
25. 900 (Approx.).
27. 7.
29. 25.
31. $x + 1 + y$.
33. x^2.
35. x^4.
37. $h^{-1}(x) = \log_3 (x + 1)$.
$D_{h^{-1}}$: $]-1, \infty)$.
39. $f^{-1}(x) = \frac{1}{5} \ln x$
$D_{f^{-1}}$: $]0, \infty)$.
41. $f^{-1}(x) = \text{Exp}\,(x/2)$
$D_{f^{-1}}$: $(-\infty, \infty)$.
43. $f^{-1}(x) = 5 \ln x$
$D_{f^{-1}}$: $]0, \infty)$.
45. 3.27 (Approx.).
47. 1.56 (Approx.).
49. 4.43 (Approx.).
51. $\text{Log}_a\,(x/y) = \text{Log}_a\, x(y^{-1})$
$= \text{Log}_a\, x + \text{Log}_a\, y^{-1}$
$= \text{Log}_a\, x - \text{Log}_a\, y$
53. From $\text{Log}_a\, u = \text{Log}_b\, v = x$,
$a^x = u$, $b^x = v$. Then
$(ab)^x = a^x b^x = uv$, or
$\text{Log}_{ab}\,(uv) = x$.
55. $\dfrac{\text{Log}_e\, 3.4}{\text{Log}_e\, 7}$.
57. $\dfrac{\text{Log}_e\, 2x}{\text{Log}_e\, a}$.
59. $\text{Exp}\,(x\, \text{Log}_e\, 2)$.
61. $\text{Exp}\,[(2x + 1)\, \text{Log}_e\, 10]$.
63. $f(1) = f(1 \cdot 1) = f(1) + f(1)$. $\therefore f(1) = 0$.
65. $g(0) = g(0 + 0) = g(0) \cdot g(0)$. $\therefore g(0) = 1$ or $g(0) = 0$.
If $g(0) = 0$, then $g(x) = g(x + 0) = g(x) \cdot g(0) = g(x) \cdot 0 = 0$, for each $x \in R$.

EXERCISE SET 7.12, PAGE 301

1. $[f + g](x) = 2x - 4$
   Domain: R
   $[f - g](x) = +10$
   Domain: R
   $[fg](x) = x^2 - 4x - 21$
   Domain: R
   $\left[\frac{f}{g}\right](x) = \frac{x + 3}{x - 7}$
   Domain: $\overline{\{7\}}$

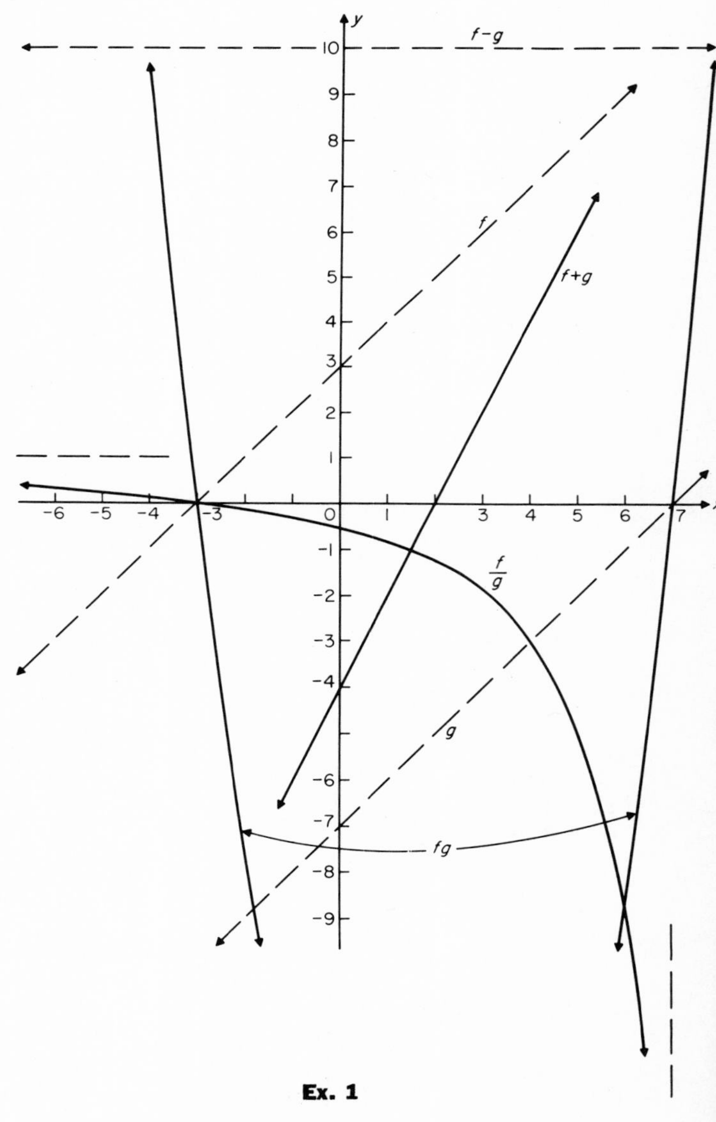

Ex. 1

3. $[F + f](x) = \dfrac{x^2 + 1}{x}$

Domain: R_0

$[F - f](x) = \dfrac{1 - x^2}{x}$

Domain: R_0
$[Ff](x) = 1$
Domain: R_0

$\left[\dfrac{F}{f}\right](x) = \dfrac{1}{x^2}$

Domain: R_0
5. $[f + g]: x \longrightarrow \text{Sin } x + 2x + 9$
Domain: R
$[f - g]: x \longrightarrow \text{Sin } x - 2x - 9$
Domain: R
$[fg]: x \longrightarrow (\text{Sin } x)(2x + 9)$
Domain: R

$\left[\dfrac{f}{g}\right]: x \longrightarrow \dfrac{\text{Sin } x}{2x + 9}$

Domain: $\overline{\{-\frac{9}{2}\}}$

7. $[a + b](x) = 2^x + 3^x$ Domain: R
$[a - b](x) = 2^x - 3^x$ Domain: R
$[ab](x) = 6^x$ Domain: R

$\left[\dfrac{a}{b}\right](x) = \left(\dfrac{2}{3}\right)^x$ Domain: R

9.–15. Answers not provided.
17. $f(x) = [g + h](x)$
where $g(x) = x$
$h(x) = \sin x.$

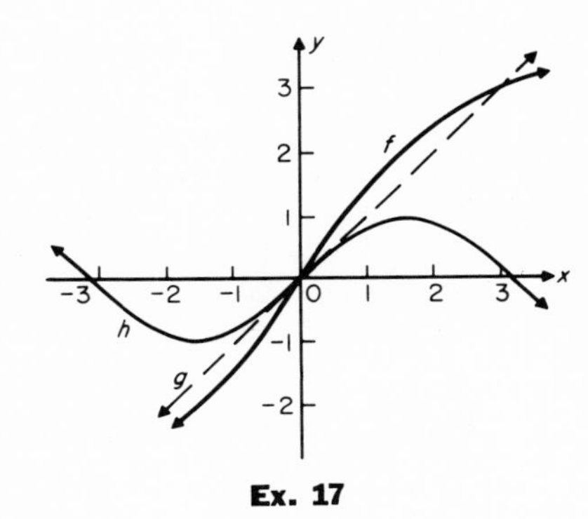

Ex. 17

19. $[G \times F^2](x) = x^2 (4 + 2 \sin x)^2.$
21. $F \circ [f \times G](x) = 4 + 2 \sin (3x^3 - x^2).$
23. $[2[(f \circ g) + h] - F](x) = 2[(3x^2 + 2) + \sin x] - [4 + 2 \sin x]$
$= 6x^2 = 6\,G(x).$
25. No. Counterexample. Let $f(x) = x$, $g(x) = 1 - x$. Both are one-to-one, but $[(f \times g)](x) = x - x^2$ is not.
27. Cos, sec. 29. Suppose f, g are odd. Then
$[f + g](-x) = f(-x) + g(-x) = -f(x) + [-g(x)]$
$= -[f(x) + g(x)]$
$= -[f + g](x).$
31. Suppose f, g are odd. Then
$[f \times g](-x) = f(-x) \times g(-x) = [-f(x)] \times [-g(x)]$
$= f(x) \times g(x)$
$= [f \times g](x).$
33. Symmetric to the origin. 35. $f_n(x)$ where n is odd.

EXERCISE SET 7.13, PAGE 305

1. Yes. $V = l^3$. 3. Yes. $C = 2\sqrt{\pi A}$. 5. No. Rectangles with sides 1:3 and 2:2 have same perimeter, but different areas. 7. Yes. $S = 6l^2$. 9. Yes. $r = \sqrt{\pi A}/2\pi$. 11. Yes. $A = P^2\sqrt{3}/36$. 13. $h(x) = 2x/3, 0 \leq x \leq 3$. 15. $f(x) = (10 - x)/2, 0 \leq x \leq 10$. 17. $g(x) = \frac{3}{5}(20 - x), 0 \leq x \leq 20$. 19. $W(x) = 12 - (7x/8), 0 \leq x \leq 8$. 21. $h(x) = \frac{1}{2}\sqrt{400 - x^2}, 0 \leq x \leq 20$. 23. $A(x) = 5x, 0 \leq x \leq L$. 25. $A(x) = 49x/2, 0 \leq x \leq 2\pi$.

27. $f(x) = C \cos x, 0 < x < \pi/2$. $g(x) = C \sin x, 0 < x < \pi/2$.
29. $b(x) = 6 \sin x/2, 0 \leq x \leq 2\pi$. 31. $f(x) = x/r, 0 \leq x \leq 2\pi$. 33. $A(x) = 8(x - \sin x), \pi \leq x \leq 2\pi$. 35. $D(x) = \sqrt{x^4 - 4x^3 + 5x^2} = |x| \sqrt{x^2 - 4x + 5}$. 37. $P(x) = 6x, x > 0$. 39. $A(x) = 5x, x > 0$. 41. $S(x) = 20\pi x, x > 0$. 43. $V(x) = \pi R^2 x, x > 0$. 45. $V(x) = 10\left[4 \cos^{-1}(2 - x)/2 - (2 - x)\sqrt{4x - x^2}\right]$, $0 \leq x \leq 4$. 47. $V(x) = \frac{32}{3}x^3, x \geq 0$. 49. $V(x) = \pi x^3/216, 0 \leq x \leq 12$.

Chapter eight

EXERCISE SET 8.1, PAGE 315

1. Tautology. 3. Neither. $P{:}\,T$, $Q{:}\,F$. $P{:}\,T$, $Q{:}\,T$. And others. 5. Contradiction. 7. Tautology. 9. Tautology. 11. Neither. False instances: $P{:}\,T$, $Q{:}\,T$; $P{:}\,F$, $Q{:}\,F$. True instances: $P{:}\,T$, $Q{:}\,F$; $P{:}\,F$, $Q{:}\,T$. 13. Tautology. 15. Tautology. 17. P & Q. Not a tautology. 19. P & Q. Not a tautology. 21. $P \rightarrow P \;\&\; Q$. Not a tautology. 23. $\sim(P \;\&\; Q)$. Not a tautology.
25. $P \rightarrow \sim Q$. Not a tautology.

EXERCISE SET 8.2, PAGE 320

1. (a) Yes. (b) Yes. (c) No. (d) $\dfrac{P \;\&\; Q}{Q}$. (e) Valid. (f) $\dfrac{2 = 3 \;\&\; 3 = 4}{3 = 4}$.

(i) Not possible. 3. (a) Both are open sentences. (b) $\dfrac{P, Q}{P \;\&\; Q}$. (c) Valid.

(d) No. 5. (a) T, T. (b) No. (c) $\dfrac{P}{Q}$. (d) $\dfrac{2 + 2 = 5}{2 + 2 = 4}$. (e) No. (g) Yes, invalid.

7. $\dfrac{P \;\&\; Q}{P}$, valid, rule of &. 9. $\dfrac{P \vee Q}{P}$, invalid, $P{:}\,F$, $Q{:}\,T$. 11. Same as 9.

13. $\dfrac{P \rightarrow Q}{P \vee \sim Q}$, invalid, $P{:}\,F$, $Q{:}\,T$. 15. $\dfrac{P}{P \;\&\; Q}$, invalid, $P{:}\,T$, $Q{:}\,F$.

EXERCISE SET 8.3, PAGE 325

1. $\dfrac{P \;\&\; Q}{Q}$, rule of &. 3. $\dfrac{P, Q \rightarrow P}{Q}$, invalid, $P{:}\,T$, $Q{:}\,F$.

5. $\dfrac{P \vee Q, \sim Q}{P}$, disjunctive syllogism. 7. $\dfrac{P \vee Q}{P}$, invalid, $P{:}\,F$, $Q{:}\,T$.

9. $\dfrac{\sim P \rightarrow Q}{\sim P \vee Q}$, invalid, $P{:}\,T$, $Q{:}\,F$. 11. $\dfrac{P}{P \vee Q}$ rule of $\vee$.

13. $\dfrac{P \vee Q,\ P \rightarrow R,\ Q \rightarrow R}{R}$, proof by cases.

15. $\dfrac{P \rightarrow Q}{(P \rightarrow Q) \vee \sim R}$, rule of $\vee$.

EXERCISE SET 8.4, PAGE 329

1. (a) Given. (b) Definition ($\cap$). (c) Substitution. (d) Substitution. (e) Given, (f) Substitution. (g) Disjunctive syllogism.

3. Proof:

1. $x \in A$.	1. Given.
2. $x \in A$ or $x \in B$.	2. Rule of $\vee$.
3. ($x \in A$ or $x \in B) \leftrightarrow x \in A \cup B$.	3. Definition ($\cup$).
4. $x \in A \cup B$.	4. Substitution.

5. Proof: (student is to supply reasons). 1. $A \subset B$. 2. $A \subset B \leftrightarrow (x \in A \rightarrow x \in B)$. 3. $\therefore x \in A \rightarrow x \in B$. 4. $(x \in A \rightarrow x \in B) \leftrightarrow (x \notin B \rightarrow x \notin A)$. 5. $\therefore x \notin B \rightarrow x \notin A$. 6. $x \notin B$. 7. $\therefore x \notin A$.

7. Proof: (student is to supply reasons). 1. $x \in A \cup (B \cap C)$. 2, $x \in A$ or $x \in (B \cap C)$. 3. $x \in A$ or ($x \in B$ and $x \in C$). 4. $x \notin B$ $(\sim x \in B)$. 5. $\therefore \sim x \in B$ or $\sim x \in C$. 6. $\therefore \sim(x \in B$ and $x \in C)$. 7. $\therefore x \in A$. 9. *Hint:* $x \in \bar{\bar{A}} \leftrightarrow \sim(x \in \bar{A})$. 11. *Hint:* First show that $x \in A \cap B$. 13. *Hint:* use "proof by cases."

EXERCISE SET 8.5, PAGE 333

1. (a) Assumption of antecedent of conditional to be proven. (b) Rule of $\vee$. (c) Definition ($\cup$). (d) Substitution. (e) Conditionalizing [steps (a)–(d)]. (f) Definition. (g) Substitution.

3. Proof:

1. Let $x \in A^*$.	Antecedent of conditional to be proven.
2. $x \in B$.	
3. $\therefore x \in A \ \&\ x \in B$.	
4. $\therefore x \in A \cap B$.	(Student is to supply reasons for
5. $\therefore x \in A \rightarrow x \in A \cap B$.	steps 2–5.)

5. *Hint:* assume $x \in B$, and show that $x \in A$ follows.

7. Proof: 1. Let $x \in A^*$. 2. $A \subset B$. 3. $\therefore x \in A \rightarrow x \in B$. 4. $\therefore x \in B$. 5. $B \subset C$. 6. $\therefore x \in B \rightarrow x \in C$. 7. $\therefore x \in C$. 8. $\therefore x \in A \rightarrow x \in C$. 9. $\therefore A \subset C$. (Reasons for each step to be given by student.)

9. *Hint:* Assume $x \in \bar{B}$, and show that $x \in \bar{A}$ follows. 11. *Hint:* Assume $x \in A$. Show that $x \in B$ follows.

EXERCISE SET 8.6, PAGE 336

1. Steps of column proof (student is to supply reasons): 1. Let $A \cap B = A$. 2. Let $x \in A$. 3. $A \subset A \cap B \ \&\ A \cap B \subset A$. 4. $A \subset A \cap B$. 5. $x \in A \rightarrow x \in A \cap B$. 6. $\therefore x \in A \cap B$. 7. $x \in A \ \&\ x \in B$. 8. $\therefore x \in B$.

9. $\therefore x \in A \rightarrow x \in B$. 10. $A \subset B$. 11. $\therefore A \cap B = A \rightarrow A \subset B$.
Paragraph proof: Suppose $A \cap B = A$. Let $x \in A$. Then $x \in A \cap B$. Therefore $x \in A$ & $x \in B$. Hence $x \in B$. This means $A \subset B$. The theorem follows.

3. (Paragraph proof only). Suppose $x \in A$. Then $\sim(\sim x \in A)$. Therefore, $\sim(x \in \bar{A})$, or, equivalently, $x \in \bar{\bar{A}}$. Thus $x \in A \rightarrow x \in \bar{\bar{A}}$, so $A \subset \bar{\bar{A}}$.
5. *Hint:* combine the proofs of Exercises 3, 4.
7. Steps of column proof: 1. Let $x \in A^*$. 2. $x \in U$. 3. $\therefore x \in A \rightarrow x \in U$. 4. $\therefore A \subset U$. (Student is to supply reasons.)
9. Suppose $x \in A \cup \emptyset$. Then $x \in A$ or $x \in \emptyset$. But $x \notin \emptyset$ for each x. (Why?) Therefore $x \in A$. (Why?) This means $x \in A \cup \emptyset \rightarrow x \in A$. So $A \cup \emptyset \subset A$.
11. *Hint:* Show $A \cap U \subset A$ and $A \subset A \cap U$.
13. *Hint:* Recall the equivalents of denials of conjunctions and disjunctions.

Answers to Exercises 15, 17 not given.

EXERCISE SET 8.7, PAGE 339

1. (Student is to supply reasons.) 1. Suppose $x \notin B$. 2. $x \in A$. 3. $A \subset B$. 4. $x \in A \rightarrow x \in B$. 5. $\therefore x \in B$. 6. $\therefore x \in B$ & $x \notin B$. This is a contradiction. 7. $\therefore x \in B$.
3. (Student is to supply reasons.) 1. Let $x_0 \in B$ & $x_0 \notin A$. 2. $\therefore x_0 \in B$. 3. $\therefore x_0 \in A \vee x_0 \in B$. 4. $\therefore x_0 \in A \cup B$. 5. $A \cup B \subset A$. 6. $\therefore x \in A \cup B \rightarrow x \in A$. 7. $\therefore x_0 \in A$. 8. $\therefore x_0 \notin A$. 9. $\therefore x_0 \in A$ & $x_0 \notin A$. This is a contradiction. 10. $\therefore$ If $x \in B$, then $x \in A$.
5. *Hint:* Use the equivalence
$$(\sim x \in A) \vee (\sim x \in B \cup A) \leftrightarrow \sim(x \in A \;\&\; x \in B \cup A).$$
7. Proof: Suppose that $x \notin \bar{B}$, i.e., $x \in B$. But $B \subset A$, so that $x \in B \rightarrow x \in A$. Therefore $x \in A$. But $x \in \bar{A}$ (given), which means $x \notin A$. Thus $x \in A$ & $x \notin A$. This is a contradiction. By the rule of indirect proof, $x \in \bar{B}$.
9. *Hint:* $A \cup \emptyset \not\subset A$ means that for some x_0, $x_0 \in A \cup \emptyset$ & $x_0 \notin A$. This means that $x_0 \in \emptyset$. (Why?)

Answers not provided for Exercise Sets 8.8, 8.9.

Chapter nine

EXERCISE SET 9.1, PAGE 352

1. $3 + 4 + 5 + 6 + 7 + 8$. 3. $0 + 3 + 8 + 15 + 24 + 35 + 48 + 63$.
5. $3 + 4 + 5 + \cdots + (n + 2) + \cdots + 15$.
7. $2 + 3 + 4 + \cdots + (n + 1) + \cdots + (k + 1)$.
9. $7 + 9 + 11 + \cdots + (2n + 5) + \cdots + (2k + 1)$.
11. $(2k + 1) + (2k + 3)$.
13. $\frac{5}{6} + \frac{6}{7} + \cdots + \frac{n+4}{n+5} + \cdots + \frac{k+1}{k+2}$.

15. $2+3+4+\cdots+\dfrac{(n+1)!}{n!}+\cdots+\dfrac{(k+1)!}{k!}$.

Alternate answer: $2+3+4+\cdots+(n+1)+\cdots+(k+1)$.

17. $1+4+9+\cdots+n^2+\cdots+64$.

Answers for 19–49 will vary.

19. $\sum_{n=1}^{9} 2n-1$.

21. $\sum_{k=1}^{7} k^2+1$.

23. $\sum_{n=1}^{m-1} (-1)^{n+1}$.

25. $\sum_{k=1}^{n} \sin \dfrac{k\pi}{2}$.

27. $\sum_{k=1}^{22} k \cot^k \left(\dfrac{\pi}{6}\right)$.

29. $\sum_{i=0}^{k-1} 4i$.

31. $\sum_{k=1}^{12} k(k+1)$.

33. $\sum_{p=k}^{k+2} p^2$.

35. $\sum_{p=k-3}^{k-1} p^2$.

37. $n+3, \sum_{n=1}^{54} n+3$.

39. $4n-1, \sum_{n=1}^{\infty} 4n-1$.

41. $\cos \dfrac{n\pi}{2}, \sum_{n=1}^{\infty} \cos \dfrac{n\pi}{2}$.

43. $n!, \sum_{n=1}^{8} n!$.

45. $(-\frac{1}{2})^{n-1}, \sum_{n=1}^{\infty} (-\frac{1}{2})^{n-1}$.

47. $3, \sum_{n=1}^{\infty} 3$.

49. $n^2+2n, \sum_{n=1}^{7} n^2+2n$.

51. $\sum_{n=k-5}^{k-1} n^2$.

EXERCISE SET 9.2, PAGE 356

1. (a) $2 = 1(1+1)$. (b) $2+4 = 2(2+1)$. (c) $2+4+6 = 3(3+1)$.
   (d) $2+4+\cdots+16 = 8(9)$. (e) $2+4+6+\cdots+2k = k(k+1)$.
   (f) $2+4+6+\cdots+2(k+1) = (k+1)(k+2)$.
   (g) $2+4+6+\cdots+2(k-1) = (k-1)(k)$.
   (h) If $2+4+6+\cdots+2k = k(k+1)$,
   then $2+4+6+\cdots+2(k+1) = (k+1)(k+2)$.
3. (a) 3 is a multiple of 3. (b) 2^4-1 is a multiple of 3.
   (c) 2^6-1 is a multiple of 3. (d) $2^{198}-1$ is a multiple of 3.
   (e) $2^{2k}-1$ is a multiple of 3. (f) $2^{4k}-1$ is a multiple of 3.
   (g) $2^{6k+10}-1$ is a multiple of 3. (h) $2^{2k+1}-1$ is a multiple of 3.
5. (a) $1 = 4$. (b) $1+4 = 2^3$. (c) $1+4+9 = 2^4$. (d) $1+4+9+16 = 2^5$.
   (e) $1+4+9+16+25 = 2^6$. (f) $1+4+9+\cdots+(k+1)^2 = 2^{k+2}$.
   (g) $1+4+9+\cdots+(k-1)^2 = 2^k$. (h) $1+4+9+\cdots+k^2 = 2^{k+1}$.

(i) If $1 + 4 + 9 = 2^4$, then $1 + 4 + 9 + 16 = 2^5$.
(j) If $1 + 4 + 9 + \cdots + k^2 = 2^{k+1}$, then $1 + 4 + 9 + \cdots + (k + 1)^2 = 2^{k+2}$.

7. (a) $\frac{1}{1 \cdot 2} = \frac{1}{2}$. (b) $\frac{1}{1 \cdot 2} + \frac{1}{2 \cdot 3} = \frac{1}{3}$.

(c) $\frac{1}{1 \cdot 2} + \frac{1}{2 \cdot 3} + \cdots + \frac{1}{n(n+1)} + \cdots + \frac{1}{100(101)} = \frac{1}{101}$.

(d) $\frac{1}{1 \cdot 2} + \frac{1}{2 \cdot 3} + \cdots + \frac{1}{n(n+1)} + \cdots + \frac{1}{(m-1)m} = \frac{1}{m}$.

(e) $\frac{1}{1 \cdot 2} + \frac{1}{2 \cdot 3} + \cdots + \frac{1}{n(n+1)} + \cdots + \frac{1}{m(m+1)} = \frac{1}{m+1}$.

(f) $\frac{1}{1 \cdot 2} + \frac{1}{2 \cdot 3} + \cdots + \frac{1}{n(n+1)} + \cdots + \frac{1}{(m+1)(m+2)} = \frac{1}{m+2}$.

EXERCISE SET 9.3, PAGE 362

1. (a) $P(1)$: 2 is an even integer. $P(k)$: $k^2 + k$ is an even integer. $P(k + 1)$: $(k + 1)^2 + (k + 1)$ is an even integer. (b) Yes. (c) Yes. (d) Yes. (e) Yes, for suppose $k^2 + k$ is even. Then $(k + 1)^2 + (k + 1) = k^2 + 2k + 1 + k + 1 = (k^2 + k) + 2(k + 2)$. But $2(k + 2)$ is even, and $k^2 + k$ is even. Thus their sum is even. That is, $(k + 1)^2 + (k + 1)$ is an even number. Thus $P(k) \rightarrow P(k + 1)$. (f) Yes.
3. (a) Yes. (b) No, $2^2 > 2^2$ is false. (c) No. (d) $2^{20} > 20^2$.
(e) Assume $S(20)$, that is $2^{20} > 20^2$. Then by multiplying each side by 2, $2 \cdot 2^{20} > 2 \cdot 20^2$, or $2^{21} > 2 \cdot 20^2$ follows. But $2 \cdot 20^2 = 20^2 + 20^2 > 20^2 + 40 + 1 = (20 + 1)^2$. Therefore, $2^{21} > 21^2$. Therefore $S(20) \rightarrow S(21)$.
(f) *Hint:* See part (e). (g) *Hint:* Assume $2^{99} > 99^2$, and show that $2^{100} > 100^2$ follows. (h) $S(k) \rightarrow S(k + 1)$ is not true for all k.
(i) No, $S(2)$, $S(3)$ are false. (j) No, $S(3)$ is false.
5. Worked in text.

7. Let $P(n)$ be $\sum_{i=1}^{4} 4i = 2n^2 + 2n$.

I. $P(1)$: $4 = 2 \cdot 1^2 + 2 \cdot 1$. (True, by observation.)

II. Assume $P(k)$, i.e., $\sum_{i=1}^{k} 4i = 2k^2 + 2k$. In expanded form,

$$4 + 8 + 12 + \cdots + 4k = 2k^2 + 2k.$$

Adding $4(k + 1)$ to both sides,

$$\begin{aligned} 4 + 8 + 12 + \cdots + 4k + 4(k + 1) &= 2k^2 + 2k + 4(k + 1) \\ &= 2k^2 + 6k + 4 = 2(k + 1)^2 + 2(k + 1). \end{aligned}$$

This is $P(k + 1)$. Thus $P(k) \rightarrow P(k + 1)$.

By parts I, II, and the Axiom of Mathematical Induction,

$$\sum_{i=1}^{n} 4i = 2n^2 + 2n \text{ for each } n \in I^+.$$

9. Let $P(n)$ be $n \geq 1$.
   I. $P(1)$: $1 \geq 1$. (True, by observation.)
   II. Assume $P(k)$, i.e., $k \geq 1$. But then $k + 1 \geq 2$, so that $k + 1 \geq 1$. But this is $P(k + 1)$. Therefore $P(k) \rightarrow P(k + 1)$. By parts I, II, and the Axiom of Mathematical Induction, $n \geq 1$ for each $n \in I^+$.
11. Let $S(n)$ be $1 + 3 + \cdots + (2n - 1) = n^2$.
    I. $S(1)$: $1 = 1^2$. (True!)
    II. Assume $S(k)$, i.e., $1 + 3 + \cdots + (2k - 1) = k^2$.
    Adding $2(k + 1) - 1$ to both sides,

$$\begin{aligned} 1 + 3 + \cdots + (2k - 1) + 2(k + 1) - 1 &= k^2 + 2(k + 1) - 1 \\ &= k^2 + 2k + 1 \\ &= (k + 1)^2. \end{aligned}$$

    But this is $S(k + 1)$. Therefore, $S(k) \rightarrow S(k + 1)$. By the Axiom of Mathematical Induction,

$$1 + 3 + \cdots + (2n - 1) = n^2 \text{ for each } n \in I^+.$$

13. Let $P(n)$ be "$\dfrac{n^3 - n}{3}$ is a counting number."

    I. $P(2)$: $\dfrac{2^3 - 2}{3} \in I^+$. (True!)

    II. Assume $P(m)$, i.e., $\dfrac{m^3 - m}{3} \in I^+$. Now

$$\frac{(m + 1)^3 - (m + 1)}{3} = \frac{m^3 + 3m^2 + 3m + 1 - m - 1}{3} = \frac{m^3 - m}{3} + (m^2 + m).$$

    But

$$\frac{m^3 - m}{3} \in I^+, \quad \text{and} \quad (m^2 + m) \in I^+. \qquad \text{(Why?)}$$

    Therefore,

$$\frac{(m + 1)^3 - (m + 1)}{3} \in I^+. \qquad \text{(Why?)} \qquad \text{But this is } P(m + 1).$$

    Therefore

$$P(m) \rightarrow P(m + 1).$$

    By the Axiom of Mathematical Induction, $\dfrac{n^3 - n}{3}$ is a counting number for each $n \in I^+$, $n \geq 2$.

Only selected answers are given for Exercises 15–58.

17. Counterexample: 1, and others.

33. *Hint:* try for large n. 37. Counterexample: $x = -1$, $n = 2$.

43. Let $P(n)$ be $(ab)^n = a^n b^n$.

I. $P(1)$: $(ab)^1 = a^1 b^1$. True since $(ab)^1 = ab$, $a^1 = a$, $b^1 = b$.

II. Assume $P(k)$, i.e., $(ab)^k = a^k b^k$. Multiplying both sides by ab,

$$(ab)(ab)^k = (ab)(a^k b^k).$$

By associative and commutative principles, this becomes

$$(ab)(ab)^k = (a \cdot a^k)(b \cdot b^k).$$

Using the definition of a^{n+1} on both sides, $(ab)^{k+1} = a^{k+1} b^{k+1}$. But this is $P(k+1)$. Thus $P(k) \rightarrow P(k+1)$.

By the Axiom of Mathematical Induction, $(ab)^n = a^n b^n$ for each $n \in I^+$.

49–53. *Hint:* Use informal descriptive arguments about lines, planes, regions.

EXERCISE SET 9.4, PAGE 369

5. Yes (remember $0! = 1$). 7. $x^9 + 9 \cdot 7x^8 + \dfrac{9 \cdot 8 \cdot 7^2 x^7}{2} + \dfrac{9 \cdot 8 \cdot 7^4 \cdot x^6}{3 \cdot 2}$.

9. $1 + 100(.03) + \dfrac{100 \cdot 99(.03)^2}{2} + \dfrac{100 \cdot 99 \cdot 98(.03)^3}{3 \cdot 2}$, or $1 + 3 + 4.455 + 4.3659$.

11. $x^{16} - 8x^{14}y^5 + 28x^{12}y^{10} - 56x^{10}y^{15}$.

13. $1 - .08 + \dfrac{90(.008)^2}{2} - \dfrac{720(.008)^3}{3 \cdot 2}$.

15. $\dfrac{17 \cdot 16 \cdot 15 \cdot 14}{4 \cdot 3 \cdot 2 \cdot 1} 2^4 x^{13} y^4$. 17. $\dfrac{16 \cdot 15 \cdot 14 \cdot 7^3 x^{13}}{3 \cdot 2 \cdot 1}$. 19. $6x^4y^4$.

Index

A

Absolute value, 110–14
  inequalities involving, 111–14
Addition:
  commutative principle for, 83
  identities in, 209–12
  inverses in, 88
  of real numbers, 83–91
Addition transformation, 100, 341
Algebra of functions, 298–391
Algebraic properties of real numbers, 69–93
Analytic geometry, 117–63
  circles, 148–51
  distance, 131–38
  ellipses, 153–55
  graphing solution sets, 119–25
  hyperbolas, 157–58
  intercepts, 141–43
Analytic geometry (*cont.*)
  linear equations, writing, 145–48
  parabolas, 160–61
  rectangular coordinates, 117–19
  sets of points, describing, 133–38
  slope, 139–41
  symmetry, 125–29
Associative principle for real numbers, 84–85
Asymptotes, 157

B

Balloon diagrams, 257
Biconditionals:
  denials of, 43
  in logic, 30–31
Binomial theorem, 366–68
Brackets, use of, 21

C

Circles, 148–51 (*See also* Rotations)
Circumcenter, definition of, 149
Closure of sets, 79–81
Column proofs, 326, 334–36
Commutative principle:
  for addition, 83
  for multiplication, 92–93
Complement:
  definition of, 326
  of sets, 64–65
Composition:
  function as a, 256–59
  indentity function for, 261
  inverse of, 274–77
  properties of, 273–74
Compound sentences, in logic, 16–19
Conditionals:
  contrapositive of, 31
  converse of, 29–30
  denials of, 41–42
  inference patterns involving, 322–25
  in logic, 20–21
  proof of, 330–32
  truth of, 25–27
Conics, 162–63
Conjunctions:
  in logic, 16–17
  truth of, 22–23
Connections, scope of, 21
Consequents, 20
Constants:
  definition of, 5
  in logic, 5–6
Contradiction, proof by, 337–39
Contrapositive of conditionals, 31
Converse of conditionals, 29–30
Coordinates:
  polar, 165–67
  rectangular, 117–19
  relations between, 191–93
Cosecant, 196, 234
  abbreviation for, 197
  inverse of, 282
Cosine, 175–79, 196, 234
  definition of, 174–75
  how to use tables for, 179–80
  inverse of, 282
  law of, 219–21
Cosine (*cont.*)
  reciprocal function of, 196
  tables for, 371–73
  values for, 178, 196
Cotangent, 196, 234
  abbreviation for, 197
  inverse of, 282
  table for, 373
Counting numbers, definition of, 3

D

Decimals, infinite, 74–77
Degrees, 175
  definition of, 168–69
Denials:
  of biconditionals, 43
  of conditionals, 41–42
  of generalizations, 36–40
  in logic, 17–19, 36–43
Dependence, concept of, 225–26
Diameter, definition of, 148
Disjunction:
  inference patterns involving, 322–25
  in logic, 17–19
  truth of, 22–23
Disjunctive syllogism, 323
Distance, in analytic geometry, 131–38
Distributive principle, 92–93
Domains of function, 237–40, 278–79
Double-angle identities, 212

E

Ellipses, 153–55
Empty set, 57
  definition of, 332
Equality, definition of, 332
Equivalence, statements of, 30
Even and odd integers, 70
Existential generalizations, 13
Existential quantifiers:
  definition of, 6
  symbol for, 9
Exp (x) values of (table), 374
Exp $(-x)$, values of (table), 374
Expanded form of sigma notation, 351
Exponential functions, 285–88, 374
  with base e, 287

F

False conclusions, 318
Focus, definition of, 160
Functions, 225–309
  algebra of, 298–301
  as compositions, 248–54
  definition of, 226, 228
  domains of, 237–40
  exponential, 285–88, 374
  $f(x)$ notation, 231–33
  graphing, 227–30, 242–54
  identity, 261
  inverse, 261–66
  logarithmic, 289–96
  mapping notation for, 242–48
  one-to-one, 267
  range of, 237–40
  relationships expressed with, 303–4
  restrictions on domain and range, 237–40, 278–79 (*See also* Trigonometric functions; specific trigonometric functions)

G

Generalizations:
  denials of, 36–40
  existential, 13
  in logic, 7–8
  proving, 12–13
Graphs:
  defined, 117
  of functions, 227–30, 242–54
  of inequalities, 121–22
  of sets of real numbers, 53–54
  of solution sets, 119–25
  of trigonometric functions, 198–203

H

Half-angle identities, 213–17
Half-line sets, 52
Horizontal line test, 269
Hyperbolas, 157–58
Hypotheses, 326

I

Identities, 87–88
  addition, 209–12
  double-angle, 212
  half-angle, 213–17
  Pythagorean, 203–7
  reduction, 184–89
  restricted, 261–66
  summary of, 188
  trigonometric, 203
Identity function, 261
Indirect proof, 337–39
Induction, mathematical, 349–69
  axiom of, 357–62
Inequalities:
  graphing, 121–22
  involving absolute value, 111–14
  polynomial, 102–4
  solving, 96
Inference, 311–47 (*See also* Logic)
  column proof, 334–36, 339
  conditionals, 322–25
  disjunctions, 322–25
  indirect proofs, 337–39
  in mathematical proofs, 326–28
  order properties, 340–46
  paragraph proof, 334–36
  patterns of, 316–20
  proof of conditionals, 330–32
  sentential variables, 311–14
  substitution, 319, 340
  tautologies, 311–14
  validity, 316–20
Infinite decimals, real numbers represented by, 74–77
Informal proofs of universal statements, 13–14
Instance of proofs, 13–14
Integers:
  definition of, 3
  even and odd, 70
Intercepts, 141–43
Interpolation, 182–83
  definition of, 326
Intersection of sets, 59–60
Intervals in sets, 51–52
Inverse elements, 88–91
Inverse functions, 261–66

Inverses:
  of a composition, 274–77
  restricting domains to obtain, 278–79
  of trigonometric functions, 279–83
Irrational numbers, 71–74

L

Language, mathematical, 47
Linear equations, writing, 145–48
Logarithmic functions, 289–96
Logarithms, tables of, 375–77
Ln(x), values of (table), 374
Logic, 5–45 (*See also* Inference)
  biconditionals in, 30–31
  compound sentences in, 16–19
  conditionals in, 20–21
  conjunctions in, 16–17
  constants in, 5–6
  denials in, 17–19, 36–43
  disjunctions in, 17–19
  generalizations in, 7–8
  informal proofs in, 13–14
  instance of proofs in, 13–14
  open sentences in, 11–14
  quantifiers in, 6–10
  synonyms in, 33–35
  truth in, 22–27
  variables in, 5–6

M

Mapping notation for functions, 242–48
Modus ponens, 323
Multiplication:
  commutative principle for, 92–93
  distributive principle for, 92–93
  inverses for, 89
Multiplication transformation, 100, 106–9, 341

N

Natural numbers, definition of, 3
Necessary condition, 34–35

O

One-to-one functions, 267
Open sentences:
  definition of, 312
  graph of, 120–21
  in logic, 11–14
Operations for sets, 78–93
Order properties:
  of real numbers, 95–115, 340–46
  transformation principles, 99–102
Order theorems, 344–46

P

Parabolas, 160–61
Paragraph proofs, 326, 334–36
Parentheses, use of, 21
Pattern sentences, 312–14
Plane, subsets of the, 117–63
$P(n)$ notation, 355–57
Points, sets of, describing, 133–38 (*See also* Analytic geometry)
Polar coordinates, 165–67
Polynomial inequalities, solution of, 102–4
Proof, 311
  by cases, 345
  column, 334–36, 339
  by contradiction, 337–39
  indirect, 337–39
  inference patterns in, 326–28
  informal, 13
  instance of, 13
  paragraph, 334–36
  types of, 326–28
Pythagorean identities, 203–7
Pythagorean theorem, 194

Q

Quantifiers:
  in logic, 6–10
  symbols for, 8–9

R

Radians, 168–69
Radius, definition of, 133, 148

Range of a function, 237–40
Rational numbers, definition of, 3, 70
Rays in sets, 52–53
Real numbers:
  absolute value of, 110–14
  addition of, 83–91
  algebraic properties of, 69–93
  associative principle for, 84–85
  commutative principle for, 83, 92–93
  definition of, 3
  graphs of sets of, 53–54
  irrational, 71–74
  operations for, 78–93
  order properties of, 95–115, 340–46
  representation by infinite decimals, 74–77
Reasoning, valid patterns of, 316–20
Reciprocal functions, 196–97
Reduction identities, 184–89
Repeating infinite decimals, 75
Restricted identity, 261–66
Revolution, 176
  definition of, 168–69
Right triangles, solution of, 193–94
Roster notation, 50–51
Rotations:
  interpolation of values of, 182–83
  tables of functions for, 371–73
  trigonometric, 168–72

S

Secant, 196, 234
  abbreviation for, 197
  inverse of, 282
Sentences:
  compound, 16–17
  conditional, 20–21
  open, 11–14, 120–21, 312
Sentential variables, 311–14
Sets, 47–67
  circle, 148–51
  closure of, 79–81
  complements of, 64–65
  definition of, 47
  ellipse, 153–55
  empty, 57, 332
  half lines in, 52
  hyperbolas, 157–58
Sets (*cont.*)
  identities of, 87–88
  of intercepts, 87–88
  intersection of, 59–60
  intervals in, 51–52
  notation in, 47–51, 50–51, 56–57
  operations for, 78–93
  parabolas, 160–61
  of points, describing, 133–38
  rays in, 52–53
  solution, 95–98, 119–25
  union of, 61
  universal, 63–64, 332
Set-selector notation, 47–48
Sigma notation, 349–52
Sine curves, 200
Sines, 174–79, 234
  definition of, 174–75
  how to use tables for, 179–80
  inverse of, 282
  law of, 219–21
  reciprocal function of, 196
  tables for, 371–73
  values for, 178, 196
Sketches, 243–48
Slope, 139–41
Solution sets, 95–98
  graphing, 119–25
Subsets, 55–57
  definition of, 326
  of the plane, 117–63
Substitution, 319, 325
  inference pattern of, 340
Sufficient condition, 34–35
Syllogisms, 323–25
Symmetry, in analytic geometry, 125–29
Synonyms, in logic, 33–35

T

Tangent, 195–96, 234
  inverse of, 282
  reciprocal function of, 196
  tables for, 371–73
  values for, 196
Tautologies, 311–14
Transformation principles, 99–102
  multiplication, 106–9
Transivity, 341

Triangles, solution of:
  arbitrary triangles, 219–21
  right triangles, 193–94
Trichotomy, 341
Trigonometric functions, 165, 174–205, 233–34 (*See also specific functions*)
  defined, 175
  graphs of, 198–203
  inverse of, 279–83
  reciprocal, 196–97
  tables, 371–73
Trigonometry, 165–222 (*See also specific functions;* Trigonometric functions)
  addition identities, 209–12
  double-angle identities, 212
  general coordinate relations, 191–93
  half-angle identities, 213–17
  interpolation, 182–83
  law of sines and cosines, 219–21
  polar coordinates, 165–67
  Pythagorean identities, 203–7
  reduction identities, 184–89
  right-triangle solutions, 193–94
  rotations, 168–72
True conclusions, 318
Truth, in logic, 22–27, 313–14

U

Union:
  definition of, 326
  of sets, 64
Universal set, 63–64
  definition of, 332
Universal quantifiers, definition of, 6
Universal statements; informal proofs of, 13–14

V

Validity, 316–20
Variables:
  definition of, 5
  in logic, 5–6
  sentential, 311–14
  unquantified, 11

X

x- and y-intercepts, 141–43

Z

Zero, 69, 87